How British Women Became Doctors:

The Story of the Royal Free Hospital and its Medical School

How British Women Became Doctors:

The Story of the Royal Free Hospital and its Medical School

Neil McIntyre

Wenrowave Press

Published in the United Kingdom by Wenrowave Press

First published August 2014

Typeset by Taylormade Book Production
Indexed by Michèle Clarke
Printed and bound by CPI Group (UK) Ltd, Croydon, CR0 4YY

A catalogue record for this publication is available from the British Library.

McIntyre, N. (Neil)
How British women became doctors: The Story of the Royal Free Hospital and its Medical School.
Neil McIntyre.
p. 618 ; cm. 24.4 x 17.0

Includes bibliographical references and index.

ISBN 978-0-9930178-0-3 (hardback)
ISBN 978-0-9930178-1-0 (paperback)

Cover Illustrations

Front cover –Top	Royal Free Hospital in 1874
Front cover – Bottom	London School of Medicine for Women c 1900
Back Cover	Royal Free Hospital and School of Medicine c 1980

To Edith Gilchrist (1913-2013) and Ruth Bowden (1915-2001) –
their enthusiasm and energy ensured that the archives of the
Royal Free Hospital and Medical School were preserved

&

To my wife Wendy and my daughter Waveney –
both graduates of the School

Contents

Acknowledgments

Many people helped me with this book. Unfortunately I cannot thank them all, having been less careful than I should have been in recording everyone's details. To those who helped but do not find their names below I can only apologise.

While working at the Royal Free Archives over the last fourteen years I had great support from three professional archivists who stored, preserved and catalogued the extraordinary collection entrusted to them. They usually found what I was looking for, made sure I treated it properly, and put it away safely afterwards! Nicky Riding (now Mrs Sugar) was followed by Victoria North (now Mrs Northwood) and she was succeeded by Victoria Rae who supervised the transfer of the collection from The Hoo to the London Metropolitan Archives. The reasons for the move to LMA were clarified for me by Andrew Rowley of the National Archives, and the LMA's Sally Bevan has helped to reassure me that those wishing to explore the history of the London School of Medicine for Women and of RFH & RFHSM will continue to be well served.

Since the Hospital and School moved to Hampstead together in the 1970s their staff and students have had a first-class service from the Royal Free librarians. For the help given to me over many years I thank not only the head librarians – Patricia Fear, Anne Fletcher & Betsy Anagnostelis – but also the other librarians, David Evans in particular. Like many others I also owe a debt of gratitude to the Royal Free's Medical Illustration department.

The staff of the British Library, the Wellcome Library, the Royal Society of Medicine Library, and the librarians at the Universities of London and Bristol, the Royal College of Physicians, the Athenaeum, and the Royal College of Physicians of Edinburgh made working in their libraries a pleasure. I also wish to thank James Beaton, Librarian, Royal College of Physicians and Surgeons of Glasgow; Robert Mills, Librarian, Royal College of Physicians of Ireland; Alan Callender, Special Collections Assistant, Robinson Library, Newcastle University, and the staff of the Camden Local Studies and Archive Centre at the Holborn Library.

Kevin Brown, the archivist at St Mary's Hospital, has been a fruitful source of articles and illustrations dealing with the early links between LSMW and St Mary's Hospital & Medical School. Jonathan Evans of the London Hospital Archives allowed me access to the records of the East London Hospital for Children. When

Dee Cook was the archivist at the Worshipful Society of Apothecaries she dug out for me details of the first women to sit its examinations. The early female medical students at Cardiff had to transfer to LSMW for clinical training. Alun Roberts, author of a splendid history entitled 'The Welsh National School of Medicine, 1893-1931: the Cardiff Years' clarified several aspects of that story.

A Swiss friend, Verena Muller, helped with details about the British women who graduated MD in Zurich (including the first one, Frances Morgan – later Mrs Hoggan). Natalie Pigeard-Micault provided similar information about early women at the Paris Medical School. Her essay 'A History of Women's Entrance into Medicine', which relates mainly to the Paris school, is available online.

Elizabeth Crawford's two books – 'Enterprising Women: The Garretts and their circle' and her monumental 'The Women's Suffrage Movement: A reference guide 1866-1928' – have been an invaluable source of information. Both contain material which is difficult to find elsewhere. She has also passed on many snippets of information that she thought (usually correctly) might interest me.

I am particularly grateful to Mrs Catriona Williams (daughter of Sir Colin Anderson and great-granddaughter of Elizabeth Garrett Anderson) for allowing me access to the Garrett Anderson letters which were held then at her house in Jersey; they are now in the Suffolk Record Office. I thank Sir Roger Bannister for kindly confirming his participation in the strenuous testing of Olympic athletes in the Hunter Street quadrangle in 1952 (see Chapter 13) and Professor John Ledingham for his views on the nature of his mother's illness in 1936 (see Chapter 11). Doctor Hussein Gezairy – the first Dean of the Riyadh Medical School and WHO regional director for the Eastern Mediterranean from 1982 to 2012 – very kindly provided information on the Royal Free's role in the creation of the Riyadh School. (see Chapter 14) I thank Peter O'Donoghue, formerly Bluemantle Poursuivant of the College of Heralds, for his formal description of the Coat of Arms of RFHSM.

Mary Ellis and Lynn Cairns, two former Registrars of RFHSM, jogged my memory about things that happened at RFHSM over the years before 1998, and Andrew Close of Human Resources at RFH helped with some queries as did Professor Stephen Powis the Hospital's Medical Director. Martin Jeffery, Pat Hennigan and John Fortune (of the RFH Estates Department) explained some of the structural changes made to the RFH complex after stage I of the building was completed.

A number of former colleagues, including Michael Green (geriatrics), Hilary Howells (anaesthetics), Bob Dick (radiology), Phyllis George & Santi Parbhoo (surgery) and Bill Tampion (biochemistry) supplied information and/or answered questions about matters related to their own departments. Bob Dick, with Patricia

Lewis Graham, described how the Free lost its radiography school. John Hopewell clarified his group's role in improving the treatment of renal failure by dialysis and renal transplantation. His own account can be found online at *http://www.bts.org.uk/MBR/General/About_Us/History/Memoir.*

I am grateful to those who read and commented on some sections of this book. They include the late Bruce MacGillivray, and his successor as Dean, Arie Zuckerman. John Carrier and Mike Spyer read several chapters, and Jennian Geddes (an RFHSM alumna and a relative of the Garrett Anderson family) read some of the early ones. George Janossy, Alison Goodall, and Ted Tuddenham provided background information on the many developments resulting from Janossy's monoclonal antibody laboratory (including the production of Factor VIII and basiliximab), as did Gillie Francis in relation to 'pegylation' and the setting up of PolyMASC. Jan Schultz and Maxine Rockoff kindly read the section on the PROMIS computer system. (See Chapter 15)

Many old students helped during the writing of this book. John Gibson, who entered the School in 1949, has presented a variety of memorabilia from its early days, including a photograph portraying the early male students. Dr Jane Griffin (Lady Jane Bingham when a student) confirmed that her mother (the Countess of Lucan) had also attended the School as a student (but with no intention of qualifying). Murdoch Laing confirmed his involvement in the 'sports car in the corridor' story in 1976 and gave what must be considered the most accurate version of it. Geoff Scott provided biographical material about his mother Professor Pearl Scott, not knowing that his parents first met in Exeter because the School was evacuated there during the war.

It is a pity that *Free Comment*, the fortnightly news-sheet which first appeared in 1957-8 and subsequently outlasted the Magazine (see Chapters 13 & 14), was not treated as a serious enough source of information to be 'collected' by the School library. It covered many topics, albeit in a somewhat irreverent manner, and gives some insight into the attitudes of staff and students. I appealed for past copies and got a good but understandably limited response from Susan Mitchley, Sally Mitchison, Paul Calloway, Roger Skinner, and Basil King (who supplied a CD containing issues from 1966-70. I quoted *Free Comment* several times. The currently available copies will be deposited in the Royal Free Library. A Festival of Arts was produced to celebrate the School's centenary in 1974. Andrew Leach kindly sent a copy of the programme – plus a CD of the sound track of the *son et lumière* on the School's history which was a highlight of the Festival. Andrew and Robert Bruce-Chwatt did the historical research and the latter wrote the script.

Finally I must thank the seventeen students who participated in the 1998 Special Studies Module that led indirectly to the writing of this book – Dale Abbotts,

Alexandra Ames, Ros Blackwood, Ben Harper, Richard Hawker, Jo Hutchinson, Caroline Lindsay, Uzma Naheed, Shamima Rashid, James Seaward, Marwa Shoeb, Jonathan Short, Samra Siddiqi, Emily Sullivan, Nazia Ulla, James Wood & Sophia Wyn-Jones.

In the final stages of the production of this book I have been greatly helped by Cengiz Tarhan, the managing director of UCL Business, and his colleagues Alex Weedon & Ana Lemmo Charnalia. Cengiz, like me, was a Continuing Trustee of RFHSM until 2008.

One person I have to thank is Craig Morris, the creator of 'Wilbur' – a freely available computer program which allows one to search all the files on one's computer for any particular word and then displays every occurrence in context. It has saved me an enormous amount of time, and I never fail to be surprised that so few people seem to have heard about it.

Illustrations

Most of the illustrations in this book are from originals belonging to the Royal Free Archives and the Royal Free Hospital. They are reproduced with the permission of Christopher Burghes, on behalf of the Trustees of the Royal Free Hospital Charity, and Professor Anthony Schapira, Vice-Dean of UCL Medical School and Director of the Royal Free Campus.

The photograph of the statue of Elizabeth Blackwell by A.E. Ted Aub (Fig 1.1) is reproduced by kind permission of Hobart and William Smith Colleges, Geneva, N.Y.

The line drawing of the Pavilion, Brunswick Square is reproduced by the permission of the Camden Local Studies and Archive Centre, Holborn Library.

The photograph of Arthur Trehern Norton is from the St Mary's Hospital Gazette and is reproduced by permission of the Imperial College Health Care NHS Trust Archives (at St Mary's Hospital).

Abbreviations – text and Refs

AABS	**Academic Advisory Boards of Studies (Med, Surg. etc)**
A & E	**Accident and Emergency (department)**
AHA	**Area Health Authority**
AASC(s)	**Academic Advisory Sub-Committee(s) (Med, Surg. etc)**
AMEE	**Association for Medical Education in Europe**
ASA	**Academic Staff Association**
Bart's	**St Bartholomew's Hospital and/or Medical School**
BMJ	***British Medical Journal***
B.Med.Sci.	**Bachelor of Medical Science.**
BMSA	**British Medical Students Association**
BoG	**RFH Board of Governors**
BPMF	**British Postgraduate Medical Federation.**
CC	**Curriculum Committee**
CMEWU	**Committee to consider limitations placed on the Medical Education of Women Undergraduates**
CSCMEWE	**Committee for Securing a Complete Medical Education for Women in Edinburgh**
CVCP	**Committee of Vice-Chancellors and Principals**
DevComm	**Development Committee**
DHA	**District Health Authority**
DHEW	**Department of Health, Education and Welfare (in USA)**
DNB	**Dictionary of National Biography**
ECR	**Extra-Contractual Referrals**
EC	**LSMW/RFHSM Education Committee**
EGA	**Elizabeth Garrett Anderson**
EGAH	**Elizabeth Garrett Anderson Hospital**
ENT	**Ear, Nose & Throat**
FGPC	**Finance and General Purposes Committee**
GCE	**General Certificate of Education**
GIR	**Gray's Inn Road**
GMC	**General Medical Council**
GP(s)	**General Practitioner(s)**

Guy's	**Guy's Hospital and/or Medical School**
HCH	**Hampstead Children's Hospital**
HEFCE	**Higher Education Funding Council for England**
HGH	**Hampstead General Hospital**
HHA	**Hampstead Health Authority**
HoDS	**Heads of Departments (RFHSM)**
HP	**House Physician**
HS	**House Surgeon**
IRC	**Interdisciplinary Research Centre**
JMAC	**Joint Medical Advisory Committee**
JPC(U)	**Joint Planning Committee (University)**
KCL	**King's College London**
KCH	**King's College Hospital**
LC	**Library Committee (RFHSM)**
LCC	**London County Council**
LEA	**Local Education Authority**
LKQCPI	**Licentiate of King and Queen's College of Physicians in Ireland**
'London'	**London Hospital and/or Medical School (now Royal London)**
LSHTM	**London School of Hygiene and Tropical Medicine**
LSMW	**London School of Medicine for Women**
LVRPA	**Lee Valley Regional Park Authority**
MAC	**Royal Free Medical Advisory Committee**
ManComm	**RFH Management Committee**
MC	**RFH Medical Committee**
MEC	**Medical Executive Committee**
MedComm	**RFH Medical Committee**
MHMS	**Middlesex Hospital Medical School**
MOH	**Medical Officer of Health**
MOS, MoS	**Members of the School**
MRCP,FRCP	**Member, Fellow of Royal College of Physicians**
MRCS,FRCS	**Member, Fellow of Royal College of Surgeons**
MP	**Member of Parliament**
Munk's Roll	**Lives of Fellows of the Royal College of Physicians of London**
NEMRHB	**North East Metropolitan Regional Hospital Board**
NETRHA	**North East Thames Regional Health Authority**
NHW	**New Hospital for Women**

NWMRHB	**North West Metropolitan Regional Hospital Board**
O & G	**Obstetrics and Gynaecology**
OSA	**RFHSM Old Students Association**
Plarr's Lives	**Lives of the Fellows of Royal College of Surgeons of England**
P	**Prospectus**
POMR	**Problem Orientated Medical Record(s)**
PROMIS	**Problem Oriented Medical Information System**
PUJC	**Pathology Unit Joint Committee**
QGM	**Quarterly General Meeting**
QMAAC	**Queen Mary's Army Auxiliary Corps**
RAE	**Research Assessment Exercise**
RCGP	**Royal College of General Practitioners**
RCP	**Royal College of Physicians of London.**
RCPEd	**Royal College of Physicians of Edinburgh.**
RCS	**Royal College of Surgeons of England.**
RFA	**Royal Free Association**
RFH	**Royal Free Hospital**
RFH Comm Man	**Royal Free Hospital Committee of Management.**
RFH & SM	**Royal Free Hospital and School of Medicine**
RFH NHS Trust	**Royal Free Hospital National Health Service Trust**
RHA	**Regional Health authority**
RMO	**Resident Medical Officer (often the most 'senior junior' doctor)**
RMW	**Registered Medical Women**
RPMS	**Royal Postgraduate Medical School (Hammersmith Hospital)**
SCPhys	**Sub-committee of Physicians**
SCR/JCR	**Senior common Room/Junior Common Room**
SSCME	**Staff Student Committee on Medical Education**
SHO	**Senior House Officer**
SJB	**Sophia Jex-Blake**
SM	**Senate minutes**
St George's	**Hospital and/or Medical School**
St Mary's	**Hospital and/or Medical School**
UCCA	**Universities Central Council on Admissions**
Westminster	**Hospital and/or Medical School**
UCH	**University College Hospital**
UCHMS	**University College Hospital Medical School**

UC, UCL	**University College London**
UCSWE	**University College of the South West at Exeter**
UGC	**University Grants Committee**
UL	**University of London**
ULU	**University of London Union**
ULAU	**University of London Athletic Union**
UMDS	**United Medical and Dental Schools of Guy's and St Thomas'**
Union Comm	**RFHSM Union Committee minutes**
UR	**Union Report**
WB	**RFH Weekly Board**

Preface

In September/October 1998 Professor John Walker-Smith and I supervised one of the new four-week 'Special Studies Modules' that had been introduced at the Royal Free Hospital School of Medicine (RFHSM) in compliance with new recommendations from the General Medical Council (GMC). The School had just merged with UCL, but existing students followed the Royal Free curriculum until qualification.[1] Eighteen 'fourth-years' took our 'History of Medicine' module and, as a group, attended lectures and visited places of medical historical interest. They also worked on individual projects. As RFHSM had just lost its independence, John and I decided that their projects should reflect the School's own remarkable history and that of the Royal Free Hospital (RFH).

Supervising the students reinforced my own interest in the subject area and brought home to me the need for a 'proper' history of the 'Free'. Its medical school, founded in 1874 as the London School of Medicine for Women (LSMW), played a key role in opening the British medical profession to women, and in removing the barriers to a university education. Several books deal with its early days. Sophia Jex-Blake describes its first ten years in *Medical Women, a Thesis and a History* (1886) – a volume that also provides an excellent account of 'medical women' from classical times to the founding of LSMW. The next thirty are covered in Isabel Thorne's brief *Sketch of the Foundation and Development of the London School of Medicine for Women, Hunter Street, Brunswick Square*. First published in 1905 it was updated by her daughter, May Thorne, in 1915.

In 1951 RFHSM's Council decided to commission a history of the School. (See Chapter 13) Two former students declined an invitation to write it, as did Florence Nightingale's biographer, Mrs Cecil Woodham Smith. Enid Hester Moberly Bell accepted the challenge, but her book *Storming the Citadel: the Rise of the Women Doctor* (1953) says little about RFH and is a skimpy account of LSMW's history (particularly after the First World War). Catriona Blake's *The Charge of the Parasols: Women's Entry to the Medical Profession* (1990) is even less informative about RFH and about the School in the twentieth century. Both authors relied almost entirely on secondary sources. Blake referenced many of her statements

[1] The new RFUCMS curriculum was introduced in 1990.

but Moberly Bell provided only a brief list of books consulted, although she had access to 'the Minutes of the Executive Committee of the School from 1874 to the present day'.[2]

LSMW opened in 1874. It would have closed in 1877 had it not achieved two goals. One was to persuade an examining body to 'recognize' it and examine its students for a degree or diploma acceptable to the GMC. The other was to persuade a 'recognized' hospital to take its students for clinical training. The King and Queen's College of Physicians in Ireland (KQCPI) helped with the first goal in February 1877, and in March RFH assisted with the second. The School was saved and serendipitously the only hospital willing to save it was the closest one.

Much has been written about the School's contribution to the training of women doctors, but historians have rather neglected the role of RFH. Despite its status as a teaching hospital it is remembered mainly as the first 'voluntary' hospital to admit patients free of charge simply because they were poor and ill, and as having been founded by William Marsden because he failed to get a dying girl admitted to hospital without a subscriber's letter. Founded in 1828 as the 'London General Institution for the gratuitous cure of syphilitic and other malignant diseases', it was named 'Royal Free Hospital' in 1837. The only book about RFH, published by its Special Trustees in 1996, is Lynne Amidon's brief *An Illustrated History of the Royal Free Hospital*. It includes some material about the School, is well illustrated and is a good read, but its text does scant justice to either institution.

RFH and LSMW were inextricably linked after 1877 – so much so that I concluded that their stories could not be told properly if told separately. I decided to write their joint history – with the added incentive that the merger with UCL allowed the School's story to be told from beginning to end. There were hints that Ruth Bowden (1915-2001, formerly professor of anatomy) was preparing a book on the School, and that Edith Gilchrist (1913-2013, an anaesthetist) was writing separately about RFH – but there is nothing to suggest either made much headway. However, between them they ensured that the archives of the School and Hospital were preserved and kept together. Had they not done so this book could not have been written. It is dedicated to them.

The Royal Free Archives is a remarkable collection of material covering the history of the School and Hospital – and of several associated hospitals. RFH's records begin with the handwritten minutes of the 1828 meeting which agreed on the

---

[2] She meant the *'Executive Council'* which met from 1874 until the School incorporated in 1898 when it split into the *'School Committee'* (later *'Education Committee'*) & '*Council*' which regulated finances.

creation of the 'London General Institution...'. Those of RFHSM start with the minutes of the August 1874 meeting that led to the opening of LSMW.

For many decades the records of both Hospital and School were somewhat neglected. This changed with the retirement in March 1970 of Gladys Barnes who was RFHSM's Assistant Secretary for over twenty years. Instead of relaxing she agreed to stay and sort out material of historical interest under the supervision of the School's librarian, Patricia Fear. In June Dame Anne Bryans, Chairman of the Board of Governors, told Council that George Qvist and Edith Gilchrist were working on RFH's archives, and that there would be an area for the display of historical records (School and Hospital) in the new building at Hampstead.

Over fifteen months Barnes collected letters, photographs & medals, stored them properly and prepared an index on about 2000 cards. She listed the portraits, furniture and equipment that had been donated; plaques recording bequests; and old ledgers and account books. A draft record was made of the physical development of the school buildings. The sudden enthusiasm for cataloguing the Free's history was probably related to the imminence of the School's centenary in 1974 (for which Ruth Bowden and Edith Gilchrist arranged an historial exhibition) and of RFH's sesquicentennial anniversary four years later.

Following the move to Hampstead some of the collection was stored in one or more rooms in the main hospital and some in a room in the basement of the library. Other material, e.g. the records of the associated hospitals, was stored elsewhere, including the basement of the Royal Free Nurses Home in College Crescent, which had been Hampstead Children's Hospital. In 1989 RFH employed Janet Foster, a professional archivist, to help Gilchrist (who had officially retired as an anaesthetist about ten years earlier). Because of the increasing demand for space within the hospital it was agreed that the archives should move to 17 Lyndhurst Gardens, Hampstead, a large house known as 'The Hoo', where it occupied a lower ground floor section on the west side of the building's south face.

The Hoo, built in 1888-90, was designed by Horace Field, an architect who also worked on alterations to the LSMW buildings in Hunter Street. For many years it was the training school for the nurses of Hampstead General Hospital (HGH) which joined the RFH teaching group in 1948. So too did Hampstead Children's Hospital (HCH) which RFH used as a nurses' training school and then as a Nurses Home prior to its sale in 1995. Hampstead General closed with the opening of the new RFH in Hampstead in the mid-1970s, and was demolished in 1978. In 1973 The Hoo became the RFH School of Radiography and Radiotherapy. Some remember it with affection as it had a tennis court and was within walking distance from the new RFH.

At the end of the 1980s there was growing pressure to improve the facilities for mental health in the community, and debate about the best way of training radiographers. The outcome was that in 1989 radiography training moved into temporary accommodation in Linden Avenue, Hampstead, prior to its transfer to the Bart's School of Radiography. The latter joined The London's School of Radiography and Radiotherapy to form the Charterhouse College of Radiography which is affiliated with City University. The Hoo became a residential home for the elderly mentally ill; it is presently occupied by the West Hampstead Community Mental Health Team (under Camden and Islington NHS Foundation Trust, which now owns The Hoo).

To render it suitable for accommodating the archives the space allocated to it at The Hoo needed modifications. Even these failed to make it an ideal repository but there were several small windowless rooms which helped to minimise the damage done to documents by light. The transfer of the archives to The Hoo was supervised by Gilchrist and Foster. The latter worked part-time until 1993 when she moved to the University of Essex. Her replacement, Lynne Amidon, was not a trained archivist. She also worked part-time while studying child psychotherapy at the Tavistock Clinic. Amidon wrote her *Illustrated History of the Royal Free Hospital* (see earlier) while at The Hoo, and returned to psychotherapy practice in October 1998. Those who followed her were all trained archivists. Nicky Riding (now Mrs Sugar) stayed until June 2001. Her replacement was Victoria North (now Mrs Northwood) who is currently head of the Bethlem Royal Hospital Archives and Museum Services. She left in August 2004 and was replaced by Victoria Rae who at the end of 2013 supervised the transfer of the archives to the London Metropolitan Archives. The last three were of great help to me.

The Royal Free Archives document the origins and subsequent fate of a hospital which, from humble beginnings, became an important voluntary hospital in London. Its story is fascinating – but that of the School is in many ways of greater historical importance as it tells how women won the right to enter the British medical profession and how, in doing so, they influenced other aspects of the lives of British women. Decisions made at the School often influenced those made at the Hospital and vice versa. This meant that cross referencing was crucial in writing this book, and working in the Hoo it was possible, with the archivist's help, to move easily and quickly between the collections.

Although the foundation of RFH antedated that of LSMW by almost fifty years the first three chapters of this book review the position of 'medical women' in medical practice before 1877 – with particular reference to the situation in Britain. Chapter 4, the early story of RFH, explains how a small Hatton Garden dispensary became a Gray's Inn Road hospital capable of providing medical students with a comprehensive clinical training. I saw no simple way of using cues from RFH's history to partition subsequent chapters, but there was an obvious approach based on that of the School, i.e. to use the Deans' terms of office. As Norton, the first Dean, served before and after the forging of the link with RFH in 1877 it seemed expedient to split his deanship into Chapters 3 & 5: they straddle Chapter 4. As the deanships of Aldrich-Blake (1914-25) and Bolton (1931-46) were both disrupted by a World War it seemed appropriate that they too should have two chapters each – namely the 'Years of War' and the 'Years of Peace'.

I did not restrict myself to the story of RFH & LSMW/RFHSM and their alumnae. In keeping with the title of the book I have tried to indicate how LSMW's success led to the admission of women to other schools (women-only or co-educational) and how opportunities for the subsequent employment of women doctors gradually increased, despite continuing prejudice against them in many quarters. Equality between 'professional' men and women is still not complete but, arguably, medicine has progressed further in that direction than most, if not all, of the other professions.

Over the years I have been struck by the prevalence in historical texts of factual errors (some of which relate to the Royal Free's history), and so, in writing this book, I tried to heed Leopold von Ranke's dictum – that the proper aim of the historian is to represent the past as it actually happened. I worked mainly from primary sources in the Archives (committee minutes, annual reports, prospectuses, magazines, etc.). However, while primary sources usually explain WHAT happened and HOW things happened, they do not always explain WHY. The minutes of meetings may fail to clarify the reasons for decisions, and motives are sometimes deliberately concealed. To allow the accuracy of the text to be checked easily I have included many references – either as endnotes or by indicating in the text the date and type of meeting to which the statement refers. I have also inserted lots of footnotes. I enjoy reading them in the books of others as they are often highly informative, even if they sometimes bring to mind Pooh-Bah's quip in The Mikado – 'Merely corroborative detail, intended to give artistic verisimilitude to an otherwise bald and unconvincing narrative'.

The Royal Free Archives are now housed at the London Metropolitan Archives (LMA). The system of referencing used when the archives were at The Hoo was created while I was writing this book, but I stuck with the simple system with which I started. The LMA has used its own system of referencing (but has matched it with that used at The Hoo). At the start of the endnotes I have tried to show how my references fit in with those at LMA – but as a result of the transfer it is possible that some items that were 'in the Royal Free Archives' may be difficult to find at LMA or may not even have been transferred there. The Royal Free Hospital library staff may be able to help in locating them.

The book is necessarily long as it embraces events occurring over about 170 years. During that time patient numbers soared and RFH and LSMW both increased enormously in size, as did their staffs. When writing about the early years I had few problems in deciding what to include and how much detail was required. It was relatively easy to describe the buildings at Gray's Inn Road & Hunter Street and the alterations made to them. However, it proved difficult to depict the larger complexes into which they grew, and to clarify the structural changes made either as planned enlargements or as repair of Second World War bomb damage. Explaining the topography of the enormous new building in Hampstead, and the changes subsequently made to it, was a bigger and sometimes insurmountable task.

There were analogous problems when writing about those employed by the Hospital and School. Initially their number was tiny by today's standards. The 'London General Institution…' opened as a dispensary in 1828 with four clinical staff – a 'surgeon', 'assistant surgeon', 'consulting physician' & 'consulting surgeon'. 'Consulting' was the adjective then used for senior colleagues no longer in active hospital practice (but usually still engaged in private practice); they would have had little or no day-to-day involvement with the dispensary. In 1877, when the LSMW students arrived, RFH had two 'physicians', an 'assistant physician', two 'surgeons' and an 'assistant surgeon' – plus several 'consulting' staff. Just before the First World War there were, along with nine junior staff, about two dozen individuals who, after the inception of the NHS, would have been considered as 'consultants'. In 1998 RFH had well over a hundred 'consultants' and a large number of junior doctors.

LSMW started with fourteen 'lecturers'; none had a full-time appointment and most taught at other medical schools. In 1914, half of the School's twenty 'lecturers' (excluding those also on RFH's staff), taught at other medical schools. There were no 'professors'. The first teacher to receive a chair at LSMW was Wood-Jones in 1915. By 1998 the School staff (pre-merger) numbered over 150 (excluding visiting professors, honorary staff, clinical staff with NHS contacts etc.). There were thirty-seven professors.

When the clinical and academic staffs were small, and there were few students, I could, when writing about them, refer to most, if not all, by name. As the numbers increased it became feasible to identify only those individuals who figured in the themes and topics chosen for inclusion in the book. However I name many staff in relation to their appointment, promotion, retirement or resignation which, although a little boring to read, helps understanding of the expansion of departments (and, infrequently, their contraction or closure), and the development of specialization – not just in clinical practice (where, e.g. 'physicians' metamorphosed into cardiologists, chest physicians, neurologists & rheumatologists etc.) but also in the basic sciences (where, e.g. physiology gradually split into biochemistry, immunology, histology, pharmacology etc.).

In any school students are arguably the most important individuals. This was certainly true of the fourteen who arrived on LSMW's first day in 1874. Twelve were battle-hardened veterans of the struggle in Edinburgh. The women students then at Girton (founded 1869) and Newnham (1871) entered Cambridge to get an education but they had no expectation of a degree. In contrast LSMW's students wanted to become 'proper' doctors and *had* to obtain a qualification allowing entry to the Medical Register. Decades elapsed before women were full members of Cambridge or Oxford (which first admitted them in 1878) and were able to graduate. By comparison the early students at LSMW were 'fast-tracked'. As a result of the political campaign waged by them and their supporters, the University of London admitted women to its degrees in 1878.

I have used a broad brush approach in trying to describe how the Free's two key institutions developed. Originally the Hospital had two main tasks – to care gratis for patients seeking its help and, as it was a 'voluntary hospital', to raise the money needed to do so. It was effectively independent, but subject occasionally to wartime requisitioning of staff and facilities. During the Second World War RFH, like other London teaching hospitals, was controlled by the Emergency Medical Service. Planning also began then for the National Health Service (NHS). After it came into effect in 1948 RFH's funding came mainly from the Government which subsequently dictated policy. For a time teaching hospitals retained some autonomy. Unlike other hospitals they did not report to a Regional Hospital Board; their Boards of Governors reported directly to the Minister of Health. 'Management' within the NHS gradually became an activity in its own right – one accompanied by a striking increase in its support staff. And while it seems self-evident that 'managers' of hospitals and medical schools should facilitate the work of 'carers' and 'educators' (and ensure it is carried out well), many would now argue that, as a consequence of increasing political interference, today's NHS 'managers' tend to hinder rather than facilitate.

The NHS proved a great success but, largely for political reasons, it was repeatedly subjected to poorly conceived and ineptly executed reorganisations.

With the 1974 reorganisation Regional Hospital Boards became Regional Health Authorities and Boards of Governors were abolished.

While it stayed solvent LSMW was relatively independent; but it had always to meet criteria (re curriculum & facilities) set by the examining boards whose qualifications met with the GMC's approval. Early in the twentieth century the provision of medical education became more expensive, particularly with advances in the basic medical sciences. As a result medical schools began seeking Government grants but those usually came with conditions attached. After 1929 Government grants, previously distributed directly to colleges, went in toto to the University Court which then decided on the allocation to colleges. Not surprisingly the University of London's influence over its medical schools increased. After the war NHS directives further reduced the freedom of action of hospitals and medical schools. Following the report of the Royal Commission on Medical Education in 1968 (i.e. the 'Todd Report') London schools were subjected to a long period of uncertainty and change that was exacerbated by the effect of NHS reorganisations on their hospitals; in RFHSM's case it culminated in what was effectively an enforced merger with UCL in 1998. (See Chapter 16)

In the book have tried to explain the background to these events, their impact on RFH and RFHSM and how they were handled by key people at the two institutions (senior administrative, clinical & academic staff, and lay members of the important School and Hospital committees). During and after the Second World War those individuals had to carry out Government policies even if they disagreed with them.

There was no nursing school until 1887/8 so at RFH 'education' was restricted initially to the ad hoc training of junior doctors by the senior clinicians responsible for them. Staff could not take pupils to the RFH until 1848; even then the wards were still officially closed to students. However, most staff wanted to teach and between 1833 and 1877 they made several attempts to start a medical school; fortunately for LSMW none was successful. (See Chapter 4)

For most of the School's existence preclinical and clinical education were essentially separate. Students were considered 'School' or 'Hospital', a distinction reinforced during World War Two when the preclinicals were evacuated – first to Scotland and then to Exeter. (See Chapter 12) The first halting steps towards integration of preclinical and clinical teaching were made in the late 1960s. However, in 1971 the GMC rejected the idea, favoured by RFHSM, of a three-year preclinical course for a B.Med.Sci. followed by a two-year clinical course leading to the MBBS. In anticipation of new regulations due to come into effect the University asked schools if they wished to organize their own curricula and examinations. RFHSM chose a school-sponsored course with school-based examinations and worked towards an integrated course meeting the GMC's requirements. A final version was submitted to the University in December 1972.

The new preclinical course began with two new interdisciplinary courses – 'Cell Studies' and 'Man and his Environment' – intended to promote integration between the 'traditional' preclinical subjects,[3] between those and the behavioural sciences, and between preclinical and clinical subjects. However there were problems with the clinical course due to start in 1976. Traditionally London's students had entered 'hospital' in two cohorts – in April and October, but the new regulations meant all were to enter in October. In 1975, RFHSM had a new Dean in place, and it was decided that the planned 'new clinical curriculum' was unsatisfactory and had to be changed. The opportunity was taken for a major overhaul. Clear 'goals' and 'objectives' were defined for the clinical years and they dictated the teaching programme and the nature of the final 'school-based' examinations which differed radically from the 'university-based' exams. Throughout there was an emphasis on clinical competence. A major part of 'in-course assessment', the importance of which had been stressed by the GMC, was conducted by one-to-one audit of the students' simulated care of 'their patients', as recorded in their own clinical notes. The last were written using Lawrence Weed's Problem Orientated Medical Record (POMR) approach. In conjunction with this RFH applied to the Department of Health for funds to import PROMIS, a remarkable computerised medical record system being developed by Weed's group in Burlington, Vermont, which is still widely considered as the best such system to have been developed. As the software would have been free, the Department of Health's unwillingness to support it then is proving more and more costly. (See Chapter 15)

Before 1877 little or no research was done at RFH. Staff members wrote on clinical topics, and William Marsden's book describing his experiences with cholera is still quoted. Some had conducted research elsewhere. Mortimer Glover, who joined RFH in 1854, discovered the anaesthetic properties of chloroform in 1842 (without recognizing its clinical potential); and Hassall was renowned for his work on the histology of human tissues and his studies on water purity and food adulteration. (See Chapter 4) For several years after LSMW opened little or no research was done at either School or Hospital. Some of the physiology lecturers, who came mainly from UCL, were gifted research workers and two, Schäfer and Starling, became the second and third holders of UCL's Jodrell Chair of Physiology.

Following the publication of the Gresham report in 1894 the University

---

[3] Primarily anatomy, physiology, biochemistry and pharmacology.

encouraged research in all its colleges, and announced that its MD and MS would henceforth be awarded not only by examination, but also via a thesis or published work based on independent research. In 1899 LSMW's new Handel Street Wing included a small research room. However, research could be costly. From 1839 the BMA allocated money annually to defray the expenses of a small number of research workers. LSMW's Julia Brinck (LRCPI 1886) received a BMA award in 1890, and a student, Janet Lane-Claypon (see below) won a BMA research scholarship in 1904; but by 1911 few other women had benefited and only about one per cent of the money allocated went to women. Most other funding for research came from wealthy donors such as Mrs. Webb who, in 1898, provided LSMW with funds for a Mabel Webb Research Scholarship (in Pathology, Physiology, or Chemistry). Mabel was her daughter, an LSMW alumna, who had just died. (See Chapter 6) Ethel Vaughan MD (MBBS 1896) won it in 1899. In 1903 it went to the brilliant Lane-Claypon. Admitted to LSMW in 1898 she graduated B.Sc. in physiology in 1903 (at UCL) and D.Sc. in 1905; she did not qualify MBBS until 1907.

At that time much of the 'big' money for research came from rich philanthropists like Sir Otto Beit. In 1910 the first Beit Memorial Fellowships for Medical Research were awarded. That year one went to a woman; two women succeeded the following year, and three in each of the next two years (but only two of the nine were medically qualified).

I have not tried to cover the research done subsequently at LSMW & RFHSM (and at RFH). Information about it can be found in the School's annual reports which, from 1913 until 1988/9, listed original papers and publications from the various departments. There were nine in 1913 (five by the anatomist Wood-Jones; two by Helen Chambers, then assistant pathologist at RFH; one from physiology by Cullis & Tribe; and one by Constance Leetham, a B.Sc. research student (who did not study medicine but was, along with Cullis and Tribe, one of the first six women members of the Physiological Society). The 1914 annual report listed another nine publications, but there were only five in 1915. The practice of listing departmental publications in the annual reports was discontinued after Zuckerman became Dean; but since then most of the LSMW/ 'Royal Free' publications, even those from the nineteenth century, can be found on the internet using a suitable search engine. Good medical librarians would be happy to assist in such a search.

Lloyd George's National Insurance Act 1911 created a national fund for medical research and the Insurance Commissioners set up a Medical Research Committee and Advisory Council in 1913. It gave some 'exceptional' researchers a pensionable salary (enabling them to devote their whole time to research); and initiated research programmes and provided funding for research by outside bodies or individuals, thus complementing the research resources of universities and hospitals. The Ministry of Health took over National Health Insurance in 1918 but the Medical Research Committee became the independent Medical Research Council (MRC) – subsequently a major source of scholarships for individuals and of funding for research projects, including very large ones.

The most important alternative source of funding, the Wellcome Trust, was created in Britain in 1936, as a legacy from Sir Henry Wellcome, a founder of the drug company, Burroughs Wellcome, which no longer produces medicinal agents. Other pharmaceutical companies give money to hospitals, medical schools and universities for research on the development of new drugs. The 'overhead' usually charged by the schools on such funding has itself become an important source of income; and if the product of the research is commercially successful the school and the 'inventors' may receive large (or very large) royalties. A school's research activities may also affect its income in another way. Since the Research Assessment Exercise was introduced in 1985/6 the perceived quality of the research done at a medical school helps to determine the size of the annual grant received from the University Grants Committee.

Not surprisingly the choice of new heads of departments at British medical schools (and those of some other countries) is often determined primarily by the research income they are thought likely to generate, rather than on their ability or willingness to ensure that most students become clinically competent, caring physicians – which surely should be the main goal of all undergraduate medical schools. Unfortunately some heads have a responsibility for undergraduate teaching and clinical practice, and gifted research workers are not necessarily the best persons to advise on these areas.

Although I have tried to present a reasonably comprehensive history of the 'Free' many stories have been left untold and this is particularly true for items that appeared either in the Royal Free magazine or the volumes of 'press cuttings'. Those who wish to delve further into some of the topics in this book or to explore different ones should look out for potential pitfalls.

Degrees and diplomas have certainly caused confusion. LSMW women could not sit for degrees and/or diplomas recognised by the GMC until 1877 when the first examination open to them was that for the LKQCPI diploma. They sat for it in Dublin. In 1878 the University of London opened its degrees to women and two LSMW students graduated MB Lond in November 1882. However, for various reasons some LSMW women wanted a qualification other than MB Lond or LKQCPI; so they sat instead for the LRCP&S Ed (from 1886), MB RUI (1890),

MB Durham (1898), etc. Many assume that those holding such qualifications had studied in Ireland, Edinburgh or Durham. In the early days most had not; they had gone there just to sit the examination – although Durham did require LSMW students to register and attend classes during their last year. Women with MD degrees from Zurich, Berne and Paris (which were not registrable in Britain) would have studied in those cities, but most British women holding them had been at Edinburgh or LSMW before 1877 and, seeing little chance of qualifying at home, had left for France or Switzerland. MD Brussels was an oddity. It was open to registered practitioners with British medical qualifications but its holders could not practise in Belgium. It was taken by those wanting to be called 'Doctor'.

Those who qualified at the 'Free' can be tracked easily. *The Medical Register*, published annually since 1859, lists all registered practitioners; but not all addresses are updated and little information is provided other than details of the qualification justifying inclusion and the date of full (and provisional) registration. *The Medical Directory* (published annually since 1845) is more informative but some doctors do not provide the necessary information or update their entries. Most practising doctors can now be found by searching on the Internet for their hospital or practice website. One difficulty with married women doctors is that while some practise under their husband's surname others retain their maiden name for professional purposes – and it can be difficult to track those who married after some years of practice.

From 1883 to 1898 the School's annual report (available in the London Metropolitan Archives) included a list of all registered medical women, not all of whom trained at LSMW. From 1899, when more and more were qualifying at other schools, the list was restricted to those who had trained (wholly or partly) at LSMW. From 1914 an additional 'topographical' list indicated the countries and towns in which former students lived (and usually worked). The Royal Free Association, founded in 1999 by the merger of the Old Students Association and Members of the School (see Chapter 16) still maintains this Directory; it has contact details for about 4,000 former students who qualified from the Royal Free.

Not all Royal Free students qualified. There is a handwritten list of all admissions between 1874 and 1927 which sometimes explains failure to qualify. There is also a typewritten list of those entering from October 1943 to September 1949. Information about those admitted in other years can be found by looking through the original individual application forms – a tedious exercise unless there are helpful clues (e.g. likely year of admission). For various reasons some wealthy and/or well connected women were admitted who had no wish to qualify; not all of these were formally admitted.

In the past the death of most doctors merited an obituary (often lengthy) in the

BMJ or The Lancet. *BMJ* obituaries are now fewer and shorter, and like *The Lancet* it tends to choose professional journalists to write 'long' obituaries. London's Royal Colleges of Physicians (RCP) and Surgeons (RCS) document the lives of past fellows in *Munk's Roll of the Fellows of the Royal College of Physicians*, and *Lives of the Fellows of the Royal College of Surgeons* (originally *Plarr's Lives…*). There are also obituaries in specialist journals, and in the national press, the *Dictionary of National Biography*, and the *Biographical Memoirs of the Fellows of the Royal Society*. *Who's Who*, *Who was Who* & *Wikipedia* are also valuable sources of biographical information – but for important points it is sensible to confirm information from *Wikipedia* (and from some of the other sources as well).

One can get a rough idea of the length of time that doctors spent at RFH from the staff list that is included in the Hospital's 'Annual Reports', along with details of donations, patient admissions & attendances, etc., and from the 'Committee of Management's report to the Governors' which often mentioned the doctors by name. After 1877 these Annual Reports, like the LSMW Prospectuses, listed the staff of both RFH and LSMW. The Hospital reports have one advantage over the School reports; submitted in January they cover the previous calendar year, so if they mention an appointment or retirement it almost certainly occurred during that year. The School reports cover the previous 'academic year', i.e. October to September. So an appointment reported during 1974/5 it could have been made from October 1974 to September 1975.

Happy reading!

CHAPTER 1

Early Medical Women

From Ancient Egypt to New York, Zurich, Paris & London

When the London School of Medicine for Women (LSMW) opened its doors to students on 12 October 1874 the General Medical Council recognized only two women as 'Registered Medical Practitioners' – Elizabeth Blackwell and Elizabeth Garrett Anderson. Blackwell's name was in the first issue of the *Medical Register* in 1859, Garrett's appeared in the one for 1866. Another woman's name should have been in the first *Medical Register* – that of James Miranda Barry who graduated MD Edinburgh in 1812. 'James' was a young Irish woman, recently identified as Margaret Ann Bulkley,[i] who posed as a man to enter medical school and maintained this subterfuge throughout a distinguished career in the Army. Her gender was revealed only after her death in 1865, aged about 75. The fact that Barry was close to retirement in 1859 may explain why she did not join Blackwell in the original list. However, her story – unlike those of Blackwell and Garrett Anderson – has little relevance to the struggle other British women had to become doctors.

Blackwell was America's first woman MD, having graduated from Geneva College in upper New York State in 1849 (see later). Although Geneva then stopped admitting women,[ii] the dam had been breached. Soon North America had several medical schools for women and its men's schools also started admitting them.[iii]

The first woman to gain a medical degree in Europe, at least in 'modern' times, was the Russian, Nadeshda ('Nadia') Suslova. She enrolled at the University of Zurich medical school in 1864 and graduated in 1867 – the year Mary Putnam, daughter of the American publisher George Palmer Putnam, was the first woman admitted to the Paris medical school.[iv]

Elizabeth Garrett qualified with a diploma from the Society of Apothecaries in 1865 (see later).[v] Keen to acquire a degree she decided to seek one in Paris where Putnam's admission had eased the way for her. In February 1869 she was allowed to enter its medical school without preliminary study at the Sorbonne.[1] On 15 June 1870 she was the first woman to graduate MD Paris,[2] but not the first British

[1] Supported by Lord Lyon, the British Ambassador to France, and with the intervention of the Empress Eugénie.

[2] A year before Putnam.

woman to receive an MD in Europe. That distinction went to the Welsh woman, Frances Morgan,[3] Zurich's second female MD, who received her degree on 12 March.[vi]

The dearth of female British doctors in the mid-19th century was not due to women's lack of aptitude or ability. They had always dealt with illness and injury within their own families, and helped other women through pregnancies and deliveries. As Jex-Blake pointed out – *'If we…try to imagine the first sickness or first injury suffered by humanity, does one instinctively feel that it must have been the man's business to seek means of healing, to try the virtues of various herbs, or to apply such rude remedies as might occur to one unused to the strange spectacle of human suffering?…few would maintain that such ministration would come most naturally to the man, and be instinctively avoided by the woman; indeed, I fancy that the presumption would be rather in the other direction. And what is such ministration but the germ of the future profession of medicine'.* [vii]

She went on to ask – *'If a child falls down stairs, and…*[is]*…seriously hurt, is it the father or the mother (where both are without medical training) who is most equal to the emergency, and who applies the needful remedies in the first instance? Or again, in the…country, where no doctor is readily accessible, is it the squire and the parson, or their respective wives, who are usually consulted about the ailments of half the parish?'* The answers seemed obvious. As health care became more specialised women naturally assumed the mantle of nurses and midwives, but for centuries they also showed they could cope with more demanding tasks when the opportunity arose.

In *'A History of Women in Medicine'* Kate Campbell Hurd-Mead noted that women doctors practised in Ancient Egypt, Greece and Rome, and in parts of Europe until the beginning of the nineteenth century.[viii]

Salerno was the first 'proper' European medical school and the forerunner of the great medieval schools of Montpellier, Paris, Bologna and Padua. At its peak in the eleventh, twelfth and thirteenth centuries it attracted students from far and wide; its women doctors, who cared for women's diseases, feature prominently in its history.

The most famous was Trotula, whose husband, John Platearius the Elder, was also a doctor. She lived in the eleventh century and is credited with several medical texts. The best known is *'De passionibus mulierum'*, which describes gynaecological operations and prevention of perineal tears in labour. There were other Salerno medical women who wrote on medical topics.[4] Salerno's importance

---

[3] Frances Morgan is better known as Mrs Frances Hoggan. (See later)

[4] Mercuriade wrote on fevers, ointments and the cure of wounds, Rebecca Guarna on fevers, urine and the embryo, and Abella on black bile.

declined as other great schools emerged; it was dissolved by edict of Napoleon in 1811.[5]

From the Middle Ages women doctors prospered at Italian universities, particularly in Bologna, where Alessandra Giliani, a prosector in anatomy with Mondino, made wonderful casts of blood vessels to aid his teaching.[ix] She died in a fire in 1326, aged 19. In 1390 Dorotea Bocchi succeeded her father as Bologna's Professor of Medicine and Moral Philosophy. There centuries later Anna Manzolini, the anatomy professor's wife, made original anatomical observations and improved teaching of the subject by creating coloured wax models. Although offered a chair at Milan she stayed in Bologna and gave her husband's lectures during his long fatal illness; elected professor of anatomy in 1760 she died in 1774. Maria Petraccini, who graduated at Florence in 1788, taught anatomy at Ferrara; her daughter, Zaffira Feretti, graduated MD at Bologna in 1800. Maria delle Donne 'received the doctoral laure' at Bologna in 1806 and was later appointed by Napoleon Bonaparte to its Chair of Midwifery.[x]

British women had no such opportunities for academic advancement – in medicine or other disciplines – as the universities, few in number until the nineteenth century, would not admit them. Other groups were also excluded. Until 1854 no one could matriculate at Oxford without subscribing to the thirty-nine articles of the Anglican Church; at Cambridge scholarships, fellowships and degrees were closed to nonconformists until 1856.

For centuries women, despite their academic isolation, were 'irregular practitioners' of medicine in Britain, despite attempts to deprive them, and male 'irregulars', of the right to practise. In 1421 a petition to Henry V prayed that '*no woman use the practyse of fisyk under payne of long emprisonment'*.[xi] The Preamble to the 1511 Act [3 Henry VIII, c II] stated: '*Forasmuch as the Science and Cunning of Physick and Surgery...is daily within this realm exercised by a great multitude of ignorant persons,...common Artificers, as Smiths, Weavers, and Women,...take upon them great Cures, and things of great Difficulty, in the which they partly use Sorcery and Witchcraft, partly apply such Medicines unto the Diseases as be very noious* [sic]*,...to the high Displeasure of God,...and the grievous hurt, Damage, and Destruction of many of the Kings liege people, most especially of them that cannot discern the cunning from the uncunning.*' Under the Act no person within the City of London or within seven miles of it was allowed to practise as physician or surgeon unless admitted by the bishop of London or the dean of St. Paul's, whose decisions were aided by four surgeons or doctors of

[5] The present University of Salerno is a distinct institution founded in 1970.

physic. Outside London, a bishop or his representative assessed applicants.[xii] Notwithstanding the unfavourable comments about them, women were examined under the provisions of this Act and licensed in this way for over 200 years.[xiii]

For millennia midwifery was the prerogative of women, even for royal births. The entry of men into 'obstetrics' followed Peter Chamberlen's invention of the midwifery forceps early in the seventeenth century,[xiv] and the fostering by male practitioners of the idea that a 'surgical' instrument must be handled by a surgeon. As women were denied surgical training midwives were doomed to categorization as inferior practitioners. However, men-midwives did not attend royal patients until Princess Charlotte's disastrous confinement in 1817 that resulted in a stillborn son and death of the mother. Victoria was the first British Queen delivered by a man; Charles Locock (later Sir Charles) attended for all her children.[6, xv]

Women distinguished themselves in other branches of medicine and surgery. Lady Anne Halkett, born 1622, daughter of the provost of Eton, served as a surgeon in the royal army at Dunfermline and at other battles. People from far and wide consulted her, often when the ministrations of men had failed. Catherine Bowler, a surgeon's wife, was renowned for treating hernias in the early eighteenth century. Jane Stephens's discovery in 1735 of a secret remedy for 'stone' aroused interest in France and Great Britain, the latter's government paid £5,000 for it in 1740.[xvi]

However, the difficulties facing medical women increased. A particular problem was that for centuries the British medical profession included three 'orders' – physicians, surgeons and apothecaries – membership of which required some form of professional education or training, from which women were effectively excluded.

Physicians, regulated by their colleges, of which they were licentiates, members or fellows, were the most prestigious group. They may have obtained a medical degree but, until the nineteenth century, their university education was that of a scholar not a practitioner. Curricula, largely theoretical, were of little practical value. Physicians wishing to practise medicine usually spent several years afterwards in clinical training, often at continental medical centres.

By contrast, surgeons and apothecaries started as apprentices. Formal education was considered relatively unimportant for a budding surgeon in the late eighteenth and early nineteenth century. Candidates for membership of the Royal College of Surgeons (MRCS) had to attend just one course of anatomy and one of surgery. Not until 1813 was it obligatory to spend a year in the surgical practice of a hospital. Apothecaries, the lowliest of the three orders, were originally shopkeepers who sold drugs – but when the House of Lords decreed in 1703 that apothecaries might

[6] The Latin for 'midwife' is 'obstetrix'; as in English there is no proper masculine equivalent.

direct and order treatment they became the general practitioners for most of the population (but could charge only for drugs, not for the advice). Apothecaries had to serve an apprenticeship before being examined at Apothecaries Hall.

The functions of the three orders overlapped. Apothecaries sometimes behaved like physicians, and vice versa. 'Surgeon-apothecaries' were supposed to satisfy the criteria of both the College of Surgeons and the Society of Apothecaries although some took only one examination. There was bickering between them, but all three orders united in their longstanding opposition to empirics, quacks, impostors – and women!

Early in the nineteenth century attempts were made to improve the regulation of the British medical profession. Dr Edward Harrison[7] reported in 1805 that 'empirical pretenders' outnumbered regular faculty by nine to one.[xvii] To weaken the position of the former the Apothecaries' Act of 1815 decreed that the Society of Apothecaries was to conduct examinations, and be responsible for most of the medical practitioners of England and Wales. Candidates had to serve a five year apprenticeship; have a competent knowledge of Latin; attend lectures on anatomy, physiology, theory and practice of medicine, chemistry and materia medica; and spend six months at a public hospital, infirmary or dispensary.[xviii] Midwifery training was required from 1827 and additional hospital practice from 1830. The Act stipulated that a Court of Examiners be '*authorised and required to examine all person or persons applying to them, for the purpose of ascertaining the skill or abilities of such a person or persons in the science of medicine, and of his or their fitness and qualification to practise as Apothecaries*; ...'. Years later the wording 'all person or persons', which clearly included women, proved crucial in the legal battle between the Society of Apothecaries and Elizabeth Garrett and her father.[xix]

The Apothecaries' Act did not solve the problem of unqualified practitioners. Concern remained about the inadequacy of many qualifications – and the lack of a register identifying properly qualified individuals. The controversial young surgeon Thomas Wakley, founding editor of *The Lancet* and a zealous reformer, was elected to Parliament in 1835. To some doctors he was a champion, to others an implacable opponent. In 1840, with two other MPs, he introduced 'A Bill for the Registration of Medical Practitioners, and for establishing a College of Medicine and for enabling the Fellows of that College to practise Medicine in all and any of its branches and hold any medical appointment in any part of the United Kingdom.' This Bill,[8] unlike the Apothecaries' Act, specified that a 'person practising medicine' was a man. It was not passed. Between 1840 and 1858 fifteen other Bills

---

[7] Lincolnshire Benevolent Medical Society inquiry into medical practice in the county.

[8] Details in Bill dated 11 August 1840 in Bills Public, House of Commons Library.

to reform the medical profession were presented to Parliament; all were abandoned, amended or defeated.

The seventeenth, carried through parliament by W. F. Cowper,[9] led to the Medical Act of 1858. It created a 'General Council of Medical Education and Registration' – to keep an annual register of qualified practitioners, approve bodies giving the qualifications, and report those that did not insist on a proper examination and course of study. Unregistered practitioners could still practise medicine (as they can today) but could not represent themselves as a 'doctor', a 'legally or duly qualified Medical Practitioner', or a member of the medical profession. Only registered doctors could be employed by the state as a medical officer, or sign certain medical certificates. Registered doctors were excused jury service. Unlike their unregistered counterparts, they could go to court to recover professional aid fees from patients (although London's College of Physicians denied its fellows that privilege!).[xx] Unregistered practitioners became second-class doctors!

Elizabeth Blackwell (Fig 1.1 Colour plate)

Elizabeth Blackwell was born in Bristol in 1821. In 1832 her family emigrated to the United States and in her mid-twenties she decided to study medicine. Many medical schools rejected her applications; Geneva College in upper New York State accepted her in 1847. She graduated in 1849 and went for postgraduate training in Paris. That November, while working at La Maternité, her left eye became infected while she was syringing the eye of a baby with purulent ophthalmia; she ended up with a glass eye.[xxi] The accident cut short her time in Paris. In October 1850 she began studying at London's St Bartholomew's Hospital – having been accepted by its dean, James Paget. She was well received, being unwelcome only in the department dealing with diseases of women and children! [xxii]

Blackwell lived in rooms at Thavies Inn (where William Marsden, founder of the Royal Free Hospital, lived for some years). One evening she was visited by Bessie Rayner Parkes and Barbara Leigh Smith – two young advocates of female emancipation.[xxiii] They became her lifelong friends – as did Florence Nightingale and Lady Noel Byron – and introduced her to a social group including the Herschels, Faraday and Russell Gurney.

Blackwell, though tempted to stay in London, returned to the USA in July 1851 and set up in practice in New York. In October 1854 she 'adopted' Kitty Barry, a 7-year-old Irish orphan rescued from the House of Refuge on Randall's Island, a reform school for juvenile delinquents/vagrants. Kitty remained with her – half servant, half daughter – until Elizabeth's death.[xxiv]

---

9 Lord Mount-Temple from 1880.

Emily Blackwell graduated MD at Cleveland, Ohio in 1854, and joined her sister in practice in 1856. A year later they opened 'The New York Infirmary for Indigent Women and Children' at 64 Bleecker Street.[xxv]

Elizabeth returned to Europe in August 1858. She visited Paris and met Dr Trelat, head of La Salpêtrière, whose wife contributed to the Blackwells' New York Infirmary. She then moved to England, keen to find out what openings existed there for women wishing to enter the medical profession.

Her arrival in London on 3 January 1859 coincided with the publication of the first *Medical Register*. Her name was included even though foreign qualifications were unacceptable unless their holders had practised in Britain before 1 October 1858. Her visit to England in 1850 was to study not to practise; but strings were pulled, primarily by William Shaen the young lawyer who made her application.[xxvi] Blackwell later wrote *'Influential friends were desirous of keeping me in England. They presented the various testimonials of English and Continental study given by distinguished physicians and credentials of American practice to the Medical Council. On this Council, of which Sir Benjamin Brodie was President, were old friends of the St Bartholomew's days. The subject was very carefully considered, and after mature deliberation this just and important concession to qualified women was authorised.'* [xxvii] Her registration gave a boost to the women's movement.

In February Blackwell met her friend Florence Nightingale who opposed the idea of women doctors. To mark Nightingale's endeavours during the Crimean War a fund had been set up in her name to support a training school for nurses. Nightingale asked her to head the school, but Blackwell, wishing to continue in medical practice, rejected the idea.

While in Paris, Blackwell prepared three talks explaining the activities of women doctors in America – one on the value of physiological knowledge; one on medical knowledge; and one on practical aspects of the women's work and its adaptability to England. The lectures, intended to stimulate interest in the medical education of women, were arranged by Bessie Rayner Parkes and the Leigh Smith sisters, and given in London, Manchester, Birmingham, and Liverpool.[xxviii]

Jessie White Mario (Fig 1.2)

Before the Medical Act of 1858 only one woman (other than James Barry) had made a serious attempt to obtain a proper medical education in Britain.[xxix] Jessie Meriton White, the daughter of a wealthy English shipbuilder, was in Paris studying radical philosophy in the autumn of 1854 when Emma Roberts, a rich widow, asked Jessie to accompany her to Sardinia to visit Garibaldi. Familiar with the writings of his fellow revolutionary Mazzini, then exiled in England, Jessie agreed. On

Fig 1.2 Jessie White Mario (1832-1906)

return to England, committed to the cause of Italian liberation, she decided to study medicine, perhaps because she had promised Garibaldi she would, when necessary, nurse his wounded soldiers.[10]

[10] She wrote to Barbara Leigh Smith in 1857 stating that her desire to study medicine originated when caring for her little brother – who, afflicted by a brittle bone disease, broke his legs many times – and for Ricciotti, Garibaldi's boy, who was also lame.

In May 1856, supported by her family practitioner, Dr Little, Jessie applied to, and was rejected by, all London's teaching hospitals. The Royal College of Surgeons refused to examine her. Helped by Shaen, a strong supporter of the women's cause, she asked the University of London *'Can a woman become a candidate for a Diploma in Medicine, if, on presenting herself for examination she shall produce all the requisite certificates of character, capacity and study from one of the Institutions recognized by the London University?'*. Jessie was optimistic but in mid-July lawyers opined that the University's Charter did not empower it to admit women as candidates for degrees. Her hopes were dashed, but in March 1857 she wrote to Barbara Leigh Smith: *'... I am glad to have made the experiment. Several medical men have assured me, that if a band of women were now to apply for admission at one or more of the hospitals, such has been the feeling excited among some of the most liberal-minded in the profession by the discussions following on my request, that it is improbable they would be refused.'*[xxx]

Jessie became more involved with the Italian circle in Britain and with Mazzini himself. The politician James Stansfeld introduced her to the Friends of Italy Society, which supported attempts to foment revolution in Italy; its members included William Ashurst (Stansfeld's father-in-law), Shaen, Peter Taylor and Samuel Courtauld (Taylor's uncle). Stansfeld, Taylor and Shaen subsequently played key roles in women's struggle to join the medical profession.

Jessie, an accomplished journalist, wrote on Italian unification for the British press. On 28 June 1857, while in Italy, she became engaged to Alberto Mario. Six days later they were arrested following a minor insurrection. On release they moved to Britain, married on 19 December, and subsequently visited America to raise money for the cause. They returned to Italy in April 1859, when Cavour provoked Austria into a war with Piedmont-Sardinia, and in 1860 joined Garibaldi for his rapid conquest of the south of Italy. Alberto was on his staff, Jessie nursed the wounded. Both participated in the war against the Austrians in 1866/7 and in the 1870/1 Franco-Prussian War when Garibaldi's army fought the Germans in eastern France.

Following the unification of the Italian peninsula in 1870 Jessie worked on three research projects, trying to raise governmental awareness of social problems such as pellagra, poverty in Naples, and working conditions in the Sicilian sulphur mines. She contributed to British, American and Italian newspapers,[11] wrote many biographies including those of Garibaldi and Mazzini,[12] plus a couple of

[11] In *The Birth of Modern Italy,* Litta Visconti Arese stated Jessie was the first English woman journalist.

[12] She also wrote biographies of Dr. Agostino Bertani, Carlo Cattaneo (with Alberto Mario), Giuseppe Dolfo, Alberto Mario (with Giosuè Carducci) & Giovanni Nicotera.

histories.[13] She died in Florence in March 1906. Her ashes were buried at Lendinara, south of Venice, next to Alberto's.

Elizabeth Garrett (Fig 1.3) [xxxi,xxxii]

Elizabeth Garrett, the daughter of Newson Garrett, a wealthy, self-made businessman from Aldeburgh in Suffolk, was the first British woman to mount a successful challenge to the male monopoly of medicine. She and her elder sister, Louie, were educated at home before spending two years (1849 to 1851) at a boarding school for ladies in Blackheath where they befriended Jane and Annie Crow from Gateshead. In 1854, while visiting the Crows, Elizabeth met Emily Davies, the daughter of Gateshead's rector. Elizabeth, Emily and Jane became committed to the women's movement.

Emily's three brothers attended public schools, two going on to university.[14] She was educated at home, which may explain why she was later to pioneer university education for women. She founded Girton College and helped to secure the admission of women to University College London.

Jane became honorary secretary of the Society for Promoting the Employment of Women – set up in 1859 by Barbara Bodichon (née Leigh-Smith) and Jessie Boucherett; Elizabeth and Emily were members. Barbara Bodichon, still young,[15] was a major figure in the women's movement following the publication in 1854 of her pamphlet *A Brief Summary in Plain Language of the Most Important Laws of England Concerning Women*. She fought to improve the legal rights of married women and, with Bessie Rayner Parkes, founded *The Englishwoman's Journal*.

Blackwell gave her first London lecture (see above) at Marylebone Hall on 2 March 1859. Later she wrote 'the most important listener was the bright, intelligent young lady whose interest in the study of medicine was then aroused – Miss Elizabeth Garrett – who became the pioneer of the medical movement in England …'.[xxxiii] However, Garrett had already contemplated a career in medicine. She had asked her father to enquire about Blackwell through his partner, Valentine Leigh-Smith, Barbara Bodichon's cousin, who provided a letter of introduction to Blackwell. Emily Davies and Barbara had met in Algiers where the Bodichons had a house; there Emily was caring for Henry, her tuberculous brother. Emily had set up a meeting between Garrett and Barbara Bodichon for early February 1859; Garrett and Blackwell then met at Bodichon's house in London after Blackwell's first lecture.

---

13 The histories were *I Garibaldini in Francia* about the Franco-Prussian War; and *The Birth of Modern Italy*, which was published posthumously.

14 The eldest, Llewelyn, read classics and was President of the Cambridge Union before becoming an Anglican priest. He was rector of Christ Church, Marylebone for thirty-three years from 1856.

15 She was born in 1827.

Fig 1.3 Elizabeth Garrett

Elizabeth attended all three of the lectures and, urged on by Emily Davies, settled on medicine as a career. The two Elizabeths corresponded after Blackwell's return to New York. Initially few knew of Garrett's plans. Legal advice was discouraging. To enter the *Medical Register* she had to qualify through a British examining body – but no British medical school accepted women. Undaunted she began preparations and took Greek and Latin lessons. Her parents were horrified when told of her plans in June 1860. Her mother remained hostile, but she won over her father and together they sought views from leading London consultants all of whom were pessimistic. In July Mrs Russell Gurney suggested some who might help. One, William Hawes, was a governor of the Middlesex Hospital. He and the Russell Gurneys persuaded Elizabeth to test her resolve with a trial period as a nurse. Through Hawes's influence she started nursing on the surgical wards at the Middlesex on 1 August 1860.

She must have impressed the surgeon Thomas Nunn, who was also the Dean; after a week he let her attend his out-patient clinic. Others also encouraged her. In October she asked the physician Campbell de Morgan, the school's treasurer, if by paying fees she could attend classes in anatomy and other subjects. He refused to accept fees but said she could, for a donation, attend the operating theatre and clinics after her three months' spell as a nurse. He provided a room for study and agreed to private tuition from the hospital's apothecary, Joshua Plaskitt. By November she was an unofficial medical student. Plaskitt taught her Latin, Greek and materia medica, and she hired Willis, a house physician at the Middlesex, as tutor in anatomy and physiology. She was living with her sister Louie and her husband at 22 Manchester Square.

In March 1861 she asked Nunn for admission to the dissecting room and to chemistry lectures. The chemistry lecturers, Heisch and Redwood Taylor, accepted her immediately; she started in the dissecting room in May. In June she received a certificate of honour for each class examination, but on 5 June she made a serious tactical error. A visiting physician asked a question during a ward round. No man responded; Elizabeth answered correctly. On 6 July over forty students protested at her presence in the school and a week later the medical school committee decided she could attend no lectures after the current series. Fortunately, before leaving at the end of July, she sat her exams and obtained the certificates needed for the Society of Apothecaries.

That summer she applied to several London medical schools. All rejected her. The examining bodies of Oxford, Cambridge, Glasgow and Edinburgh refused to examine her, as did the Royal College of Surgeons when she applied to take its diploma in midwifery. Her only hope was the Society of Apothecaries. The original Apothecaries Act of 1815 gave the Society the right to examine and license candidates in medicine. As noted earlier the Act, still in force, referred to 'all person or persons' – without specifying gender. To satisfy the Apothecaries' requirements Elizabeth had to serve an apprenticeship, and take three years of lectures, demonstrations and hospital attendance. Plaskitt accepted Elizabeth as an apprentice in June 1861; this allowed her to apply to the Apothecaries for registration as a student. Their Council, opposed to examining women, took legal opinion on the terms of the Society's charter and learned it had no grounds for refusing her. In late August the Society therefore agreed to examine her if she fulfilled its regulations. One requirement, apprenticeship, she had satisfied. To spend three years in British medical schools was to prove more difficult although she had the option of taking private lessons with recognized teachers from these schools.

Bessie Rayner Parkes introduced Elizabeth to Dr John Chapman, proprietor of *The Westminster Review*, who put her in touch with his former teacher, George Day, Regius Professor of Medicine at St Andrews. Day suggested she spent the winter studying the subjects needed for matriculation as a university student, and recommended scientific reading with a private tutor and attendance at courses of lectures – one on botany at the Pharmaceutical Society, Tyndall on physics at the Royal Institution, and T. H. Huxley on natural history and philosophy at the South Kensington Museum. After Huxley's first lecture Elizabeth entertained some of the other ladies in the audience – including Sophia Jex-Blake, to whom, according to Manton, she took an instant dislike.[xxxiv]

In April 1862 Elizabeth applied to matriculate at the University of London. She and Emily Davies lobbied its senators and wrote to the national press; the Senate rejected her application by one vote. Newson Garrett consulted the Attorney General and was told, as was Jessie White, that its charter did not allow the University to admit women. A new charter was being prepared; Newson sent a memorial proposing that the University and its examinations be opened to women. At Senate on 7 May George Grote, the Vice Chancellor, proposed that the new charter should allow admission of women. There were ten votes on each side; Lord Granville, the Chancellor, gave his casting vote against the motion, following the convention that a casting vote was given to the status quo.

Elizabeth now decided to try Scotland. Overcoming her dislike of Jex-Blake, who was studying in Edinburgh, Elizabeth wrote asking about the prospects of admission to its medical school. Jex-Blake, with characteristic generosity, replied 'come and see'. Elizabeth stayed with her for two weeks from 30 May. Sophia arranged a weekend trip to the Trossachs to celebrate Elizabeth's twenty-sixth birthday on 9 June.[xxxv] Together they sought help from influential people in Edinburgh, but a meeting of medical men rejected Elizabeth's application to the Edinburgh school by 18 to 16. She and her father then went to St Andrews to meet George Day, who encouraged her and offered to tutor her. She decided to return there in October. In September she passed the preliminary examination in arts at Apothecaries' Hall – a necessary preliminary to its professional examinations.

On returning to St Andrews Elizabeth applied for matriculation. There was no examination. She simply paid the Secretary, McBean, a pound for the ticket making her a member of the University, and acquired class tickets for chemistry and anatomy lectures. However, the Senate told McBean he had acted without due authority. On 1 November he tried to return her pound; she refused to take it.

Day was effectively excluded from subsequent Senate meetings because they were held in an upstairs room; crippled by a climbing accident in 1857, he could not climb the stairs.

On 15 November Senate ruled 'the alleged matriculation of Miss Garrett to be null and of no effect'. She took legal advice on whether payment of the fee constituted a contract binding on the professors at St Andrews. Opinions were conflicting. James Moncrieff, the Lord Advocate in Edinburgh, considered her ill used by the Senate of St Andrews. He thought she might be admitted to classes, and get damages for expenses incurred, but that there was no way a woman could be admitted to a university degree. Elizabeth contacted *The Scotsman*, whose editor, Alexander Russel, was to become a strong supporter of medical women. But not everyone was sympathetic. On 22 November the British Medical Journal noted 'The female doctor question has received a blow…at St Andrews University. It is…time that this preposterous attempt…to establish a race of feminine doctors should be exploded.'

Although she could not graduate Elizabeth could still qualify with a diploma from Apothecaries' Hall. She remained at St Andrews and studied anatomy and physiology with George Day. She wrote to Apothecaries' Hall to establish that its examiners would accept this private course of lectures. The reply was encouraging, demanding only 'that the certificates on the various subjects required by the Court be obtained from recognized lecturers of acknowledged schools of medicine.'

Elizabeth left for Edinburgh in May 1863 and approached James Young Simpson, the famous obstetrician. Nine years earlier, he had accepted Emily Blackwell as his assistant. Now he welcomed Elizabeth, but referred her for teaching to his colleague Alexander Keiller. In three months she witnessed over a hundred deliveries and attended twelve herself.

On return to London Elizabeth worked at practical anatomy, and needed to complete the clinical practice required for the LSA. From October 1863 to March 1864 she was taught anatomy by Louis Stromeyer Little,[16] a young demonstrator at the London Hospital Medical School (later an orthopaedic surgeon). Clinical practice was a bigger problem, and in February 1864 she had to settle for 'nursing experience' at the London. Fortunately she was supervised by Nathaniel Heckford, the resident *accoucheuer*, who became a good friend. By August she had conducted

[16] Louis Little was the son of Dr W.J. Little who had helped Jessie White Mario with her applications to London's medical schools. (see earlier)

55 deliveries. Heckford certified she had successfully completed her studies in 'Midwifery and diseases of women, and vaccination.' Some staff and students at The London complained about her pretence of being a nurse.

That June a young woman turned up, eager to become a fellow student. Elizabeth entertained her to tea, summed her up as 'crude and dogmatic' and politely dismissed her.[xxxvi] However, the following year she and Emily Davies supported a Miss Colborne who sought to attend classes at a number of medical schools. Colborne was admitted at St Bartholomew's but forced out by the implacable hostility of the male students.[xxxvii]

In April 1864 Elizabeth applied for admission to the examination for the licence of the Royal College of Physicians believing 'that in the interest of the public and for the honour of the profession, women should be subject to the severest tests open to men'. The College's counsel opined that 'the language of the Charter and of the Bye-Laws precludes the College in granting licences practice to Females, and also from admitting them to examination for a license'. Her application was rejected.[xxxviii]

Elizabeth began her last year as a student in October 1864. Little taught her morbid anatomy, and Stephen Goodfellow gave her the lectures on the principles and practice of medicine which he gave at the Middlesex, where she walked the wards until the end of her last statutory period of clinical practice in March 1865. At the Middlesex she met John Ford Anderson – a young Scots physician and brother of her future husband. Professor George Harley of University College London gave her the final course of lectures – on toxicology and forensic medicine.

The Society of Apothecaries, realising that Elizabeth was determined to qualify, wrote that they could not admit her to the final examinations. Newson Garrett threatened to sue. The Apothecaries took legal advice before capitulating. She took the examination on 28 September 1865 with seven male candidates. She passed!

Elizabeth practised from her new home, 20 Upper Berkeley Street, which her father had rented for her. She shared it with Jane Crow, now Secretary of the Society for Promoting the Employment of Women, and it became a hive of political activity. A meeting of fifty governesses held there in January 1866 resulted in the formation of the London Association of Schoolmistresses. Two months later Barbara Bodichon asked John Stuart Mill to submit a petition supporting enfranchisement of women property owners,[17] and Elizabeth and Emily Davies presented it to him. Although defeated in parliament on 7 June it was well supported. The committee that collected the signatures used the drawing room at Upper Berkeley Street as an office,[xxxix] and in November it became the

[17] Applicable only to widows & spinsters; married women's property belonged to their husbands!

Enfranchisement of Women Committee – the first British suffrage society. Its secretary was Elizabeth's sister, Louie Smith. After Louie's death from appendicitis in February 1867, aged 35, Elizabeth eschewed active involvement in the suffrage movement for many years.

Garrett's Little School

Having qualified, Elizabeth wanted to help other women to enter the profession. On 9 January 1866 she wrote to her mother – *'we are framing a scheme of this kind; – to take a house close by here,…and to turn the ground floor into a dispensary for women & children with me for the doctor – the three pupils wd…share the benefits of what practice there was and it might become the nucleus of a hospital with beds. The upper rooms could be used as a school, one room for dissections, another for lectures, others for private study, library etc etc. We propose getting men…[from]…men's schools to teach the pupils here, rather than attempting to get new men recognized as teachers, solely for us, by the General Medical Council. I should be general manager of the school, tutor to the pupils as well as medical attendant in the dispensary, and I should have as much power as would be wanted to keep things straight. The lecturers would naturally be friendly to me & wd be willing to let me share in their work and this wd be the best way of creeping into a position as teacher wh[ich] should be recognized by the Medical Council. One advantage of the scheme is that it wd not cost much, & that if students did not come forward when the three now ready to begin should have ended their course, there wd be no disgrace in just shutting up the class rooms & going on alone with the dispensary. There wd be no real school formed, as the lecturers wd all teach in virtue of their position elsewhere; each lecturer wd be asked only to give one course for a certain term wh students wd continue to pay as if for private lectures; if more students came forward, the course cd be repeated yearly, but if they did not, the three now beginning sd merely go thro' their curriculum & leave others to arrange in the same way for themselves when they come. I hope you & the dear father will understand the scheme & think as well of it as I do…'* [xl]

The house taken was 69 Seymour Place where, on 2 July 1866, Elizabeth opened St Mary's Dispensary for Women and Children for treating the poor of Marylebone. The three pupils were Frances Morgan, Sarah Goff and Ellen Phillips.[18] They passed the preliminary examination in Arts of the Society of Apothecaries on 25 January 1867 (Frances with honours). On 14 February the Society's Court of Examiners, alarmed about more women qualifying, decided it would no longer accept *'certificates of lectures, or of anatomical instructions, delivered in private*

[18] Goff & Phillips, not Dunbar & Atkins as stated in Manton's biography of Garrett Anderson.

to particular students apart from the ordinary classes of recognized, public, medical schools.' This ruled out qualification through its examining board because no such school would accept women. The Royal College of Surgeons could have examined them. Nathaniel Heckford (1842-1871), who had taught Garrett at the London Hospital, married Sarah Goff on 28 January, three days after her examination. In March he approached the Royal Free Hospital which, in 1865, had been approved for study for the MRCS and asked if it would receive ladies as pupils; this initiative was not followed up.[xli]

The three potential pupils went their separate ways. Ellen Phillips and her sister Mary were Quakers. In July 1867 they opened a small dispensary for women and children at 13 Virginia Row, Bethnal Green. In 1868 it moved to 25 Hackney Road as the North Eastern Hospital for Children and in 1908 it became the Queen's Hospital for Children. Ellen married Alexander Fox, another young London Hospital doctor. They moved to New Zealand. After his death in 1876 she returned to Britain and died in January 1890.[xlii]

Sarah and Nathaniel also founded a hospital, the East London Hospital for Children, which opened at Shadwell on their first wedding anniversary. Garrett was appointed visiting medical officer in March 1870 and held the post until October 1873. There she met her future husband, James George Skelton Anderson, financial adviser to the hospital and vice-chairman of its Board.[19] Sadly Nathaniel died of tuberculosis on 14 December 1871. Sarah moved to South Africa in 1878, returning to England in 1901.[xliii] In 1942 the two hospitals combined to form the Queen Elizabeth Hospital for Children.

Frances Morgan enrolled at Zurich. There her ability and personality made her a legend.[xliv] She graduated 12 March 1870. Frances studied in Vienna, Prague and Paris before returning to Britain. Excluded from the *Medical Register* because of her foreign degree she was a medical 'second-class citizen' in March 1871 when she joined Garrett (now Mrs Garrett Anderson) at the St Mary's Dispensary. Frances Morgan was arguably the most brilliant of the early medical women, and the first in Britain to do high quality medical research. But she would have had no career had it been realised that, aged 17, before she started her medical studies, she had had an illegitimate child in Brussels.[xlv]

Garrett's was not the first attempt to set up a women's medical school in London. In 1864 Dr James Edmunds opened the Female Medical College at 4 Fitzroy

[19] In 1854 Skelton joined the shipbrokers James Thompson & Co, headed by his uncle, James Anderson. By 1863 it was Anderson, Thompson & Co, and in 1869, following the death of the last Thompson it became Anderson, Anderson & Co. In 1878 it joined the Green family of ship owners and shipbuilders to found the Orient Steam Navigation Company.

Square. It did not provide a full medical education, just instruction in midwifery to educated women.[xlvi] However, Edmunds opened a new area of employment to middle-class women and enabled their pregnant peers to be attended by one of their own class and gender. While its alumnae were ineligible for the *Medical Register* they probably made childbirth safer.

In a letter to her father on 10 January 1866 Elizabeth wrote that Frances Morgan, then a prospective apprentice, had *'been to Dr Edmunds at the Fem Medical College thinking I was there. He had impressed her with the conviction that he & his colleagues were either humbugs or very ignorant and she was greatly pleased to find I did not advise her to join them. Miss Goff, the lady with me yesterday, gave them £50 as one donation & yet she now knows they are doing more harm than good & that they can teach students nothing. She urged me very much to get some public statement made separating me from them, as she thinks the connection they try to make people think exists does me considerable harm. However this may be I think it must be left to time. I should not like to go openly against them,* [nor for]*...my friends to do so...*`[xlvii]

On 23 April 1867 Elizabeth's younger sister, Millicent, married Henry Fawcett. Although blind following a shooting accident he was professor of political economy at Cambridge and the Radical Liberal MP for Brighton. Years earlier he had proposed to Elizabeth! Millicent became one of the great leaders of the suffrage movement and a founder of Newnham College, Cambridge; Henry supported the women's movement vigorously until his death in 1884.[xlviii]

While Garrett was engaged in her pursuit of the Paris MD (see earlier) another woman began fighting for the right of British women to study medicine. To Garrett's chagrin it was Sophia Jex-Blake who, with four other women, entered the University of Edinburgh in 1869. Garrett gave them little support, although she was involved with Lady Amberley's[20] offer of a scholarship to be awarded on the results of the matriculation examination in October 1870.[xlix]

In 1870 Elizabeth became involved in two political issues. W.E. Forster's Education Act, passed in August, led to compulsory education in Britain and ensured provision of schools in areas lacking them. Locally elected school boards were empowered to build schools, provide teachers, and insist on attendance. The Marylebone Working Men's Association – husbands and fathers of Garrett's dispensary patients – asked her to stand in November for election to the new London School Board. There were seven candidates for election as the representative for Marylebone. She polled 47,858; T.H. Huxley took second place with 13,494. Her vote was larger than that of any other candidate in the whole of

[20] Lady Amberley was Bertrand Russell's mother,

London; Emily Davies was the only other woman elected to the London School Board, on which Elizabeth served for three years.[21]

The other issue was the Contagious Diseases Acts of 1864, 1866 and 1869, intended to minimize the problem of venereal disease, which caused great concern to the Army and Navy. In Britain prostitutes were punished only if they annoyed others, but in most European countries the police regulated prostitution and enforced medical examination of prostitutes. The first Act, applicable only to certain garrison towns, allowed a Justice of the Peace (JP) to order a woman's examination and detention for treatment for up to three months if a senior policeman believed her a prostitute suffering from a disease described in the Act. The 1866 Act allowed periodical medical examination for up to a year, and detention for up to six months, and preliminary information about suspected disease was no longer necessary. The 1869 Act involved more towns and allowed detention for up to nine months.

Many groups, including the British Medical Association, Church dignitaries and heads of schools and universities, thought the system of inspection should become universal. However, the women's movement, led by Josephine Butler, considered the Acts unjust. A movement to repeal them was supported by liberal politicians including James Stansfeld and John Simon, Medical Officer to the Privy Council.[22]

The women's movement looked to the two practising women doctors for support. They got it from Blackwell, but not from Garrett who, in 1870, wrote to the *Pall Mall Gazette* supporting the Acts.[1] Many in the women's movement never forgave her. Jex-Blake and her fellow students in Edinburgh also failed to support those working for repeal but, as we shall see, they could not possibly have risked any further alienation of Edinburgh's hierarchy.

Garrett married Skelton Anderson on 9 February 1871.[23] His father, the Rev. Alexander Anderson, was a Scottish Presbyterian minister before he opened a small school in Aberdeen; he and his wife had twelve children. Elizabeth had met Skelton's brother, Dr John Ford Anderson, while at the Middlesex Hospital.

The first Married Women's Property Act had been passed in 1870 and Elizabeth insisted that her earnings (though not her capital) were legally secured to her. On 28 July 1873 their first child, Louisa, was born.[24] Margaret was born in September 1874 but died in December 1875. The third and last child, Alan, was born in March 1877. Louisa and Alan were to play major roles in the story of the London School of Medicine for Women.

---

[21] Emily Davies was elected for Greenwich.

[22] A Repeal Bill, introduced by Stansfeld, was eventually carried in March 1886.

[23] At the Scottish Presbyterian church in Upper St George's Street.

[24] Louisa, like her mother, became a doctor.

Somewhat surprisingly, given the hostility of most members to women doctors, Garrett Anderson was elected to the British Medical Association in 1873. Dr Stewart, Ford Anderson's chief at the Middlesex, and secretary of the Metropolitan branch, arranged her election. Two years elapsed before provincial members realized what had happened.

Blackwell prospered in New York. In May 1860, she and her sister Emily moved their Infirmary from Bleecker Street to 126 Second Avenue, which could accommodate students.[li] They were assisted by Philadelphia graduates seeking practical instruction in medicine: one was Rebecca Cole, America's first black woman doctor.[lii]

During the American Civil War (April 1861 to April 1865) Blackwell helped to find nurses for the United States Army. Subsequently the Blackwells' infirmary obtained a charter incorporating it as a women's medical college. They organized a full medical course lasting four years (instead of the usual three) and set up an examination board independent of the school's teaching staff – an arrangement commonplace in Britain but unusual in America. Emily was the school's Dean until it incorporated with Cornell University in 1899.

The first fifteen students entered the Women's Medical College of the New York Infirmary on 2 November 1868; private students, including Sophia Jex-Blake, had already been tutored by the Blackwells at the Infirmary. Jex-Blake was in the first formal class, but within weeks returned to England because her father was mortally ill.[liii] Five of the first group graduated in 1870 – the year the subway opened in New York.

Blackwell herself returned to England in 1869. On 16 June she wrote to Barbara Bodichon – *I am coming with the one strong purpose in my mind of assisting in the establishment, or opening of a thorough medical education for women, in England. – As soon as the Doctorate is freely attainable by English women, I shall feel as if my public work -- my own special pioneer mission, were over -- but not until then. While working for this object, I shall hold consultation hours, for any ladies, who may wish to seek my medical advise. . . . I will ask you, dear friend, not to mention my plans to Miss Garrett or any other acquaintance, at present; It is known that I make a trip to Europe this summer, but not that I propose passing the winter there, and it would not be well that this latter point should be known just yet.*[liv]

On settling in London Blackwell lived for months with Barbara Bodichon. The latter's friends included Dante Gabriel Rossetti, George Eliot and her lover George Henry Lewes, Mrs Crawshay, Anna Goldsmid, Frances Power Cobbe and the philosopher Herbert Spencer. Charles and Fanny Kingsley converted Blackwell to Christian Socialism.

In April 1870 Blackwell set up house and practice at 6 Burwood Place; but medical practice played little part in her life, income from American investments making it unnecessary.[lv] She involved herself in many reform movements few of which had much impact. One exception was the 'National Health Society', which also involved Barbara Bodichon, Anna Goldsmid and Ernest Hart, the editor of the *BMJ*. Founded in February 1871 it promoted the dissemination of sanitary knowledge among the general population and invented the motto 'Prevention is better than cure'. Frances Morgan (later Mrs Hoggan) was its first secretary. For two and a half years, from May 1870, Elizabeth gave a home to a little boy. Only eight months old on arrival he became Sir Henry Paul Harvey, diplomat and editor of the *Oxford Companion to English Literature*.[lvi]

After a trip to France in September 1872 Blackwell suffered fever and rigors, probably due to cholangitis; it became a recurrent and serious problem. As she wrote in her autobiography *'I was attacked by illness, which proved so serious that in 1873 the Burwood Place establishment was broken up, and my plan of life necessarily changed. During the next three years I vainly endeavoured to resume my London work, but was frequently obliged to seek health in change of residence and foreign travel'*.[lvii] She left for Europe in April 1873 and did not return to London for a year.

Although both Blackwell and Garrett Anderson expressed their keenness that British women should be provided with a complete medical education they were not the ones destined to achieve that goal. In Edinburgh, and then in London, a more determined woman battled to help women qualify and enter the *Medical Register* as 'proper doctors'. It was she, Sophia Jex-Blake, who made the breakthrough.

CHAPTER 2

Sophia Jex-Blake:

Failure in Edinburgh, Success in London

Sophia Jex-Blake (Fig 2.1) [1, i, ii, iii]

Sophia Jex-Blake was born at Hastings on 21 January 1840. Her father, Thomas, was a proctor of Doctors Commons, a professional association of Admiralty and ecclesiastical lawyers. She was educated at home before attending several small boarding schools where she was considered highly intelligent but a difficult pupil!

In October 1858 she enrolled at Queen's College, Harley Street, an Anglican college founded by F. D. Maurice and his colleagues at London's King's College in 1848. It was the first place to provide higher education for women in Britain. After two months, to her father's horror, she took paid employment there as a mathematical tutor. Without payment she also taught book-keeping at the Society for the Employment of Women, and tutored a class of children at Great Ormond Street.

Early in 1862, following the break-up of an intense relationship with Octavia Hill,[2] Sophia went to study in Edinburgh. Later that year she went to familiarise herself with women's education in France and Germany, returning to Brighton in May 1863. Two years later she visited America for a similar purpose.[3] She had introductions to Dr Lucy Sewall and Ralph Waldo Emerson. The former, then 28, was resident physician at the New England Hospital for Women and Children, of which her father, Samuel Sewall – judge, abolitionist, and supporter of the women's movement – was a founder. Sophia helped at the hospital. She wrote reports, filled in for a sick dispenser, started attending clinics and ward rounds and began to contemplate medicine as a career.

In June 1866, she came home to discuss her future with family and friends. She wrote *'most people are much more in favour of Medicine than I expected, except Miss Garrett, who thinks me not specially suited'*. After returning to Boston in September she enrolled as an anatomy student at Lucy's old school, the New

1 The biographies by Margaret Todd (Ref i) & Shirley Roberts (Ref ii) provide details of Jex-Blake's life. The best account of her struggle to provide women with a medical education is her own book. (Ref iii)

2 A housing reformer and co-founder of the National Trust.

3 Macmillan published her findings in 1867 as *A Visit to Some American Schools and Colleges.*

Fig 2.1 Sophia Jex-Blake (1840-1912)

England Female Medical College. On 11 March 1867 she and Susan Dimock wrote requesting admission to Harvard Medical School.[4] A letter of rejection was sent on 8 April. Both letters appeared in the *Boston Daily Advertiser*. Thanks to Oliver Wendell Holmes, Brown-Sequard and others, they received clinical teaching at the Massachusetts General Hospital for about eight months. In January 1868 they made another unsuccessful attempt to enter Harvard.

In March Sophia left for New York. She attended private classes at the Blackwells' Infirmary, and Dr Moseley, chief demonstrator at Bellevue Hospital,

[4] Dimock (MD Zurich 1871), an American, was lost in a shipwreck off the Scilly Isles in 1875.

taught her dissection and practical anatomy. When the Blackwells' new medical school opened on 2 November 1868 Sophia was in its first entry;[5] two weeks later she left for England having heard her father was dying.

Sophia now decided to try to study medicine at a British university. Her brother Thomas and Josephine Butler[6] both consulted friendly university professors. Henry Sidgwick[7] held little hope of success at Cambridge or Dublin. David Masson, Professor of Rhetoric and English Literature at Edinburgh, wrote to Butler that he and Sir James Young Simpson would meet Sophia, but were pessimistic about her chances in Scotland.

Sophia went to Edinburgh in March 1869. Masson, her main supporter, wrote reminding John Balfour, Dean of the Faculty of Medicine, and Robert Christison, Professor of Materia Medica and Therapeutics, that Paris had admitted Mary Putnam and Elizabeth Garrett and, with other foreign Universities, had set an example in allowing women to enter for medical degrees. Sophia's strongest supporters in the medical faculty were Balfour, Hughes Bennett and Simpson; sadly the last died in the spring of 1870. Alexander Russel, editor of the *Scotsman* and an advocate for the feminist movement, helped to publicise Sophia's cause.

On 20 March she applied to attend lectures. The medical professors agreed, but only for that summer term. The Senatus Academicus (the Principal and all professors from every faculty) voted 14 to 4 in her favour on 27 March. However there was trouble ahead. Christison,[8] her main enemy, implacably opposed to admitting women, was the only person sitting on all five bodies that would determine the fate of prospective medical women – the Medical Faculty, the Senatus, the University Court, the University Council and the Infirmary Board.

The University Court, which met in strict privacy, had eight members – the Rector, the Principal, the Lord Provost, and appointees of the Chancellor, the Rector, the Senatus, the Town Council, and the General Council of the University. It received two appeals against the Senatus decision – one from 180 students, the other from Muirhead, Professor of Civil Law, who thought the question had not been fully considered. On 19 April the Court '... considering the difficulties at

[5] Blackwell disliked Jex-Blake. In 1868 she wrote to Barbara Bodichon: 'Miss Jex-Blake is coming to join our class – I'm afraid she won't be very amenable to discipline – but very certainly she must work harder than I have yet known her to do, if she is to gain our diploma.' [EB letter to Barbara Bodichon 28 Oct 1868; EB Collection, Special Collections, Columbia University Library]. Quoted in Sahli – see Ref 2 Chapter 1 (p. 165 – Ref 172).

[6] For her own publishers, Macmillan, Sophia was writing on 'Medicine as a Profession for Women' in *Women's Work and Women's Culture (1869),* edited by Josephine Butler.

[7] A founder of Newnham College, Cambridge.

[8] Christison was a distinguished physician and toxicologist; he was created a baronet in 1871.

present standing in the way of carrying out the resolution of the Senatus, *as a temporary arrangement in the interest of one lady,* and not being prepared to adjudicate finally on the question whether women should be educated in the Medical classes of the University, sustains the appeals and recalls the resolution of the Senatus'.[iv]

This decision was final. Masson said three of the five who voted favoured medical education of women, but given the students' appeal they feared a disturbance if Sophia was admitted. However, he thought an application from six to twelve ladies would succeed. The Principal concurred – *'if a sufficient number of ladies could be found to constitute a small extra-academical class in medical subjects, the University of Edinburgh would be willing to make arrangements for the teaching of such a class, and to examining the lady pupils with a view to awarding them medical degrees'.* [v]

On 15 May Isabel Thorne, hearing of the Court's concern about 'a temporary arrangement in the interest of one lady', wrote offering to join Sophia in a new application. Aged 35, and married with four children, Thorne had lived in China, but returned to Britain with two daughters in 1862. Her husband, Joseph, returned permanently in 1874. Isabel attended Edmunds's Female Medical College when it opened in 1864. Two years later she studied practical midwifery at the City Lying-In Hospital, and practised as an *accoucheuse* in London before deciding to study medicine. She passed the preliminary examination in Arts at the Society of Apothecaries before it ruled, in February 1867, that candidates for its LSA had to have attended a recognized medical school. Having made some arrangements to study in Paris she decided to switch to Edinburgh.[vi]

More support emerged. Josephine Butler told Sophia about Edith Pechey, a woman at Leeds who wished to become a doctor. Pechey had been educated at home by her father, a Baptist minister at Langham near Colchester; her mother taught her Greek.[vii] She joined the fray with two others – Mrs Helen de Lacey Evans, a young widow from Edinburgh, and Matilda Chaplin, one of Isabel Thorne's fellow students at the Female Medical College. Chaplin's mother lived near Barbara Bodichon, and had signed the 1866 women's suffrage petition.

In 1869 Sophia considered possibilities in London. She went along when her mother consulted Thomas King Chambers, a physician at St Mary's Hospital. He supported the idea of women doctors, and thought most London medical schools would accept women as students if they paid for separate anatomical teaching. Arthur Norton, the anatomy lecturer at St Mary's, agreed to teach them. The women applied to all the London medical schools, without success. They wrote to St Mary's as follows:

18 June 1869. *3 Maitland Street, Edinburgh,*

Sir,

We the undersigned request admission as perpetual pupils to the Medical School of St. Mary's Hospital. We are desirous if possible of separate provision for the study of anatomy both by lectures and by dissections and we are ready to be responsible for any extra expenses in which the School may be involved by such an arrangement.

We are, sir,

Yours obediently, Sophia Jex-Blake, Mary Edith Pechey, Isabel Thorne.

The School Committee, anticipating problems with male students, resolved '*that the Dean…inform Miss Blake that the School Committee decline to accede to the request contained in her letter and that she…communicate this decision to the other ladies who…signed the letter.'* Although they did not receive the help they requested, the contact with King Chambers and Norton was to prove invaluable, and Walter Cheadle, elected Dean at that meeting, also became a strong supporter of the women.[viii]

Sophia returned to Edinburgh and asked the Senatus to recommend matriculation of women as medical students if taught in separate classes, for which she guaranteed the fees. She also asked the University Court to remove its veto.

The Medical Faculty and the Senatus approved special classes for women, as did the University Court on 5 July. Efforts followed to support the women planning to study medicine in Edinburgh. Lady Amberley (Bertrand Russell's mother) wrote in her diary on 14 August 1869: *'Miss Garrett is anxious to get some scholarships at Edinburgh for the women who are likely to be allowed to study there as medical students next winter as the senate have admitted them and it has only to be confirmed by the General Council and Chancellor. I have settled to give one of the scholarships of £50 for three years. Miss Garrett gives a third of another.'* [ix]

The following Court resolutions were approved by the General Council on 29 October, sanctioned by the Chancellor, and inserted in the University's *Calendar* under the title 'For the Education of Women in Medicine in the University'.[x]

1. *Women shall be admitted to study of medicine in the University;*
2. *The instruction of women for the profession of medicine shall be conducted in separate classes, confined entirely to women;*
3. *The Professors of the Faculty of Medicine shall, for this purpose, be permitted to have separate classes for women;*

4. *Women, not intending to study medicine professionally, may be admitted to such of these classes, or to such part of the course of instruction given in such classes, as the University Court made from time to time think fit and approve;*
5. *The fee for the full course of instruction in such classes shall be four guineas; but in the event of the number of students proposing to attend any such class being too small to provide a reasonable remuneration at that rate, it shall be in the power of the Professor to make arrangements for a higher fee, subject to the usual sanction of the University Court*
6. *All women attending such classes shall be subject to all the regulations now or at any future time in force in the University as to the matriculation of students, their attendance on classes, Examination, or otherwise;*
7. *The above regulation shall take effect from commencement of session 1869-70.*

Teachers were recruited for the classes, and Sophia helped the other women prepare for the matriculation examination on 19 October. There were 152 examinees; the five women took four of the first seven places. On 2 November each received a matriculation ticket as a *Civis Academiae Edinensis* – they were the first women undergraduates in any British university.[9] They also registered as medical students with the General Council of Medical Education and Registration.

Sophia moved into No 15 Buccleuth Place with her maid Alice and Edith Pechey. Isabel Thorne's family shared an apartment in Lauriston Place with Matilda Chaplin. Chemistry and physiology courses began in November. All seemed well.

When in March 1870 the women sat for examinations Edith Pechey came third in chemistry. As the two men above her were repeating the class she should have been awarded the Hope scholarship – endowed by a former professor of chemistry with money received for giving lectures to ladies! But it went to a man. The teacher, Crum Brown, explained that Edith was not strictly a member of the class as the women received tuition at a different hour. Paradoxically, he awarded her the bronze medal, for which only class members were eligible, and in the published list placed the women according to their marks. There was widespread public indignation, fuelled by comments in *The Times*, *Spectator* and even the *British Medical Journal*. Pechey appealed to the Senatus which decided, by one vote, that she was not entitled to the Hope scholarship but, also by one vote, that the women should have ordinary class certificates! Many years later Isabel Thorne wrote that

[9] Except for James Barry. (see Chapter 1)

this dispute caused much bad feeling and probably accounted for so many of their subsequent difficulties.[xi]

At the University's next General Council (i.e. all graduates who had registered as members), Masson's motion that women should attend ordinary classes was lost by 47 to 58. Even the Dean, who wanted them in his ordinary botany class, had to teach them separately. Allman would not take two classes for natural history so the women approached Alleyne Nicholson of the Extra-Mural School; his courses were outside the jurisdiction of the university. The university recognized lectures by extra-mural teachers approved by the College of Surgeons or Physicians, but only four such classes could bc taken towards the degree. Nicholson's male students agreed the women could join them. This first 'mixed class' continued through the summer of 1870.[xii]

For the new academic year the original five women were joined by Emily Bovell and Mary Anderson; the latter was the sister of John Ford Anderson, Elizabeth's old Middlesex friend, and of Skelton Anderson, Elizabeth's future husband. The group, soon known as the 'Septem contra Edinem', needed teachers for anatomy and clinical subjects which started in the second year. They were welcome at Patrick Heron Watson's surgery lectures, and Peter Handyside, the only recognised extra-mural teacher of anatomy, admitted them to his ordinary class and into the dissecting-room. These mixed classes infringed the University Court's second resolution on the medical education of women, but when this issue was raised the Senatus did not interfere, thanks to the Principal's casting vote, and so the classes continued. On 28 October the General Council considered extending facilities for the women students but, after Christison asserted that Queen Victoria opposed women in medicine, the motion was lost by 46 to 47 – one of the many defeats by an agonisingly small margin.[xiii]

For clinical teaching the women applied to the Royal Infirmary, the only Edinburgh hospital big enough to fulfil the requirements for registration. Its Board of Managers refused the application on 31 October 1870. It was asked to reconsider. Handyside and Heron Watson supported the women, and papers were presented from clinicians willing to allow female students to attend their wards. Most of the Managers, a small group elected by and from contributors to the Infirmary, were prepared to accede, but the women's opponents got the matter deferred for a week. Before it was reconsidered about 500 male students signed a petition against admitting women to the Infirmary; that settled the matter.[xiv]

The male students' behaviour now deteriorated, culminating on 18 November 1870 with the infamous 'Riot at Surgeons' Hall'. The *Courant* (the only Edinburgh morning paper unfavourable to the women) reported – *'Shortly before four o'clock, ...when the ladies arrived at the college, nearly 200 students assembled in front of the gate...[the ladies]...advanced towards the gate, the students opening up their ranks to allow them to pass. On reaching the gate it was closed in their face. Amidst the derisive laughter ..., it must be said to their credit that a number of students cried "shame." In a short time the janitor opened one leaf of the gate and the ladies were admitted ..., but not before some...had been considerably jostled. The anatomical classroom...was crowded to the door, and...[because]... of the noise and interruption, Dr Handyside found it utterly impossible to begin his demonstrations. With much difficulty, he singled out those students belonging to his class, and, turning the others out of the room, he was about to proceed, when the pet sheep which grazes at the College was introduced to the room, a student jocularly remarking that it would be a good subject for anatomical purposes. Poor 'Mailie' was kept a prisoner, and the lecturer was allowed to proceed.'* Apparently Handyside said *'Let the sheep remain, it has more sense than those who sent it here.'* [xv]

There was more trouble after the class, but the women were protected by a male escort led by George Hoggan[10] and Robert Wilson, both lifelong supporters of women in medicine. One of the women was Mrs Kingsley, wife of the editor of the *Daily Review*; her husband, like Alexander Russel, championed the women's cause. She attended classes not to qualify but to identify with the cause. Wilson told Edith Pechey the real cause of the riots was the professors' attitude to the women; warning of more trouble, he recruited the 'Irish Brigade' of students to help. The indignation aroused by press reports of the 'Riot' was far greater than that over the Hope Scholarship.[xvi]

Managers of the Royal Infirmary were elected annually at a contributors' (subscribers) meeting. Owing to overcrowding the one on 2 January 1871 was moved to St Giles' Cathedral. Duncan McLaren, MP for Edinburgh, was there supporting the women. Twice widowed, his third wife was Patricia Bright McLaren, the Quaker suffragist. His daughter Agnes, already engaged in suffrage work, was Sophia's friend and in November 1872 became a fellow medical student. The Lord Provost proposed six men favouring admission of the women; a doctor from the Infirmary proposed the six already on the Board. A petition was read, signed by 956 women of Edinburgh, expressing *'our earnest hope that full facilities for hospital study will be afforded by the managers to all women who desire to enter the medical profession'*. After a heated discussion the women's slate was defeated by 88 to 94.[xvii]

---

[10] In 1874, Hoggan married Dr Frances Morgan; it was Britain's first 'medical marriage'.

The Lord Provost, William Law, stung by the defeat, called a meeting which created a *'Committee for Securing a Complete Medical Education to Women in Edinburgh'* (CSCMEWE). Its goals were to understand the real difficulties of the case; to secure admission of women to Edinburgh University on ordinary terms, though not necessarily in mixed classes; and to provide them with suitable hospital instruction. Crucially, it also decided to 'aid them in obtaining such legal assistance as may be required to ascertain and assert their rights as matriculated students of the University, and as registered students of medicine'. Many important and influential people supported it. The Lord Provost was its Chairman, Louisa Stevenson its Honorary Secretary.[xviii]

Sophia, a contributor to the Infirmary, spoke at the election meeting and said, rather impulsively, *'This I do know, that the riot was not wholly or mainly due to the students at Surgeons' Hall. I know that Dr Christison's class assistant was one of the leading rioters – and the foul language he used could only be excused on the supposition I heard that he was intoxicated. I do not say that Dr Christison knew of or sanctioned his presence, but I do say that that I think he would not have been there, had he thought that the doctor would have strongly objected to his presence.'* Dr Christison objected to the suggestion that his assistant Craig (also a medical student) was intoxicated; Sophia replied *' if Dr Christison prefers that I should say he used the language when sober, I will withdraw the other supposition.'* Craig brought an action for libel against Sophia.[xix]

The case, which started on 31 May 1871 and lasted two days, was reported in the *Scotsman* and other papers as a remarkable example of legal chicanery. Reliable people had told Sophia that Craig was a ringleader in the riot, but she did not see him. Her counsel therefore advised her not to give evidence, allowing the truth to emerge through questioning of Craig and other witnesses. Because Sophia did not enter the witness box Craig's counsel, Shand, objected successfully to all questioning of Craig and other witnesses relating to his involvement in the riot; it was not even established he was present. The jury found in his favour, but assessed damages at one farthing.[11] Sophia had to pay the entire cost – £915 11s 1d. One of the jury wrote to the *Scotsman* claiming the Clerk of the Court misled them on several issues; they did not intend damages to be awarded against Sophia and, but for the Clerk's opinions, their verdict would probably have favoured her. A lawyer suggested Sophia should appeal, on the grounds either of the Clerk's interference or that the decision of the judges was wrong.[xx]

Within weeks well-wishers covered the whole cost of the libel action,[12] and after all expenses were paid £100 was added to a 'nest-egg' for funding women's

---

[11] A farthing was a quarter of a penny (at that time 240 pennies made a pound).

[12] Thomas Jex-Blake sent money to pay half his sister's expenses; it was not needed.

hospitals staffed by women. Mrs Henry Kingsley and Louisa Stevenson (called 'Pussy' by the women students) were the treasurers of the fund.[xxi]

The women's difficulties continued. Because Surgeons' Hall rescinded *'permission given last summer to those lecturers who desired to admit ladies to their classes'* they had to organize separate classes in another building. More worryingly, the original students had taken the four classes allowed with extra-mural teachers. The next subject was Christison's; he refused to take them at a university class. In June 1871 Sophia asked the Senatus either to appoint special University lecturers, or to relax the regulations so that they could take more extra-mural classes. However, on 28 July her appeal was rejected by a single vote; Lister seconded the motion against the women.[xxii] The Lord Provost's new committee (CSCMEWE) took legal advice and in September the Lord Advocate and the Sheriff, Patrick Fraser, said the University could make any necessary provision for the completion of the ladies' education, and that the Medical Faculty was bound to admit the ladies to professional examination in the subjects they were already qualified to pass.[xxiii]

The last point was important; it was rumoured that new women entering would be unable to take the Preliminary Examination in Arts and matriculate – and, more seriously, that those who had been studying for two years would be excluded from the First Professional Examination on 24 October 1871. Wilson, the University Secretary, wrote on 13 October that he told the Clerk to receive the money for the latter exam, but that the Medical Faculty then instructed the Dean to inform each woman *'that your name and your fees...were received in error by the Clerk...as a candidate for the first professional examination..., but that the Faculty cannot receive you for such examination without the sanction of the Senatus Academicus'*.

A similar letter, sent to Sophia the day before the Preliminary Examination, stated the Dean was *'interdicted by the Faculty from giving examination papers to ladies on the 17th and 18th curt. Kindly communicate this fact to the ladies whose names you some time ago handed in to me for this examination'*. The ladies (Mundy, Dahms & Miller) were already in Edinburgh.[xxiv] As Patrick Fraser had declared such action illegal the Dean allowed the examinations to take place but told the women that following representations by Christison the Principal had decided they could not matriculate. On appeal the Senatus, on 21 October, permitted them to matriculate and told the Medical Faculty to examine those taking the First Professional Examination. All passed; sadly, owing to her efforts fighting their battles, Sophia did not take the examination.[xxv]

These results were not the only reason for celebration. Mary Anderson became

Mrs Marshall in autumn 1871.[13] In October Mrs de Lacy Evans became engaged to Mr Russel of the *Scotsman*; and in December Matilda Chaplin married her cousin, William Edward Ayrton, a young engineer. Only de Lacy Evans gave up her studies.

Friends wanted to persuade the University to appoint special university lecturers, or to relax the regulations so that the women could take more extra-mural classes. At General Council Dr Alexander Wood moved that *'the University Court…is bound in honour and justice to render it possible for these women who have already commenced their studies, to complete them'*. Nine thousand women signed a memorial in support. Shrewdly, Professor Turner (an opponent) quoted Sophia's letter to the Dean two years earlier signalling her willingness *'to withdraw my application altogether if, after due and sufficient trial, it should be found impracticable to grant me a continuance of the favour which I now request'*. An amendment leaving the matter to the Senatus and the University Court was carried by 107 to 97.[xxvi] But, as Sophia pointed out in the *Scotsman,* the letter quoted referred only to the tentative proposal that she, without matriculation, should attend Balfour and Allman's summer courses; this proposal the University had rejected, *'deferring the whole question till a permanent plan could be arranged and formerly sanctioned by all the necessary authorities, — which was finally accomplished after eight months of consideration and delay'*.[xxvii]

The Senatus debated the matter on 30 October 1871. CSCMEWE had written that, *'in the event of special lecturers being appointed…to give qualifying instruction to women, the Committee…guarantee the payment to them of any sum…fixed by the Senatus for their remuneration, in case the fees of the ladies are insufficient for the purpose; and…are willing…to provide such rooms and accommodation as may be required for the delivery of the said lectures, if it* [is]*…impossible for the University to provide space for that purpose.*' The Senatus, having agreed the women should take the First Professional Examination, decided against any steps enabling them to complete their education and voted, by 14 to 13, to recommend to the Court that the November 1869 regulations regarding female students be rescinded, without prejudice to the rights of those already in place. As 18 of the 35 professors of the University protested against this decision the regulations could not be rescinded; instead, on 3 January 1872, the Court confirmed them. Everything remained *in statu quo*. [xxviii]

However, two long legal battles then started – the first about the election of the managers at the Royal Infirmary; the second about the University's responsibility for allowing the women to complete their course and to graduate.

[13] Sadly her husband died within months; their son died at birth.

At the annual meeting of contributors to the Royal Infirmary held on 1 January 1872 the election of managers turned again on admission of women students to the wards. This time the six 'women's candidates' were elected by 177 to 166. Masson then proposed *'That henceforward all registered students of Medicine shall be admitted to the educational advantages of the Infirmary without distinction of sex, – all details of arrangements, however, being left to the discretion of the managers'*. This was carried unanimously because those opposed had left en masse.[xxix]

Two weeks later it was announced that twenty-eight firms, thirty-one ladies and seven doctors voted for the women and fourteen firms, two ladies and thirty-seven doctors against. The Lord Provost was forbidden to declare the new managers duly elected, on the ground that the votes of firms were incompetent, and that they had determined the majority! The *Scotsman* commented *'it mattered nothing that firms had voted ever since the Infirmary was founded; that contributors qualified only as members of firms had ..., sat over and over again on the Board of Management, and on the Committee of Contributors...that the firms whom it was now sought to disqualify had been among the most generous benefactors of the charity ... The firms had voted in favour of the ladies, and the firms must go, if, at least, the law would (as it probably will not) bear out the medical men in their reckless endeavour to expel them.'* The issue went to court but the firms' votes were not declared valid until 23 July. The case then went to a higher court and the final judgment, favouring the women on all points, was delayed until December.[xxx]

So in 1872 the women could not enter the hospital because the incomplete Board of Managers carried on without the newly elected contributors and ignored the Statute enacted in January. When the final judgment came the women's party – worried that new managers, unfriendly to the women, might be elected at the next annual meeting – called a contributors' meeting for 18 December, and another for 23 December. They voted to admit women to the Infirmary; their visits were to be separate from those of the men, and they could only go to wards if invited by the relevant doctors. The women got their tickets and began to attend the wards with Heron Watson and George Balfour.

Unfortunately at the election in January 1873 the ladies' slate lost by 279 to 271, making further concessions unlikely. However the surgeon Heron Watson taught the women gratis on Sunday mornings. The managers tried to stop him – arguing he should observe the Sabbath – but Cowan, the new Lord Provost, attended a Sunday session and persuaded the managers to allow the teaching to continue. The physician Balfour gave the women an hour in his wards three times a week, plus opportunities for practical work. A sense of fair play led Dr Peel Ritchie, who was unsympathetic to the women's cause, to give up his men's class at the Royal Dispensary to teach the women instead.[xxxi]

Some supporters encouraged the women to go to law to ensure they could finish their studies and graduate. Sophia made a last appeal to the University Court. She sent it the opinions of the Lord Advocate and Sheriff Fraser – that the University was empowered to matriculate women in 1869, that resolutions passed then amounted to a permission to women to *'study medicine'* in the University, and that the women were therefore entitled to demand the means of doing so, and that if these means were refused, the legal mode of redress lay in an Action of Declarator.

On 8 January 1872, five days after confirming the November 1869 regulations, the Court, with Christison as its only medical man, decided not to comply with the women's requirements for teaching – the whole question being *'complicated by the introduction of the subject of graduation, which is not essential to the completion of a medical or other education'*. The women should give up the idea of graduation and be content with certificates of proficiency. Sophia pointed out that *'though a degree is not essential to a medical education, it is absolutely indispensable to any practical use of it, — that is to any lawful practice of the medical profession'*. She offered to waive the question of graduation, pending an authoritative decision about the powers and duties of the University, if arrangements could be made for the women to continue their education. The Court agreed; but it would count no classes taken as 'qualifying', and it would not help them to become legally qualified doctors. So the women brought an Action of Declarator. On 27 March the Senatus decided to defend the summons, although six members[14] protested there was no just cause to oppose admission of women to the study of medicine.[xxxii]

The historic lawsuit came before Lord Gifford, the Lord Ordinary, on 17 July 1872. Sheriff Fraser and John McLaren argued the case well. The latter (later Lord McLaren) was the son of Duncan McLaren MP, and junior counsel in Sophia's libel case. Gifford found that, *'according to the...constitution and regulations of the...University of Edinburgh, the pursuers are entitled to be admitted to the study of medicine...and...to all the rights and privileges of lawful students in the said University, subject only to the conditions...in the said regulations of 12 November 1869:...that the pursuers, on completing the prescribed studies, and on compliance with all the existing regulations of the University preliminary to degrees, are entitled to proceed to examination for degrees in manner prescribed by the regulations of the University of Edinburgh.'* He also stated that while the Senatus could not direct professors to admit women to their ordinary classes, and that the University Court could do so only by altering certain regulations, the Court could

[14] Professors Hughes Bennett, Masson, Calderwood, Lorimer, Charteris & Ballantyne Hodgson. Only Hughes Bennett was a member of the Medical Faculty.

recognize extra-academical teachers who could give instruction in separate classes.[xxxiii] The women and their supporters were delighted.[15]

Owing to the difficulty of arranging classes the women scattered for the summer of 1872. Matilda Chaplin Ayrton & Emily Bovell went to Paris; Massingberd Mundy & Anna Dahms to Dr Lucy Sewall in Boston; and Edith Pechey to the Endell Street Lying-in Hospital in London. One student, Rose Anna Shedlock, went to Italy for five weeks in May 1872 to obtain evidence about the admission of women to the principal Italian universities. Shedlock then also went to Paris, and in 1878 married Émile Roux, a young man destined to become one of the great French medical scientists. Sadly Shedlock died in 1879.[xxxiv]

Sophia remained in Edinburgh. On the strength of Lord Gifford's judgment she rented a small house to serve as a medical school and arranged the winter's teaching. She engaged Dr George Hoggan to teach practical anatomy but, although he had been a lecturer with Handyside, the University would not 'recognize' the teaching he gave that winter.[16]

Matters in Edinburgh came to the attention of Parliament, perhaps because of Sophia's talk to a large meeting at St George's Hall, London on 25 April 1872 at which the Earl of Shaftesbury took the chair. That August Sir David Wedderburn MP proposed reducing funding for Scottish Universities by a sum equal to the combined salaries of Edinburgh's medical professors. No vote was taken as it was hoped the University would accept Gifford's judgment.[xxxv] However, the University appealed and Edinburgh's Court of Sessions reversed the judgment in June 1873. Five judges were for the women, seven against (including Shand, who defended Craig in the libel trial, and Mure, the judge in that case).[xxxvi] They decided that by admitting women to the University in 1869 the University Court acted illegally; the authorities were therefore excused responsibility for the women, who had to pay the expenses of both sides – about £850. Although the women took extra-mural classes until March 1874 the reversal of the judgment effectively ended the hard fought 'Battle of Edinburgh'.

In those difficult days the women's behaviour was admirable. The younger ones pursued their education where and how they could. In the summer of 1873 they studied medical jurisprudence with Dr Littlejohn,[xxxvii] and the following winter took clinical medicine with George Balfour. Isabel Thorne arranged for other extra-mural lecturers to teach midwifery, materia medica and pathology – the lecturers for the last two subjects having to apply to the University of St Andrew's for the recognition necessary to 'legitimise' their lectures. Sophia took honours in all subjects.[xxxviii]

---

[15] One who wrote to congratulate Sophia was Frances Anstie – see later.

[16] Rose Anna Shedlock was a witness at Hoggan's marriage to Frances Morgan in 1874.

After the reversal of Lord Gifford's judgment Sir David Wedderburn gave notice, on 29 July 1873, of a bill to grant Scottish Universities the power to educate women in medicine and to give them ordinary medical degrees.[xxxix] However, Garrett Anderson, opposed to Sophia's efforts in Edinburgh, argued in *The Times* of 5 August 1873 that the time was not ripe for medical education of women in Britain. Although she had tried to set up a small school herself in 1866, she now suggested women could best serve the cause *'by going to Paris to study medicine, and returning here as soon as might be to practise it.'* She recognised that Paris graduates could not register as medical practitioners in Britain but made light of this disadvantage. As a practical approach to the problem her suggestion was clearly absurd. Sophia wrote a long, detailed reply,[xl] arguing that while *'no means of education are provided at home, only a very small number of women will ever seek admission to the profession…few things would please our opponents better than to see one Englishwoman after another driven out of her own country to obtain medical education abroad, both because they know that on her return after years of labour, she can claim no legal recognition whatever, and because they are equally certain that, so long as no means of education are provided at home, only a very small number of women will ever seek admission to the profession.*'

In April 1871 Sophia had met James Stansfeld, MP for Halifax, when she spoke at a suffrage meeting in London, Stansfeld was a friend of Jessie White (Mario) who had sought medical training in London in 1856. (See Chapter 1) His wife, Caroline Ashurst, was a prominent suffragist. Stansfeld, a barrister, did not practise law; his income came from his Swan brewery in Fulham.[xli] Elizabeth Wolstenholme told Sophia that Stansfeld supported medical education for women and would help. Sophia met him again in April 1872 when she spoke at St George's Hall. That December he introduced her to three colleagues in Gladstone's government; John Simon, Chief Medical Officer of the Local Government Board (of which Stansfeld was President); Lord Ripon, Lord President of Council; and Robert Lowe, then Chancellor of the Exchequer.[xlii]

Wedderburn's Bill needed the Liberal Government's support if it was to pass and Sophia's links with Stansfeld, Lowe and other ministers were now invaluable. She contacted Lowe, now Home Secretary, and in January 1874 met Sir John Lubbock, Lord Aberdare, Grant Duff, Thomas Hughes and the Russell Gurneys.[xliii] Lowe, the University of London's MP, received a memorial from 471 graduates, including 61 medical graduates, supporting degrees for women. It was organised by Dr Alfred Shewen, a medical graduate.[17] Lowe said he would bring in a suitable bill if Cabinet colleagues would support it. However, Gladstone dissolved

17 Shewen later taught at LSMW. He married Edith Pechey's sister.

Parliament and then lost the election. In February Disraeli's Conservatives formed a new government. Wedderburn had not stood for re-election.

At Stansfeld's suggestion Sophia contacted Russell Gurney, a Conservative MP,[18] to suggest he take up a bill with Lowe (now out of office). Gurney said he would support a bill brought in by Lowe, but Stansfeld thought it unwise to have it introduced by an ex-Cabinet minister. In March 1874 W.F. Cowper-Temple (simply Cowper until 1869) told Stansfeld he would support a good bill and asked Sophia for 'a lawyer who knows the subject and will frame a bill or advise about it'. She suggested White Millar, her solicitor in Edinburgh. Cowper-Temple persuaded Gurney, Orr Ewing and Dr Cameron to sign a bill that would 'remove doubts as to the powers of the Universities of Scotland to admit women as students and to grant degrees to women'. Parliament received sixty-five petitions supporting it – from the town councils of Edinburgh, Aberdeen, and Linlithgow; the City of Edinburgh; the Edinburgh lecturers who taught the women; 26 Scottish Professors, including 13 from Edinburgh and the Principals of St Andrews and Glasgow; and one from 16,000 women. There were only four petitions against the Bill; three from the old enemies in Edinburgh – the University Court, Senatus and the Medical Faculty – and the fourth from the University of Glasgow, which opposed it despite the favourable views of its Principal.[xliv]

The bill's second reading was fixed for 24 April 1874 but Lyon Playfair, Edinburgh University's MP, had it postponed – 'in order that his University might have time to consider the subject'! This effectively shelved it for another year. Subsequently he used Parliamentary machinery to shelve it indefinitely. However, the motion was debated on 12 June 1874 and Cowper-Temple, Stansfeld and others supported it. Speeches by the two Edinburgh members were in marked contrast. Duncan McLaren (Town) said intelligent inhabitants of Edinburgh would vote nine-tenths in favour and *'If two or three of the Professors would only take a voyage around the world, the whole question would be settled before they returned. Where male students paid three or four guineas for each class, the ladies paid eight or ten guineas, so money was no obstacle. There was no difficulty...except want of will, and that arose from medical prejudice, — at least that was the opinion of [most] people in Edinburgh.*' Lyon Playfair (Gown), who had supported Sophia in 1869, had a harder task. *Punch* thought him 'one in a perplexity between his constituents and his convictions.' Although no vote was taken the publicity helped the women, but there was no hope of returning to Edinburgh. They could have appealed to the House of Lords, but as Stansfeld wrote three years later, 'that would have meant further indefinite delay and further heavy expense, and then, if the

[18] In 1870 Russell Gurney introduced the Married Women's Property Bill.

result were favourable, a probable refusal of the University to act on their ascertained powers.'[xlv]

At the end of October 1872 Sophia had taken the examinations she deferred a year earlier. She failed. Devastated, she thought her natural history paper was unfairly treated. Edith Pechey sought T.H. Huxley's opinion on the paper. It was unfavourable. When commenting on the parliamentary proceedings in 1874 *The Times* stated it was 'amusing…that one of the Ladies who had rendered herself most conspicuous should…have failed under the test of examination.' Isabel Thorne wrote in *The Times* of 18 June 1874, mentioning Sophia by name, that it was 'devotion to our cause which led to her failure…she had borne the brunt of the battle, and had spared her fellow-students all the harass and worry of the struggle, and had thus enabled them to enjoy the leisure requisite for passing their examinations.'

Sophia, furious at this explanation of her failure, was now guilty of a serious error of judgment. She wrote to *The Times* (20 June) implying unfair treatment in the examination. Five of the six examiners replied and Huxley wrote defending his friend Wyville Thomson (who was away on the *Challenger* expedition).[19] Sophia challenged them to submit her papers, and those of candidates who had passed, to an unbiased referee. To their suggestion that she could have appealed to the University Court, the Senatus or the Medical Faculty she pointed out that those she was accusing would then have judged the issue. But public opinion, like her friends, was against Sophia. Louisa Stevenson and Isabel Thorne both wrote to her about the 'irreparable' damage the letter had done. Prudent friends stopped Edith Pechey from publishing a letter suggesting that if Huxley had examined Edinburgh's male students ninety per cent of them would have failed.[xlvi]

While at Edinburgh the women explored the possibility of studying somewhere else. In 1873 they approached Birmingham, St Andrews, the Irish schools and Newcastle Medical School (affiliated to the University of Durham), but to no avail. With no chance of a degree they tried, unsuccessfully, to arrange qualification as licentiates of the Royal Colleges, or of the Apothecaries in either London or Dublin.[xlvii]

After Gifford's judgment in 1872 Francis Anstie sent Sophia a letter of support. She now asked him about prospects at Westminster Hospital. On 6 December 1873 he wrote *'…I do not see…any practical plan at present. At Westminster…possible that my colleagues would consent to separate classes. But the fatal objection is want of space;…I fear there is no way, except by the ladies raising money enough to found a School for themselves…[Then] I, and I think others, would…go out of*

[19] The *Challenger* expedition helped to lay the foundations of oceanography.

our way to afford them teaching. But the difficulties about clinical teaching seem very great'. Six days later he thought the Westminster Hospital School staff would not surrender their position as teachers of male students – *'... your best course would be to take some premises in London, and build a thoroughly good School, fit for first-class teaching of the theoretical courses...if that were done you would get teachers. And with a solid evidence of sincerity and energy in your work I believe the hospitals, or some of them, would...grant you hospital practice.'* He wrote again on 2 July 1874 to tell Sophia that London University's Senate had rejected Convocation's petition to admit women to all its degrees. *'I think there is nothing for it now but...to form a School for yourselves...I do not think there would be any very great difficulty in obtaining clinical instruction and in becoming recognised by some of the corporations. I am sorry to have had no better luck as your champion. But there is no doubt just now for some reason or other, a strong current of adverse opinion'*. Arthur Norton also assured Sophia that *'a thoroughly good School might be organised, apart from the existing schools, but with friendly lecturers gathered from any or all of them'*.[xlviii]

Sophia travelled from Perthshire to London and met Anstie and Norton on 13 August. With King Chambers they recruited medical friends willing to start a school for the women displaced from Edinburgh. A meeting was arranged to which Garrett Anderson, eight months pregnant, was invited. She wrote expressing her reluctance to attend. She may have wished to distance herself from a project with no chance of success or, disliking Sophia, she may not have wanted Sophia to receive the credit for opening the profession to women. Sophia replied the day before the meeting took place:

Hampstead, 21st August 1874

'If I kept a record of all the people who bring me cock and bull stories about you, and assure me that you are "greatly injuring the cause" I might fill as many pages with quotations as you have patience to read, but, beyond defending you on a good many occasions, I have never thought it needful to take much notice of such incidents, still less to retail them to you.

Nor do I much care to know whether or no certain anonymous individuals have confided to you that they lay at my door what you call 'the failure at Edinburgh,'— inasmuch as the only people really competent to judge of that point are my fellow workers and fellow students, such as Professor Watson, Professor Bennett, Miss Stevenson, Mrs Thorne, Miss Pechey, Dr Watson, and Dr Balfour, and I do not fancy that it is from any of these that you heard the comments in question.

It can, as I say, serve no purpose whatever to go into this sort of gossip which is very rarely indeed founded on any knowledge of fact; but, quite apart from any such discussion, I am more than willing to say that if, in the opinion of a majority of those who are organising this new school, my name appears likely to injure its chances of success, I will cheerfully stand aside, and let Mrs Thorne and Miss Pechey carry out the almost completed plans.

So much for your second objection [to joining the Council of the School] which I have taken first, because I feel that the other is for your own consideration and Dr Anstie's, and that it is needless for me to say anything on the point.

In conclusion let me say that I never said it "did not signify" whether you joined the Council (though I did say that I believed the School was already tolerably secure of ultimate success). I think it of very great importance, both for your credit and ours, that there should, as you say, be no appearance of split in the camp, and I should greatly prefer that your name should appear on the Council with Dr Blackwell's and those of the medical men who are helping us.'[xlix]

On 22 August 1874 Sophia, Anstie and Norton met at Anstie's home, 16 Wimpole Street, with Edith Pechey, Drs Burdon-Sanderson, Buchanan, Sturges and Cheadle, and the surgeon George Critchett. King Chambers took the chair. Despite the advanced stage of her pregnancy Garrett Anderson attended.[20]

The first resolution was that a *'school be formed in London with a view to educating women in medicine and of enabling them to pass such examinations as would place their names on the Medical Register'*. Anstie (Fig 2.2) was to be Dean. After qualifying at King's in 1856, he was elected Assistant Physician (1860) and Physician (1873) at Westminster Hospital.[l]

The Provisional Council of the new school was to include only qualified medical practitioners – namely those present plus Elizabeth Blackwell, Dr Archibald Billing, Dr Frank Payne and Mr Berkeley Hill; Sophia was to attend as Honorary Secretary. Except for Dr Murie (physiology) and Dr William Smout Playfair (midwifery) the lectureships went to members of the Council. The School was to open on 12 October 1874 – fifty-one days later! Although Garrett Anderson was a member of Council, it was some time before she took any part in the daily life and work of the School.

On 29 August Sophia, Isabel Thorne, Cheadle and Norton were made trustees of any funds or property to be acquired. Sophia resigned as Honorary Secretary, not wishing to hold two positions. The Provisional Council drew up regulations and set

[20] From this point most of the detail about the story of the School comes from the minutes of Council, and I give dates of Council meetings to facilitate reference.

Fig 2.2 Francis Anstie (1833-1874)

fees – subject to confirmation by a permanent council. The three-year course of lectures required by examining boards was to cost £80, or £85 if paid in annual instalments; separate subjects cost £8.8.0 during the winter, £5.5.0 in the summer. Fees were lower for students who had been at Edinburgh. Those not intending to practise medicine could attend classes on payment of the relevant fees.

That meeting accepted the offer of Ernest Hart, editor of the *British Medical Journal (BMJ)*, and a prominent member of the Jewish community, of a scholarship of £57 for three years. It also invited him to join the Provisional Council. His second wife Alice (née Rowland), was a medical student in Paris, and joined the new school in its first year.

At its third and fourth meetings (on 2 & 5 September) Council agreed the Dean should write to the Society of Apothecaries and the Colleges asking for a list of the requirements to be met before they would recognize a medical school. The Colleges were to be informed that the objective of the London School of Medicine for Women (LSMW) was the education of women.

At those meetings the trustees and the Dean were empowered to take suitable premises for the school. Funds were needed. Thirteen individuals each gave £100.[li] They were Sophia and her mother; Isabel Thorne, her husband Joseph, and her brother-in-law Augustus; E. M. Smith a friend of the Thornes from Shanghai; Andrew Coventry (of CSCMEWE); Mrs Holland of Liverpool; Edward Pease of Darlington; Jonathan Priestman of Newcastle; Walter Thomson, a Scotsman resident in India who had given £1000 to the women when they were in Edinburgh;[lii] Mrs Pennington; and Sir Francis Goldsmid MP. The Priestmans and Penningtons were famous radical liberal families, linked by marriage to the Brights and McClarens. Garrett Anderson did not contribute.

Sophia found *'a wonderfully suitable premises'* – the Pavilion House, 30 Henrietta Street, Brunswick Square, on the Foundling Hospital estate. Her diary entry for 15 September states *'Actually signed lease and got possession of 30 Henrietta Street. Rigged up some kind of beds and slept there that night, — Alice coming from Wales to help me.'*[21] Her stay there was brief. By 9 October she occupied 32 Bernard Street, her new private residence.[liii]

On 19 September the Foundling Hospital committee considered Sophia's request to put up a garden room to use for lectures and dissection. It refused, objecting to the Pavilion being used other than as a private dwelling house. However, dissection took place at the School despite the Foundling's unwillingness to condone it officially.

In 1873 Tommy Cooke opened his celebrated private anatomy school in the burial ground of St George the Martyr – the ground being outside the Foundling's jurisdiction; Cooke, an American raised in France, was apparently a mediocre surgeon but a remarkable anatomy teacher, popular with those needing to re-sit examinations. His school, entered via Henrietta Mews, off Henrietta Street, contained a dissecting-room and a tank for seventeen cadavers.[liv] Although within a hundred yards of the Pavilion there is nothing to suggest any LSMW woman attended it.[22]

---

[21] According to Todd (p88) Alice was Sophia's maid from 1860.

[22] Cooke lived at 40 Brunswick Square. He died in 1899 but the school continued until about 1914. One of his daughters married R. R. Garratt, RFH's Secretary from 1911-1934.

Fig 2.3 The Pavilion Holborn (from 1820s Bill of Sale)

The Pavilion had been a grand residence. (Fig 2.3) An 'advertisement of sale' dated 1810 described it *'...on the ground plan nearly 100 feet by 35, and lawn upwards of 100 feet square...The suite of principal apartments, extending 100 feet in front, and opening to a Varender* [sic], *or Stone Colonnade six feet wide, communicates with the Pleasure Ground or Gardens, laid down in Lawn, and planted with Shrubs. They consist of a Vestibule; Library or Audience room, 17 by 15; Eating room, 25 by 17; Hall, 12 by 10.6; Drawing room 24 by 17; and Withdrawing-room, 17 by 14: a singular and commodious Staircase, 16 feet diameter; Waiting room, and all other suitable offices; Coach-house and 4-stall stabling, etc. with Loft and Coachman's room over ditto. The Bedrooms,...* [seven], *...are all on one Floor, detached from the servants, and particularly airy. The exterior parts of the Edifice have not been less attended to, in architectural proportion & symmetry.'* [lv]

Helen Webb, writing in 1924,[lvi] described it as she first saw it in the late 1870s.

'*... I knocked at its door, a little postern in the wall of what was then Henrietta Street, now Handel Street...opened by...Miss Fanny Butler...She brought me into the little room on the left near the door, which I afterwards knew well as Miss Heaton's office...As Miss Butler talked I looked out on the beautiful garden...all green grass with shrubs and great burdock plants. In the middle stood the weeping ash,...The garden was surrounded on three sides by high walls,...bounded on the* *south by Henrietta Street, by Wakefield Street on the east, and on the north by the backyards of the houses in Compton Street. The entire length of the western side was occupied by the house, of which...nothing now remains. The back of this building was against the houses in Hunter Street,...destroyed to clear the site for the present School. The old house, once a charming villa, dated from the early...19th century,...said to have been built by Frederick Duke of York, son of George III.*[23]

Standing at the little postern in Henrietta Street one looked straight along a stone-flagged verandah which ran the whole length of the house. On to this the French windows of all the downstairs rooms as well as the hall door opened on the left. (Fig 2.4)

Fig 2.4 The Pavilion Verandah

...Walking along the verandah one first passed the door of a little passage, into which the Secretary's office opened, then came the window of that office, and after that the windows of a room, which in summer was the chemical laboratory and in winter the lecture room. This room was also entered from the Secretary's office, a way chiefly used by the lecturers and new arrivals. Half-way along the verandah one reached the hall door, which opened into a wide hall with a beautifully proportioned double staircase. (Fig 2.5) *On the left in this hall was the door of the*

[23] According to Scharlieb (*Reminiscences*, p71) & Lord Riddell (*Dame Louisa Aldrich-Blake*, p.49) it was the home of Mrs Fitzherbert, George IV's mistress but there may have been confusion with her house at Brunswick Sq. Brighton.

Fig 2.5 Pavilion Staircase

Chemistry room,...and on the right that of the "long room," so-called because it extended to the far end of the building. It had three or four windows onto the verandah,...the original drawing-room of the house. For us it was a dissecting-room in the winter, in summer a lecture-room. Upstairs were several small rooms it is hardly necessary to describe, which were used for various purposes. While those on the ground floor were lofty, with elaborate cornices and handsome doors, those above were low, with small square sash windows.'

Alice Hart, also writing in 1924, described the building in 1874 as consisting '*of a long, low white house, standing in a forlorn and neglected garden,...From the ceiling of the drawing room, which became our dissecting room, still hung the chandelier with its cut glass pendants:...but the whole place was dreary and comfortless'*.[lvii]

Council met in the new building on 5 October. Anstie had died unexpectedly on 12 September, aged forty.[24] Norton became Dean, and King Chambers a trustee. It was Elizabeth Blackwell's first attendance. Her letters at the time reveal her low opinion of Sophia, and her inflated opinion of her own importance to the new school. She wrote: *I find myself...drawn in more & more into the organization of a "London School of Medicine for Women"...begun...rather prematurely by Miss Jex-Blake, supported by a highly esteemed physician Dr. Anstie -- Miss Jex-Blake is a dangerous person from her power and want of tact -- Dr. Anstie controlled her, but he suddenly died – I now seem compelled to step in and try now for my experience and judgment can supply the control that has suddenly been lost. There is great danger of mischievous scandal arising -- for this belligerent woman has already threatened to go to law with two powerful corporations in London! -- I cannot explain all the complications -- but it is one of the most difficult pieces of business I ever undertook, and I don't know whether I shall succeed – there is a large nominal Council but quite unaware of the danger of Miss J.B.'* [lviii]

Blackwell was also scathing about the men helping Sophia – *'at present Miss J. B. holds the money, has rented a building in her own name, and has no acting committee to guide matters, only an almost nominal "Council" which has no stated meetings or records of its proceedings. She has promised a certain number of men £100 each to lecture for the school, and I really think that the money is the only thing that most of them care for.'* [lix] These remarks appear to have been made before Blackwell attended her first Council meeting. They are clearly unjustified. The meetings were fully documented, and the men who served as lecturers proved loyal supporters of the school despite opposition from the profession at large. There is no evidence that any were paid unduly large sums to lecture.

Norton, who proved an admirable choice as Dean, was only thirty-three. Following a brilliant undergraduate career he qualified in 1862 from St Mary's, but even before qualifying was made Demonstrator of Anatomy. In 1866 he became Lecturer in Anatomy and was elected Surgeon to out-patients. Two years later, at

[24] In June 1882 James Anstie, a cousin, presented the School with a portrait of Francis Anstie.

Fig 2.6 Arthur T Norton (1841-1912)

the ridiculously young age of twenty-five, he was given charge of in-patients. He replaced Walter Coulson, who became *persona non grata* at St Mary's because he sought to combine his general surgical post there with a specialist urological post at St Peter's Hospital. In 1870 Norton took charge of the new Department for Diseases of the Throat at St Mary's. He joined the English Ambulance in France during the Franco-Prussian War and, on 12 September 1870 was visited at Arlon by Elizabeth Garrett, an old friend. Five years later he was active in the formation of the Volunteer Medical Staff Corps, a precursor of the RAMC, and became Commandant of the London Companies. (Fig 2.6) [lx]

On 10 October Council decided to ask Sir Francis Goldsmid to be the School's Honorary Treasurer. Liberal MP for Reading, and the first Jewish barrister and QC, he and his wife were strong supporters of the women's movement. His father, Sir Isaac Lyon Goldsmid, the first Jewish baronet, had helped University College to buy its Gower Street site. Father and son promoted emancipation of Jews in Britain, and were founders of the West London Synagogue. Both served as treasurer of University College Hospital. Although Sir Francis joined LSMW's Governing Body he declined the post of Treasurer. His refusal proved serendipitous as it resulted in the appointment of James Stansfeld.

After seven weeks of hectic activity the London School of Medicine for Women opened, on schedule, on 12 October!

CHAPTER 3

Arthur Norton (1) (1874-77)

The First Three Anxious Years of LSMW

Fourteen students enrolled when the London School of Medicine for Women (LSMW) opened on 12 October 1874. Twelve had been at Edinburgh, namely Isabel Thorne, Sophia Jex-Blake, Edith Pechey, Mary Marshall, Alice Ker, Ann Clark, Isabella Foggo, Elizabeth Vinson, Jane Russell Rorison, Agnes McLaren, Edith Shove[1] and Elizabeth Ireland Walker (who took anatomy only). The 'new girls' were Jane Elizabeth Waterston, from South Africa, and Fanny Jane Butler. Six more enrolled that winter – Mrs Annie De la Cherois, Mrs Alice Hart, Mrs 'Ninon' Kingsford,[2] Mrs Drysdale Vickery and two physiology students, Marion Newell and Amy Smith. In the summer of 1875 Isabella Bartholemew and Marie von Thils made the total twenty-two.[i]

Sixteen of the nineteen who intended to qualify and register with the GMC did so. Two of the others qualified only in Europe – Kingsford in Paris in 1880 and von Thils in Zurich in 1878 – and were therefore ineligible to join the register. Isabel Thorne was to sacrifice her career for the sake of the School (see later).

Vinson gave up her studies; Alice Hart (née Rowlands) was forced to abandon them. Her husband, Ernest Hart, himself a doctor, was a member of LSMW's Provisional Council – but also editor of the *British Medical Journal* (*BMJ*). Members of the British Medical Association (BMA), opposed to women doctors, thought it inappropriate that their editor's wife should become a doctor and so Alice left the School after four years.[ii] Hart had previously worked at *The Lancet* where he was unsympathetic about Elizabeth Garrett's initial professional struggles; but he became her friend and a strong supporter of medical women.

---

1 Isabel Thorne lists them in *Sketch of the Foundation and Development of the London School of Medicine for Women*. Scharlieb's obituary of Shove (BMJ 14 Dec 1929) did not mention Edinburgh, but noted that Shove had been '*apprenticed...for five years with Dr Prior Parvis of Blackheath,...a consistent advocate of medical education for women*'. Shove did not matriculate at Edinburgh but passed the Preliminary Examination in Arts at the Society of Apothecaries in April 1874, and registered with the GMC as an Edinburgh medical student.

2 'Ninon' Kingsford was the pen name of Anna Kingsford – author & owner of the *Lady's Own Paper*. She was a vegetarian, campaigner for women's rights, and opponent of vivisection. She graduated MD Paris in 1880, practised unregistered in London & was interested in mystical subjects.

Alice's sister was Dame Henrietta Barnett who, in 1907, founded the Hampstead Garden Suburb Trust; four years later she started the girls' school that still bears her name.

William Broadbent joined the Provisional Council in October; he was the ninth member closely associated with St Mary's Hospital. The other eight were Norton, the newly appointed Dean of LSMW; Hart and Cheadle, both former deans of St. Mary's Hospital Medical School, plus King Chambers, Critchett, Burdon-Sanderson, J. F. Payne and Charlton Bastian. Colleagues at St Mary's, unhappy about the situation, discussed it at a meeting of their Medical School Committee on 27 October. The twenty-three members present, a record attendance, voted by 14 to 8 '*That the School Committee, without wishing in any way to dictate to their colleagues,* [thought it]...*not expedient that teachers in St Mary's School should connect themselves with the London School of Medicine for Women, such connection being deemed to be highly injurious to the interests of St Mary's School: it is therefore the earnest hope that the gentlemen referred to will be induced to reconsider the course they have taken.'* Those gentlemen did not reconsider and no further action was taken. The new Dean, Dr. Shepherd, wisely scotched the idea of further discussion on 1 December.[iii]

Initially LSMW's Provisional Council had two relatively simple tasks – to sort out the School's organisation and to consolidate the teaching programme. It also had two more difficult ones – to persuade an examining body to recognise the School and examine its students, and to find a hospital willing to provide clinical training. Failure to do either would render LSMW unable to attract students or to raise money for their training. Norton asked the nearby Royal Free Hospital (RFH) for help. On 26 October 1874 its medical staff '*having heard the letter of Mr Norton read in reference to the admission of Female Students to the practice of the Royal Free Hospital decline to entertain the question.*'[iv]

In October a 'Laws Committee' (Blackwell, Cheadle & Sturges) was set up to draft the School's rules. The Edinburgh committee (CSCMEWE) requested involvement and were allowed one representative to confer with the 'Laws Committee'; they selected Louisa Stevenson. New contributors to the School, also granted a representative, chose Jex-Blake.

On 30 December the Provisional Council agreed on a Governing Body that included its own members – plus present contributors, the executive committee from Edinburgh, teachers of the School (ex officio), donors of £20 or more, and selected future graduates of the School. Two weeks later it decided to include 'persons of eminence and influence known to be favourable to the medical education of women'; the first such group were Charles Darwin, Lady Crompton,

Dr Cameron MP, Revd Llewelyn Davies (Emily Davies's brother) and Henry Fawcett MP (husband of Millicent, Garrett Anderson's sister). No President was chosen. Lord Aberdare, the Dowager Countess of Buchan, the Bishop of Exeter, the Dowager Lady Stanley of Alderley,[3] and the Earl of Shaftesbury were made Vice-Presidents. At its first meeting on 2 June 1875 the Governing Body agreed the School's constitution.

An 'Executive Council' (teachers plus an equal number from the Governing Body) replaced the Provisional Council. It first met on 2 July 1875. Stansfeld, now Honorary Treasurer, was elected Chairman ex officio. He had been a minister throughout Gladstone's first administration (December 1868 to January 1874), was the first president of the Local Government Board and a close friend of Shaen, the School's solicitor.

LSMW's teachers, as good as those at any other London school, were committed to teaching medicine to women. Except for Blackwell and Garrett Anderson, they all also taught at men's schools where young clinicians usually covered 'minor' subjects like botany, materia medica, pathology and forensic medicine before progressing to lectureships in medicine, surgery and midwifery. The clinicians, being 'honoraries', were not paid for looking after hospital patients, and their income from teaching depended on student numbers and on the number of lectures given.

Norton was originally chosen to teach anatomy but, on becoming Dean following Anstie's death, he asked Reeves to replace him. Mears, who joined Reeves as a demonstrator, could not attend every day so Samuel Fenwick was made assistant demonstrator in September 1875;[v] all three were from the London Hospital.[4]

Chemistry was taught by C.W. Heaton of Charing Cross Hospital, the brother of Jex-Blake's secretary. James Murie, due to teach physiology, switched to comparative anatomy (not due to start until the summer session), and on 13 October 1874 Edward Schäfer and Eugene Dupuy were appointed jointly in his place. Dupuy resigned in November because he could not teach physiology *'without illustrating...by experiments on animals'*. Upset by *'the decision or rather sentiment of some of the members of the Council of the School that I should not perform any [such] experiment.'* he deplored being *'compelled to withdraw before the influence of a prejudice which I was far from believing to be still so powerful in this country.'* However he helped by lecturing one day a week.[vi] Schäfer ran the

3 Her daughter Lady Amberley would have been involved, but had died that year.

4 Mears's marriage to Isabella Bartholomew, who qualified in 1881, was the first between an LSMW student and one of her teachers (but far from the last). Their son, James, was born 1883.

first physiology exam but subsequently responsibility for physiology passed to Walter Rivington from the London Hospital who joined the Provisional Council in October 1874.

Dupuy clearly underestimated the widespread and growing opposition to vivisection. Within a year Frances Power Cobbe[5] and George Hoggan founded the Society for the Protection of Animals Liable to Vivisection (also known as the 'Victoria Street Society'). Lord Shaftesbury was its first president and main parliamentary spokesman; Stansfeld was a vice-president. Bills for the total abolition of vivisection were presented to Parliament every year from 1876 to 1884. Other LSMW supporters opposed to vivisection included Blackwell, Shaen, Duncan McLaren and Lord Aberdare (although Aberdare did not favour total abolition).[vii]

Following a Royal Commission on vivisection a Cruelty to Animals Act was passed in 1876. It meant individuals and institutions had to be licensed for animal experiments. No woman held a licence until 1898 and LSMW did not register for such experiments until 1912 – after another Royal Commission supported vivisection subject to legal control and after the GMC encouraged schools to teach experimental physiology to male and female students. Until then LSMW's students saw live experiments at other institutions.

During LSMW's second year Rivington's demonstrator was Joseph Needham, a brilliant young student at the London Hospital. His son, also Joseph, and also a biochemist, became a famous historian of Chinese science and civilization. Rivington resigned in October 1876;[6] fortunately no physiology (or anatomy) was scheduled for that winter. Six months later Schäfer was asked to return and continued teaching at LSMW until appointed Jodrell Professor at University College (UC) in 1883.[viii]

The academic year was made up of a long winter session of six months or so, and a shorter summer one. Only chemistry, physiology and anatomy were taught during the first (winter) session; medical schools generally did not teach anatomy in the summer as warm weather rendered dissection on the cadavers unappealing. Some subjects were to be taught in alternate years.

Five subjects were taught in the summer of 1875 – botany (Stokoe), materia medica (Octavius Sturges, later joined by Donkin), mental pathology (Sankey from UC who taught gratis), comparative anatomy (Murie) and practical chemistry. Lectures on surgery and practice of medicine began in October 1875. George

---

[5] Frances Power Cobbe was a member of CSCMEWE.

[6] King Chambers & Garrett Anderson may have triggered Rivington's resignation when, in March 1876, they complained to Council that their students knew little physiology and asked that this be remedied.

Cowell covered surgery (replacing the original appointee Berkeley Hill). Forensic medicine (Shewen), ophthalmic surgery (Critchett), and midwifery and diseases of women (Playfair) were to be taught in the summer of 1876. Playfair[7] dropped out and Garrett Anderson, not originally chosen as a teacher, agreed to take over his subjects. However she opted out of teaching midwifery and diseases of women when King Chambers asked her to teach medicine with him in place of Anstie. She suggested Frances Hoggan, a Zurich graduate, should teach midwifery but Council rejected the idea because Hoggan was not then registered. Instead the task went jointly to Blackwell and Ford Anderson, Garrett Anderson's brother-in-law. No botany was taught in the summer of 1876; students were told the Pharmaceutical Society's course would satisfy the Examining Boards.

Because initially LSMW had no hospital link Council guaranteed fixed fees for each lecturer. A hundred guineas was paid for each course during the second long winter session; the anatomy demonstrator got fifty pounds. When Cheadle started teaching pathology in October 1876 Jex-Blake considered his course inadequate for the Scottish examining boards, and four months later complained that his fifty guineas for twenty-two lectures was more than double the usual rate; Critchett got twelve guineas for twelve lectures on ophthalmic surgery. King Chambers proposed one guinea a lecture as the standard rate.

For three years there was a poor attendance at courses and examinations. One reason was that some students, being exempt from subjects they passed in Edinburgh, were not in London. From July 1875 Edith Pechey, still unqualified, worked for a year as Lawson Tait's house surgeon at the Birmingham and Midlands Hospital for Women – having replaced Louisa Atkins who, like Hoggan a Zurich MD, was not yet eligible for the Medical Register. Isabel Thorne spent most of the second academic year in Paris, where her son Yoell was born in February 1876.[8,ix] Alice Ker had no examination to sit in 1876. At Jex-Blake's suggestion she spent much of the year in Boston, studying with Lucy Sewall at the New England Hospital for Women.

Another reason for absenteeism was that some of those enrolled at LSMW, e.g. Mary Marshall, Ninon Kingsford, Alice Vickery and Alice Hart, were also studying in Paris, while Agnes McLaren was in Montpellier (where she was the only female medical student). Marshall, McLaren and Kingsford graduated with a French MD, but Kingsford was not to register with the GMC. Vickery qualified LKQCPI in 1880. When Hart asked the Great Northern Hospital (later the Royal Northern) if

---

7 William Smout Playfair was the brother of Lyon Playfair, MP for the University of Edinburgh in 1874. The latter supported Jex-Blake in 1869 (see Chapter 2).

8 There is no suggestion in her diary that Thorne registered as a student in Paris.

she could attend its wards in 1876 (thus supplementing her hospital studies in Paris), she was accepted as a student from Paris – not LSMW[x] – even though she took class examinations at LSMW in the summer of 1875 and winter of 1875-6. Sadly she was made to abandon her studies (see earlier).

Some ex-Edinburgh students sat class exams at LSMW. Five did so during the winter session of 1874-5 (Clark, Foggo, Ker, Vinson & Shove), three in the 'summer' of 1875 (Clark, Ker & Marshall) and two in the 'winter' of 1875-6 (Ker & Rorison); however, none did so in the 'summer' of 1876 and none took all of the exams. Butler, one of the two new arrivals during the first year, did take all the examinations; Waterston sat exams only in the Summer Session.

The School's problems were reflected in the low student entry in October 1875; only six enrolled, two for physiology alone. This brought the total number at LSMW to seventeen as some of the original students had left. Only two of the new entry qualified – Adela Bosanquet (LRCPI 1883) and Janet Monteath Douglas (LKQCPI 1880).

The first prospectus (Winter 1874-5) noted that '*a register of desirable lodgings, etc, in the neighbourhood of the school is kept by the Secretary, Miss Heaton, to whom all students not already resident in London are advised to apply for information and advice*'

There was no 'student life' as such during LSMW's first three years, owing to the small number of students and the erratic attendance. The students made their own entertainment. Alice Ker, who lived with Jex-Blake in Bernard Street, worked hard but also had an active social life. She visited relatives and friends in London, attended parties, the theatre and concert halls, and frequented the 'Saturday Pops' held in the afternoon at St James' Hall; there she often sat behind George Eliot.[9] She also enjoyed sporting occasions (e.g. the Oxford v Cambridge boat race).

However, there was probably little frivolity at the School. Alice Hart – in the Jubilee issue of the Magazine in November 1924 – recalled '*the grim earnestness of the first students', and Garrett Anderson's plea to her 'to try and induce the students to go to some dances at her* [EGA's] *house; but it was in vain'*. Most were devout Christians, and their informal Bible reading group, which met weekly from the spring of 1875, could be considered the first of LSMW's 'clubs and societies'.

As its students could not qualify and register without passing the necessary examinations the School tried to persuade one of the nineteen examining bodies to

9 RFH Archives has a copy of Ker's diary (1875) plus excerpts from her unpublished autobiography – both rich sources of information about the life of LSMW students during the School's first year or two.

recognise it for this purpose. Some responded that they were legally unable to examine women, unless new legislation was introduced. Cowper-Temple's Bill to give Scottish Universities the power to admit women (postponed from 24 April 1874) had its second reading on 3 March 1875 but was lost by 153 votes to 196. Three weeks later Cowper-Temple, now an LSMW governor, introduced another Bill, *'to permit registration of degrees from the five specified Universities of France, Berlin, Leipzig, Berne and Zurich'* – if held by women. It was deferred. On 16 June Lord Sandon, in reply to Stansfeld, said the Government was prepared to consider medical education for women. John Simon, medical officer of the Privy Council, asked the GMC for its views. Its members opined *'that the study and practice of medicine and surgery, instead of affording a field of exertion well fitted for women, do, on the contrary, present special difficulties which cannot be simply disregarded; but the Council are not prepared to say that women ought to be excluded from the profession'.*[xi]

While matters were proceeding Simon suggested the women apply to sit for the 'Licence in Midwifery' of the College of Surgeons. It was, surprisingly, a registrable qualification that allowed its holders to practise in specialties other than midwifery. Sophia, Isabel Thorne and Edith Pechey applied to the College in December 1875. Its legal advisors said it might be compelled to examine the women and their certificates of attendance were therefore accepted on 17 February 1876. Critchett, LSMW's lecturer in ophthalmic surgery, persuaded the College to admit them to the usual examination plus an extra exam in anatomy and surgery with the chairman of the Board. However the examiners promptly resigned and pressure was applied to prevent anyone replacing them. The women's examination was 'postponed'. More than a year later Stansfeld wrote *'Since then there have been no examiners and no examination; but there was immediately a meeting of the Obstetrical Society, at which a vote of thanks to the members of the examining board was carried by "universal acclamation".'* [xii]

On 2 March 1876 the Lord President (the Duke of Richmond) met an LSMW deputation to discuss registration of women as medical practitioners.[10] He made no promises but in May the Government supported Russell Gurney's Bill to enable all nineteen examining boards to admit women to their examinations, *if they chose to do so*. The Act became law on 11 August 1876.[xiii] It was the first major breakthrough.

The General Medical Council was happy about a purely permissive Act. So too were the women and their supporters; they reasoned that if one examining board

[10] Lord Aberdare, Lord Shaftesbury, Stansfeld, Mr Forsyth MP, Mrs Pennington, Jex-Blake, Garrett Anderson, King Chambers and Norton. Lord Aberdare, Richmond's predecessor as Lord President, set up the meeting, (CM 1876: 25 Feb)

agreed to examine them others would follow, while if none did so the case for compulsory action would be overwhelming. In September 1876 two students, Edith Pechey and Edith Shove, solicited support from the King and Queen's College of Physicians in Ireland (KQCPI) and the Queen's University of Ireland; both agreed to admit women to examinations and diplomas on the same terms as men if they complied with the regulations.[xiv] However, Queen's University demanded one session's attendance at a college in Cork, Belfast or Galway. To allow students to start at Galway the following month Stansfeld and three friends guaranteed fees of £400 over five years, but the scheme fell through because of the hostility of one Galway professor.[xv]

Stansfeld now sought formal recognition of LSMW by the Irish College. At its meeting in Dublin on 2 February 1877 Dr Smith, who had visited LSMW, declared its facilities satisfactory. The next day the College's Registrar, Maggs Finney, wrote to Stansfeld: '*... on the 2nd instant a resolution was passed recognizing the Lectures delivered, and Instruction given, in the London School of Medicine for Women.*[xvi]

The first three women to obtain the Irish diploma and join Blackwell and Garrett Anderson on the Medical Register did not train at Edinburgh or LSMW. They were Zurich graduates. Eliza Walker Dunbar was admitted as a licentiate (LKQCPI & LM)[11] in January 1877 and Frances Hoggan and Louisa Atkins in February. Jex-Blake and Edith Pechey followed in May; both had graduated MD Bern earlier that year. The four women qualifying LKQCPI & LM in 1878, who also had foreign MDs,[12] brought the number of women on the Medical Register to eleven. The qualification LKQCPI was sometimes referred to humorously as the alphabetical licence to practise. One wag suggesting the letters stood for 'Licensed to Kill, Qualified to Cure, Patients Invited.' [xvii]

LSMW still needed a hospital for clinical teaching. In March 1876 the Royal Free staff again refused to help. The School's 'Hospital Practice' committee, set up in February 1875, approached the East London Hospital for Children and the German Hospital, Dalston. It also asked the President of the Local Government Board to admit students to its new hospital in Cleveland Street, but rules under the Metropolitan Poor Act prevented use of such asylums for medical instruction.[xviii] The London Hospital was the School's first choice, but its long-standing opposition to female students was unanimously endorsed by its medical staff in July 1876.[xix] The only hospital willing to take women was Garrett Anderson's New Hospital for Women, which had moved from Seymour Place to Marylebone Road in 1874;

[11] 'LM' means Licentiate in Midwifery.

[12] Annie Reay Barker & Anna Dahms (both Paris), Ann Clark (Berne) & Agnes McLaren (Montpellier).

small and serving only women it was unacceptable to examining bodies, but LSMW students visited it on a fairly regular basis, either walking there or travelling by train or bus.[xx]

The situation was serious. On 24 January 1876 Council heard that several students (including Mary Marshall, Alice Ker, Mrs Grant {née Rorison} and Isabella Foggo) had left owing to lack of hospital facilities;[13] it feared others would follow suit.

Two months earlier Norton and Reeves, the anatomy lecturer, reported an approach by a gentleman (wishing to remain anonymous) who contemplated establishing a new hospital. In April 1876 he offered to build one with 100 beds if the Governing Body would provide £5000 for initial expenses. Women students would be guaranteed admission for five years, on payment of the usual fees. Stansfeld met him, was impressed, and felt he would honour his agreements but Council would not act on so vague a plan.[xxi]

By May LSMW's funds were almost exhausted. Stansfeld, emphasizing the difficulty of raising money if the hospital problem remained unresolved, stressed the need to keep going because Russell Gurney's enabling Bill was coming before Parliament. He promised to approach George Moore, a trustee at RFH.

On 18 July Council debated closure of LSMW. Opinions were divided. Garrett Anderson thought no new students should be admitted, but wanted classes to continue that winter to complete the three-year curriculum. Jex-Blake said if they did not continue for junior and senior students she would start a new school in Edinburgh. Norton's suggestion that LSMW might become a high-class school of midwifery was firmly rejected. Eventually it was agreed classes should go on to the end of the next winter session. That October five new students were admitted, including the brilliant young Helen Prideaux (see later).

Sophia, unable to attend a special meeting of Council on 31 July, wrote to Stansfeld – *'I have received intelligence pointing to a possible solution of our hospital difficulty. As, however, the persons concerned insist upon absolute secrecy ..., I shall be glad to know whether the Executive Council will empower me to...act for them in this matter, until I can...lay the whole facts before them.'* [xxii] Stansfeld believed the scheme practicable, but nothing came of it; the nature of the 'possible solution' remains a mystery.

On 16 October 1876 Stansfeld again promised to talk to George Moore about RFH. Sadly, Moore died on 21 November following an accident. Soon after Stansfeld (Fig 3.1) wrote to Sophia,

---

[13] Ker, Grant and Foggo applied for re-admission in January 1878. Ker worked with Sewall in Boston in 1876. She graduated MD Bern and qualified LKQCPI in 1879; Marshall took the Paris MD and LKQCPI in 1880. Grant and Foggo qualified LKQCPI in 1880.

Fig 3.1 James Stansfeld (1820-1898)

'I met Mrs Garrett Anderson at dinner the other day; she did not seem to have much hope or plan about the School in any way. I have however something to tell you I think you will be rather pleased to hear. Mrs Stansfeld and I went to Clapham

today to call on the Hopgoods, with whom we had become friendly at Whitby: and Mr Hopgood is Chairman of the Board of the Gray's Inn Lane Hospital. We found them both with us, but strange to the question. I am to send Mr Hopgood something to read, and he is to consider whether anything is possible there; he does not appear to be in awe of the staff.

Just as I had begun to talk the Editor of the Contemporary Review[14] *came in and listened and expressed general sympathy in a timid way, but asked me if I would write him a paper shewing a practical way and outcome; and I undertook at once to do so.*

The paper I can manage though I am glad to think I shall be likely to see you before I send it; but in dealing with Mr Hopgood I very much wish you were here...What time in January shall you be back, probably time enough for us to act together in the matter.'[xxiii]

On 5 January 1877 Stansfeld wrote to her again – *'I shall not consult anyone if I can avoid it. I think you and I have the best chance of managing it alone'*; and, in a positive mood, on 13 January – *'I congratulate you seriously and sincerely; it was time to get that particular anxiety off your mind,*[15] *and to be MD at all events...I will defer what I may have to say till we meet; but we'll win and no mistake.'*[xxiv] Hopgood (Fig 3.2) was a solicitor who acted for Cubitts, the large building firm occupying the site to the north of RFH. He wrote to Stansfeld – *'I shall be at home all Sunday...on receiving a formal application...it shall be...submitted to our Weekly Board, — I think they will...summon a special meeting of the Committee of Management, whose decision will be final for the current year!...My wife feels such a deep interest in the success of the movement...*[*she*] *may be put down as a subscriber or guarantor...of £100.'* [xxv] Sophia visited Hopgood with Stansfeld.

At RFH's Weekly Board on 15 February Hopgood read Stansfeld's letter proposing that the women students might attend the daily visits of the physicians and surgeons and receive lectures on clinical subjects. Two weeks later three of the medical staff – O'Connor, Cockle and Rose[16] – attended and agreed to the proposal. Gant wrote opposing it. The Board, noting that RFH appeared the only establishment in London able to provide the School with clinical instruction, thought it just and right to offer it. Their decision was not entirely altruistic. Although there were only sixteen students the School guaranteed fees to the medical staff of at least £400 a year for five years. Stansfeld also hinted that wealthy friends of the School would support the first large London hospital to

[14] Stansfeld may have meant the magazine *Nineteenth Century*.

[15] Sophia's graduation at Bern.

[16] See Chapter 4.

Fig 3.2 James Hopgood (1811-1897)

admit women students, and guaranteed additional annual subscriptions totalling at least 300 guineas. On 14 March 1877 RFH's Committee of Management unanimously approved admission of the women. That year the opening of its new Victoria Wing improved the clinical facilities available at RFH.[xxvi]

On 17 March Stansfeld reported the happy outcome to Council which appointed King Chambers, Sophia and Norton to join him in discussions with RFH. Stansfeld told the students that in October they would be fully provided with clinical instruction.

Without RFH's agreement to take the students LSMW would have closed. It had made no plans for tuition in the summer of 1877 so the students were told to spend the time studying midwifery, pharmacy and vaccination! They attended the dispensary practice of the New Hospital for Women, and Pearce, the public vaccinator at Westminster, was hired to teach them at his practice in Horseferry Road.

The momentous decisions of the Irish College and RFH allowed Norton to write in June to Miller, Registrar of the GMC – *'I beg to inform you that the London School of Medicine for Women to which the Royal Free Hospital is attached for the purposes of clinical instruction is now a Recognised Medical School & to request that in the future you will kindly enter upon the Register the names of students studying at this School.'* Miller replied enclosing the resolution *'That a copy of the Recommendations of the Medical Council be forwarded to Mr Norton, and that he be informed that Students are entered on the Register, provided the conditions laid down in these Recommendations have been complied with.'* [xxvii]

During April and May a formal agreement was drawn up between the School and RFH. LSMW guaranteed to pay not less than £715 in fees and subscriptions (a sum underwritten by Stansfeld, Frederick Pennington, and Skelton Anderson).[xxviii] For clinical students it agreed to pay £45 for a four year course or, if paid separately, £20 for one year, £15 for the second and £15 for a third year; a fourth year would be free. Female students were only to be admitted through LSMW; there would be no male students. Clinical staff agreed that students could accompany them on ward visits, attend out-patients and post-mortem examinations, and be appointed as dressers and clinical clerks. The staff were to lecture each year on medicine and surgery.

Jex-Blake must have been delighted that her goal was finally achieved. Her joy was short-lived. At Council on 7 May Stansfeld announced *'the time had now arrived...to consider the appointment of a person or persons to carry on the important work which was before the School. It would require...various qualities such as power of organisation to ensure the success of the public meeting and to raise the large funds now needed, and tact and judgment to enable the arrangements connected with the workings of the school and its students to go on smoothly with the Hospital.'*

Discussion of this matter resumed at a special meeting of Council four days later when the proposal to appoint a paid Secretary under the orders of Council was agreed unanimously. Stansfeld then proposed the appointment of an Honorary Secretary. Garrett Anderson asked what such an officer would do. Norton explained there was much work for which he had no time and which a paid clerk could not undertake. Jex-Blake said Norton had remained Dean on the understanding that he dealt only with business connected with the medical classes. She dealt with correspondence, minutes, reports and communications with public and press; they were time-consuming duties she would gladly transfer to an Honorary Secretary. Stansfeld argued that they could expect such services from a paid secretary only by paying a salary higher than they could afford. Council agreed to appoint an Honorary Secretary and a sub-committee (Mrs Thorne, Stansfeld and Norton) was asked to prepare a scheme defining the duties and position of the proposed Honorary Secretary.

The matter was discussed again on 19 May when Jex-Blake was in Dublin becoming a licentiate of the Irish College. Those present (Garrett Anderson, Louisa Atkins, Bennett, Bastian, Cheadle and Miss Du Pre) accepted the sub-committee's document defining the duties of an Honorary Secretary. The Dean was to be responsible for all classes, directions to students, student and staff discipline, and communications with lecturers and Hospital authorities, and was to sign all documents and letters related to his duties. The Honorary Secretary was to assist with correspondence, prepare minutes and reports, conduct LSMW's financial business, and see that accounts were properly kept. To secure control over the School, its relations with RFH, its own subscribers and the public, the Executive Council was to meet regularly and frequently. For urgent official acts that could not await a Council decision the Honorary Treasurer, the Dean and the Honorary Secretary were to act jointly, subject to subsequent confirmation by Council. The proposed paid official was to be called 'Assistant Secretary'; she was to act under the direction of the Dean and Honorary Secretary, and fulfil other duties required by Council. According to the minutes 'a lengthy discussion then ensued with regard to the selection of the Honorary Secretary and it was finally agreed to postpone the nomination until the next meeting.'

Garrett Anderson was absent from Council on 30 May when King Chambers and Jex-Blake proposed that Mrs Thorne be urgently requested to undertake the office of Hon Secretary. For some reason the vote was postponed until 12 June when, with fewer present, Isabel Thorne (Fig 3.3) was elected unanimously. The position of Assistant Secretary was to be offered to Miss Heaton, sister of the chemistry lecturer, who had done clerical work for Sophia since the School opened.

Much has been written about the events of May 1877. Sadly two pages, probably relating to the 19 May meeting, have been carefully cut from the Council minute book.[17] Mrs. Thorne's diary states simply that 'In May 1877 I undertook to

[17] Elizabeth Crawford noted their excision in *'Enterprising Women; the Garretts and their Circle'* London: Francis Boutle, 2002. p 87. Crawford suggested the pages were torn out; in fact they were carefully removed using a razor blade or similar instrument.

Fig 3.3 Isabel Thorne (1834-1910)

be Hon. Sec. of the London School of Medicine for Women which obliged me to go frequently to London.' [18]

The only source of evidence, apart from the Council minutes, is Margaret Todd's biography of Jex-Blake. However, Jex-Blake was Todd's main source of information and Jex-Blake herself may not have been fully aware of the events of May 1877. One cannot check Todd's original sources because Sophia left Todd her 'papers, letters, diaries, letter books, case books and all other private documents', and requested that they should be burnt without examination if Todd predeceased her. Todd committed suicide soon after the biography was published. She appears to have acquiesced with Jex-Blake's wish that all her papers, letters etc. should be destroyed.[xxix]

Todd was certain Sophia wanted and expected to be Honorary Secretary so that she could continue the work she had been doing without the title. *'She had conceived it [the School], brought it forth, tended it, fought for it, – done most of the daily work it involved, with the help of a lady secretary she herself had trained. Until she was a qualified doctor, however, she did not wish her name to appear either on the Council or on the Governing Body. In all the early papers it occurs only as Trustee.'* However, her enforced absences to take examinations in Bern and Dublin gave people a chance to do without her. Todd suggested that, as Sophia was not always easy to work with, some did not wish her to return to take up the reins. Sophia probably guessed something was up, as she wrote to Stansfeld that the honorary secretaryship was too onerous to be undertaken except at the unanimous wish of those concerned. She suggested that Isabel Thorne, Louisa Atkins or Garrett Anderson might care to undertake the task. She probably thought the first two would refuse, and that Garrett Anderson, overwhelmed with other work, could not possibly have entertained the suggestion.[xxx]

However, according to Todd,[19] on 19 May '*Mrs Thorne proposed S.J.-B as Honorary Secretary, and someone else proposed Garrett Anderson, both nominations being duly seconded. Mrs Anderson was in a difficult position, and said so frankly. She did not wish to take an unfair advantage over her colleague; but if it was to be for the good of the School —? Mr Stansfeld and the Dean (Mr Norton, who was always S.J.-B's staunchest supporter) were somewhat at a loss, and so no doubt were others; it was not an easy situation for anybody. After some talk the meeting was adjourned. Everything pointed to Mrs Anderson's election.*[xxxi]

[18] The Thorne family lived at Sevenoaks in Kent and moved to Lewes in Sussex in 1879. Isabel did not move back to London until December 1895, having taken a lease on 10 Nottingham Place, so the post of Hon. Sec. was clearly not a full time task.

[19] But not according to the remaining Council minutes.

Sophia could not have accepted the election of Garrett Anderson, who had showed little support for the women in Edinburgh, opposed the formation of the School in London and had to be persuaded to attend the first meeting at Anstie's house. Although rich, she did not help the School financially in its early days, and was prepared to close it to new entrants in the summer of 1876. Furthermore she had never hidden her dislike of Sophia. However, Todd thought Sophia, over and above her personal feelings, was genuinely concerned – firstly that Garrett Anderson was too busy to undertake so big a job and that she would effectively only be lending her name, and secondly that she lacked the necessary insight and imagination.[xxxii]

Isabel Thorne's election was probably the best solution. She was *persona grata* with all parties, and no one had better credentials. 'About the best possible,' Sophia wrote in her diary, 'So much better than I.' However, Thorne must have been a little sad. Since enrolling at James Edmunds's Female Medical College thirteen years earlier she had wanted to qualify as a doctor. At Edinburgh she took all her classes with distinction, but had the opportunity to pass only one professional examination. Now she sacrificed her own ambition and made the success of the School her main object in life.[xxxiii]

With Isabel Thorne's election as Honorary Secretary Jex-Blake, as we shall see, was no longer as dominant a figure at LSMW, and in 1878 she returned to Edinburgh (see Chapter 5). This left the way open for Garrett Anderson to play an increasingly important role in the running of the School, culminating in 1883 with her election as Dean.

What was Garrett Anderson doing during LSMW's first three years? Initially she was not a key player. When it opened she was busy with her family and in consolidating her clinical practice. Her second daughter, Margaret, was born 9 September 1874, eighteen days after the original meeting at Anstie's house. Sadly Margaret died in December 1875 after an illness beginning in October.[20] That month EGA was due to start teaching the Practice of Medicine together with King Chambers but it seems unlikely, given Margaret's illness and death, that she did so until early in 1876. Although EGA was a reluctant participant at the original meeting she attended 25 of the 44 Council meetings held up to March 1877. Five of those missed coincided with Margaret's illness; and the last five probably related to the birth of Alan Anderson on 9 March 1877, a delivery supervised by Elizabeth's sister-in-law, Mary Marshall, then still a medical student.[xxxiv] As her

[20] Tuberculous meningitis according to Manton (Ref xxxvii on p. 248), but tuberculous peritonitis according to Louisa Garrett Anderson (Ref xxxv on p. 200)

daughter Louisa later pointed out 'In these years of early marriage EGA proved that the medical woman can do her duty as a wife and mother and that a wife and mother need not forfeit medical practice.'[xxxv]

Garrett Anderson also had outside interests. She enjoyed music, attended concerts, and founded a quartet which played at members' homes. In March 1875 a holiday in Italy with her sister Millicent was her first parting from Skelton and their daughters. She arranged an audience with Pope Pious IX to have her old cook's rosary blessed.[xxxvi] But the trip's highlight was a visit to Garibaldi, one of her heroes. In her old age his signed picture still hung in her bedroom.[xxxvii]

Her practice prospered; she cared for many rich and influential ladies and their families, reporting some of her more interesting cases in the *British Medical Journal*. In August 1875 she attended the Edinburgh meeting of the BMA with Frances Hoggan. EGA had been a member since 1873; Hoggan was the newly elected second woman member. Both presented papers – Garrett Anderson on 'Dysmenorrhoea', Hoggan on 'A new histological process for staining tissues.'[xxxviii] The President that year was Christison, Jex-Blake's *bête noire* in Edinburgh and still strongly opposed to women doctors. A call for a referendum on female membership resulted in a postal vote that November; three-quarters of respondents opposed admission of women, but no action was taken. At the Manchester meeting in 1877 EGA further infuriated BMA members by commenting on a paper by Wilson Fox, professor of clinical medicine at UCL. In 1878 Lister and others proposed expelling the two women. A BMA sub-committee was set up to examine the legal status of lady members, and BMA groups nationwide voted against admitting them. A BMA meeting on 8 August 1878 agreed 'That no female be eligible as a member of the Association'. Hoggan's membership was declared invalid because she was not on the *Medical Register* when elected (although she was when her membership was rescinded!). Garrett Anderson was not expelled.[xxxix]

Hoggan (then Frances Morgan) had joined EGA at her Seymour Street dispensary in March 1871, and went with her to the Marylebone Road when the dispensary was transformed into the New Hospital for Women. She assisted at surgical operations but became concerned about EGA's surgical competence and suggested that a man, Dr Willam Appleton Meredith, an experienced gynaecologist who helped in difficult cases, should undertake all abdominal surgery. Louisa Garrett Anderson wrote that Hoggan 'fell from grace' over this issue.[xl] Hoggan resigned in April 1877.[xli] (See also Chapter 6)

The acceptance of LSMW by the King and Queen's College of Physicians in Ireland and then by the Royal Free Hospital effectively laid the 'foundation stone' for the medical education of women in Britain and, because of its mighty empire, in many other countries as well. When other examining bodies also opened their qualifications to women LSMW students switched their allegiance to London University and Edinburgh rather than face the more arduous journey to Dublin. The Royal Free, however, was the closest hospital to the School and the two institutions were to remain inextricably entwined for over a hundred and twenty years – to the great benefit of both.

The next chapter describes the story of RFH up until 1877 and explains why it was such a suitable partner for LSMW, and why it was not already a teaching hospital for men.

CHAPTER 4

The Royal Free Hospital (1928-1877)

From Greville Street to Gray's Inn Lane

The Royal Free Hospital (RFH) was founded in 1828 by William Marsden (Fig 4.1) who was born in Sheffield in 1796. He served an apprenticeship with a local chemist and druggist before leaving for London in 1816. There he worked with Dale, a surgeon-apothecary at Holborn Hill, studied at St Bartholomew's Hospital and married Elizabeth Ann Bishop, then aged fourteen, in 1820. He qualified MRCS in 1827. That December, according to the Marsden legend, he found a sick girl on the steps of St Andrew's Church, Holborn. Unable to get her admitted to a London hospital, because admission required a letter from a hospital subscriber or governor,[1] Marsden paid a poor widow to give her a room until she died, unidentified, two days later.[i]

Shocked by the experience he decided to found a free hospital and called a meeting at Gray's Inn Coffee House[2] on 14 February 1828.[ii] (Fig 4.2) Those present decided *'to found a charitable institution in this metropolis for the gratuitous cure of syphilitic and other contagious diseases to receive the benefits of which the only recommendation shall be the poverty and disease of the afflicted applicants'*. The resulting 'London General Institution for the gratuitous cure of Malignant Diseases'[3] was ahead of its time in accepting for treatment patients with syphilis and other venereal diseases; they were rejected by most hospitals whose supporters resented paying for the consequences of sin! [iii]

Governors at the new Institution paid a guinea a year per vote, or ten guineas for a life governorship with one vote. In February 1828 a 'collector' was appointed to raise money, in part by calling at governors' houses for their subscriptions. In 1830 the second collector, Higgins, was dismissed for theft and replaced by a resident full-time 'assistant secretary' named Penny. Godfrey Goddard, a young lawyer and Marsden's neighbour in Thavies Inn, became honorary secretary; Pascoe St Leger

---

1 Money received from subscribers was the main source of income for hospitals at that time.

2 The site of the Grays Inn Coffee House (1695) is now occupied by the 'Cittie of York' pub (22 High Holborn) which includes much of the interior of the old building.

3 The word 'malignant' then covered many disorders. In 1851 Marsden founded another hospital for what we now call malignant diseases. His Free Cancer Hospital is now the Royal Marsden Hospital.

Fig 4.1 William Marsden (1796-1867) by Baugniet

Grenfell was the honorary treasurer. Goddard left under a cloud in 1831, having embezzled over £63 from general funds; B. F. Watson took over as honorary secretary.[iv]

The consulting physician was David Uwins, physician to Peckham lunatic asylum and a convert to homoeopathy; John Painter Vincent from Bart's was

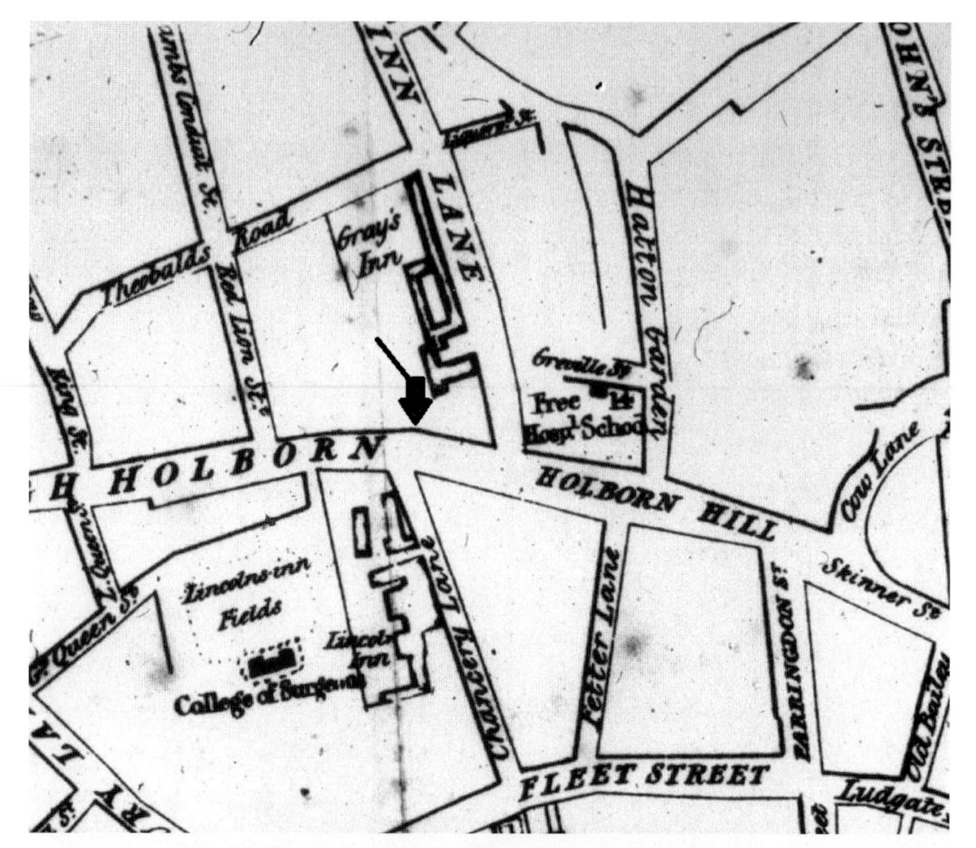

Fig 4.2 Site of Gray's Inn Coffee House indicated by arrow

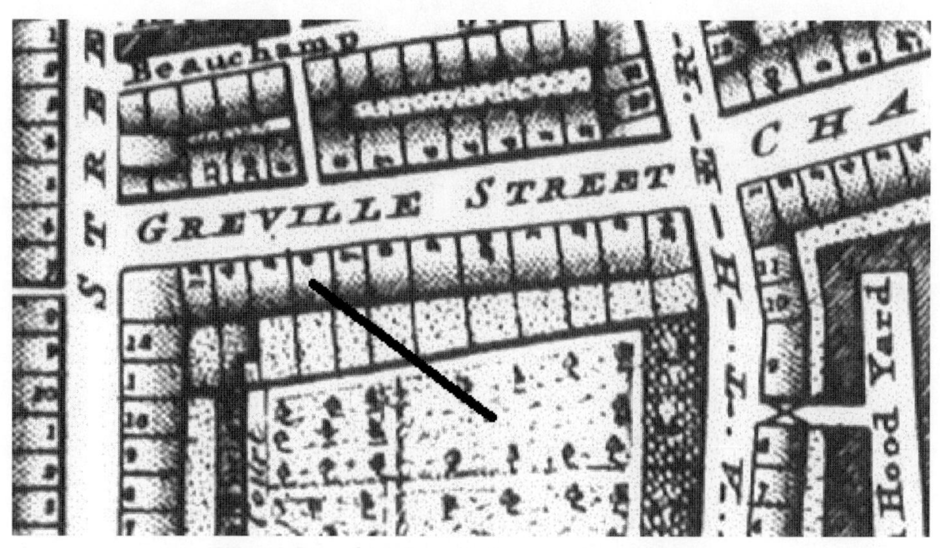

Fig 4.3 Site of 16 Greville Street indicated by line

consulting surgeon and Marsden surgeon. The assistant surgeon appointed soon fell ill and was replaced by Greville Jones, a young governor. The 'consultings' attended weekly, the surgeon and assistant surgeon daily (except Sundays). The staff could not take pupils to the Institution, accept rewards directly or indirectly, or practise midwifery. All treatments were free.[v]

In March the governors took a lease on 16 Greville Street, a four storey house in Hatton Garden.[4] (Fig 4.3) The first patients were seen there on 17 April. The apothecary, Weston, was given two furnished rooms in the house and the two upper floors were sub-let.[vi]

The Institution provided advice and medicine – and *'the Surgeons...extended their services to visiting within a certain distance such patients as were unable from disease to attend the establishment.'* [vii] The Institution treated over a 1000 in the first year and more than 4000 in the year ending February 1832. Treatment at Greville Street was free so other hospitals, and many doctors, saw a threat to their incomes and influence.

Initially there were no in-patients, although the Committee contemplated receiving 'in door patients' from the start.[viii] When Asiatic cholera struck in February 1832 London's hospitals would not take cholera patients. The Committee gave notice to the top floor tenant, commandeered the apothecary's accommodation and placed fifty straw mattresses in the empty rooms; it employed a nurse and orderly and the housekeeper became 'Matron'. The first of 524 cholera patients was admitted on 20 February; only 108 perished.[5,ix] Marsden recorded his experience with cholera, which included intravenous infusion of saline fluids, in *'Symptoms and Treatment of Malignant Diarrhoea; better known as Asiatic or Malignant Cholera'*, first published in 1834.[6]

In October 1832, with cholera on the wane, the governors agreed that patients with other illnesses might be admitted.[x] However, they reversed this decision in January 1833 following the resignation of Watson, the honorary secretary, who considered the move too risky. Debts were £350, assets only £240 (which included £103 in the building fund) and patient numbers were increasing.[xi]

When cholera flared up again in August 1833 the staff was increased to two physicians, two surgeons and two assistant surgeons.[xii] Vincent, President of the Royal College of Surgeons in 1832, had resigned and Alexander Tweedie,[7]

---

[4] The original building was demolished in the 1930s to make way for the back of the Prudential Assurance Building at 138-142 Holborn.

[5] During the two years from 23 February 1832 to 25 February 1834 (covered by 5th & 6th annual reports)

[6] Three further editions followed; his son edited the last (published in 1871, after William's death).

[7] Sandwith, Marsden's biographer, states that he named his son Alexander (b 1832) after Tweedie.

physician to the London Fever Hospital,[8] joined Marsden as surgeon. The new assistant surgeon soon left and Philip Bennett Lucas replaced him in June 1834. The second physician, Michael Ryan, was not appointed until November 1834.

In October 1834 the Committee, now wanting to admit in-patients, considered taking a contiguous house in Greville Street.[9] The terms offered were unfavourable and so No. 16 was rearranged to create two wards – one male and one female.

Four honorary secretaries had come and gone when, in July 1835, William Hugh Fenn was employed as a paid secretary; he was to play a major role in the Institution's history. A month earlier its patron, William IV, approved a change of name to 'Free Hospital, Greville Street'.[10,xiii]

A scandal erupted on 7 July 1835. Francis Abbott (a governor, and later Marsden's father-in-law) complained that Tweedie and the new apothecary, William Hentsch, were endorsing a secret quack remedy for gonorrhoea. Its manufacturer, Franks, also a governor, had nominated Hentsch as apothecary. Eventually the pair were sacked – Hentsch on 23 February 1836, Tweedie a week later.[xiv] Tweedie prospered; he remained physician to the Fever Hospital, became physician to the Foundling Hospital and in 1838 was elected FRS for his work on fever.[xv]

However, the issue was damaging. About twenty governors stopped subscribing and the physicians Uwins and Ryan resigned, as did Lucas the surgeon; only Marsden and Greville Jones remained to care for patients. Pascoe Grenfell resigned as treasurer and was replaced in April 1836 by George Grote, a banker and MP for the City of London. In 1827 Grote, age 33, was the youngest of the original Council of the self-styled 'University of London';[11] he and his wife Harriet were strong supporters of the women's movement.[xvi]

The 'Free Hospital Medical School'

The Tweedie–Hentsch scandal coincided with an attempt to start a medical school at the Free Hospital. Until the 1830s London had no 'proper' medical schools. Students at its famous hospitals attended classes either at the hospital (as at Guy's, St Thomas' and The London) or at privately run schools where virtually all the teachers were clinicians. This system was threatened when University College and

---

[8] The London Fever Hospital stood where King's Cross station stands now; it moved to Islington in 1849 and became the Liverpool Road branch of RFH in 1947.

[9] It was the one to the west of No 16.

[10] Thanks to Robert Peel, then Home Secretary, the Institution had royal patronage from its first year. George IV was Patron until he died in 1830. William Frederick, second duke of Gloucester, was its first President; when he died in 1834 the Duke of Buccleuch succeeded him.

[11] Later known as University College London, and now as UCL.

King's College[12] appointed medical faculties *ab initio*, and made plans to found associated hospitals. North London Hospital, opened in 1834, was renamed University College Hospital in 1837; King's College Hospital opened in 1840. The old institutions responded. In September 1833 *The Lancet's* annual educational issue carried separate advertisements for private schools and hospitals; in 1834 the advertisements were for a hospital and its associated school, e.g. the 'London Hospital School and Practice'.

Following enlargement of the Free Hospital's medical staff in August 1833 the Committee contemplated *'affording those officers the means…of establishing a Medical School in connection with the hospital'.*[xvii] On 1 September 1835 Marsden moved that *'the honorary medical officers of this establishment are authorised individually to deliver lectures in the consulting room of the hospital at times convenient to themselves subject to the approval of the Committee and in no wise interfering with the ordinary business of the Charity'.*[xviii] *The Lancet* of 26 September noted, under 'Free Hospital, Greville Street, Hatton Garden', that from Monday 3 October Dr Uwins would lecture on medicine four times a week, and Greville Jones would lecture daily on anatomy, physiology, pathology and surgery.

The staff became more ambitious. In 1836 the 'Free Hospital School' advertised in *The Lancet*. Greville Jones was to teach anatomy, physiology and pathology, J. Barnes materia medica, and Barnes & Bishop medical jurisprudence. Greville Jones and John Gay, who replaced Tweedie and Lucas, were to organize dissections. Students would practise 'chemical manipulation' under Bishop, the new apothecary. The school failed. It was 1848 before *The Lancet's* educational issue next made mention of the Free Hospital – where 'Pupils can obtain permission from the medical officers to attend the practice of this hospital'.

The 'Royal' Free Hospital

Victoria succeeded to the throne on 20 June 1837. She and her mother, the Duchess of Kent, had been patrons of the Free Hospital from 1835. It requested her continued patronage and a change of name, and received the following reply:

'Whitehall, September 26th 1837

Sir,

I am directed by Lord Russell to inform you that the memorial of the Committee of Management and the Governors of the "Free Hospital", Greville Street, Hatton Garden, praying her Majesty's patronage and permission to call this Institution the Royal Free Hospital, has been laid

[12] Founded in 1829.

before the Queen. And I am glad to add that Her Majesty has been graciously pleased to consent to be the Patroness of this Institution and to allow it to be called the "Royal Free Hospital".

I am, Sir, your obedient servant, F. Maule' [xix]

Subscriptions and donations increased, but the financial situation remained precarious. Fenn resigned as secretary in February 1838 but remained on the committee. Charles Legh took the post for a year; the Reverend R. C. Packman was then secretary until 1846. In February 1838 Hume Weatherhead was appointed physician, a post left vacant after Uwins and Ryan resigned in 1836; Marsden became 'Medical Director'.

Late in 1838 the hospital received its first legacy (£450). In 1839 Queen Victoria donated £50. The finances improved. 17 Greville Street was purchased for £833,[xx] and the number of beds rose from 30 to 72. This allowed changes in practice. Although all remained involved in RFH's general practice its staff began to specialise. Hume Weatherhead covered pulmonary disease; Marsden dealt with scrofulous, cancerous and other malignant diseases; and John Gay treated patients with deformities.[xxi] Greville Jones was resident house surgeon. Extra beds also allowed the Committee to agree that *'...respectable females admitted...be placed in a ward by themselves apart from those of a more unfortunate class'* , i.e. away from prostitutes or women with venereal disease; this decision was to have major repercussions (see later).[xxii]

More than 12,000 patients were treated in the year after 17 Greville Street was acquired; 555 were admitted, including some urgent midwifery cases. But when the extra beds opened in January 1840 the newly established medical committee wanted more. It urged the main Committee *'to continue...increasing the accommodation for in-patients; and...suggest[ed]...building a hospital in the environs of the Metropolis, on some high and dry situation, whereby pestilential and contagious maladies, would be removed from the heart of this too crowded city, and where the patients would be more speedily restored and consequently a greater number benefited at the same cost'.* [13,xxiii]

The Committee began searching for a suitable site in April 1841. Several were offered, including Corporation of London land at Holloway.[xxiv] RFH had to raise money for a new building and that year Lord Robert Grosvenor (Whig MP, and son of the first Marquess of Westminster), a great supporter of RFH, petitioned Parliament for *'a grant...towards erecting a more commodious building'*. The

[13] This move, to Hampstead, was made in 1974!

Chancellor of the Exchequer turned down the request, not wishing to set a precedent that might trigger approaches from other hospitals![xxv] Around that time Marsden also suggested *'...branch Establishments being opened in various parts of the Metropolis, on the same free principle as that which governs this Hospital, for the relief of Out-Patients and that Medical Officers for the same be elected in their several localities for the due performance of the duties belonging thereto.'* [xxvi] The Committee agreed to seek sites for these establishments, but the novel idea came to nothing.

Gray's Inn Road

In July 1842 Marsden reported that the premises of 'Messrs Seddons, formerly the City Light Horse barracks situated in Gray's Inn Lane, would be disposed of upon such terms as he thought very advantageous'.[xxvii] George IV used Seddons, a famous furniture manufacturer, to refurnish the private apartments at Windsor Castle. When the King died in 1830 Seddons's bill for £179,000 was disputed and £30,000 was withheld.[xxviii] The firm had to leave its premises in Aldersgate Street. It moved to an old barracks in Gray's Inn Lane originally occupied by the City Light Horse (or Light Horse Volunteers) – a yeomanry regiment raised in the late eighteenth century when a French invasion was feared; it was used subsequently to quell urban riots. Cavalry training and manoeuvres were then possible in the fields off Gray's Inn Lane (a name changed to 'Gray's Inn Road' in 1862). The officers were city merchants and bankers.[14]

On 4 August a Mr Stevens presented the governors with a glowing report on the property: *'... it would scarcely be possible to obtain in London premises already built so easily convertible to the requirements of your Institution. The rooms are large, well ventilated and for the most part fitted out with warm water apparatus for heating them...accommodation may be provided for from 350 to 400 patients without any extension of the premises. The cost to build would not be less than £12000. The cost to alter for present purposes would not be less than £500...I do not think...a more favourable opportunity would present itself...as regards situation or adaptability to the purposes of your Institution.'* [xxix] (Fig 4.4)

The governors bought the lease from the Calthorpe estate, calculating their liability at about £13,000. To expedite matters Hume Weatherhead, Marsden and Fenn personally guaranteed rent and outgoings until the financial situation was stable; they were made trustees and all RFH's property was invested in their names.[xxx] Seddons leased part of the premises until 1852; the rest was converted

[14] Spencer Perceval, the only British Prime Minister to be assassinated, was a member from 1794 - 1803.

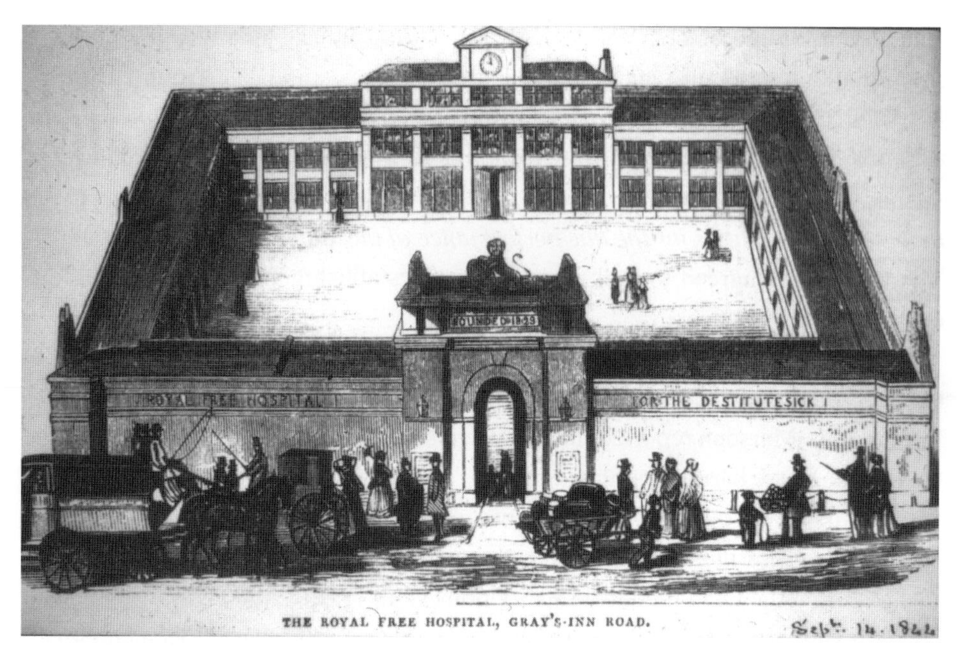

Fig 4.4 RFH 1844

into a hospital. The first out-patients attended on 16 January 1843; in-patients transferred from Greville Street two days later.[xxxi]

Lord Robert Grosvenor and Samuel Gurney, a renowned philanthropist and banker, led the fund raising efforts. The Queen headed the subscription list. The Bank of England, the Corporation of London and many city companies and merchants pledged support. [xxxii]

On 5 June 1845 Fenn resigned both as a trustee and from the Committee, following an attack on his character by Robert Bell of Norris Castle, Isle of Wight.[xxxiii] The nature of the attack is unclear. He was soon reinstated but management may have been lax during his absence; the financial situation deteriorated and for several months Committee meetings were inquorate.

The *Humanitas* Affair

A second scandal hit RFH. Late in 1845 *The Times* carried four letters criticizing the hospital written by *Humanitas*, who remained anonymous. On 25 November he claimed two girls from Windsor, both with pulmonary tuberculosis, were refused entry on 18 November even though the syphilis ward had empty beds. One died next day at a local tavern. The Secretary, Packman, responded that respectable women could not be admitted to the syphilis ward, and that the girls had been offered a cab to the City of London Union to await a bed.

On 27 November RFH's Committee decided that henceforth '*no application for admission was to be rejected without investigation by an Honorary Medical Officer and that a room should be set aside for such applicants who could not be immediately admitted to the wards.' Humanitas*, well informed, reported this on 5 December claiming that the girls were not 'respectable women' and could have entered the syphilis ward. He also implied irregularities in RFH's management and in application of its funds.

He attacked RFH's management again on 10 December, advised subscribers to remove certain groups from the Committee, and suggested that potential contributors should withhold donations until matters improved. Finally, on 16 December he reported the second girl's death. He visited Windsor to check the girls' stories and, having found other women treated for venereal diseases at RFH, he questioned the Hospital's apparent emphasis on such conditions.[15] He changed tack a little, arguing that hospitals like RFH should be public establishments, or provided by the state – *'not left to individual speculators, who can make a trade of disease, by obtaining a control over the funds and the elections, misusing the one, and causing endless disappointments in the other'.* He implied that RFH medical officers were chosen through private influence and intrigue, not for their scientific competence and professional ability.

Surprisingly, when the Committee reviewed *The Times* correspondence on 22 December it did not discuss RFH's financial situation, ostensibly because the accounts were being prepared for audit before the forthcoming AGM. However, the claims of *Humanitas* had substance and on 5 February 1846, while Marsden was in mourning for his wife, a review of RFH's liabilities led the governors to adopt the most rigid economy.[xxxiv] However, they still agreed salaries of 100 guineas for the Secretary and the Chaplain; and in early March, when stock had to be sold, Fenn was appointed Superintendent of the Counting House Department at a salary of 150 guineas.

In January 1846 they asked Thomas Wakley, editor of *The Lancet*, to join the Committee. Warily, he replied on 2 February *'...the daily journals of Thursday last...*[reported]*...that the debts and liabilities...of the Free Hospital amount to between £7,000 and 8,000...what funds or means...will enable the Committee to discharge their present engagements?'* [xxxv] He declined the invitation.

The governors were worried. On 2 April Marsden announced that Charles Pearson, the City of London Solicitor,[16] had inspected the RFH accounts for Lord Robert Grosvenor and his friends; they suggested the Committee should retire and that they would assume responsibility.[xxxvi] However, like Wakley, they pulled out when told that RFH's liabilities made the deal unduly risky.[xxxvii]

---

[15] RFH was of course founded to treat patients with syphilis and similar diseases.

[16] In 1837 Pearson was the first to lobby for an underground railway in London.(See – Inwood, S. *A History of London*, London: Macmillan, 1998, p 549.

On 4 June the Committee reviewed the accounts from 1 January to 9 May. Income was well short of expenditure. They owed £3000 on the RFH buildings, other liabilities totalled about £4400, and there was £4.6s.7d in the bank! Tradesmen demanded payment and the Hospital's bankers, Prescott, Grote and Co, wanted £499 to settle an overdue bill of exchange. At that meeting Grote resigned as treasurer, ostensibly because he had retired and moved to the country.

Action was needed. The Earl of Airlie, John Masterman, John Walter and Thomas Wakley were invited to inspect RFH.[xxxviii] The changes they suggested were agreed on 2 July. A Weekly Board of eleven Committee members took over immediate management of RFH from its Director (Marsden) who was not a member but was expected to attend. They abolished the paid chaplaincy, stopped paying the Secretary and withdrew gratuities for the honorary medical officers; other salaries were cut. Masterman, Grote's successor as MP for the City of London and a fellow banker, replaced him as treasurer in August.[xxxix]

Over £800 was needed quickly to prevent personal annoyance by creditors. At a special Committee meeting on 22 June the nine who attended donated £110 and lent £550; requests for contributions were sent to non-attenders. Some debts were settled, but in early July RFH could afford to use only 20 beds for in-patients.

Why was the financial situation so bad? Packman, the secretary, absented himself for much of the summer of 1846. When Fenn wrote on 25 August asking when he would return he was still indisposed! On 23 September the Weekly Board[17] threatened to stop his salary. A week's receipts were missing; his assistant said Packman had the money, and he was asked to return it with £24 due from the previous year's account. At the AGM in January 1847 Packman was dismissed. Marsden, Medical Director and Trustee, and effectively the manager, may also have been guilty. Six years later Wakley wrote to Gay 'The remarks…[were] made …confidentially [like the] statements…made by me to you in Bedford Square,[18] respecting the mal-appropriation of the funds of the Royal Free Hospital by one of your present colleagues and his then coadjutors.'[xl] If Wakley was referring to the financial problems of 1845/46 Marsden was the only medical colleague still on the staff!

Income fell markedly in 1846, perhaps owing to the criticisms of *Humanitas*, but the new system of management minimised the damage. Out-patients increased by 25%, but although debt fell by over £500 in-patient numbers were still restricted because of the fear of further indebtedness.

Thomas H. Wakley (Wakley Jr.) was elected surgeon to RFH in August 1846. Given his father's involvement with RFH that summer, charges of nepotism were

---

[17] Its first meeting had been on 9 September.

[18] Bedford Square was Wakley's home

inevitable. Wakley Sr. joined RFH's Committee at the AGM on 26 January 1847 and served until his death in 1862. At that AGM an attack on Fenn by the Rev Dr Worthington, who argued that a trustee should not also act as accountant, was deemed unjust. Within days Fenn was re-elected superintendent of the Counting House department and of the secretary's office; Worthington's chaplaincy was revoked.

The Weekly Board worked well. At the end of 1847 debt, excluding the mortgage, was less than £2300, and thus £3000 lower than a year earlier. Income was up by £815, current expenses were discharged weekly, and fresh liabilities were less than £900. Even so two large wards remained closed and only twenty in-patients were 'allowed' – although this number was often exceeded.[xli]

There was money available for worthy causes. On 18 December 1846, in Gower Street, the dentist James Robinson extracted a tooth painlessly from a Miss Lonsdale who was anaesthetised with ether. Three days later, at UCH, Liston performed the first surgical operation done using ether anaesthesia in England. This emphasizes the speed with which ether was adopted for surgical procedures after the famous operation at the Massachusetts General Hospital on 16 October 1846. When in January 1847 RFH's dentist, Scott, wished to buy apparatus for administering ether the Weekly Board said order the best available. In February 1848, after Scott's death, James Robinson became the dentist at RFH.[xlii]

In 1848 a fall in income was attributed to European turbulence, caused by revolutions in France, Prussia, the Austrian Empire, and the states that constituted the new Italy. Britain was spared such problems but its economy suffered. Even so RFH reduced its debt by £2000. The following year receipts were over £5500 and all liabilities incurred before 1848 were cleared, along with most of that year's arrears. Fifty beds reopened and 'classification' of patients resumed (i.e. the separation of respectable women from prostitutes, the trigger for the problems with *Humanitas)*.

Hospital Staff

In 1844 William Wilson joined Weatherhead as Physician at RFH. Two years later he moved to Florence as physician to the British Legation and eventually died there in 1896. Weatherhead, a prolific writer on medical topics, left about the same time as Wilson.[19] His replacement Thomas Bevill Peacock, who had a major interest in heart disease, was for three years RFH's only physician; he left for St Thomas' in 1850.[xliii]

---

[19] Weatherhead died in June 1853.

James Newton Heale, appointed physician in 1850, proffered his resignation in October 1851 complaining of ill-treatment by some RFH staff. The Weekly Board could not confirm his claim and he moved to the County Hospital at Winchester.[xliv] His replacement at RFH, Richard Chambers, was also a Physician at the Free Cancer Hospital founded by Marsden at 1 Cannon Row, Westminster in 1851.[20]

William Brinton, an RFH physician from 1852, moved to St Thomas' in 1860. Elected FRS in 1864 he died three years later. After Chambers died unexpectedly in 1853 Arthur Hill Hassall (Fig 4.5) joined Brinton at RFH. Hassall, previously apprenticed to his uncle Sir James Murray, a fashionable Dublin physician, qualified MRCS in 1839 and LSA in 1841. However his major interest then was biological research. In 1845 he became a Notting Hill general practitioner but 'deciding to qualify myself for the higher branches of the medical profession' he passed the London MB in 1848 and in 1851 added MD and MRCP to his medical qualifications. Even so, although distinguished in other aspects of medicine, he was an odd choice as physician at RFH. Even as a student he was a keen microscopist and biologist – and his name is known to medical students everywhere because of 'Hassall's corpuscles' of the thymus gland, described in 1849 in his '*The Microscopic Anatomy of the Human Body*' which was the first text on this subject. The following year another book of his – '*A microscopical examination of the water supplied to the inhabitants of London and the suburban districts*' – called for improvement in the quality of the city's water. Subsequently Hassall's reports in *The Lancet* on adulteration of food led to legislation against the practice (and to his nickname 'Mr Analytical Commission').[xlv]

On 10 January 1849 the Weekly Board supported Marsden, Gay and the physician Peacock in recommending that Weedon Cooke, a young surgeon at RFH should be appointed as Surgeon *Accoucheur*. However, the Committee was reluctant to embrace obstetrics, believing it conflicted with the charity's original purpose. Instead Cooke became medical officer for diseases of children.

In 1850 a sub-committee appointed to review the physical condition of the hospital and its organization reported to the Weekly Board on 11 May that the wards were clean but other places were dirty and/or needed repair. It suggested a better use of space, and staff duties were spelt out in detail. To ensure its recommendations were carried out it proposed that '*one competent person…direct and control the general management of the different departments of the Hospital*'. Marsden became the first Superintendent.

Legal costs, and expenditure on repairs, compulsory under the lease, dashed the Committee's hope of freeing itself from past debts by the end of 1850. However,

[20] Now called the Royal Marsden Hospital it moved to its present site in Fulham Road in 1862.

Fig 4.5 Arthur Hill Hassall (1817-94)

the outstanding mortgage was reduced by £2000 in 1851, thanks to two large legacies, and the following year all arrears to the end of 1851 were paid off except for the remaining mortgage of £1000.

The main event of 1851 was the Great Exhibition, held in Hyde Park from 1 May to 15 November. The resulting increase in railway traffic led to more accidents and many of those injured on the Great Northern Railway were taken to RFH.[21] Railway accidents continued rising and in 1866 the directors of the Great Northern

[21] As King's Cross station did not open until 1852, they would have come from the temporary station on Maiden Lane (later York Road, now York Way).

Railway doubled their subscription to RFH to £50 year – for services rendered to those injured in accidents on their line.

The Dismissal of John Gay (Fig 4.6)

On 30 March 1853 the weekly *Medical Circular* carried a 'biographical notice' of John Gay, surgeon at RFH since Tweedie's dismissal in 1836. It did not flatter RFH or its staff – *'This unattractive structure might be easily mistaken…for its near neighbour, the House of Correction… The subject…is principal surgeon…, and, considering the disadvantages [of] being connected with a hospital of its character, has obtained a degree of celebrity of which many other surgeons…might feel proud. Nothing but genius of a high order for the practice of surgery, would have enabled Mr Gay to force himself into conspicuity despite so many obstacles'*. It claimed the position RFH had assumed following Gay's original appointment to the 'petty institution in Greville Street' was due almost solely to his efforts.

Surprisingly RFH's Committee (with Wakley Sr. in the chair) did not discuss the article until 13 July. Gay, asked about his role in the matter, wrote on 19 July – '*I am not in any way responsible for the personal or general observations which it contains…I did not see them in manuscript or proof, nor was I aware of their nature prior to their publication.*' He was asked to place corrections in the *Medical Circular*. On 3 August he confessed to receiving a proof before publication but denied reading it. He said the editor (George Ross of Farringdon Street) would print a letter from him, with corrections. He showed the Committee a copy of the letter, but it was not the same as the version published the following week – in which Gay stated he was not the 'principal surgeon' of RFH, Dr Marsden being the senior, and requested the editor to admit that he, Gay, was neither responsible for the opinions contained in the 'biographical notice' nor aware of their nature before publication.

Gay thought this would satisfy the Committee. But the editor's accompanying comments were inflammatory. Ross wrote that while Marsden was 'principal surgeon' in the *official* sense, Gay was not simply the 'principal surgeon', but the only surgeon at RFH. Ross was unaware that Marsden had 'performed a capital operation in his life,' and offered to publish any operative report he might submit. Finally, he suggested the treatment of Gay was a detestable plot.[xlvi]

The Committee, with no doctors present, met again on 10 August. Understandably, they were sceptical about Gay's claim that he had not read the proofs, and unhappy about his delay in writing to Ross and his failure to correct statements about the character of the hospital. He had forfeited their confidence.

The *Medical Circular* of 17 August explained RFH's attitude to Gay: *'…the "Lancet" clique…wish[ed] to establish a medical school…, but…cannot muster,*

Fig 4.6 John Gay (1812-1885)

among them all, either museum, drawings, or brains…efforts have been made to transfer the Hunterian School to the Royal Free Hospital, but, hitherto, without success…Mr Gay, the "principal surgeon" to the hospital, was averse to the design,…without his concurrence, the school could never be established, or, if established, be anything else save a butt for laughter. Mr Gay constitutes an impediment to the vanity of the faction; but for him, one son might be advertised as a LECTURER IN SURGERY! another, perhaps, as a LECTURER IN MEDICINE !! And MR ANALYTICAL COMMISSION, who has already performed, in his own person, the astounding synthetic feat of rolling four or five single gentlemen into one, might not be unwilling to submit to a re-division, and to distribute himself among four or five offices.'

On 14 December the Committee decided to dismiss Gay; the governors concurred on 30 December. A *Medical Circular* editorial two days earlier was again provocative – Gay's problem was *'towering to too great a height, and dwarfing the already puny stature of such of his colleagues as pretended to be his rival'*. Ross suggested the Wakleys were the problem; he claimed that Wakley Sr., editor of a rival journal, and Wakley Jr., personally antagonistic to Gay, had both attended the original meeting on 13 July.[22] Gay had told Ross: *'The Committee secretly let some premises…to Dr Marsden, Mr Thomas Wakley [Jr.], and Mr Gant, for…a medical school. They had summoned me a fortnight before to a conference with themselves and my colleagues, to* [consider]*…forming a school; but…the projected meeting did not take place and to that of the 13th of July I was not invited.'*[xlvii]

More than 120 governors were present on 30 December. Peacock, the physician who left RFH for St Thomas' in 1849, railed against Gay's dismissal and Gay also spoke. An amendment supporting him was lost by 87 to 36; a very large majority carried the original motion.

The subsequent response was extraordinary. According to the *Medical Circular* (19 Jan), over a thousand doctors met at the Hanover Square Rooms on 18 January 1854. Many expressed reservations about the 'biographical notice' but support for Gay was overwhelming. Rose Cormack and Ballard resigned as lecturers at the proposed new medical school. (See below) Meetings supporting Gay were held all over the country, and reported in detail in the *Association Medical Journal* (later to become the *British Medical Journal*) edited by Rose Cormack.

[22] Wakley Sr. was in the chair; Wakley Jr.'s attendance was not recorded in the minutes of the meeting.

The Inquest

Gay, like Tweedie before him, did not suffer unduly from his dismissal, becoming surgeon to the Great Northern Hospital (later the Royal Northern) until his death in 1885.[xlviii] But he did not leave RFH quietly. On 13 April 1854 Weedon Cooke and Wakley Jr. operated for bladder stone on a three-year-old boy; no stone was removed. The patient died three days later. Palmerston, then Home Secretary, ordered a full inquiry which began on 20 June. Two surgeons who examined the child before Weedon Cooke claimed there was no stone. One was found in the bladder at autopsy, but only the urethra was entered at surgery.[xlix]

At the inquiry Evans, a solicitor, testified that initially Gay, urging secrecy, had employed him to investigate the child's death. Evans therefore offered to act for the parents, without charge, and suggested an inquest. Gay, wanting a barrister present, asked Evans to brief Ballantine, an enemy of the Wakleys. Weedon Cooke's solicitor, Steele, was an RFH governor; he wished to avoid bad publicity and proposed a private examination but Gay insisted on a public hearing. However he could find no doctor willing to give evidence and, concerned that his complicity with Evans might be revealed, wanted to cancel the inquest. Having been given £100 by Steele, Evans returned Gay's retainer of £8 and gave £20 to the father telling him nothing would be gained by the inquest. The father cancelled it – but he then changed his mind and sought help from Lord Dudley Stuart MP, who in turn contacted Palmerston.

Weedon Cooke was innocent in this skulduggery. Ballantine acted for the parents at the inquest. Surprisingly, Gay confirmed Evans's testimony but denied any wish to injure the hospital, or anyone in it, although he suggested it was mismanaged. He claimed there was a move to re-instate him at RFH. Wakley Sr. said Marsden and Wakley Jr. were not opposed to this, but influential governors vowed to resign if Gay returned. The jury found that the child died of inflammation caused by an operation unskilfully performed by Cooke and Wakley Jr; it declined to give an opinion on other matters.[l]

The Royal Free Hospital Medical School of 1853

The *Medical Circular's* comments about plans for a medical school were well founded. On 8 June 1853 the Hunterian School of Medicine in Bedford Square asked the Weekly Board for use of part of the RFH premises. Hassall, Gay and Wakley Jr. turned up to a meeting to which RFH's medical officers were invited. Frederick J. Gant represented the Hunterian School,[23] and it was offered the top

[23] He may have suggested RFH to his colleagues because he was befriended some years earlier by George Crawshay of the Welsh iron family, a governor and major benefactor of RFH.

room and two rooms on the right hand of the inner gateway for about sixty guineas per annum.[li]

However, on 6 July, the Weekly Board heard that it was Marsden, Wakley Jr. and Gant – not the Hunterian School – who now wanted space for a 'Royal Free Hospital Medical School'. They believed 'the Committee…will…use their best endeavours to extend the Hospital accommodation…to get it recognised by the College of Surgeons, and…that immediately the Hospital shall be recognised, the School and Hospital shall be united, and three members of the Committee of the Hospital together with Dr Marsden, Mr T.H. Wakley, and Mr F.J. Gant shall jointly govern the School.' [lii]

On 13 July, before discussing Gay's 'biographical notice', the Committee agreed to this proposal and asked the Weekly Board to consider what changes were needed to unite the school and RFH. Gay had attended the meeting on 15 June; given the *Medical Circular* article it would hardly have been surprising if he was deliberately excluded from subsequent ones.

The 'Free Hospital School' of 1836 had failed. However, from 1848 pupils could arrange with a medical officer to attend the practice of RFH although its wards were officially closed to students. In 1851 and 1852 *The Lancet's* annual educational issue advertised clinical instruction for ten guineas for six months, and twenty guineas for 'perpetual' status. The advertisement claimed RFH had 134 beds.

RFH took the new plan seriously. The founding trio asked the Weekly Board on 10 August 1853 if they could rent the whole of the first floor of the centre building at the back of RFH, as well as parts already taken by them, and got immediate possession. Two weeks later Marsden suggested building a new ward to meet the College of Surgeons bed requirement. The Committee agreed. A tender of £550 was accepted. The work was to be completed by 1 October![liii]

All seemed well. On 17 September *The Lancet* carried a half-page advertisement for RFH and its 'Medical and Surgical School', which was due to open on 1 October.[24] Dr Tyler Smith, physician *accoucheur* at St Mary's Hospital, was to give the inaugural address on 4 October. The School section mentioned the teachers, the times and cost of their courses, and examinations and appointments to clinical posts. The most famous teacher was Robert Knox, the former Edinburgh anatomist who in 1848 was involved, but exonerated, with the murderous body snatchers Burke and Hare. The only hospital staff listed as teachers were Wakley Jr. and Hassall. These points were not lost on Ross; in a scathing editorial in the *Medical Circular* on 28 September he wrote:

[24] The advertisement claimed that RFH had 160 beds, 26 more than the preceding year.

'The truth...is, this School is not recognised, and has...no title to a place among the educational establishments of the metropolis...

'...this Free Hospital School enjoys the questionable honour of having the names of only TWO of the medical officers of the hospital figuring on its staff! Which two does the reader suppose are the distinguished men selected...to fill the professorships in the school?[25] *MR THOMAS WAKLEY, JUN., and MR ANALYTICAL COMMISSION!...All the other officers hold aloof from the job...*

'Where is that honest man and eminent surgeon Mr Gay? Taking care of his honour. Where is the accomplished physician Dr Brinton? Shunning bad company...

There are two other gentlemen well-known in the anatomical, surgical, or resurrectional — we hardly know which — annals of Edinburgh, which Dr Knox might very appropriately introduce to aid him in the anatomical department. With this addition the staff will be complete.'

However, RFH had jumped the gun. A medical school needed recognition by an examining body. No application was made to the College of Surgeons until mid-September; its Court of Examiners received it on 7 October. Three College delegates – Caesar Hawkins, South, and the President, Guthrie, inspected RFH and reported back to the Court on 7 November. Three days later the College rejected the application. It wrote to Fenn that it could not recognise RFH or attendance at the lectures delivered in the School of Medicine and Surgery connected with it; the letter made five points.

1) *There were no more than 80 or 90 patients at RFH; 150 were required to satisfy the RCS Council's regulations for a Metropolitan hospital.*
2) *Wards to receive the additional patients were incomplete, unlikely to be ready for some time, and inadequate to accommodate the proposed numbers safely.*
3) *Lectures on anatomy, chemistry and other subjects were to be given in the surgical operating theatre. Council thought it improper for anatomy to be taught where surgical operations were performed, and that chemistry needed a theatre expressly adapted to the purpose and a chemical laboratory.*
4) *The collection of normal and pathological museum specimens was inadequate for teaching anatomy, pathology, and surgery.*

[25] In those days the term 'professor' was used somewhat indiscriminately and did not necessarily signify a university appointment.

5) Arrangements for out-patients were insufficient, both for due attention to patients, and for the accommodation of students wishing to observe the practice.[liv]

The College of Surgeons could not have recognised Knox as a teacher of anatomy despite his pre-eminence in the field. John Henry Osborne obtained a diploma from the College of Surgeons of England in August 1845 having studied medicine for only nine months. He falsified certificates of attendance from many teachers including Knox, with whom he claimed to have studied in 1839 (while still a pupil at Nottingham Grammar School!). When Osborne's qualifications were challenged in 1847 Knox apparently told the English college that his own signatures were genuine, but later told the Edinburgh College of Surgeons that they were forgeries. Incensed by his attitude, Edinburgh withdrew his recognition as a teacher, and informed all the licensing boards about its decision.[lv]

On 8 October 1853 the Edinburgh College, learning of Knox's appointment at the RFH Medical School, reminded its English counterpart of the previous correspondence and asked it to inform RFH. On 11 November the English College wrote to Fenn rejecting RFH's application and wrote to tell Edinburgh it would not accept certificates of attendance from Knox. However, on 26 November it wrote telling Edinburgh it had been unnecessary to 'inform RFH' as its school had not been recognised.[lvi]

On 19 November the College of Surgeons told Fenn that RFH pupils who were already registered with the College, and who could arrange entry to a recognised School and Hospital within one week, would have their attendance recognised for the whole session. At the Middlesex Hospital Medical School Committee on 21 November its secretary, Campbell de Morgan, read a letter from Gant proposing that the RFH pupils should attend the Middlesex until suitable arrangements were made at RFH.[lvii] The Middlesex lecturers rejected the proposal. Three days later Gant told them that RFH lecturers wished the students to attend the Middlesex for the entire session. The Middlesex staff admitted them, agreeing that they should return to RFH if its School opened for the next winter session. Gant's autobiography, published in 1905,[lviii] suggested about fifty students transferred to the Middlesex Hospital. However, on 26 November 1853 the Council of the College of Surgeons received from de Morgan a note that fourteen *'above named gentlemen have been transferred from the Royal Free Hospital and have been received at the School of the Middlesex Hospital from this day to the end of the present session'*.[lix]

RFH's medical school did not re-open. In April 1854 the Middlesex agreed that the pupils could remain for the summer courses of lectures, and on 5 October 1854 approved 'an application...from Mr Hutchinson — a student transferred from the Royal Free Hospital last session [to] be admitted as a second and third year's student on payment of £20 each session'.[lx]

The College of Surgeons' decision proved a happy one. Had RFH's application been approved it could not, twenty-four years later, have accepted students from the London School of Medicine for Women, and the opening of the medical profession to women might have been significantly delayed. However the decision must have been a bitter blow to Marsden, Wakley Jr. and Gant. Only the last was to teach women at the new school in 1877.

The Crimean War

The Crimean war lasted from March 1854 until the treaty of Paris in February 1856. The British public, concerned about the troops' sufferings, contributed to new patriotic funds. Prices rose, donations to RFH fell. In September 1854 a severe cholera epidemic led the house surgeons to complain about the increased patient load. Asked to deal with this, if necessary by adding more medical staff, Marsden appointed his son Alexander [26] as assistant surgeon on 11 October – three weeks after his twenty-second birthday!

In 1854 in-patient numbers were again restricted because funds were short. Even so further appointments were made. In April Gant was appointed assistant surgeon pro tem, an honorary appointment without salary; in November he opted to be a resident house surgeon at 50 guineas a year.[27] On 6 December Mortimer Glover was appointed physician (if able to qualify LRCP within six months); Victor De Meric was appointed surgeon, Joseph Sampson Gamgee, who had acquired a veterinary diploma before qualifying MRCS in 1954, was made assistant surgeon and J. E. Savory assistant house surgeon. On the same day Alexander Marsden was given leave to join the Army; he worked at Scutari, Sebastopol and with the ambulance corps, and returned with the Crimean and Turkish medals.

In February 1855 the Weekly Board was asked to select for the army other doctors who would return to RFH when no longer needed by the 'War Department'.[28] As bed numbers were still restricted RFH was happy to oblige. Gant resigned his lowly new position and left in March. Three others were given leave of absence. Glover, still not an MRCP, went in April and Gamgee followed in August;[lxi] it is not clear whether De Meric went to the Crimea.

Gamgee was appointed surgeon to the British Italian Legion and had charge of the hospital at Malta during the Crimean war. He wrote asking if he might

---

[26] He had qualified LSA 1853, MRCS 1854.

[27] Gant's autobiography notes that he took consulting rooms at 13 Old Cavendish Street in 1852.

[28] They were not to be Commissioned Medical Officers of the British Army.

resume his duties as Assistant Surgeon at RFH in October 1856, but within weeks of making this request he tendered his resignation and became a surgeon in Birmingham.[lxii]

Glover returned in February 1856, managed to pass the LRCP in July, and was duly appointed Physician. However, the Weekly Board of 11 December 1856 heard that on the previous Saturday Glover was found drunk at the hospital – apparently not for the first time – and that several patients had left, after objecting to his prescribing for them. Within days Glover resigned.[lxiii]

Glover's story was a sad one. He was born in 1815 in South Shields, near Newcastle. In 1829, aged fourteen, he was apprenticed to an Edinburgh surgeon. He enrolled in the University's Faculty of Medicine the following year and qualified LRCSEd in 1837. In 1839 he defended his thesis ('*On the physiological and medicinal properties of bromine and its compounds*'), graduated MD, and moved to join the staff of the Newcastle School of Medicine and Practical Sciences. In 1842 he was the first to describe the anaesthetic properties of chloroform – having administered it intravenously to two dogs – but he failed then to appreciate its clinical potential. Apparently destined for a distinguished academic career he seemed to lose direction after joining RFH in 1854 – almost certainly because of an addiction to chloroform and opiates and possibly alcohol. Despite this he still published in the medical press. On 10 March 1859 Glover married Sarah Hickman, who had escaped from Colney Hatch Asylum, but a week later she was taken back to the asylum. He died on 11 April. An inquest followed an autopsy performed by Gant. On the death certificate the coroner, Wakley Sr., reported '*Accidental death by overdose of chloroform taken as a sedative*'.[lxiv]

Understandably the war had most effect on RFH's surgeons. The physicians Brinton and Hassall remained in post. In September 1855 the Weekly Board accepted William O'Connor's offer to perform Glover's duties during his absence. In August 1956, despite Glover's return, assistance was still required by the physicians, perhaps for the reasons mentioned above, and at Brinton's request O' Connor was elected Assistant Physician on condition that before RFH's next AGM he obtained the necessary qualification, as Glover had done.[lxv]

That O'Connor did not meet this condition seems evident as the Weekly Board minutes of 10 June 1858, state 'As a bill is probably about to pass during the present session altering the rules of admission to the Royal College of Physicians, Dr O'Connor's term for fully qualifying according to the rules of this hospital was extended three months longer.' There is no evidence that he ever met the original requirement, but it may not have been necessary; the new Medical Register recognised all registered doctors as equal under the law so there was no requirement for specific diplomas.[lxvi]

The Sussex Wing

Despite the College of Surgeons' rejection of the proposed medical school RFH made plans to improve the Hospital and to accommodate eighty more in-patients. It offered 20 guineas for the best design for a new frontage and wings; £3000 was allocated to the project and the Trustees were authorised to borrow up to £5000 using the premises as security. A design was agreed and a builder's tender for £3690 was accepted in August 1854, but the money ran out and the work was postponed.

However, with the financial turmoil of the late 1840s a potential source of funds had been overlooked. In June 1844 RFH's Committee agreed, following the death in 1843 of Augustus Frederick, Duke of Sussex (George III's sixth son), that if *'subscribers to the Sussex Memorial Fund...consider [building a]...wing to the Royal Free Hospital the most fitting mode of [remembering]...the Duke of Sussex' the Hospital would support the project and guaranteed £1300 towards a 'Sussex Wing' and a bust or statue of the late Duke.*[lxvii]

Fenn was asked to check the fund in March 1852 but there is no record of his findings. By March 1855 it held over £1600. Representatives of the fund and RFH met at Somerset House on 5 June and agreed to build a new wing. When the first stone was laid on 30 July there were refreshments in the boardroom, and the Foundling Hospital's juvenile band played for the guests. The Welsh School, next to RFH, provided facilities for the assembly of the Freemasons attending.[29] The handsome and commodious new buildings (Fig 4.7) were opened in June 1856.[30] The Duke's statue was placed at the front of the Sussex Wing. The sculptor, John Thomas, made no charge. He and Florence Nightingale became the first honorary life governors of RFH in July 1856.[lxviii]

Florence Nightingale and her Fund

In November 1855 a national fund was created to enable Nightingale to establish a training school for nurses. Gant, who had worked at Scutari, suggested in April 1856 that RFH should ask for its support. In August O'Connor met Carter Hall, joint secretary of the Nightingale Fund, and they met subsequently with Marsden and Bowyer, a Weekly Board member. In November Bracebridge, a trustee of the fund, wrote that Nightingale's attention would be called to RFH.[lxix]

In February 1857 O'Connor and Smith, the new Hospital Secretary,[31] visited

[29] The Duke of Sussex had been Grand Master of the Freemasons.

[30] During construction of the Sussex wing Marsden & Nelson, a governor, visited new hospitals in Paris & Brussels to study their 'numerous contrivances & improvements tending to increase the comfort of patients and convenience of medical officers'. WB 13 Sep 1855

[31] Stanford Skey Smith, connected with RFH for over 20 yrs, succeeded Fenn, who died suddenly in 1857.

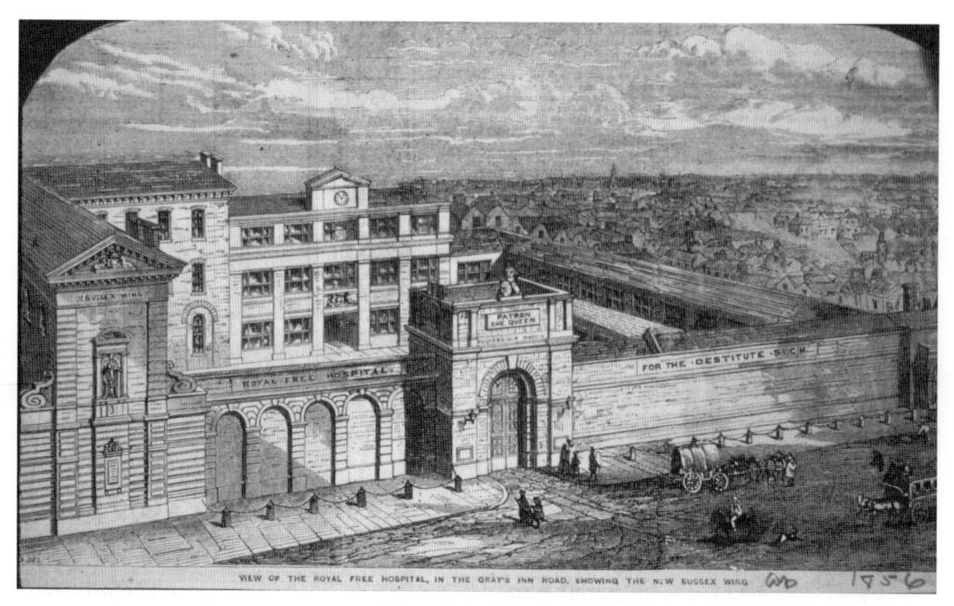

Fig 4.7 RFH 1856

Samuel Carter Hall to whom O'Connor wrote on 16 February: *'Since our conversation...occurred to me to give you...particulars relating to the origin, condition and prospects of* [RFH, and] *the principle on which it is founded, and...leave it to your better judgment to submit this...or not to Miss Nightingale...The situation...is at once open, airy, and convenient to all parts of the Metropolis,...in point of salubrity being better situated than any similar institution in London...in the centre of very large and extensive neighbourhoods chiefly composed of the artizan* [sic] *class who unable to pay for medical attendance, are prevented being reduced to absolute pauperism through the great facility afforded...by the Royal Free Hospital...resident medical officers being always in attendance for that purpose. The Hospital has no endowments – it depends solely on voluntary support to carry out the good its founder originally intended.*

To make it the most useful and extensive hospital in England nothing would contribute more than its connection with...Miss Nightingale –...there is space to accommodate 500 patients [plus those]...*now admitted... It is situated [near] the Fever Hospital, the Foundling Hospital, the Hospital for Children, and its close proximity to the Great Northern and North Western Rails – makes it convenient for easy removal of nurses to the different parts of the country. Adjoining...is a well arranged and commodious house...used as the Welsh Charity Schools, having a spacious garden in the rear and separated from the road by a large space of ground. That building is now on sale – next to* [it] *is Trinity Church, to which for religious purposes...easy access...without going through the public entrance to the church.*

If...you think it advisable...a more detailed account...[can]... be forwarded to Miss Nightingale...I shall...communicate your wish to the Secretary. ...'

The next day, Carter Hall sent O'Connor's letter to Nightingale and enclosed a newspaper cutting reporting the recent annual meeting of the RFH governors.[lxx] He wrote '*... I should much blame myself,...if...the subject of the Free Hospital were to "slip through", and the power to give it consideration came "too late...The Doctor and the Secretary called upon me at my house, and I said I would...forward to you any communication...with the understanding that you would notice it or not, as you found it convenient...But I presume...from the inquiries and observations I have made,...this hospital would be favourably viewed by you. There is certainly none with so many capabilities and so many merits.'*

On 18 March 1857 Nightingale visited the hospital – apparently unexpectedly. The Steward reported her visit to next day's Weekly Board and said she 'expressed approval of the internal arrangements – the whole of which she examined minutely'.[lxxi] A year later she asked for information about nursing at the hospital over the preceding ten years.[lxxii] As the Nightingale School did not open until 1860 these early approaches were clearly premature, but as a reward for his efforts RFH elected Carter Hall an honorary life governor.[lxxiii]

In its annual report for 1857 the Committee referred to the events that had affected charitable institutions – the Crimean War, floods in France in 1856, the Indian Mutiny (which began in January 1857), and the failure of American banks and railway companies that caused panic in the autumn of 1857.[lxxiv] However, the high income in 1856, and the generosity of George Moore and his friends, who raised £1715, allowed RFH to meet current expenses and pay off £1865 of debt. Moore became one of its major benefactors.

In 1858 Edward Masterman replaced his father as Treasurer. That year the Committee noted that 'its principle of free admission has at length been happily endorsed by its partial adoption in some other medical institutions'.[lxxv] In 1859, after many legal problems, 17 Greville Street, purchased in 1839 for £833, was sold by public auction for only £570, RFH's mortgage had risen to £5000,[32] but two bequests helped to reduce it by £1500. Following a bequest of £1800 early in 1860 the Committee considered the financial position to be more satisfactory at the end of that year than at any former period.

In 1862 Thomas Wakley died following an accident in Madeira.[33] That year negotiations took place with St Thomas' Hospital which had sold its site near

---

[32] Presumably to cover the building of the Sussex Wing.

[33] On 16 May 1862, a past member of the Committee, Joseph Bond, gave RFH 150 guineas and three valuable oil paintings by distinguished masters to show his respect for Wakley.

London Bridge to the Charing Cross Railway Company and was rebuilding at Lambeth, opposite the Houses of Parliament. Its Treasurer, Baggallay, asked RFH in May whether it could make beds available for St Thomas' patients while the work was in progress. RFH offered its old wards but St Thomas' wanted the whole of the new Sussex wing and suggested RFH patients occupy the old wards. After detailed discussions Baggallay wrote on 19 June about arrangements made to keep the St Thomas' establishment together.[lxxvi] It moved to Newington, and occupied former pleasure gardens with a music hall and zoo!

The entire mortgage on the GIR premises was paid off in 1861. In 1863 the plan to clear all remaining debts, and use any surplus to increase accommodation for in-patients, was put on hold so that RFH could purchase its freehold from the fourth Lord Calthorpe[34] for £5265, well below its market value.[lxxvii] George Moore, now chairman of the Committee, co-ordinated a special appeal. He joined William Marsden, Henry Hoare Jr., Rev J. B. Owen and Alexander Marsden as a trustee. The year's receipts, including the money raised for the freehold, amounted to £10,558, a sum exceeding all years except 1843.

A notable event in 1863 was Charles Dickens's presidency at RFH's thirty-fifth anniversary festival, held at the Freemasons Tavern on 6 May. During his splendid address he pointed out that RFH was – *'a free hospital…no recommendation is needed by the suffering creature who seeks admission; no letter from a governor or subscriber has with difficulty to be hunted out. "Look at me, look at me; I am sick, I am poor, I am helpless, I am forlorn." Those are the patient's credentials.'* Dickens also helped many other hospitals to raise funds – by speaking or by writing articles about them.[lxxviii]

In the late stages of the freehold negotiations there was a curious episode. On 9 July 1863 George Moore wrote resigning as Chairman of the Committee, commenting 'I'm sure you cannot be surprised at this resolve, after the treatment I have received.' He was asked to reconsider and offered any explanations he might require at the next Weekly Board.[lxxix] He sent the following reply via the chairman of the Board, asking that it be entered in the minutes:

Bow Church Yard *15 July 1863*

I little thought when I consumed so much of my valuable time and put myself under so many obligations to my friends to raise the £4350 in Donations, and £120 annual subscriptions for your Hospital but I should have been compelled to leave it through the conduct of the Founder. I have received the Resolution of the Quarterly Meeting urging me to withdraw my

[34] Who succeeded his elder brother in 1851.

resignation but I cannot do it upon principle as I only know one way of serving charitable institutions – the first is to collect all the money I can and the second is to see to the expenditure of every shilling to the greatest possible advantage and this will never be the case as long as the Founder has supreme sway. His first letter to me after I had resolved to do all I could to raise the money to purchase the Freehold was to the effect he had never asked anyone for a shilling and never would. Had he not frustrated my canvas for funds I should have raised a much larger sum and the rotten system of getting into debt and depending upon Legacies to get you out, need not have been resorted to. Believe me I feel great humility in thus withdrawing from an Institution I have endeavoured to serve faithfully and honestly for the last twelve or 15 years and I cannot do so without thanking you and the other members of the Committee for their courtesy. As I disapprove of the management I beg leave to cancel my annual subscription and also that of my firm of £20 a year each. May I request of you to record this letter on your minutes as my justification.[lxxx]

General Watkins replaced Moore as chairman of the Committee. The reason for the dispute is unclear, but one can sympathize with his concern over the 'rotten system of getting into debt and depending upon legacies to get you out' which had characterized the hospital's existence from its beginning. Despite Moore's enormous contributions to RFH the Weekly Board, while regretting the affair, recorded their confidence in and respect for Marsden, and especially for the urbanity and courtesy with which he always cooperated with the Board. Moore remained a trustee, and after Marsden's death in 1867 he resumed his financial support for the hospital.

In October 1864 the Weekly Board expressed concern about the explosives kept by Eley Brothers[35] in the neighbouring premises, but it seems to have been unnecessary.[36] RFH's architect, Innes, was more worried that the Eleys' plan for a new building on the hospital's south wall would interfere with future plans for an extension.[lxxxi] When subsequently Moore pointed out that the windows of Eley's new building would overlook RFH Innes said the hospital must secure the future right to erect a new wing on the south side to the height deemed necessary. If windows overlooking RFH were allowed to remain for 20 years they would become 'ancient lights'; Messrs Eley could then legally prevent building in front

[35] Even now a famous cartridge manufacturer.

[36] In 1883 Eley brothers applied for a licence to extend their business in Gray's Inn Rd. RFH's committee thought the effect of the proposed licence would be to diminish rather than increase the risks attending the manufacture at Eley's. Cubitts, also near Eley's, came to the same conclusion.

of them.[lxxxii] In July 1875 Eley Bros agreed to pay a shilling a year to use and enjoy their 'lights', without obstruction by the hospital, until such time as RFH built on the ground then occupied by the out-patient department.[lxxxiii]

In May 1865 (eleven years too late!) the Royal College of Surgeons recognised certificates of pupillage and dresserships at RFH for the MRCS, thus indicating the Free's improved standing. The Committee reiterated its desire to start a medical school, but still needed money to provide the requisite number of beds.[37, lxxxiv]

In October 1865 there was again a threat of cholera. To avoid delay two wards, isolated from the rest of the building, were made ready to receive patients with the disease and were used during the cholera outbreak of 1866, part of the last great pandemic.[lxxxv]

William Marsden died at the Star and Garter Hotel, a famous hostelry at Richmond Hill, Surrey on 16 January 1867, aged seventy-one. He had spent almost forty years at RFH and sixteen at his Cancer Hospital at Brompton. James Hopgood, chairman of the RFH Committee, offered £200 annually for five years to support a 'Founder's Ward' or 'Marsden Ward'. As a new ward was available, vacant and highly suitable his offer was accepted.

Within weeks of William's death a subcommittee appointed to consider the duties of the General Superintendent suggested the post was unnecessary. Alexander Marsden (Fig 4.8) had carried out the duties during his father's long illness, but while the Weekly Board had agreed to this in August 1862 it now rejected a proposal that he should take over as General Superintendent. However the Committee overruled it and appointed him at a salary of 150 guineas.

His stewardship proved a disaster. Early in 1868 correspondence in the *British Medical Journal (BMJ)* accused him of advertising, and of unprofessional and mysterious prescribing.[lxxxvi] On 23 May *'A Physician'* requested *'he* [Marsden] *should also obtain from the Board of the Royal Free Hospital,...some explanation of the anomalous position he holds in that institution, being at the same time one of the visiting surgeons, and a paid officer fulfilling the duties of general superintendent without residence. In pursuance of this latter appointment, he attends the committees from which other members of the staff are excluded, and he receives a handsome salary for work which in every other institution is cheerfully and gratuitously done by medical committees. He is, at one in the same time, the superior in authority over the staff, their inferior, as being a salaried household officer, and their compeer as one of the junior officiating surgeons of the institution.*

[37] It was this recognition by the RCS which, in 1867, triggered Heckford's approach, on behalf of Elizabeth Garrett, to ask whether RFH might receive women as pupils. (See Chapter 2).

Fig 4.8 Alexander Marsden (1832-1902)

Such a jumble might be productive of serious results in the hands of an unscrupulous man. But I submit that, as a precedent, it is woefully bad...With a donation and legacy list showing the clear receipts of £120,000, it [RFH] *is now in such an incomprehensible state of impecuniosity that a finance committee was appointed to ascertain how the money had gone. The resulting report has not, so far as I know, been published. I am not aware that any other hospital has ever appointed one of its staff to exercise similarly autocratic power in regard to professional matters.'* [lxxxvii]

In July three articles about RFH in the *BMJ* were reported extensively in *The Times*. They criticized many aspects of RFH's organization – the poor condition of the buildings, furniture and surgical appliances; its record keeping; poor attendance of the medical staff (the general superintendent being the greatest sinner); the incompetence of the matron and steward (a mother and son); poor organization of the clinical services; and profligacy in expenditure. *The Times* of 10 July noted *'The reporters of the British Medical Journal forbear making any comment upon the supposed duties of the gentleman called "general superintendent," because, since they have commenced their labours, he has resigned'.* '[lxxxviii]

When Alexander resigned in July 1868 he asked to remain on the Committee and Weekly Board. Six months later he resigned from both and cut his weekly out-patient work from two days to one. In 1873 he stopped attending out-patients, owing to his busy private practice and time spent as senior surgeon to the Cancer Hospital. He wanted to remain on the RFH staff, but without beds. His colleagues objected to his remaining Surgeon on this basis and suggested he and Wakley Jr., joint editor of *The Lancet* since 1866, should be Consulting Surgeons.[lxxxix] The Committee agreed. Marsden was not replaced; his beds were divided among the other medical staff; Wakley's beds had been appropriated by his colleagues in 1867.

Hassall had had chest problems for some years, and in 1866 suffered from haemoptysis. Colleagues complained about his absence from RFH and in 1867 his beds (and those of Wakley Jr.) were distributed among the other honoraries. In 1869 he moved to the Isle of Wight and opened a TB sanatorium in Ventnor. From 1878 he practised in Switzerland and Italy and died in San Remo in 1894 aged 77. Surprisingly in RFH's annual reports his name remained on the staff list as 'Physician', not 'Consulting Physician', until 1879.[xc]

Walter Rickards was appointed physician at RFH on 10 October 1867 and was soon honorary secretary of the Medical Staff Committee, a post he relinquished in April 1870 when the surgeon Hill took over. Rickards left RFH in 1877 on the grounds of his own poor health and that of his wife and child. He was not replaced. Instead, to help RFH cope with an increasing out-patient demand, William Allen Sturge was appointed to a new assistant physician's post.[xci]

In 1866 the City experienced a major financial crisis, triggered indirectly by the death in 1856 of Samuel Gurney, a major benefactor to RFH in 1843, and head of Overend, Gurney and Co., a major London discount house held in the highest regard. His successors speculated unwisely and in 1866 the company's bankruptcy caused widespread panic.[xcii] Within three months 180 financial companies collapsed, including Agra and Masterman's Bank, part owned by Edward Masterman, RFH's treasurer. It held the savings of Indian Army officers and imperial civil servants; fortunately RFH had only £153 in the bank at the time! The events of 1866 provided the last example of a run on a British bank until the collapse of Northern Rock in 2007.

Following this crisis annual subscriptions and legacies fell and financial difficulties arose. In October 1868 RFH considered raising money against its buildings to pay off debts, but its solicitor, Hyde, wrote that the Charity Commissioners could not sanction mortgaging any estate to pay debts, as opposed to repairs, buildings and improvements. Furthermore no one would lend money without the Commissioners' sanction, and borrowing would be difficult as there was no rent to pay the interest.[xciii]

After Alexander Marsden's resignation the Committee reorganised the paid staff, considered too large and expensive, dispensed with an assistant secretary, messenger and collector, and stopped paying a medical superintendent. Morgan, the dispenser, retired; the new dispenser had only one assistant. The Rev J. B. Owen, chairman of the Weekly Board and Hospital Chaplain, gave up his Chaplain's salary of 100 guineas, but received £50 for expenses. The new secretary, James Stephen Blyth, late secretary of Kings College Hospital, received almost £100 less than Smith, who resigned owing to ill-health. The total saving was £679. Only the house surgeon, matron and steward escaped the cuts! [xciv]

Even so the AGM in February 1869 heard that RFH owed £5632! A ward was closed, and the medical staff offered to help – by raising funds and by reducing expenditure in the wards and on out-patients. They prepared a hospital pharmacopeia, hoping to simplify prescribing, lessen work in the dispensary, and reduce drug costs. In January Hopgood reported that he and Owen had explained the financial position to those druggists owed money, hoping some would reduce their bills. However, trouble with druggists persisted, perhaps because of the potentially deleterious impact on them of a pharmacopoeia.

Reporting of the hospital's difficulties by the national press proved beneficial. The annual report for 1868 stated 'An influential Daily Paper,[xcv] after giving a graphic account of the Hospital, winds up an impressive appeal, in the following terms of encouragement: *We cannot conclude this sketch of...the Royal Free Hospital without expressing...[the] great need for its continued existence, and for a more extended pecuniary support than it has at any time obtained. The Board of Managers admit that there has been reason for the hostile criticism to which they have been subjected; but they shew that they are determined to deserve the support of the public by prompt and we hope, complete amendment. They will have many difficulties to surmount, and they can only surmount them with public aid. Let that aid be given at once, and generously, on the understanding that in every respect there shall be a wise administration of funds.'*

Fortunately 1869 was a good year. Income, over £12,000, was the largest since the hospital was founded; almost £4000 of debt was paid off. RFH was made more comfortable and attractive to patients. The overall bed number rose from 40 to 74 and the number per ward fell from 24 to 16. Medical and surgical cases were separated in three surgical and two medical wards. Out-patient numbers fell to 47,783, and only 825 patients were admitted that year, because of bed restrictions during the first six months when money was still tight.[xcvi]

Income fell again in 1870. Many annual subscribers died and the public contributed large sums to relieve the sick and wounded following the onset of the Franco-Prussian War. Even so, the Hospital freed itself from debt. A new operating theatre was finished. The old operating room in the central (east) block was converted into a comfortable post-operative ward, with six beds for female patients. It was called Elizabeth Ward, in honour of Mrs James Hopgood. Her husband paid for the conversion, and furnished and maintained the ward for many years.[38] The surgery for reception of casual cases (i.e. the casualty department) was doubled in size. A covered vestibule was erected at the entrance of the Sussex Wing to protect patients from cold and draughts; the back court of the hospital was levelled and sown with grass, and laid out with gravelled walks for the use of patients. The old Board Room was transformed it into a handsome apartment more than twice its former size.[xcvii]

Each of the honorary staff had a dresser or clerk – a student at one of the medical schools – who lived in and assisted the house surgeons; the arrangement satisfied all parties. When in March 1870 the medical staff suggested that each officer should have three dressers, as in other hospitals, the Weekly Board rejected the idea. In reply the surgeons again wrote raising the question of the hospital's educational role: [xcviii]

> *To the Weekly Board of the Royal Free Hospital*
>
> *... It has been often expressed by many members of the Board as desirable that a School of Medicine should in course of time be instituted. As a preliminary to that it is now, in accordance with the rules of the College of*

[38] In 1871 friends of RFH commissioned a marble bust of Hopgood by W. Calder Marshall & gave it to the Hospital.

Surgeons, possible to begin a school without any expense to the Board. All surgical students are now required to pass through a six-month dressership, and the dresserships at this Hospital are recognised by the College of Surgeons, so that we should at once by having more dressers or pupils derive personal advantages from their assistance, and the minor surgical duties of the Hospital would be more efficiently performed under the direction of the Surgeon or House Surgeon.

We have the honour to be, gentlemen, your obedient servants
Weedon Cooke, Victor De Meric, Alexander Marsden, Frederick Gant, John D. Hill

On 14 April the Weekly Board agreed on three dressers for each surgeon, provided their attendance and responsibilities were carefully regulated. The surgeons decided dressers should attend twice daily, and 'be gradually introduced to the full performance of their duties by practical instruction, first in the more simple cases of the out-patients department.'

The importance of these dresserships became evident when, on 3 August 1871, the Weekly Board heard from Hill, the Medical Staff Committee's secretary, of an offer 'so conducive to the well working and status of the Hospital' that they hoped it would be sanctioned by the Board. UCH's Medical Committee decided on 26 July, that 'Professor Erichsen be requested to obtain a written agreement from the official representatives of the Royal Free Hospital on the proposed terms that this Hospital pay £100 yearly for the privilege of appointing 20 dressers annually to the Surgeons of the Royal Free Hospital each dressership to be tenable for six months.' [xcix]

Despite Hill's apparent enthusiasm the medical staff rejected the proposal from UCH.[c] Had they accepted, the history of RFH would have been very different as it could not then have accepted women students six years later.

Nursing

There were originally no trained nurses at RFH but, according to its first Register of Nurses, Jane Dunwoody, who trained at St George's was made Head Nurse in 1868. The British Nursing Association (of Cambridge Place, Paddington)[39] took over all nursing at RFH in 1870. It provided eighteen trained nurses and a resident Lady Superintendent for £276 a year plus board and lodging. They were quartered in the central block of the building and their dormitory displaced the anatomical and pathological museum. Nursing became more efficient and the treatment of patients, and the moral and religious tone of the nurses, was deemed eminently

[39] Not to be confused with the British Nurses' Association founded in 1887 by Mrs Bedford Fenwick.

satisfactory.[ci] They were trained according to the system set up at the Nightingale Fund Training School, which opened at St Thomas' in June 1860.[cii]

Nightingale's choice of St Thomas' seems serendipitous. Unenthusiastic about her fund she tried to withdraw from its administration in March 1858. But she was patroness and organiser – and had £45,000 to spend. She asked her friend Elizabeth Blackwell to head the new nursing school, but Blackwell, committed to medical practice, refused. In 1859 Nightingale looked for a suitable hospital and a lady superintendent. After negotiations with the London Hospital fell through she considered other hospitals before settling on St Thomas' with which she was involved for another reason. Because St Thomas' lay in the path of a planned line from London Bridge to Charing Cross the Charing Cross Railway Company made a generous offer for its land. The hospital's governors could not decide whether to sell the whole site or only part of it. Whitfield, St Thomas' Resident Medical Officer, sought Nightingale's opinion in February 1859.[40] She advised the sale of the whole site – and a move to Lambeth where the new St Thomas' opened in 1871.[ciii]

Carter Hall had suggested RFH as a suitable site for the new nursing school in 1857. It was again considered for a Nightingale Training School in 1872. Henry Bonham Carter, the poet Arthur Hugh Clough's successor as the fund's secretary, considered moving the school, or spreading the fund's work more widely, when its agreement with St Thomas' ended. He wrote to Nightingale on 2 February, 'Of the London hospitals the Middlesex would be most desirable. My endeavours to get a footing there some years ago [1866] failed and I did not get any response…Something might be done at the Royal Free and I should be glad to go over the Westminster.'[civ]

The link forged between the British Nursing Association and RFH was a great success. It charged for only 15 nurses in the first year; three were provided free. It then decided eighteen were actually needed; the cost rose by £69 p.a.[cv] In May 1872 Miss Coles, the Lady Superintendent, who died in 1874, acquired a registering skin thermometer for taking the patients' temperatures.[cvi] Her successor, Miss Carberry (hence Carberry Ward), served until her death in 1887. The arrangement with the British Nursing Association ended had ended in 1884 but most of the nurses stayed on. RFH started its own School of Nursing, run by the Matron, Eugenie Barton, in 1888. The London Metropolitan Archives holds a detailed account of the structure and furnishing of the wards, and of the accommodation and training of nurses at RFH, in a manuscript dated 1874/5.[cvii]

[40] Whitfield had corresponded with Nightingale from 1856 because he taught nursing students.

The Siege of Paris, which lasted four months, ended in January 1871. British sympathies during the Franco-Prussian War were initially with the Prussians, but shifted to the French underdog. London alone sent £80,000 worth of provisions to the starving in Paris. Because money was being raised for Paris and business was slack RFH's Committee cancelled the annual dinner; that further reduced donations. Although subscriptions fell in 1871 legacies covered that year's liabilities.

In 1871 a laboratory was added to the dispensary allowing many preparations, expensive when bought from druggists, to be prepared in-house. Two rooms above the out-patient department were fitted up temporarily as isolation wards and proved invaluable in the smallpox epidemic of 1871-2 when they housed patients pending transfer to the smallpox hospital. The post-mortem room floor was laid with concrete to prevent absorption of deleterious matter; a new room was added where bodies could be viewed by the coroner and jury before inquests.[cviii]

In 1876 legacies totalled over £18,000, including one for £11,000 from the Rev. Gautier Milne[41] and one for £3000 from George Moore.[42] They allowed planning for three new blocks in a scheme for the complete reconstruction of the east and south sides, except for the existing east wards which received new windows. Both east and south sides were to rise to the height of the Sussex wing (Fig 4.9). The largest block, started that autumn, included a wing with three wards holding a total of fifty beds, a new out-patients' department in the basement, a dispensary, and a covered way linking it with the other buildings.

1877 was RFH's fiftieth year, and arguably the most important. Finances were sound; the available beds were always full. The first new block, the Victoria Wing, costing about £13,000, was completed in the autumn, and opened to patients in January. It held three large wards, each 105 ft by 22 ft, named after three major benefactors – Milne, Thomas Boys,[43] and Wynn-Ellis.[44] During its construction out-patients were seen only under special circumstances; consequently the year's attendance was only 5099, having been 25,668 the year before.[cix]

Work on the second new block, involving the south part of the east side, began in the spring of 1878 As their quarters had to be demolished to build this block nurses were provided with temporary accommodation in two of the Sussex Wing

---

41 The City of London Hospital for Diseases of the Chest also received £11,000.

42 Moore, who prospered from the lace industry, was one of RFH's great benefactors. He was killed by a runaway horse in Carlisle in November 1876 while on his way to speak at the Nurses' Institution.

43 Boys bequeathed £5500 in 1865; it was received in 1876.

44 Wynn-Ellis bequeathed £4000 in 1875.

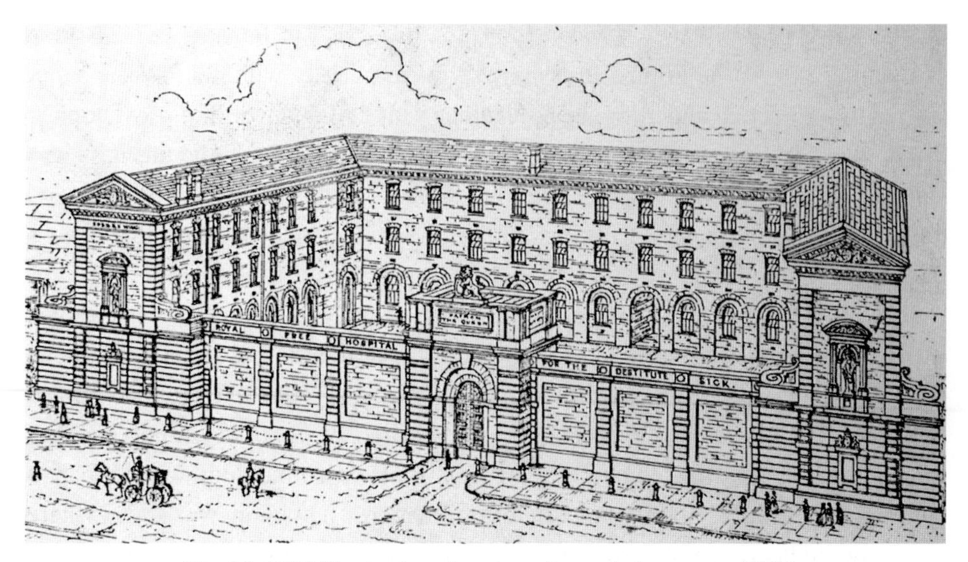

Fig 4.9 1876 illustration showing planned changes to RFH

wards. When these wards reopened RFH had 150 beds. In addition to nurses' quarters, the second block provided accommodation for the Lady Superintendent, a large meeting room, a private room for the medical staff, a students' room, and isolation wards. The estimated cost was just over £8000.

The last block, contiguous with it, was to accommodate a post-mortem room, the dead-house and the museum.[cx] All were still in use over ninety years later.

However, the event that enhanced RFH's status and gave it a special place in medical history was its decision, perhaps a reluctant one, to admit women students for clinical training. The circumstances leading to that decision were described in Chapter 3.

CHAPTER 5

The Deanship of Arthur Norton (Part 2) 1877–83

From Diplomas to Degrees

In April 1877 LSMW had an examining body that recognized its students and a hospital that give them a clinical training. The future seemed bright. To secure that future money was needed and one of Isabel Thorne's first tasks as Hon. Secretary was to organise the fund-raising meeting held at St George's Hall, Langham Place on 25 June 1877. The Earl of Shaftesbury took the chair. The event, a great success, was widely reported in the national press.[i] The speakers – Henry Fawcett, Cowper-Temple, Garrett Anderson and Jex-Blake – emphasized the need for women doctors in Britain and India and thanked supportive parliamentarians. They also appealed for money. Stansfeld said £5000 was needed to cover running costs for five years. £2600 had already been promised and the target was reached within months. However there was no appeal for capital funds, which may explain why LSMW failed to acquire the lease of 30 Henrietta Street (including 7 & 7a Hunter Street) when it was sold in January 1879. Council allocated £750 for its purchase; it went for £1060.[ii]

In February 1878 LSMW received a major bequest from Mary Ann Oakes of Paramatta, New South Wales – 134 shares in the Bank of Van Diemen's Land.[1] Worth £10,700, and paying 6% interest, it was meant to be a permanent endowment. However William Shaen, the School's solicitor, disliked holding shares with an unlimited liability and suggested selling them. The widower George Oakes visited London that October and agreed to the sale – providing the proceeds were invested to provide a permanent income in accordance with his late wife's wishes. Sadly the price of the shares fell and they realised only about £4000.[iii] Oakes, a member of New South Wales's Legislative Council, died in Sydney in 1882 after being run over by a tram.[iv]

The School's second large legacy, £450 from Miss Watts of Islington, came in 1881 but more capital was needed. Money for scholarships was provided by the National Association for the Promotion of the Medical Education of Women in

[1] Now called Tasmania

Edinburgh, and its sister group in Birmingham. Eliza Orme, a major supporter of women's rights, funded a travelling scholarship.[2]

In March 1878 the School revised its constitution, partly because it did not allow LSMW to charge additional fees when extra courses were introduced. The new version called for one meeting of the Governing Body each year instead of four, clarified the Executive Council's powers, and recognized the office of the Honorary Secretary.

In June Council discussed whether women could receive a partial education at LSMW before going as missionaries to India. It decided that, except by special permission, students would only be admitted if they intended to complete a course leading to registration; however, those not intending to practise medicine could attend certain classes as an 'amateur'.[v]

The highlight of 1878 was the opening of degrees to women by the University of London. Although Convocation had voted for it in May 1874[vi] the University's charter forbade it, so Convocation voted for a new charter in January 1876.[vii] Before it was enacted Russell Gurney's 'Enabling' Act of August 1876 empowered the University to examine women in medicine. In December 1876 Edith Shove applied formally for admission to the London examinations. Senate granted her request in February 1877 by a vote of 14 to 7; of its medical members Sir William Gull, Sir James Paget and Archibald Billing voted in favour; Sir William Jenner (the Queen's physician), Richard Quain and Sharpey voted against.[3,viii]

Because women could not take a non-medical degree without a new charter or another Act many doctors opposed Senate's decision arguing, somewhat cynically, that Gurney's Act was unjust – benefiting only women wishing to take medical degrees. At Convocation on 8 May, by 144 to 116, members carried the motion 'That it is inadvisable for this University to admit women to degrees in medicine, before it shall have considered the general question of their admission to degrees of all Faculties': 109 medical graduates voted in favour, only 9 against. The plan misfired. On 15 January 1878 Senate laid before Convocation the draft of a new charter admitting women to all degrees; it was approved by 241 to 132. During the debate Sir William Jenner said he *'had but one dear daughter, and he would rather follow her to the grave than allow her to go through such a course of study'*. His daughter became an ardent suffragist![ix]

The necessary supplemental charter was granted, and in July the School applied for recognition as a medical school. The University recognized LSMW and RFH

---

[2] Eliza Orme (1848-1937) had studied at University College and became a distinguished barrister.

[3] Gull & Quain were also members of the GMC. Billing was a member of LSMW's Provisional Council.

in November. On 12 December, Carpenter, the Registrar, wrote to Norton from the University's offices at Burlington Gardens – *'Dear Sir, I have the pleasure of informing you that I have now received the approval by the Home Secretary of the recognition, by the University of London, of the London School of Medicine for Women, and of the Hospital.'* [x]

The Conjoint Examination Threat

However, a new problem had arisen. On 6 May 1878 LSMW's Council discussed a Bill that, despite Gurney's Act, might have stopped women obtaining a registrable qualification. Under the Medical Act of 1858 individuals were included in the Medical Register if they possessed any one of the many degrees and diplomas granted by the licensing bodies, even a licentiateship in midwifery. Many thought this unsatisfactory, believing that a registered doctor should show evidence of training in medicine, surgery and midwifery. In 1870 Lord Ripon (Gladstone's Lord President) brought in a Bill to establish 'conjoint' examining boards: badly worded, it caused confusion and was dropped. The GMC's proposal that licensing bodies should combine to form a conjoint board in each of the three kingdoms[4] met with general approval – and the Government removed the legal difficulties that prevented London University, the Apothecaries and the Royal College of Surgeons forming a conjoint board.[xi]

The English licensing bodies agreed a scheme in 1877 and, at the GMC's request, the Duke of Richmond (the new Lord President) introduced a Bill specifying that individuals should be able to register only if they held a 'double qualification' – either two diplomas, one in medicine and one in surgery, or a diploma from a conjoint board. The women were understandably concerned; they could register only via the Irish College of Physicians and had no access to examinations at a surgical college. The University of London degree, access to which was imminent, was an MB (Bachelor of Medicine). Its BS (Bachelor of Surgery), unlike its MD, MB and MS, was not registrable; those taking it had to have passed the MB. Unmodified, Richmond's new Bill would have prevented women from registering unless they took both the London MB and BS. A deputation from LSMW[5] met Richmond on 31 May 1878 to explain the problem. Fortunately his Bill encountered difficulties. Ripon's Bill advocated compulsory conjunction; although Richmond's suggested voluntary conjunction the licensing bodies still disagreed about it. The Government tried to amend it, but the Bill was dropped; with it, for a while, went the whole conjoint scheme.[xii]

---

[4] England, Scotland & Ireland.

[5] Norton, Isabel Thorne, Jex-Blake, Annie Clark, Louisa Atkins & Garrett Anderson. The last wrote a long letter on the subject to *The Times* of 8 May.

In October 1877 Garrett Anderson gave the inaugural address to a now complete medical school.[6] Nine new students entered; thirteen began clinical studies. Because RFH did not cover all clinical specialties tuition was needed elsewhere to satisfy the requirements of examining boards. The Central London Throat and Ear Hospital, Gray's Inn Road, accepted the women students and in January 1878 its secretary wrote that the surgeons enjoyed teaching the ladies and would do so on a permanent basis: Lennox Browne lectured on the throat and taught laryngoscopy; Llewellyn Thomas covered diseases of the ear.[xiii]

In December 1878 the Irish College of Physicians, then the School's only examining board, announced that students must attend a hospital with designated fever wards. Norton approached William Broadbent,[7] senior physician at the London Fever Hospital, who persuaded its committee to admit the women, stating that his colleague Cayley was not opposed. However on 26 January 1880 Cayley wrote to Miss Heaton that he and Dr Mahomed (Broadbent's successor) were unaware of that agreement, and that the days proposed clashed with their arrangements with Guy's. To resolve the problem Cayley took the women on different days.[xiv]

RFH was usually helpful about clinical teaching and in 1879, asked to provide clinical experience in ophthalmology and gynaecology, it created departments for these specialties. It assigned five beds to Critchett, the ophthalmic surgeon,[8] and six to Hayes, newly appointed as Physician for Diseases of Women.[9,xv]

It was less helpful over obstetrics. Initially clinical students, still few in number, spent three months at the British Lying-in Hospital in Endell Street. However, from October 1880 the Irish College would not accept three months at a lying-in hospital plus three in a gynaecological dispensary in lieu of six months attendance at a recognized lying-in hospital.[xvi] With increasing student numbers LSMW clearly needed access to more maternity beds.[xvii] It approached the York Road Lying-in Hospital and Queen Charlotte's Hospital (then in the Marylebone Road); but they lacked accommodation for students and could not help.[xviii]

In May 1881 Norton suggested RFH should open a maternity department – with Hayes as its head and a dedicated resident medical officer (RMO) as his assistant. The School offered to pay Hayes and to take rooms nearby for three students, but the RMO post proved a stumbling block. LSMW wanted it filled by a registered

---

6 Lutzker's biography of Pechey-Phipson (1973) states erroneously that Pechey gave the address in 1877. She gave the one in 1878.

7 Norton's colleague at St Mary's and a member of LSMW's Provisional Council,

8 Critchett resigned from RFH in 1881 on appointment at St Mary's. Mackinlay replaced him.

9 In 1879 Hayes was also elected as Physician for Diseases of Women at King's College Hospital.

woman doctor who would live-in with the obstetric students. The medical staff, unwilling to accept a woman doctor, suggested entrusting the duties to a resident midwife. Norton accepted those terms, but in February 1882 RFH's Weekly Board abandoned the scheme, considering it too great a responsibility unless a qualified male RMO assisted Hayes.[xix]

LSMW also approached the New Hospital for Women (NHW), then in Marylebone Road, but its staff did not want an attached lying-in hospital. NHW considered establishing an outpatient department that would have cost LSMW about £200 a year;[xx] but this did not happen until 1891, after NHW moved to the Euston Road (see later).

The Clapham Maternity Hospital was open to LSMW students. It was founded in 1889 by Annie McCall who had qualified in 1884. As a student she had done three months' midwifery at Queen Charlotte's which took male and female students. She wrote 'there were five such training centres in London: Queen Charlotte's Hospital; York Road Hospital; Endell Street; a hospital near Angel Corner, near the Marble Arch; and the Jewish Maternity Hospital, East London'.[xxi] Presumably LSMW used them all. Residence may not have been obligatory. In discussions with the NHW, Norton proposed that, instead of renting quarters for the students, patients could be given the students' addresses as happened at UCH and other schools. One LSMW student arranged a second spell at Queen Charlotte's in 1882; she paid 12 guineas for one month's residence and two month's 'out door attendance'.[xxii]

Issues arose over propriety when the female students started clinical work. In February 1878 the RFH staff decided that in outpatient clinics male cases whose examination might involve 'exposure', including those with venereal disease, should be seen last – so that the ladies might withdraw. The handling of such cases in the wards and operating theatre was left to the surgeons' discretion.[xxiii]

There were other teething problems. On 21 December 1882 Council heard complaints that inpatients' meal times were disturbed by students and agreed that *'Clinical Clerks and Dressers are admitted to the wards for the performance of their duties from 10 to 12 a.m. and from 2 to 4 p.m. Special leave from...medical officers will be required for admittance at other hours.'*

Of the nine students admitted to the School in October 1877 three were partial students taking only anatomy and/or physiology. Five of the other six qualified – including Julia Swaagman (see later) and Arabella Kenealy. The latter was a well-known author, as was her sister Annesley (who entered LSMW in 1879 but soon gave up medical studies). The only one not to qualify was Mrs Mary Eleanor Lawrie, a wealthy lady, then aged forty-one, who lived at 1 Chesham Place,

Belgravia. On learning that RFH was to accept women students she applied to its Weekly Board for immediate enrolment and, able to attend only in the morning, asked to be dresser to the Senior RMO.[xxiv] That request was refused, so she enrolled at LSMW. Although still a student for the 1881 census, she took no class examinations during the course.[xxv] In February 1882 she presented the School with a valuable Zeiss microscope for use by the clinical students.

In the autumn of 1878 eight new students enrolled, including Annie McCall, Julia Cock, Matilda Chaplin Ayrton, Katherine McDonogh and Catherine Mitchell. Subsequently Cock was one of LSMW's deans – the first to have been a student there. In 1871, while with Jex-Blake at Edinburgh, Matilda Chaplin had married her cousin, the electrical engineer William Edward Ayrton. In 1873 she accompanied him to Japan; there she opened a school for midwives, lecturing via an interpreter,[10] and also conducted anthropological research. In 1877, after developing tuberculosis, she returned to Europe and qualified MD Paris in 1879 and LKQCPI in 1880 prior to entering practice in Sloane Street. She died in 1883.[xxvi]

Katherine McDonogh (Mrs Frikart), the thirteenth woman added to the *Medical Register* (as Eliza Foster MacDonogh-Frikart), had the dubious distinction of being the first woman to be struck off. Already a Zurich MD (1877) she joined LSMW in October 1878, qualified LKQCPI in 1879 and became a house physician at the New Hospital for Women. She had a Swiss address in the *Medical Directory* from 1881-86, and one in Torquay from 1887-94, although much of the latter period was spent in Australia. There she advertised her practice, thus violating the declaration she took when admitted LKQCPI. The Irish college wanted her removed as a licentiate and in November 1893 reported her to the GMC, whose president, Sir Richard Quain, had opposed entry of women to London University degrees in 1877. The GMC rescinded her Irish qualification and demanded her attendance in May 1894 for consideration of her Zurich degree.[xxvii]

She did not attend.[xxviii] The *BMJ* of 9 June referred to her as *'a lady doctor (of Zurich) who caused offence in Victoria by her clamant placards and newspaper advertisements of her "phenomenal skill". Her vaunt that she is the "only duly qualified and registered lady specialist in Australasia" will now have to be modified'*, because the GMC deemed that she had *'sinned against the honourable traditions of the profession and...removed her from the Register'*. In 1896 following a complaint from a Dr Morris Evans she was summonsed for unlawfully using the title 'Doctor of Medicine', contrary to the Medical Act. Evans had posed as a gardener and feigned illness; at his request she issued a certificate that he was

[10] She held a certificate in midwifery from the London Obstetric Society, the only medical qualification then open to women in Britain.

unfit for work, and signed herself MD. As she was an MD Zurich the judge dismissed the case.[xxix]

The only 1878 entrant to cause concern at the time was Mitchell – a council member of the Malthusian League, newly founded by the physician George Drysdale. The League was pilloried by the national press because it promulgated information about birth control[xxx] – a subject that the LSMW curriculum ignored for many years.[xxxi] Worried about admitting Mitchell, Council was horrified to find that her sister, Mrs Swaagman,[11] another Malthusian council member, was already a student at LSMW – as was Drysdale's common-law wife Alice Vickery, a League Vice President.[12] Some wanted to reject Mitchell and expel the other two, but the Fawcetts argued that LSMW should not appear responsible for the opinions of all its students. Shaen advised that control over women students should mirror that exercised in medical schools for men, and pointed out that, while admission could be refused without giving a reason, expulsion might trigger an action for damages. Council therefore admitted Mitchell and took no action over Vickery and Swaagman. All three withdrew from the Malthusian League's Council and promised to have no connection with it while still students.[xxxii] When Chaplin Ayrton died (see later) the Mitchell sisters took over her Sloane Street practice.

Anna Dahms, another of the Edinburgh group, also applied for entry in 1878. Although unqualified she was the first house surgeon at the New Hospital for Women in 1875.[xxxiii] Already MD Paris (1878) she was not formally admitted as a student but was allowed to attend RFH. She and Chaplin Ayrton wanted to register in Britain, and presumably needed further hospital instruction in London before taking the Irish exam. Dahms, who qualified LKQCPI in 1878, was later medical officer to the Post Office in Manchester.

In October 1879 fifteen new students entered, including Mary Scharlieb (see later) and Jane Harriet Walker. The latter, famous for her work on tuberculosis, was to be the first president of the Medical Women's Federation. She was created Companion of Honour in 1931.[xxxiv] Some left before qualifying – among them Annesley Kenealy and Mary Alice Palmer. The latter's father, George Palmer, was MP for Reading and a founder of the biscuit manufacturers Huntley and Palmer. In 1885 Mary married Augustus Waller, who had taught her physiology. She became a major supporter of LSMW, where their daughter Mary taught physics for many years (see later).

---

[11] Swaagman had three children before beginning medical studies.

[12] Alice Vickery & Isabel Thorne studied at the Female Medical College. Vickery had become its secretary in 1872; even so LSMW appeared unaware she was Drysdale's wife and a mother. After qualifying in 1880 she reappeared as Vice President & lecturer for the Malthusian League. [see Crawford E. *Enterprising Women* . p 311, ref 46]

Of the 36 admissions during the three years from October 1880 eighteen qualified. About thirteen had had no intention of qualifying. One of these was Elise Morgan, Frances Hoggan's illegitimate daughter, who entered in 1880 to study chemistry; Elise passed the Preliminary Examination in Arts at the Apothecaries but did not pursue a medical career.[xxxv]

Women planning to take the London MB had to pass the University's Preliminary Scientific Examination (PSE) even if they had passed an 'equivalent' test and were well along in their medical studies. LSMW had to arrange special instruction for it. The Pharmaceutical Society covered botany and organic chemistry, and Professors Carey Foster and Oliver Lodge (later Sir Oliver) taught physics to mixed classes at UCL. The first six women to start such studies were fortunate that UCL's Edward Schäfer, also LSMW's physiology lecturer, agreed to teach them zoology – probably because his sisters were at school with Scharlieb's sisters.[xxxvi] The six were at different stages of training. Edith Shove had entered LSMW in 1874, and was a student anatomy demonstrator. Helen Prideaux and Connie Hitchcock arrived in 1876, Julia Cock in 1878, while Scharlieb and Emily Tomlinson both entered in 1879. Hitchcock and Cock gave up working for the MB and qualified LKQCPI; the other four passed the PSE.

Shove was the first woman to pass any form of 'medical' examination at London University when, in July 1880, she and Scharlieb took the Intermediate Examination (covering anatomy, physiology, organic chemistry and material medica). Somewhat surprisingly, given her overall academic record, Scharlieb failed anatomy. A year later Prideaux won the gold medal and exhibition for anatomy, Scharlieb took first-class honours in materia medica and pharmaceutical chemistry, and Tomlinson gained second-class honours in organic chemistry.[xxxvii] Tomlinson, a great friend of Helen's, was visiting the Prideaux family home at 22 Woburn Square on the day of the 1881 census.

Scharlieb and Shove took the London final MB together in November 1882 and became the first two women to graduate in medicine at a British university.[13] Shove, already LKQCPI, had entered the *Medical Register* in 1881; she now graduated in the second division with honours in medicine and obstetric medicine. Scharlieb, a licentiate of Medicine, Surgery and Midwifery from Madras Medical College (1878), took only the London MB; she passed in the first division, took the gold medal in obstetrics, was top in forensic medicine, and in the second-class in medicine. Soon afterwards she passed the BS with second-class honours.

[13] The first women to obtain any sort of degree were the four who graduated BA in London in 1880; their course was shorter than the medical course .

Tomlinson qualified MB in 1883 but went blind soon afterwards and never practised. In 1884 Prideaux graduated with first class honours in medicine and obstetrics, and second class in forensic medicine.[14] She then passed the BS with third-class honours.[15] Appointed house surgeon to the Children's Hospital, Paddington, she died there of diphtheria on 29 November 1885. Much was expected of Prideaux, who was greatly loved by staff and fellow students. A postgraduate scholarship was set up in her name. The first Prideaux Scholar, Florence Nightingale Toms, used it to study obstetrics in Vienna.

In November 1880 Council decided that while women with a diploma from a European, Indian or colonial university, or an American college with a minimum curriculum of three years, could be admitted gratis to RFH for clinical lectures and post-mortem demonstrations, they could not take any hospital post or attend tutorial classes without charge. In the summer of 1881 Mary Jane Hall (MD Boston) became LSMW's first 'post-graduate' student.[16] Council asked Lucy Sewall's advice about potential American visitors. She replied that only two American medical schools open to women had a regular three year curriculum – the Blackwells' College linked to New York Infirmary and the University of Michigan – and from February 1881 graduates of those schools were allowed to enter RFH.[xxxviii]

In March 1883 Edith Shove was appointed Medical Superintendent for the female staff of London's General Post Office.[17] Lucy Cradock, LKQCPI 1883, took a similar post at Liverpool,[18] as did Dahms at Manchester. All three owed their appointment to the foresight of Henry Fawcett, one of LSMW's Governing Body and husband of Garrett Anderson's sister, Millicent; unfortunately Fawcett died in 1884. As Postmaster-general in Gladstone's government he derived great pleasure in extending the employment of women; but his enthusiasm for this was not shared by the mandarins of the Civil Service who considered women inferior to men even if they held professional qualifications,. At the time of Shove's appointment the Treasury professed to believe that the new "she-Dr" looking after women at the Post Office was unable or unqualified to treat men, perceiving her as *'...a peculiar*

[14] Prideaux, who had an outstanding academic record, took eight years to qualify – presumably because she switched to take the London MB.

[15] A third class honours did not equate with a third class degree.

[16] Excluding 'foreign graduates' studying at LSMW to be able to register through the LKQCPI.

[17] According to Scharlieb's autobiography [p 56] and her obituary of Shove (BMJ 1929: 14 Dec) Shove was a shy, little lady who spoke out loud to herself. Publication of her reports for the Post Office on telegraphist's cramp and other problems was precluded by her official position.

[18] Cradock was elected to the prestigious Liverpool Medical Society in 1888.

Dr…for 1150 females leaving 6100 males to be treated by two doctors giving them 3050 patients each! So surely it would be far better if it is necessary that another doctor should be appointed, to appoint a male who would be available for "all hands", instead of appointing one suitable for a limited number.[xxxix]

Shove, like her male counterpart, was allowed a month's leave each year but had to provide her own locum. The male Medical Officer and his deputy covered each other's leave. Her salary of £300 a year, increasing by £20 a year to £450, was lower than the £400 to £600 recommended by Fawcett; a male Medical Officer was paid £800-£1000 p.a.. As we shall see, such attitudes persisted for decades in the Civil Service. Although senior women might outrank men, they did not have charge of them – even if they were lowly messengers.

Although its students could now qualify through the Irish College and the University of London LSMW still sought other portals of entry to the profession. London's College of Physicians debated admission of women to its examinations in March 1878. Sir George Burrows, an ex-President, and Charles West (founder of Great Ormond Street Hospital for Sick Children) moved '*... that the College do steadily adhere to the terms of its Charter and do not grant its licence to practise physic to women'*. Henry Maudsley and James Pollock moved an amendment – that women should receive the licence if they met the requirements. Their opponents argued that to make women work was a retrograde step, that the College's purity might be endangered if women 'contracted any of the ordinary relationships of life' and that it would be unseemly to admit women and men to similar examinations. The original resolution was carried by 69 votes to 16.[xl] Maudsley, the psychiatrist after whom the Maudsley Hospital is named, was a convert to the women's cause; however, his earlier views, that intensive study was harmful to women and that post-pubertal exertion, mental or physical, might cause menstrual disorders and sterility,[xli] were still being widely used as arguments against medical education of women.

On 7 February 1882 Council had approved Prideaux's proposal to seek examination by the Society of Apothecaries. She had received the top mark in its Arts examination in January 1876, and won the Gold Medal and Exhibition in Anatomy at the University's Intermediate Examination in 1881. The Apothecaries response to her application was that they would consider it when she attended a school recognized by their Court of Examiners. Shaen pointed out that their regulations referred not to a school or hospital 'recognized by their Court of Examiners' but to 'any recognised School or Hospital' and that LSMW was recognised both by the Irish College and the University of London. He applied for examination on the ground that Prideaux had passed London University's Intermediate Examination – but the Apothecaries would not budge.[xlii]

As the School grew it needed a museum and a library. On 9 March 1878 Council discussed the museum of James Blundell, a celebrated teacher of obstetrics, recently deceased. Built up over 100 years by teachers at Guy's, it included about 900 preparations in bottles, many dried specimens and bones, forty plaster casts, obstetric instruments, and some valuable old books by Hunter and Smellie. As the Hunterian Museum had no space for it his executor, Dr Wilks, offered the collection to LSMW, which purchased it for £70. King Chambers suggested that the School should also use RFH's own museum. Mrs Thorne found it in good order but it lacked a catalogue and no one seemed responsible for it.[xliii] Alexander Marsden, its curator from 1869, had resigned in 1872. It was made available for teaching and a catalogue was prepared; the Hospital's Annual Report for 1880 announced that the fittings of the museum, recently relocated, were almost completed.[19,xliv]

King Chambers was a founding father of LSMW. In 1864 his left leg had been removed as treatment for a popliteal aneurysm, and in 1878 he also lost his right leg, which was similarly afflicted. He gave up most professional activities the following year.[20,xlv] Horatio Donkin replaced him as Garrett Anderson's co-lecturer on the Practice of Medicine.

At the meeting at which Blundell's museum was discussed Garrett Anderson suggested creating a School library for study and reference. Appointed honorary librarian, with a budget of about £100, she asked colleagues to recommend books for purchase. In response Sankey donated a comprehensive set of books on mental pathology, King Chambers gave 100 volumes, and subsequently many teachers followed suit. In 1882 the writer Anne Gilchrist presented the medical books left by her daughter Beatrice, who had entered LSMW in 1875 but committed suicide in 1881. When Buchanan Baxter died in 1885 his widow presented the library with 200 volumes.[xlvi]

In 1878 Garrett Anderson produced *The Student's Pocket Book,*[xlvii] a small volume of over 90 pages that slipped easily into a pocket. Her intention was to 'supply medical students with means of registering some of...[their] important...clinical work, [so it] shall be easily available for after reference'. She hoped that it would also 'serve to guide their reading and pathological study in

---

19 The RFH museum was created for the short-lived medical school opened in 1853. Gant collected specimens from Paris & Edinburgh but the RCS still considered it inadequate as a medical school museum. RFH bought it from Marsden, Wakley Jr. and Gant for £380 in 1859. In 1870 it was displaced to provide a dormitory for nurses; two years later the specimens went on display in a large room at the back of the hospital.

20 King Chambers continued to act as physician to an insurance company and after 1881 represented Oxford University on the GMC. He died in 1889, aged 71.

connection with each disease as it comes under their notice in the wards, and…help to keep before their minds the range of subjects which they have to overtake'.

The left-hand pages listed diseases or morbid conditions under headings such as "Diseases of the Nervous System,…the Respiratory System, .. the Female Organs of Generation, etc". Six columns on the right hand pages allowed the student to record how she had encountered the condition – four had the headings 'Seen: Lecture: Museum: PM seen' – to indicate if there was an entry about it in her 'Casebook', and to note 'Books Read' about the topic. Spare pages at the end were for a bibliography and notes, and the binding had a slot for a pencil.

In the 1883-84 prospectus LSMW recommended 1 Byng Place, where Miss Grove was the Principal, and Russell House, Tavistock Square, with Miss Cail as Superintendent, as suitable residential accommodation for its students. The demand for such establishments increased.

Initially LSMW had none of the clubs and societies associated with college life. The Bible reading group met weekly from the spring of 1875. In October 1878 its eleven members[21] wanted it properly established. Council granted them use of a room. In February 1882 it approved a more secular request – a tennis court in the garden for which the students offered to pay. It was ready in October and tennis became a major sporting and social activity at LSMW.

On 6 May 1879 women doctors met to found the Association of Registered Medical Women (ARMW).[22] Those present resolved that all registered medical women be invited to a meeting followed by a dinner on Tuesday, 11 May 1880; that the notice, requesting papers for presentation, should be sent out in January; and that Eliza Walker Dunbar should be Hon. Secretary. Blackwell was the first president. Ten members attended that 'second' meeting at LSMW; one paper was read. Afterwards they dined at 'The Trafalgar' inn in Greenwich. Although registered herself, Frances Hoggan refused to attend because unregistered women were excluded even if well qualified;[23] she never joined, nor did she join the Medical Women's Federation founded in 1916.

The eleven present at a meeting on 3 May 1881 formulated a protest against exclusion of women from the International Medical Congress to be held that summer in London. Even so, during the first week of August they entertained

---

21 Adela Bosanquet, Jane Waterston, Helen Johnston, Janet Monteath Douglas, Isabella Bartholomew, Alice Marston, Alice Ker, Fanny Butler, Annie Jacob, Annie McCall and Elizabeth Lougheed.

22 The minutes do not record where the 6 May meeting took place or who was present.

23 She may have been protesting the exclusion of Emily Bovell and Anna Kingsford (both MD Paris). Bovell replaced Hoggan when she resigned from the New Hospital for Women in 1877.

several hundred of those attending the Congress at a garden party at LSMW.[xlviii] Subsequently attendance at the annual meetings of the Registered Medical Women was patchy; six turned up in 1882 and four the following year. The largest attendance at any of the first ten meetings was fifteen in 1888.

School and Hospital Staff

Reeves taught anatomy for six years. William Pope Mears, his demonstrator from 1875, left in 1878 to become head of anatomy at the University of Durham's School of Medicine where he was highly regarded.[xlix] His textbook '*Schematic Anatomy*' appeared in 1882. In 1890 he and his wife (Isabella Bartholomew, LRCPI 1881), a Tynemouth general practitioner, went to China as missionaries but owing to his poor health they returned home in 1893.[l]

For a while Reeves took the whole class. Alice Ker, still unqualified but very competent, was his demonstrator.[24] (see Chapter 3) When Reeves resigned in 1880 Walter Ottley and Albert Leahy ran anatomy as half-lecturers. Stanley Boyd, a young surgeon at Charing Cross Hospital replaced Ottley when the latter resigned in June 1882. The following year, without giving notice, Leahy joined the Indian Medical Service.[li] Boyd then lectured alone for about twenty years. In 1889 he married Florence Nightingale Toms who had been a student anatomy demonstrator when he arrived at LSMW. Toms's studies were interrupted during her brother's illness and Helen Prideaux replaced her as demonstrator. Toms returned, qualified in 1888, and was awarded the first Helen Prideaux Scholarship (see earlier); she was not related to *the* Florence Nightingale.

In anticipation of more students it was decided in July 1877 that anatomy and physiology should be taught every year. In October Schäfer, now head of physiology, persuaded Council that first-year preclinical students should not work in the Hospital. In 1881 his histology demonstrator was Victor Horsley,[lii] who qualified that year at UCH and later became a leading figure in British medicine. Horsley, like Schäfer, supported the cause of medical women. The latter resigned in 1883 to succeed Burdon-Sanderson as Jodrell Professor of Physiology at UCL. Schäfer was only thirty-three and had been an FRS for five years. Augustus Waller replaced him at LSMW.

In December 1877 Elizabeth Blackwell, wintering in Nice owing to ill-health, resigned her co-lectureship in midwifery.[liii] Louisa Atkins took her place. Atkins, a Zurich MD, had worked as an unregistered resident medical officer at the

[24] Applications from Ker, Mrs Grant (née Rorison) & Mrs Foggo for re-admission to LSMW were approved in January 1878. All three originally entered in 1874. Ker's aunt, Louisa Stevenson, paid for a year's stay at Bern, where in 1879 Ker graduated MD (and qualified LKQCPI). Ker's great friend Annie Clark had graduated MD Bern in 1878.

Birmingham Hospital for Women for three years. After registering in February 1877 she moved to the New Hospital for Women.

In April 1877 Shewen resigned as co-lecturer in Forensic Medicine. In December Jex-Blake suggested that Bond, Dupré's co-lecturer at Westminster, should replace Shewen, but Council wanted Jex-Blake to take the post. In March 1878 she announced she was leaving London,[25] withdrew her candidature on 6 May and Bond was appointed. However, on the same day Council created a chair of Hygiene with Jex-Blake and Edith Pechey as co-lecturers. Sophia held this appointment for over eleven years despite her move to Edinburgh a few weeks later; Pechey, although living and practising in Leeds, held it until she went to India in 1883.[liv]

The clinical staff at RFH received relatively little attention in early accounts of the School's beginnings. The senior staff was surprisingly small and only four were listed as lecturers in LSMW's first report after it linked up with RFH – the two physicians, William O'Connor and John Cockle, and two surgeons, Gant and Rose.

William O'Connor, the senior physician, who worked at RFH for over twenty years, died in 1880. His *Lancet* obituary considered him best known for treating 'stomach and neuralgic affections' and for managing children's diseases. It also noted that he 'was the first Catholic since the Reformation…appointed to a large public hospital or similar institution in England.'[lv] Cockle, appointed in 1859, was, unusually for the time, both FRCS and FRCP. A chest physician, and expert on aneurysms of the thoracic aorta, he had a large private practice.[lvi]

Walter Rickards retired from RFH for family reasons in 1877. He was not replaced as Physician. Instead, to satisfy an increasing outpatient demand, William Allen Sturge was appointed to a new assistant physician's post. Sturge became pathological demonstrator at RFH in 1878 and replaced Cheadle as lecturer in pathology at LSMW.

Sturge, commemorated eponymously through the Sturge-Weber syndrome, trained at Bristol and UCH. In 1876 he studied neurology with Charcot in Paris. There he met Emily Bovell (MD Paris 1877), who had been at Edinburgh with Jex-Blake. They married in 1877 and practised together in Wimpole Street. That year Bovell, although unregistered, replaced Hoggan at the New Hospital for Women. However she developed tuberculosis, so in 1881 Sturge left RFH and they moved to Nice where Emily died in 1885.[26] Samuel West replaced Sturge as assistant physician.

---

[25] And asked for the return of the microscope she had lent the School.

[26] For many years he was considered one of the Riviera's ablest physicians. Queen Victoria made Sturge a Member of the Royal Victorian Order (MVO) in recognition of his services there to her and her family. A year after Emily died Sturge married his nursing assistant. In 1907, he retired to Suffolk and became an enthusiastic archaeologist. He died March 1919.

At that time two sets of pathology lectures were given at LSMW – in alternate summers. Sturge tackled most of the 1883 set, presumably while escaping the heat of Nice. He resigned as lecturer in September 1884. The surgeon, Frederick Eve, curator of the museum both at Bart's and the RCS, replaced him, but Eve soon left RFH and it was Quarry Silcock's name which followed that of Sturge in LSMW's prospectuses.

Evan Buchanan Baxter, a young physician raised in Russia, replaced Sturge as physician at RFH. He already held the chair of materia medica and therapeutics at KCL, his alma mater. He fell ill in 1883. Samuel West, lecturer in Materia Medica from 1882, took over his beds and Harrington Sainsbury from UCH acted as locum for his outpatient work. Baxter died aged forty-one, in 1885.[lvii]

The surgeon William Rose, like O'Connor and Cockle, agreed to accept women students in March 1877. Gant, the senior surgeon, did not, and although he soon recognised their educational prowess he remained unconvinced of their suitability as doctors – and particularly as surgeons.[lviii] Rose, an outstanding young surgeon, was appointed in 1875 after Hill's death from erysipelas. In 1888 he resigned from RFH on appointment as professor of surgery at King's College Hospital where he had been assistant surgeon.[lix]

Harrison Cripps was made assistant surgeon in 1877. He resigned in 1879 after 'an accidental poisoning of his system, occurring in the performance of his hospital duties'. Subsequently he became a distinguished rectal surgeon at Bart's. His replacement James Shuter, like Cripps an assistant surgeon at Bart's, died unexpectedly in November 1883 from an overdose of morphine; he was replaced by Frederick Eve.

LSMW's agreement with RFH expired in September 1882. The School requested renewal on the existing terms, but RFH wanted payment made to Hayes (gynaecologist) and Mackinlay (ophthalmologist) whose departments were created in 1879 at LSMW's request. Ford Anderson and Critchett[27] were the lecturers on those subjects. The School argued that it paid clinicians for lecturing and pathological demonstrations, not hospital work; outpatient teaching was meant to be entirely honorary. Even so, it hinted that Hayes and Mackinlay would be paid as lecturers, and asked that students should see their in-patients. Stressing financial difficulties, it pointed out it was the only school supporting its hospital's general funds, its contributions being guaranteed by Stansfeld, Skelton Anderson and Frederick Pennington. In July Pennington requested relief from this responsibility.

[27] Critchett died in November 1882; he was a major & constant supporter of medical education of women.

John Westlake, QC, husband of a School governor, accepted it. In October 1882 RFH generously offered to waive such contributions if Hayes and Mackinlay were paid £30 a year each for clinical instruction. LSMW accepted and the new agreement was signed.[lx]

Relatively little building was done at either School or Hospital between January 1878 and the middle of 1883 except for the completion of the three new blocks at RFH (see Chapter 4). Both the centre quadrangle and the back courtyard of RFH were smartened up, and the whole of the latter was laid with tar paving; in the main quadrangle the centre plot was turfed, the roadways were macadamised, and footpaths of tar paving were laid and edged with granite kerbstones.[lxi]

In 1879 the RFH Committee addressed a long standing concern – patients suffering owing to the noise of the heavy traffic passing constantly along Gray's Inn Road. RFH asked the St Pancras Vestry to alleviate the problem by paving the road with wood. It agreed, but the work was delayed because springs in the area caused flooding of the Victoria Wing basement which lacked a direct communication with the deep storm-outlet drain because the Metropolitan Board of Works had refused to sanction one. Drainage was necessary before work could start on the road so the Vestry agreed to connect RFH with its own drain at the corner of Ampton Street, about 400 feet away. The wood paving was done in 1880.[lxii]

The Departure of Jex-Blake

Jex-Blake spent several months at London hospitals honing her clinical skills before leaving for Edinburgh. There, in June 1878, she put up her plate at 4 Manor Place – as the first woman doctor in Scotland! Three months later she opened an outpatient dispensary at 73 Grove Street, Fountainbridge, where poor women were treated for pennies. Old friends welcomed her back and Heron Watson, George Balfour and Peel Ritchie supported her practice loyally. Sophia employed a cook, housemaid, coachman and several other servants, her servant Alice having retired to Wales.[lxiii]

Initially her practice prospered. Her mother wintered with Sophia, spending summers with her son at Rugby where she died on 8 July 1881. Soon afterwards a young assistant at the dispensary died unexpectedly. She had been working on fat solubility and there was speculation that ether, a fat solvent, contributed to her death. As a result Sophia lapsed into a prolonged depression during which she was supported by her old friend Ursula Du Pre. The Manor Place practice was closed, others ran the dispensary.[lxiv]

In September 1983 Sophia returned to practise at a new home, Bruntsfield Lodge, rented from her old friends the Burn Murdochs; there she saw her wealthier patients. The dispensary's work increased and it moved to a larger house at 6 Grove Street; it had room for five beds, which were opened in 1885 (see Chapter 6).[lxv]

On 20 February 1883 Isabel Thorne informed Council that Norton was resigning as Dean. He continued as lecturer in surgery, a post he also held at St Mary's where he was senior surgeon from 1881. He remained on LSMW's Council and when Stansfeld resigned in 1891 took over as Honorary Treasurer.

On 13 March Donkin proposed and Louisa Atkins seconded a motion that Mrs Garrett Anderson be nominated for election as Dean. Despite her depression Jex-Blake attended and proposed an amendment, seconded by King Chambers, 'that Dr Edith Pechey be proposed for election as Dean of the School.' The amendment was lost; the original resolution was carried by 14 votes to 1. At the next Council meeting Garrett Anderson's nomination to the Governing Board as Dean was confirmed unanimously; at the Governors' meeting on 7 May Elizabeth Blackwell proposed, and Mr Bond seconded, the motion that Mrs Garrett Anderson be elected Dean.[lxvi]

Shirley Roberts stated that although Sophia remained a governor and Trustee she never attended another meeting of the Executive Council.[lxvii] However, the records show that she chaired the 116th Meeting of Council held on 3 March 1885. Her name remained on the list of Members of Council until the Annual Report for 1889, the year she resigned as lecturer in hygiene.

CHAPTER 6

Elizabeth Garrett Anderson (1883-1903)

Synergy in Action – Consolidation and Expansion

At Burlington House on 10 May 1883 Garrett Anderson's first official duty as Dean was to present to Lord Granville, the University of London's Chancellor, Mary Scharlieb and Edith Shove – the first two women awarded a medical degree by a British university. Twenty-one years earlier Granville dashed EGA's own hopes of qualifying with a degree rather than a diploma when his casting vote prevented admission of women to the University.

Her first Council meeting, on 22 May, was more mundane. She announced that Lady Granville would present the prizes in June and that Millicent Fawcett [1] would propose the vote of thanks. Council agreed the Worshipful Company of Cutlers could borrow old instruments from the museum for a cutlery exhibition at Salters' Hall; Joseph Thorne, the Hon.Sec.'s husband, and a strong supporter of LSMW, was the Master Cutler!

In June Council rejected the idea of linking with Victoria University,[2] formed in 1880 by amalgamating Manchester's Owen's College, Liverpool University College and Yorkshire College, Leeds. The second British university to award degrees to women, it split subsequently into the independent universities of the three cities.

London University was founded in 1836 to examine and confer degrees on students from London's University College and King's College, and from other 'approved' institutions within the United Kingdom. However in 1858 a new charter allowed students from anywhere to sit for its degrees (except for medical degrees). Internal and external students took the same examinations until 1900, but even in London itself there was no link between the teachers and the examining body. The staff of University College (UCL) and King's College (KCL) coveted Victoria University's power to confer degrees on its own students, and in 1884 London's teachers set up an 'Association for Promoting a Teaching University for London'. They hoped to gain control over their own students' syllabuses and examinations

---

[1] Garrett Anderson's sister.

[2] Council first mooted the idea of linking with Victoria University on 29 July 1879 – before it opened.

and to change the university from a mere examining body into an institution giving teachers a major role in its governance.[i] It faced strong opposition from supporters of the 'external' system – especially those in Convocation, which feared for its own privileges if colleges and teachers became more powerful.

When in April 1885 the Dean became LSMW's representative on the committee of the 'Association' she was on a long holiday to Australia, travelling by courtesy of the Orient Line;[3] Norton (the acting Dean) or Stanley Boyd attended in her absence.

In 1887 UCL and KCL, arguing that separating examining and teaching was detrimental for university education, petitioned the Privy Council for a charter for an 'Albert University of London', including medical schools, with faculties and boards of studies. However, the petition led to the resignation of a third of UCL's Council who were unhappy about teachers conferring degrees on their own students.[4,ii]

A further complication was that London's Royal Colleges of Physicians and Surgeons were also petitioning for degree-giving powers; LSMW opposed this unless women could take the degrees. A Royal Commission was set up in May 1888 under Lord Selborne to deal with both petitions, and *'to inquire whether any and what kind of new university or powers is or are required for the advancement of higher education in London'*. It included three lawyers and three 'teachers' but had no medical members.

The commission rejected the Royal Colleges' petition and opted for a teaching university in London. However, differences between the lawyers and 'teachers' led to confusion.[iii] The Senate, trying to reconcile interested parties, reached agreement with the powerful medical lobby but Convocation vetoed the resulting scheme in May 1891.[5] The Privy Council recommended a charter for 'Albert University' but, following widespread opposition and parliamentary objections, consent was withheld in March 1892.[iv] Had London's medical schools become colleges of Albert University their students could have sat a less exacting final examination than that for the University of London's MB.[v]

Another Royal Commission, the 'Gresham Commission',[6] was appointed in April 1892 under Lord Cowper. Seven of his twelve fellow commissioners

---

3 Founded jointly in 1878 by her husband's company, Anderson, Anderson & Co. and F. Green & Co.

4 A process considered analogous to auditing one's own accounts.

5 Mary Scharlieb was one who spoke against it; see Cooke, History of RCP London: vol 3, p952.

6 So called because it was suggested that if the new university incorporated Gresham College to become 'Gresham University' there would be a link with the rich City of London.

understood London's problems and there were three medical members – Sir William Savory, a Bart's surgeon; Sir George Humphrey, a surgeon at Cambridge; and John Burdon-Sanderson, professor of physiology at UCL from 1870 until 1883.[vi]

After its publication in January 1894 the Commission's report, similar to Selborne's, was better received. It recommended reconstructing the university so that it would be able *'while retaining its existing powers and privileges, to carry out...the work...required of a teaching University for London, without interfering with...those important duties...performed as an examining body for students...from all parts of the British Empire'*.[vii]

There were to be internal and external students. Many institutions in London, including the medical schools, were to become 'schools' of the University – retaining their separate identities, but with teachers appointed or recognised by the University. Research was to be promoted. The Commissioners proposed a Senate, an Academic Council (influenced mainly by the sixteen faculty members of Senate), a Council for External Students (dominated by the sixteen representing Convocation), plus a system of Faculties and Boards of Studies. A statutory distinction was thus made between internal and external students, and their degree examinations developed along different lines. (See also Chapter 7). Adoption of this system was not immediate. The report recommended reform by legislation – not a charter. The requisite Act of Parliament, not passed until 1898, established a commission to frame the necessary statutes for the University, whose administration moved from Burlington Gardens to the Imperial Institute in South Kensington in 1899.[viii]

Meanwhile there were developments in parliament and at other universities and examining boards that had the potential to affect medical women. On 25 June 1886 the Act to Amend the Medical Act was passed. Subsequently no one could register without passing an examination covering medicine, surgery and midwifery. But the Act did not create the concern provoked in 1878 when Richmond's Bill specified that only a 'double qualification' should be registrable. Then women had little access to surgical examinations;[7] by 1886, in both Ireland and Scotland, they could qualify through a conjoint diploma, or add a surgical diploma if they already had a 'medical' qualification.

Following the Medical Act of 1858 the King and Queen's College of Physicians in Ireland and the Irish Royal College of Surgeons had contemplated a joint qualification. When these two Irish Colleges reopened negotiations for the giving of a double qualification in November 1883 no agreement was reached. The

[7] London also had a separate BS degree but its MB had a surgical component.

physicians would not include Apothecaries Hall in the plan. However the surgical college would '*grant its licence to persons holding degrees or licences in medicine from other bodies…including the Apothecaries Hall of Ireland'* and in January 1885 it admitted women to all examinations.[ix]

The Irish College of Surgeons recognized LSMW and in 1886 Mrs Mary Dowson, a student and then teacher at LSMW, became the first female LRCSI, having qualified LRCPI in 1884. The College also admitted women to its medical school; Agnes Shannon was the first in 1885 but she did not go on to qualify.[x] The surgeons subsequently gave way over Apothecaries Hall and the Irish Conjoint Board was established in 1886. The first woman awarded the Irish conjoint diploma was Florence Nightingale Toms in May 1888.[xi] The King's and Queen's College of Physicians in Ireland became 'The Royal College of Physicians of Ireland' in October 1890; the qualifications LRCPI and LRCP&SI date from that time. The first Irishwoman to obtain the LRCP&SI was Emily Winifred Dickson in 1891. She was elected FRCSI in 1893; that year she also graduated MBBCh at the Royal University of Ireland.[xii]

The Royal University of Ireland (RUI) was founded in 1880 following the University Education (Ireland) Act 1879. Its examinations were open to all, including women and students at the Catholic University,[8] two groups that were previously unable to take recognised University degrees. Queen's University was therefore dissolved in February 1882; its colleges at Cork, Galway and Belfast survived but had no special relationship with the RUI (which awarded the degrees). The first LSMW student to graduate MB RUI was Eleanora Fleury, an Irishwoman; she took first place at the final examination in 1890 as she had done in the intermediate examination in 1887. In 1893 she was awarded the MD RUI with a gold medal. Four other LSMW students also qualified through the Royal University.

Trinity College, Dublin admitted three women to its medical school in 1904. One, Eva Jellett, transferred from the Royal University in 1904, having studied at the Catholic University Medical School in Cecilia Street. In 1905 she was Trinity's first woman medical graduate; her late father, a former Provost, was the only Board member to support admission of women when the idea was first mooted in the early 1870s. Until 1936 Trinity's women medical students had their own anatomy department with a separate dissecting room and reading room. The Belfast Medical School admitted its first three women in 1889: they were two sisters from Newry – Elizabeth Gould Bell and Margaret Smith Bell – plus Harrietta Rosetta Neill; Elizabeth qualified in 1893, the others in 1894. Two women graduated at Cork in

[8] Founded in 1854.

1898, and in 1902 Christina Caldwell Dagg became the first female to enter Galway medical school, but she did not go on to qualify.[xiii]

In Scotland 'double qualifications' (i.e. LRCPEd, together with either LRCSEd or LFPSGlas) were introduced in 1859.[xiv] In 1884 the two Edinburgh Royal Colleges and the Faculty of Physicians and Surgeons of Glasgow[9] created a Conjoint Board awarding the 'triple qualification'[xv] – LRCPEd, LRCSEd, LFPSGlas – usually abbreviated for practical purposes to LRCPSEd. Women could not take Scottish qualifications until 1886 but the 'triple' was to prove more popular with LSMW students than the examinations in Dublin. Iszet Mead (later Mrs. Haythornthwaite) and Emma Littlewood (Mrs. Slater) were, in 1886, the first LSMW students to pass the 'triple';[10] that year no LSMW student failed a formal examination.

Obviously LSMW students wanted to be examined in London. The Royal Colleges of Physicians and Surgeons had agreed on a Conjoint Board early in 1883. However, in March 1884 they wrote to the GMC withdrawing from the 1877 scheme, which had envisaged a single Examining Board for England that also involved the Society of Apothecaries and the four English universities then awarding medical degrees.[11] The first 'LRCP, MRCS' examinations were held in January 1885; they were not open to women until 1909.[12]

The Society of Apothecaries needed either to combine with a board providing a surgical qualification or run its own surgical examination. It applied to the GMC for permission to appoint three surgical examiners. Garrett Anderson and Isabel Thorne were clever. When supporting the application they asked the GMC to persuade the Society to admit women to its examinations. When, on 17 May 1887, the GMC approved the application making the Apothecaries' licence registrable under the 1886 Act it stated it was *'not unwilling to express the hope that Examining Bodies, may, if within their powers, find it desirable to admit women on equal terms with men to the privilege of Examination.'*

At last the Society opened its doors to women and on 23 March 1888 it accepted Isabella Macdonald's application to sit for its new licence. She qualified on 14 April – the second woman granted a licence to practise by the Society,[13] *'and the first to include Surgery'*.[14]

---

9 It was the 'Royal Faculty' from 1909, and became a Royal College in 1962.

10 Not Jessie Hunter and Sarah Gray in 1888, as claimed by Hull & Gayer-Kordesch in '*The Shaping of the Medical Profession*'; Hambledon Press: 1999. p46. James Beaton, Librarian of RCPS Glasgow gives pride of place to Mead in November 1886.

11 Oxford, Cambridge, London & Durham.

12 See Chapter 7.

13 Garrett Anderson being the first.

14 After passing London MB later that year Macdonald joined Edith Pechey at the Cama Hospital in Bombay. Three yrs later she returned and was Out-patient Physician at NHW. She died 1947.

Although women could obtain the Scottish diplomas from 1886 they still could not study medicine in Scotland. Jex-Blake, now well established in Edinburgh practice, was asked to help. She recruited two lecturers willing to teach women at Surgeons' Hall and guaranteed the fees. Eight women started classes in the autumn of 1886, including Margaret Todd[15] and Grace Cadell; Cadell had enrolled at LSMW in October 1884 but returned to Edinburgh for family reasons.[xvi]

The women needed a library, laboratories, and access to hospital instruction – in other words a medical school. Suitable premises were available; in 1876 Sophia, Ursula Du Pre and Louisa Stevenson had purchased No 1 Surgeon Square, previously used as a medical school. Its lecture rooms and laboratories were refurbished, and a library and sitting-room added. In October 1887 it opened as the 'Edinburgh School of Medicine for Women' with Sophia as Dean; her friends G.W. Balfour, Agnes McLaren, Heron Watson, White-Miller, Mrs Alexander Russel and Ursula Du Pre formed the Executive Committee. The school offered a complete training and was recognized by the Scottish examination board. Sophia arranged clinical training at the Leith Hospital, which was recognised by Edinburgh's Royal Colleges of Physicians and Surgeons. In 1888 Sophia became the first accredited woman lecturer in the extramural system; she taught midwifery, having passed the requisite examinations with distinction.[xvii]

Isabel Thorne was unhappy, believing that Jex-Blake and her Edinburgh friends should have supported LSMW instead of founding a second medical school for women.[16] Thorne's stance seems unrealistic given the long distances some women would have needed to travel.[xviii] However, her main concern might have been loss of revenue from fees. In November 1890 a Dr Maxwell told Thorne a Miss Tillinghast enrolled at Edinburgh paid fees of £61; LSMW's were £115. He said missionary societies would struggle to support LSMW without concessions. In December he wrote that he had been misled; missionary ladies paid £85 at Jex-Blake's School – but still much less than LSMW's fees.[xix]

Initially all went well at Jex-Blake's new school but problems arose when more students arrived, one being Cadell's sister, Ina (Georgina). Some of them resented Sophia's strict discipline. Students were meant to leave Leith Hospital's wards by 5 p.m. to ease the nurses' work. However, at 5 p.m. on 8 June 1888 the Cadells and two others watched the house surgeon, Juckes, examine a patient with a head injury. Asked by the Lady Superintendent to leave Grace Cadell told her she had no business interfering as Juckes had invited them. Sophia reprimanded the culprits

---

[15] Later Jex-Blake's companion and biographer.

[16] In May 1878, Dr Muschet of Stirling requested details of LSMW's foundation.He wished to start a women's school in Glasgow. Council replied it was undesirable to start more medical schools for women given the difficulty of making them self-supporting.

before the whole class and drafted an apology for their signature; Ina Cadell later retracted her apology.[xx]

The school split into two factions. Margaret Todd and others remained loyal to Sophia. The Cadell sisters, the most outspoken of the hostile group, were expelled. They brought an action for damages, each claiming £500 compensation for interruption of their studies. In July 1889 the judges found for the Cadells but awarded them only £50.[17] Sadly the school was to pay a much higher price.[xxi]

Soon after the Cadells' exclusion the school's most gifted pupil, Elsie Inglis, encouraged by rich and influential friends, left and established the Medical College for Women at 30 Chambers Street. Its facilities were poor but its fees were lower and its rules less restrictive. When it opened in 1889 many students from Sophia's school enrolled there. Lacking access to an Edinburgh hospital its students travelled initially to Glasgow Royal Infirmary. In July 1892 they were accepted by Edinburgh Royal Infirmary. Two of its Board of Managers also served on the Committee of the Chambers Street College; ironically, one was Sir Alexander Christison, son of the late Sir Robert Christison![xxii]

Sophia's school still had loyal supporters. The remaining students accepted her firm leadership, and many remained her friends. Indian students introduced by Edith Pechey[18] received a special welcome and several lived at Bruntsfield Lodge. Edith visited in 1892 and distributed the prizes at the end of the academic year.

Margaret Todd was now Sophia's main companion. In 1887 Todd bought Louisa Stevenson's share of the School's building and in 1894, now registered, she was appointed assistant physician to the Hospital and Dispensary for Women and Children; she became Sophia's professional assistant as well as her closest friend. Todd was a successful author with the pen-name 'Gordon Travers'; two of her novels, *Mona Maclean* (1892) and *Growth* (1906), drew on her experience as a medical student. Todd also coined the term 'isotope' for chemically almost identical atoms with different atomic weights,[xxiii]

The report of the Commission set up in 1888 to review the charters of the Scottish universities led to the Universities' (Scotland) Act 1889 that allowed Scottish universities to graduate women. Edinburgh opened its medical degrees to them in 1894 but would still not admit them. However, it recognized the two women's schools and Jessie Macgregor (Surgeon Square School) and Mona Geddes (Chambers Street College) became its first female medical graduates on 1 August 1896. That day Geddes, Garrett Anderson's niece,[19] married Dr Douglas Chalmers

[17] During the summer term of 1889 Ina Cadell was a short stay student at LSMW.

[18] Now Mrs Pechey-Phipson

[19] She was the daughter of Skelton Anderson's sister 'Nellie'.

Watson. During the First World War she organised the medical service of the newly formed Women's Auxiliary Army Corps.

Edinburgh did not need two women's medical schools. The Chambers Street College benefited from its affiliation with the Royal Infirmary. Numbers fell at Surgeon Square which closed in 1898. However Jex-Blake's Edinburgh Hospital for Women and Children flourished. Sophia founded it in 1885 by adding beds to her Dispensary. In 1897 there was a public appeal to enable it to move to a larger site. The Committee chose Sophia's residence, Bruntsfield Lodge, as its new home and she sold it for a reasonable price. In March 1899 it became Bruntsfield Hospital, where only women doctors were appointed. After her school closed Sophia retired, and in May 1899 she moved to a house called 'Windydene' in Mark Cross, Sussex, a few miles south of Tunbridge Wells.

Edinburgh was no longer the only place in Scotland where women could study medicine. Glasgow's Queen Margaret College for Women started a medical school in 1890;[20] fourteen enrolled. Although taught separately the women shared some lecturers with the men, took the same examinations, and received clinical instruction at Glasgow's Royal Infirmary. In 1891 Marion Gilchrist, on behalf of all the women, applied to enter the University of Glasgow under the terms of the 1889 Act; the following year she and fifty-five other women entered the medical faculty. She graduated MBCM in 1894. Although Alice Cumming and Dorothea Lyness also graduated that year Gilchrist, owing to a high commendation, was and is considered Glasgow's first graduate.[21, xxiv]

In 1892 Aberdeen opened all faculties to women; the first arrived in 1894 and entered mixed classes. The medical school's first woman student was Myra Mackenzie of Auchtergavin, Perthshire. In 1895 she joined 268 men; she graduated in June 1900.

The ancient University of St Andrews could grant medical degrees, but although medicine was taught there from the fifteenth century it had no proper medical school until the end of the nineteenth century – mainly because the small local population could not support a hospital large enough for clinical training. After University College Dundee was founded in 1881 adequate clinical facilities gradually became available. The 1889 Act allowed Dundee's University College to join the University of St Andrews, with the object *inter alia* of establishing a conjoint University School of Medicine. It opened in 1898 with six women in the first class. The University admitted women to all courses in 1902.

In 1895, following two years of negotiations, LSMW and St Andrews drew up an agreement which would have allowed LSMW women to graduate at St Andrews

[20] Queen Margaret College was founded in 1883.

[21] Gilchrist was the first to graduate in any subject.

even if they had studied only at LSMW/RFH. However, none did so because the House of Lords declared the St Andrews University Court invalid. Similar discussions between LSMW and the University of Glasgow that year also proved sterile.[xxv]

Provincial medical schools had started opening to women in England (and Wales). The first to do so was Bristol Medical School founded in 1833. In 1893 it amalgamated with University College, Bristol – the predecessor of the University of Bristol which received its charter in 1909. Florence Elizabeth Perry entered the Bristol school in 1891. She enrolled with seventeen men, including her future husband, an Australian named Frederick Willey; twelve of the men qualified as doctors and two became dentists. Perry moved on to London and, as Mrs Willey, studied at LSMW, graduating MB London in 1900. As Lady Barrett she became dean of LSMW in 1926. (See Chapter 10) No more women were admitted to study medicine in Bristol until 1905. The University could not award its MBBCh degree until 1912. Until then Bristol students took a variety of qualifying examinations.[xxvi]

Twenty-eight students enrolled when Cardiff's medical school opened in 1893; two were women – Mary Elizabeth Phillips and Victoria Evelyn May Bennett. Until 1921 its students could only study preclinical subjects in Cardiff and went elsewhere for clinical training. Phillips moved to LSMW in 1897 and graduated MB Lond in 1900. Bennett followed her there in 1899, qualifying LSA in 1903.

Two LSMW students, Margaret Joyce and Grace Harwood Stewart, were in 1898 the first women to graduate MB BS Durham; their classmate Claudia Rowse graduated MB but did not sit the BS. The following year LSMW's Selina Fitzherbert Fox qualified MB BS; in 1903 she was the first woman to acquire the Durham MD. The first to complete the whole course at Durham was Mary Evelyn DeRusett (later Mrs Howie); she graduated MBBS in 1902 having entered the Newcastle College of Medicine in 1896. LSMW women, as external students, had to register for a year, and take two courses in the winter session and two in the summer, but they did not need to reside at the University.[xxvii]

Although Owen's College, Manchester admitted women from 1883 none initially was a medical student. However in 1899 its Senate debated the motion that women wishing to study medicine should be sent 'to other available institutions'; it decided the whole purpose of the college was that students '*could obtain* [education] *at home without expensive resort to distant seats of learning*' and rejected the motion by 22 to 2. That year saw the entry of Manchester's first two women medical students – Catherine Chisholm, BA (classics) 1895, and Catharine Corbett. Chisholm graduated in medicine in 1904 and Corbett in 1905. Chisholm later founded a children's hospital in Manchester.[xxviii]

When the University of Birmingham opened in 1900 thirty-six medical students enrolled; three were women. The first woman to matriculate and subsequently take MBChB was Florence Margaret Price of Carmarthen. She entered the medical school with her elder brother Ernest Henry Price; their father was a Welsh doctor. The other two were Edith Dora Grove of Walsall, aged 21, and Helen Gertrude Greener of Erdington, aged 26. Before starting in Birmingham Florence had passed the First Professional Examination as a student of the Chambers Street School in Edinburgh. Most of her time as a student was spent in Birmingham, but according to the Medical Directory of the time she graduated from both Birmingham and Edinburgh. Greener entered LSMW for a year in 1904, but graduated with a Birmingham degree in 1905.

Only 27 women had entered the medical register before EGA became dean. Of the first 16 all but two had had to acquire the KQCPI diploma,[22] even though all but one had an MD from the USA, France or Switzerland.[23] Nine had registered as students of LSMW but, having completed relevant courses at other medical schools, had spent relatively little time there.

In 1883 these early medical women were relatively settled. Blackwell had more or less retired. Atkins, Marshall and de la Cherois worked with EGA at her New Hospital for Women. Hoggan practised independently in London. Walker Dunbar ran a Dispensary for Women and Children in Bristol – so too did Jex-Blake in Edinburgh where Agnes McLaren worked at the Canongate Medical Mission. Annie Clark was at the Midland Hospital for Women in Birmingham, where Annie Reay Barker (MD Paris 1877) was RMO before joining Clark on the staff. Dahms had opened a Dispensary for Women and Children in Manchester and was the first woman to practise there; in 1884, the Manchester Medical Society refused her access to its library. Alice Ker headed the Mill Street Dispensary in Leeds. Mrs Mears practised in Tynemouth near Durham. Edith Shove and Lucy Cradock worked for the Post Office, in London and Liverpool respectively. Janet Monteath Rushbrook and Mrs Jane R(ussell) Grant (née Rorison) had London addresses in 1883 but were not obviously in practice; Grant appeared to resume work a few years later. Julia Cock, unwell after qualifying in 1882, had not yet started work. Edith Pechey, Foggo, Butler, Marston, Scharlieb and Hitchcock were in India; Jane Waterston, had returned to South Africa; McDonogh (Mrs Frikart) gave a Swiss address.[xxix]

---

[22] The two were Blackwell & Garrett Anderson. Ker's MD Bern came after she took the Irish diploma.

[23] The exception, Waterston, LKQCPI & LM 1879 trained almost exclusively at LSMW/RFH. Chaplin-Ayrton, who died July 1883 was left out of the list of registered medical women in the 1882-3 Annual Report; she had been in practice in Sloane Street.

Many more women were now expected to qualify – but finding them employment was not easy. Male practitioners would not accept them as partners or assistants and, except in large towns, they would have fared badly had they competed against men. Few hospitals had employed a woman – even as a junior doctor – and only one had employed them at a 'senior' level.[24] The main hope of the newly qualified was to join hospitals or practices already run by women. The first and best of these was EGA's New Hospital for Women, created in 1872 by adding ten beds to the St Mary's Dispensary in Seymour Place that EGA had set up with backing from her wealthy father. In 1875 Anna Dahms (then unqualified) became its first house surgeon and Louisa Atkins (then unregistered) joined EGA and Hoggan as a visiting physician. Bovell (MD Paris, also unregistered) replaced Hoggan in 1877 (see earlier); her resignation owing to illness in 1881 led to the appointment of Annie de la Cherois (KQCPI 1881). EGA's sister-in-law, Mary Marshall, also became a visiting physician around that time.[xxx]

When Jex-Blake went to Edinburgh in 1878 she chose the path followed by EGA and opened the Edinburgh Provident Dispensary for Women and Children at 73 Grove Street, Fountainbridge; there she treated the poor for pennies.[25] In 1885 she moved to larger premises at 6 Grove Street where she founded the Edinburgh Hospital for Women and Children by opening a six-bed ward. (See Chapter 5) Catherine Urquhart, recently qualified at LSMW, was appointed Resident Medical Officer. Subsequently the hospital moved to Bruntsfield Lodge, Jex-Blake's former residence. (See above)

Before EGA retired as Dean, more hospitals were staffed by medical women. The new ones, mostly general hospitals with admission restricted to women and children, included the Clapham Maternity Hospital, and Jane Walker's TB hospital in Nayland on the Essex/Suffolk border.

The number qualifying each year from LSMW remained in single figures until 1888. Those medical women who were actively employed were getting busier, so collectively their own practices, dispensaries and hospitals could accommodate the small number of new women doctors wishing to work in Britain.

From 1883 the School's annual report included a list of all registered medical women with addresses for many. In 1889 there were two lists – registered women who had been educated wholly or partially at LSMW and RFH, and those who had not studied at either place. From 1899, when women were qualifying at other schools, only those trained (wholly or partially) at L(RFH)SMW were listed. Subsequently the list was of 'all former students'.

---

24 'Senior' here implies a doctor was in 'secure' employment – without need to move on at some stage.

25 She had a separate private practice, firstly at Manor Place and then at Bruntsfield Lodge.

By 1903, when Cock became Dean, there were 320 names in the list: 19 worked at RFH and 33 at the new Euston Road premises of the New Hospital for Women (see above); seven were at the Clapham Maternity Hospital and School of Midwifery (and its associated clinics)[26] founded by Annie McCall.

In the School's early years the annual reports commented on the appointment of all registered medical woman (not just former students) to posts likely to have involved competition with men – e.g. those of Shove, Cradock and Dahms at the Post Office in 1883 and 1884; Annie Clark at Birmingham's Children's Hospital (1884); Helen Prideaux to the Children's Hospital, Paddington (1885); Julia Cock as Medical Examiner to the Government Insurance and Annuities Fund for Women Proposers in the Metropolitan District (1887); Helen Webb as Assistant Medical Officer at Homerton Fever Hospital (1889) – the first relatively permanent large hospital post given to a woman (Sarah Gray having been clinical assistant there the year before); and Agnes Henderson at Holloway Sanatorium – the first woman employed at an asylum for mental diseases. But in the early 1890s, when such appointments had become more common, most were simply listed in the annual reports.

Men's attitudes to medical women were changing, albeit slowly. At its AGM at Nottingham in 1892 the BMA voted almost unanimously for women's admission as members,[xxxi] and after the ban was lifted the following year Mary Scharlieb was the first admitted. However male enthusiasm for recognition of women doctors was far from widespread. In the summer of 1893 the British Laryngological Society discussed admission of women, two having applied to become Fellows. Its Council was unanimously in favour, but the masses rejected the idea although they did agree women could attend meetings as visitors.[xxxii]

In 1896 the BMA's East Anglian Branch chose Garrett Anderson (EGA) as its president for 1897-8. Her presidential address 'On the Progress of Medicine in the Victorian Era', given on 27 May 1897, is printed in the October issue of LSMW's magazine.

During EGA's deanship the number of positions available to registered medical women gradually increased, both in clinical practice and in public services. But what was given with one hand was sometimes taken back by the other. By 1894 there were 2807 women employed at the Post Office's headquarters and 10345 men. Spencer Walpole, Secretary to the Postmaster General, asked the Treasury to increase the salary of the Female Medical Officer (Shove) and to appoint an Assistant Female Medical Officer. The latter request was approved. Miss Madgshon was appointed Assistant Female Medical Officer in October 1895; but

[26] Battersea District Maternity and Albert Dispensary.

the Treasury refused to increase Shove's salary because the appointment of an assistant would ease her workload.

The degree of opposition to women doctors varied from group to group. It was driven almost entirely by prejudice and was rarely if ever related to dissatisfaction with their qualifications or clinical performance. At the end of 1901 matters relating to the employment of three women became a matter of public interest.

When Macclesfield Infirmary appointed Miss Murdoch Clarke as house surgeon its medical staff resigned en masse – but continued to see their patients. Alarmed by this the governors offered Clarke a year's salary to resign. She refused initially but did so in late December 1901 when the staff threatened to stop caring for patients. The British press carried the story, but remarkably the most detailed account was in the *Morning Post* of Cairns, North Queensland, on 4 February 1902. Within weeks Clarke announced she would open her own practice in Macclesfield.[xxxiii]

On 16 November 1901 the BMJ announced Miss E.S.M. Walker was to become assistant M.O. at the Toxteth Park Workhouse because her predecessor, Miss Blackadder, was marrying another doctor. Walker's appointment was approved – but by a narrow majority, and she had to promise she would stay for eighteen months.[xxxiv]

For the women's movement the third story was the most encouraging. In October 1901 Jane Gilford Cox resigned as the junior assistant M.O. at Bracebridge Pauper Lunatic Asylum. Her work there, and that of her female predecessor, Dr Green, had been satisfactory, and there was little or no opposition to appointing a third woman.[xxxv]

It was galling to those qualifying at LSMW that they could not get jobs at their own hospital. In 1888 Frances Harris had been made curator of RFH's museum and Hester Russell, Jessie Hatch and Maud Chadburn – all senior students – followed her in that post. In February 1891 Council made an unsuccessful approach to RFH about opening some resident posts to women. Aldrich-Blake became the first medically qualified woman curator in 1892 and as a tentative arrangement was also made assistant to Frederick Silk, the anaesthetist. A succession of new women graduates followed her as curator,[27] and when Vaughan took over the museum following Webb's death in October 1898 'Assistant Pathologist' was added to the title. In 1900 the job was split; Vaughan remained curator and Frances Ivens was made Clinical and Assistant Pathologist, a post which passed on to Louisa Woodcock.

The breakthrough came in 1894; when Silk resigned Aldrich-Blake was made

[27] ML Dobbie 1893, Effield Greene 1894, Edith Knight 1895, & Mabel Webb 1896, 1897 & 1898.

anaesthetist to RFH, and Annie Piercy and Mabel Jones her senior and junior assistants. The following year Aldrich-Blake was appointed surgical registrar and anaesthetist, and Mrs Percy Flemming (née Emily Wood) as medical registrar.[xxxvi]

In March 1898, perhaps encouraged by these events, 51 LSMW students and 32 qualified former students petitioned RFH about opening its resident posts to women stating: *The need…is very pressing,…difficult to obtain such appointments at other hospitals in the absence of the practical experience which we should gain as residents at the Royal Free…at most … children's hospitals…candidates who have not previously held at least one resident appointment are not considered…this is the case at Great Ormond Street, the Victoria Hospital for Children at Chelsea, and the Manchester Children's Hospital at Pendlebury.* RFH's Secretary, Conrad Thies, replied that the Weekly Board and Medical Committee were sympathetic but noted *'serious practical difficulties in…such appointments at a general hospital. During the past few years various responsible posts, such as registrars, anaesthetists, clinical assistants, and curator of Museum at this Hospital, have been given to medical women, and the Board are prepared to recommend further appointments if the difficulties referred to can be overcome.*[xxxvii]

After prolonged negotiations the two first women residents were appointed on 24 April 1901 – Louisa Garrett Anderson as house surgeon (HS) to Berry (women patients) and Hayes, and Louisa Woodcock as house physician (HP) to the female patients of West and Sainsbury; they took their turn at casualty work. Appointing them may not have been the magnanimous gesture it appeared. Isabel Thorne's diary states that at an RFH committee she suggested, unofficially and privately, that if female residents were appointed she would give £100. Burt, the Weekly Board's Chairman said for £1000 it might entertain the idea. Garrett Anderson and her husband promised £100, as did Augustus Thorne, Isabel's brother-in-law; '… *the £1000 was soon guaranteed and in July 1900 Mr. Burt announced at the prize giving that two of the resident posts would be opened to women students of the School; this was carried out in May 1901.*' [28, xxxviii]

There was another major development in 1902 when, following Hayes's decision to spend more of his time at King's College Hospital as Professor of Practical Obstetrics, Mary Scharlieb, in competition with male applicants, was elected as Physician for Diseases of Women at RFH, with Ethel Vaughan as Assistant Physician. No similar appointments were made in other specialties for many years.

EGA was greatly helped by the School's supporters. Sadly Shaen died suddenly

---

[28] The jobs were not advertised. Louisa wrote to her mother from Paris on 25 March 1901 'Have you actually sent my applications for the R.F.H.? It is very funny not advertising the posts.'

in March 1887. Henry Henderson, a colleague at Shaen Roscoe, replaced him as the School's solicitor. In January 1891 Stansfeld resigned as Hon Treasurer and Chairman of Council. He would have left a year earlier, because of political and other pressures, but was persuaded to stay on. Henderson replaced him on Council and Norton took over as Hon. Treasurer, a role Henderson assumed when Norton left London in 1897.

Stansfeld was not replaced as Chairman of Council as the School's constitution made no mention of a Chairman.[29] Mrs Fleming Baxter chaired three meetings, but subsequently various individuals took the chair, depending on who was present. There was also no provision for a Chairman of Council in the new rules (the Memorandum and Articles of Association) that came into force after LSMW incorporated in 1898.

Stansfeld died in February 1898, James Hopgood a few months earlier. It was the latter who, at Stansfeld's request, persuaded RFH's staff to accept the women students in 1877. He remained on RFH's Weekly Board until 1888 and the continuing good relations between School and Hospital owed much to his influence. Hopgood and his wife, Elizabeth, who died in 1890, were major benefactors of both institutions.

When EGA took over as Dean LSMW's financial situation was poor; there were few students and expenses were high. However, money for scholarships was still relatively easy to obtain. In 1885 John Byron of Lancaster left £691 for a scholarship to assist ladies needing financial help. The first Byron scholar, Gabrielle Breeze, entered the School in 1881, but struggled subsequently with examinations and the scholarship was withdrawn;[xxxix] she eventually qualified MB Lond in 1892 and became a missionary in Morocco.

On 14 October 1884 LSMW celebrated its tenth anniversary with a conversazione. The students erected a tent in the garden, and decorated the School with flowers, pictures, flags, pottery, coloured lamps and Chinese lanterns. Guests included the Dowager Lady Stanley of Alderley, Frances Hoggan, Mary Marshall, members of the Governing Body and RFH staff. Jex-Blake was not present! [xl]

Clubs, Societies and the Magazine

In 1883 the Bible reading group flourished, and tennis was played in the garden, but there were no 'clubs and societies' at LSMW. A Debating Society, founded in January 1886, was mentioned in the Prospectus for 1886-7; a Tennis Club was added the following year. The Tea Club, whose members paid to take tea in the

---

29 Stansfeld was elected chairman ex officio at the Executive Council's first meeting in February 1875.

Common Room, first appeared in the Prospectus for 1888-9 (but was probably formed before the Debating Society). Subsequent years saw the appearance of the Students Weekly Bible Reading and the Medical Women's Monthly Prayer Union (1890-1); the Students Library (1892-3); the Students' Volunteer Missionary Union (1894-5), and the Dramatic Society (1896-7). The first time the Students' Societies were mentioned under a single heading was in 1897-8, when the new Students Medical Society was top of the list.

The first meeting to discuss launching a magazine was held on 29 January 1895. As many clinical students could not attend a second meeting was held on 31 January; it elected a Committee of Management, consisting of the editor, a Hospital sub-editor, School sub-editor, treasurer, secretary, and a representative from each year. Miss Cock and Mrs. Flemming acted as a 'Reference Committee'. Mrs Willmott Evans (née Annie Frances Piercy, MB 1893) was the first editor. The first issue, printed by the Women's Printing Society, appeared in May 1895. On its first page the statement 'Work is as it is done' appeared; it became the Magazine's motto.[30]

The new journal was a great success. Produced for about 80 years its back numbers provide information about the social, sporting and professional life of LSMW and RFH, and about examination results, the fate of old students, and births, marriages and deaths.

Early in 1897 the original magazine committee resigned.[31] The journal's supporters met on 26 March. After the first editor reviewed the magazine's early history a new committee was elected. Florence Stoney was to be editor until Mabel Webb took over In November; Cornelia Sheldon-Amos was Hospital sub-editor. After Webb's unexpected death from peritonitis due to a perforated gastric ulcer in October 1898[32] Louisa Garrett Anderson and Constance Long co-edited for a year. Louisa then became editor, with Long as the magazine's secretary. Frances Ivens replaced Louisa as editor in November 1903.[xli]

The magazine's name, initially 'Magazine of LSMW and RFH', was changed in October 1897 to 'Magazine of RFHSMW'. In October 1899 'Magazine of the London (Royal Free Hospital) School of Medicine for Women' appeared on the cover, but the inside page heading remained 'Magazine of RFHLSMW' for many years.

LSMW's First Major Building Works

In February 1881 Edith Shove suggested building a room in the garden to provide a separate classroom for students studying for the London MB. As the landlord would have demanded compensation Council instead allocated one of the museum

[30] According to the *Magazine* for January 1899 Mabel Elizabeth Webb suggested the motto.

[31] No reason was given in the Magazine for the resignation of the whole committee.

[32] Webb was then Curator and Assistant Pathologist at RFH.

rooms to them. Space was not then a problem. Only eight students entered in October 1883; two were already MDs, and one studied only physiology. However when eighteen arrived in 1884-5 (fifteen of whom qualified) the School seemed overcrowded. As even greater numbers were anticipated more space was clearly needed; rooms were re-arranged in the main building and Shove's plan was resurrected.

In January 1885 Yuill[33] obtained estimates for a garden room intended for dissection. The District Surveyor, Hayward, chosen as architect, advised discussion with the landlord to forestall an increase in rent on renewal of the lease in 1892. Such an increase could have been avoided had the School acquired the lease, either when Ashton bought it in 1879 or at auction in May 1882, after Ashton's death, when the Dean and Hon. Sec. fixed a limit of £950; it sold for £955! In May 1885 the owner accepted an offer of £1045. The Foundling Hospital's Governors still objected to teaching of anatomy on the premises,[xlii] but in March 1886 agreed to an iron room being erected on the south side of the garden. After completion it was used as a lecture room, not for dissection. Louisa Garrett Anderson found it *'unsightly and uncomfortable – an oven in summer and a noisy ice house in winter with rain on the corrugated iron roof.*'[xliii]

The main building was rearranged and its heating and lighting upgraded. The students' sitting and dressing rooms were enlarged and refitted, and new laboratories – anatomical, physiological and chemical – came into use. While these changes were in progress lectures were delivered at the Hospital. The work was completed late in 1886.

The expansion was timely. The average student intake over the previous twelve years was about 12, the highest being 22 during the first year. In 1886-87 it was 27; in the next three academic years the intake was 25, 34 and 32.

The cost of the alterations, £1155, included £200 for the iron room. Clearing the debt took two years, and triggered a dispute with Jex-Blake. On 29 May 1888 Council decided to sell stock to meet the deficit. Jex-Blake, still a Trustee, objected to selling investments to meet current expenses, and to taking such action without the 'previous sanction' of the Governing Body. She asked that the minute books be sent to her for perusal.[34] On 15 June the Hon. Sec. said she had told Jex-Blake the sale was to meet capital expenditure, not 'current expenses', and that the words

---

[33] A civil engineer, EGA's friend (and Skelton's cousin), and a member of RFH's General Committee.

[34] At the June Council meeting the Hon. Sec. said Jex-Blake borrowed the minute books while preparing a new edition of '*Medical Women*' but she and Miss Heaton were uneasy about having let them out of the School safe. On 26 October 1888 Council ruled they should not be removed from the School premises.

'previous sanction', although in the 1875 Constitution, were not in the revised version of May 1878. Mrs Thorne then found an earlier, seemingly pertinent, resolution related to the Oakes shares, and a special meeting of the Governing Body on18 July 1888 found that Council had acted properly in selling the stock.[xliv]

Two years later Council again decided to sell stock to pay for building work; again Jex-Blake called for a Governors' meeting. The Hon. Sec. sent her details of the July 1888 meeting and the summons for a meeting on 5 May 1890 at which the Governing Body approved the sale of stock to pay for the alterations. This satisfied Jex-Blake.

Enlarging the Hospital

Building also went on at RFH. Following the work done in the late 1870s only the front (west side) of the Hospital was essentially unchanged since the 1840s. It had only one storey, the other three wings now having three, and its outside facade had no windows. (See Ch 4, Fig 4.7) It held the Board Room; a laboratory and dispensary rooms – which were inadequate for their purpose and a potential fire hazard; and inferior rooms and dormitories accommodating resident medical officers and servants. The interior was squalid, and by 1888 the roof was so rotten that repairs would have been wasted on it. Extensive reconstruction and renovation were needed urgently.

It was decided to rebuild the wing and thus provide a much needed children's ward; a more suitable casualty room; laboratory and dispensing rooms matching the standard of other departments of the hospital; better provision for the resident medical officers and domestic servants; and additional accommodation for the increasing number of women students attending the hospital.[xlv]

In 1890 Harvey, the architect, prepared plans for a new front block in harmony with the improvements made elsewhere at RFH. It was to have three floors and an imposing frontage commanding public attention. At a meeting at the Mansion House in 1892 a fund was set up to raise the estimated cost of £20,000.

There was reluctance to begin until the money was raised but further deterioration, and a pressing need for a better casualty room, dictated a start to building in 1893. The old building had already been knocked down by the time the Marquis of Dufferin and Ava, RFH's President, then ambassador in Paris, wrote to *The Times* of 10 October 1893 trying to raise the £12,000 still needed.[xlvi]

The new front buildings, called the 'Alexandra Wing', (Fig 6.1) were handed over by the contractors late in 1894,[35] and formally opened by the Prince and Princess of Wales on 22 July 1895. Facilities for casualty patients were improved;

[35] The Lord Mayor, Sir George Tyler Bt., inspected them in October.

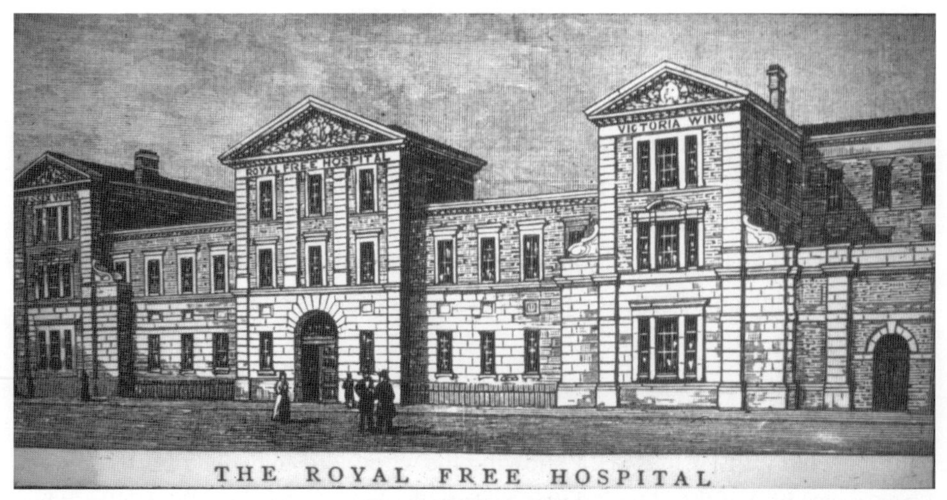

Fig 6.1 RFH in 1895

there was a new dispensary, new isolation wards, a laundry, and proper accommodation for medical officers and servants. There were other improvements at RFH. External and internal wood and ironwork were repainted; the west ends of the Sussex and Victoria Wings were cleaned and repaired; ward lavatories and bathrooms were altered to improve sanitation; the floors of Marsden and Crawshay wards were re-laid with oak. The operating theatre was upgraded, extra accommodation was provided for students, and the open space in the centre of the quadrangle was enclosed and turfed.[xlvii]

The second five-yearly agreement between LSMW and RFH expired in September 1887. There was little change in the terms of the third agreement, but in June 1890 some RFH Committee members questioned the expense incurred in associating with LSMW, as clinical fees went to the medical staff and none to RFH. Their concern, stemming from discussions going on in the House of Lords, was that money subscribed for charitable purposes was being spent in other ways. Mrs Thorne thought the clinical staff would oppose reduction in their fees, but agreed that the £100 to £120 needed to maintain the School at RFH should not come from Hospital funds. Eventually it was agreed that LSMW would pay RFH four per cent of fees received for School purposes, and that the Weekly Board would take a percentage of clinical fees. There was clearly good will on both sides.[xlviii]

However, when the draft of the fourth agreement was discussed in January 1893, RFH's medical staff complained about the exclusion of students other than those from LSMW, and that School fees had risen more than Hospital fees. They made several demands – including the right to take private male students at RFH (which LSMW rejected); that lectureships, when vacant, be offered to RFH staff; and that

Hospital fees be restored to their former level, (which LSMW's representatives agreed but Council did not).[xlix]

In letters to the medical staff on 4 and 30 March Isabel Thorne pointed out that LSMW did not profit from reduced Hospital fees, and that in 1887 RFH staff had agreed to reduce fees (Hospital and School) owing to competition from other women's schools. School fees had increased to cover additional expenses resulting from the curricular changes demanded by examining boards in 1892. The School paid clinicians for extra teaching, but there was no justification for increasing the basic Hospital fee. The new five-year curriculum was unlikely to involve RFH staff in more teaching, as some of the clinical teaching required (e.g. in lunacy, fevers and paediatrics) would not take place at RFH; only time would tell whether it would create extra work. RFH staff rejected this point and wanted clinical fees raised by five pounds. As Scottish clinical fees were lower than at RFH Council had contemplated reducing total fees to £105 but it had not done so even though several LSMW students had moved to Glasgow and Edinburgh, where the cost of living was also lower.[l]

In May, Roughton, the Hon Sec of RFH's staff, wrote that, as increasing clinical fees meant charging students more, his colleagues acceded to the agreement, providing fees would rise when LSMW's financial situation improved. Council resolved that 'when the accounts…show a sufficient surplus a share…shall be divided among the Lecturers of the School and Hospital according to a schedule…agreed…by the Executive Council.' [li]

India

In India the women's death rate from childbirth and disease was very high – partly because many Muslim and Hindu women would not consult male doctors. The Zenana Bible and Medical Mission to India was founded in 1852 to reach women that lived in a 'zenana' [36] and were thus cut off from normal community life. In 1867 Surgeon Corbyn started a school – in Bareilly, Uttar Pradesh – which taught medicine to local Christian women and others uninhibited by purdah.

In 1871 Mary Scharlieb, a British woman married to a barrister, began training as a midwife in Madras. Realising that studying medicine would be more useful she contacted Surgeon-General Balfour, head of the medical service in Madras. His suggestion that women should enter the local medical college aroused opposition but despite this Scharlieb and four others entered classes for women in 1875. Scharlieb obtained her Medical Practitioners' Certificate in 1879, returned to England and continued her training at LSMW.

The first medically qualified LSMW woman to go to India was Fanny Butler,

[36] The part of a house in which women of high-caste families were secluded.

LRCPI. In 1880 she went to Jabalpur where she died in 1889. Another LSMW woman, Edith Bielby, went earlier but unqualified. She entered LSMW in 1877 intending to become a medical missionary, but after only one session left for Lucknow where she ran a dispensary and then a small hospital. In 1882 she returned to finish training at LSMW. The Maharani of Punna, her patient, gave her a message for Queen Victoria,[37] to let the latter know 'what the women in Indian zenanas suffer when they are sick'. After meeting Bielby the Queen, opposed to the idea of women doctors,[38] showed an interest in the suffering of her Indian women subjects. In 1883, before Scharlieb returned to Madras, Victoria received her at Windsor. Scharlieb claimed that the Queen's physician, Sir William Jenner, implacably opposed to women doctors, tried to prevent her visit but that Victoria listened instead to Henry Acland,[39] a friend of Scharlieb's.[lii] Ill-health forced Scharlieb's return to London in 1887. While she was in India her children stayed in London with Professor Schäfer and his wife.[liii]

George Kittredge, an American businessman in Bombay, read Frances Hoggan's article in the *Contemporary Review* of August 1882 describing the problems of providing medical care for Indian women. To recruit women doctors he set up the Medical Women for India Fund, Bombay. Contemporaneously Mr Pestonjee Cama offered, if the government would provide the site, to build in Bombay a women's hospital to be staffed by women doctors. Kittredge met Edith Pechey in Paris in 1883 and persuaded her to become senior medical officer of Cama's hospital. That December she started work in Bombay, but the hospital did not open until 1886. Charlotte Ellaby, MD Paris, joined her in Bombay in November 1884.

In December 1884 the Earl of Dufferin succeeded the Marquis of Ripon as Viceroy of India. Queen Victoria asked Dufferin's wife to set up a 'National Association for Supplying Female Medical Aid to the Women of India'. The Countess of Dufferin's Fund, instituted in August 1885, was to bring women doctors to India, open women's hospitals and wards, and train Indian women as medical practitioners, nurses and hospital assistants. LSMW's prospectus for 1887-8 announced its Council was *'authorised by the National Association...to offer two Scholarships, entitled the 'Jubilee'*[40] *and the 'Dufferin' Scholarships, each...of £25 a year for four years, to ladies willing to prepare for the practice of medicine in India, and who require pecuniary assistance to do so...One scholarship will be awarded at the discretion of the Council to students of LSMW who...wished to*

[37] Empress of India since 1876.

[38] She had threatened to withdraw her patronage from the International Medical Congress of 1881 if women were allowed to attend.

[39] Acland was then Regius Professor of Medicine at Oxford, and President of the GMC.

[40] It marked the fiftieth anniversary of Victoria's accession to the throne.

compete, at the end of their first Winter session; the other will be an entrance scholarship, to be awarded September 1887, the subject of the examination being the same as that of the ordinary entrance scholarship.'

The first scholarship awarded, in 1887, was a 'Jubilee' scholarship. Despite falling ill after the first day of the examination Lillie Jones won it, being the only competitor. In 1891 Lady Reay, Lady Aitchison and Lady Lyall became vice presidents of LSMW; all supported the women's cause in India and the Countess of Dufferin's Fund.[41]

Women awarded a Dufferin Fund scholarship were expected to spend at least five years in India. If they reneged money received was to be repaid with interest. In 1890 marriage led Ellen Ward, the Dufferin Scholar of 1888, to cancel her agreement with the Fund. The money repaid was transferred to Mildred Staley, the runner-up for Ward's scholarship.

In 1883, before the Dufferin initiative, an Indian Medical Scholarship Fund had been established at LSMW; it was advertised in the prospectuses for 1883-4 and 1884-5 but not subsequently. The first scholar, Florence Sorby, qualified in 1888, but it is not clear whether she went to India. LSMW's Annual Report for 1889 noted she was 'studying abroad', but in 1890 she was Mrs Orford, living in Pontefract.[liv]

Money from the School's fund was transferred to the Countess of Dufferin's Fund to provide a separate scholarship called the Stuart Mill Scholarship,[42] as requested by Miss Edington, the principal contributor. Stuart Mill scholars were supposed to practise in India but after qualifying in 1894 the first of them, Ethel Bentham, (1890), worked at the Blackfriars Provident Dispensary for Women and Children and the New Hospital for Women, and then moved to Newcastle, returning to London in 1909. An ardent suffragist, and a prominent Labour politician, she was elected Labour MP for East Islington in 1929 but died in 1931.

In April 1897 Council approved Lady Dufferin's suggestion that the Stuart Mill scholarship should go alternately to an Indian student coming to London and to an English student going to India. The October 1898 award, for an Indian resident, native or Eurasian, went to Alice Sorabji who graduated MBBS in 1905. In 1908 she married the British surgeon, Theodore Leighton Pennell, who had worked in India since 1892, mainly in Bannu (now part of Pakistan) near the Afghanistan border.

The most famous Indian women student at LSMW was Rakhmabai,[43] (Fig 6.2) whose stepfather was a surgeon in Bombay. In 1875, aged eleven, she was married to a distant relative but remained at her stepfather's house. In 1883 her husband

---

[41] The 'Jubilee' and 'Dufferin' Scholarships were advertised in the LSMW prospectus until1893-4.

[42] Notices about the Start Mill Scholarship appeared in LSMW's prospectus until 1906-7.

[43] 'Rukhmabai was a widely-used mis-spelling'; she only used 'Rakhmabai'.

Fig 6.2 Rakhmabai (1864-1955, arrowed) and fellow LSMW students

requested she move to the marital home. Her refusal triggered a prolonged legal struggle, which reached the Privy Council and was widely reported by the British and Indian press. In 1887, following an out-of-court settlement, her husband renounced all rights to her. Encouraged by Edith Pechey she entered LSMW in 1890 thus satisfying her long-standing desire to study medicine. She qualified through the Scottish triple in 1894, and the following year returned to India. She was a close friend of Bertrand Russell's first wife, Alice Pearsall Smith.[lv]

Further Building Works at LSMW

As student numbers increased LSMW had to decide how to make the best use of its premises. To justify erecting a large new building it was essential to have a long lease, but the Foundling was reluctant to provide such leases in case a leasehold enfranchisement Bill became law. In September 1889, acting on Council's behalf, Sir Owen Roberts, a Lieutenant for the City of London and Clerk to the Clothworkers' Company, persuaded the Foundling to *'grant a building lease for 80 years...at a rent of £210 per annum, [providing...] that the plans...of any building... be first submitted...for approval. That the buildings are not to be used for...dissection, but only as lecture or class rooms, museums, etc. the old materials to remain the property of the Lessee in lieu of a peppercorn rent...the premises referred to are...the Pavilion with the garden attached thereto, and numbers 7a, 7, 8, 9, 10 & 11 Hunter Street. Signed, W L Wintle, Secretary.'* Council considered the terms too onerous and asked for modification of the conditions. [lvi] Another eight years elapsed before the long lease was finally agreed.

In the meantime Council decided to link 7 Hunter Street with the Pavilion, and to use the former's main room for anatomical lectures and another as a materia medica museum. LSMW consulted the architect Horace Field. Following its purchase of the lease in May 1885 the School had to ensure repairs were done at No 7. The tenant, who did so only after a court action, refused to pay costs awarded against him, threatened legal action for alleged damage during building in 1886, and upset his neighbours. Although LSMW's solicitors forced him to sell his sub-lease in 1888 he remained at No 7 until June 1889. The house, then filthy and swarming with vermin, needed fumigation, the drains needed clearing, and fifteen layers of paper had to be removed from the walls. Work to render it habitable cost £40, and the District Surveyor then found an unsafe wall needing rebuilding.[lvii]

In October 1887 the Metropolitan Board of Works changed the name of Henrietta Street to Handel Street, as there were two other Henrietta Streets nearby. The new name commemorated Handel's local connection; several of his greatest works, including the *Messiah*, were first produced at the Foundling Hospital.[44]

Field's proposals for connecting No 7 and the Pavilion were not effected immediately as Council hoped for better terms for a long lease. Offered possession of 8, 9, 10 & 11 Hunter Street for about £2300 in February 1890 it declined the Foundling's offer of a long term lease as it would have had to surrender not only the lease for 30 Handel Street (now the School's official address) and 7 & 7a Hunter Street, but also that for 8, 9, 10 & 11 Hunter Street (which it had not yet obtained). To buy a new lease and rebuild on the present site would cost about £15,000 and ground rent would more than treble. Furthermore, Council contemplated building elsewhere as Mr Prideaux had found a 17,700 sq.ft. plot in Calthorpe Street, near RFH, with a freehold price of £6000. Prideaux offered £3500, but the price rose to £6750 and no further action was taken.[lviii]

Council decided to carry out Field's proposals – which would cost £800 more than his original estimate of £1000, because of the problems at No 7 (see above) and the defects found in the Pavilion's drainage system. On completion in October 1891 LSMW had two chemical laboratories, a materia medica museum, a well-lighted museum, a library, an enlarged anatomical department, a fine students' common room and a room for Council and other meetings, as well as the physiology laboratory. Changes were also made in the dressing-rooms, lavatories

[44] In 1919 Council (25 Jun) rejected the Foundling's idea of changing Handel Street to Elgar Street.

and domestic offices. After inspecting the improvements, a Mr. Matthew Whiting gave Miss Heaton a cheque for £1,000.[45] There was no public prize-giving in 1890 owing to the building work.[lix]

When LSMW opened in 1874, the parallel plots of the two disused burial grounds of St. George, Bloomsbury, and St George the Martyr, Queen Square, occupied the land to the east of the corner of Wakefield and Henrietta streets. The Kyrle Society, founded in 1877 by Octavia and Miranda Hill 'to give pleasure to the poor', converted the ground of St George, Bloomsbury, into a public garden which Princess Louise opened in July 1884.[lx] The other cemetery was soon added to it, and from 1890 the enlarged garden was accessible from east and west ends. (Fig 6.3) It made the journey from LSMW to RFH a short pleasant walk, much of it on an asphalt path, bordered by trees and flowerbeds; it passed a tombstone marking the grave of a granddaughter of Oliver Cromwell.[lxi]

In 1890 Garrett Anderson's New Hospital for Women transferred from 222-224 Marylebone Road (which held 26 beds) to 144 Euston Road (with forty-two beds).[46] The new building, much closer to LSMW, had a large out-patient department, comfortable wards and a medical women's institute with a good library. Facilities for students were excellent. More importantly, it provided posts for recently qualified women doctors. Nearly all the medical staff were past students of LSMW. A maternity department opened in 1891, the year Scharlieb was appointed to the staff. EGA retired from it in 1892.

Not surprisingly, given the effort expended in moving the New Hospital, the Dean stated in October 1890 that she could no longer keep in touch with the students.[47] She tried to resign, but Isabel Thorne, arguing that LSMW would suffer, suggested the 'experimental' appointment of a Sub-dean who was to organize the Hospital posts, attend Hunter Street to meet students, and visit those at RFH. By December Julia Cock had assumed these duties; in 1894 she moved her office to RFH, and the School's Assistant Secretary helped her for two hours a week. Her title was changed to Vice-dean in 1899.[lxii]

Louisa Garrett Anderson wrote that '*a partnership of outstanding harmony followed between the dean and sub-dean. Miss Cock had the vision of a statesman and her loyalty to the dean was one of real friendship.*' [lxiii] Evidence of this

[45] Whiting, a silk merchant and well known philanthropist, also gave money to King's College Hospital.

[46] This move was triggered by Lord Portman's refusal to renew the lease on the Marylebone Rd premises.

[47] In her mother's biography (p 230) Louisa Garrett Anderson wrote EGA's main defect as dean was her inability to remember students and struggling to find the right name even for the last gold medallist.

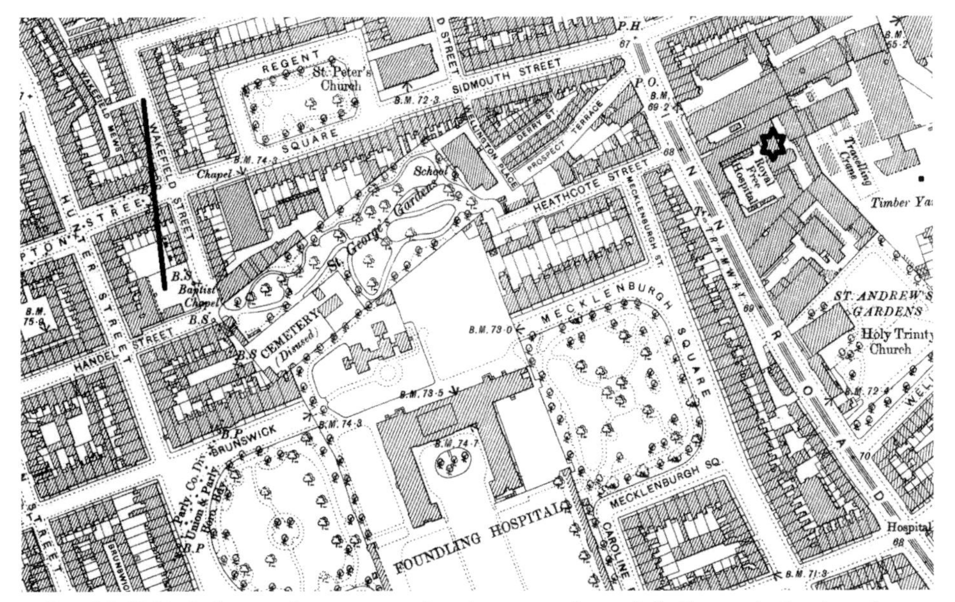

Fig 6.3 1894 Ordnance Survey map showing route through St George's Gardens from RFH (star) to LSMW (bottom of line)

friendship appears in a letter written by EGA to Skelton Anderson on 7 April 1899 while holidaying in Italy – '*Miss Cock and I have done very well together. She does not like much exercise so I have not had a chance of doing the least too much. She is however thoroughly sympathetic about all pretty things and she has excellent taste.*'[lxiv]

Mr and Mrs Stubbings served as porter, cook and housekeeper from the opening of LSMW and lived in the Hunter Street building. They left in 1890 because their daughter Harriet was getting married; without her they could not provide luncheon and refreshments. They received a testimonial and a gratuity of £20. Their replacements, the Myers, soon resigned because Mr Myer's part-time duties at LSMW clashed with his other job. The cook to Miss Carberry, RFH's Matron, was Mrs Lambert, wife of the anatomical porter. She became cook/ caretaker at LSMW and her husband, helped by a new assistant, took over all portering duties. Lambert was a great success; his carpentry and gardening saved the School much expense.[lxv]

Further Building at LSMW & the Need for Incorporation

In December 1891 the School paid £300 for the sub-lease of 8 Hunter Street. In May 1892 it bought the superior lease to 8, 9, 10 and 11 Hunter Street for £425 from Mrs Elliott who lived at No. 11 which was sub-let after she vacated it. No. 8 was incorporated into the School that summer and provided rooms for pathology lectures, for Mrs Clarke Keer's practical pharmacy class, and for operative midwifery as well as for a library and a lavatory. In September 1892 the ground landlord agreed that a brass plate carrying the School's name could be placed on the door of 8 Hunter Street, although 30 Handel Street remained the official address until incorporation of the School in 1898 (see later).[lxvi]

Despite these improvements the Annual Report for 1892 stated *that – The time will soon come when the rebuilding of the School must be undertaken. The present School buildings are very old and as the number of students increases it will become more and more necessary to house better the School. The Council, however, wish to carry on their work as long as they possibly can in the present houses, as certainly not less than £20,000 will be needed when it becomes absolutely necessary to rebuild.*

A sub-committee that analysed LSMW's accounts over the previous five years reported in February 1895. Ordinary annual expenditure had risen from £2451 to £3635. Extraordinary expenditure – on leases, buildings and alterations – was £3027. Except for interest on the balance of the Oakes legacy School fees were the only income and all Hospital fees went to RFH. From 1874 to 1889 there had been deficits almost every year. From 1889 to 1893 fees covered ordinary expenditure and left a surplus, but enlarging the School took not only the surplus but also £565 from the Oakes legacy, £1160 from donations, and £488 interest on investments. There was little in reserve. Expenditure in 1893-94 again exceeded income, partly because lecturers were paid extra for more classes. Worryingly, the sub-committee could not envisage improving the School's finances without loss of efficiency.[lxvii]

However, money was available for new buildings. In May 1892 the Attorney General asked whether £3000 from a bequest would fund a scholarship or buildings carrying the donor's name, and in June 1893 LSMW received £3089 in new consols[48] for buildings to include a Pfeiffer Laboratory, and a tablet commemorating Emily Pfeiffer. Weeks later the Gilchrist Educational Trust[49] offered £50 a year for a five year scholarship and, if it approved the plans, £500 towards a Gilchrist laboratory. The former was accepted immediately but planning for the latter was delayed as there seemed little prospect of building given the financial situation – so the building fund gathered interest until the time was ripe for a public appeal.[lxviii]

Early in 1896 Charlotte Payne-Townshend, a rich Irish heiress, became an 'amateur' student of anatomy and physiology. That September she gave LSMW £1000; from the annual interest £5 was to go to the library, £5 to the common room, and the rest towards bursaries for students needing help, but the trust deed allowed

[48] British government securities without redemption date and with fixed annual interest.
[49] Founded by John Borthwick Gilchrist (1759-1841)

the £1000 to be invested in School buildings. Payne-Townshend was elected a governor and joined the Executive Council in January 1897. She married George Bernard Shaw in 1898.[lxix]

On 4 November 1896 the Dean told Council that, owing to the large entry that year (about 37), the premises were crowded. She suggested a plan for rebuilding. Although RFH staff were opposed to it Council gave its approval. A subcommittee[50] was appointed to elaborate on the scheme, report on finances, and consider the advisability of incorporating the School; RFH chose James Berry and three colleagues to 'consult' with it. The Dean wasted no time in raising funds. *The Times* of 11 December published her letter seeking contributions for the New Hospital and for the School Building Fund; within a month £800 was received for the latter.

On 15 December Council discussed taking a new long-term lease before starting to build. The Foundling offered one of 80 years at £300 a year if the School's Trustees would guarantee to spend £16,000 on the property within 10 years. Council now agreed that LSMW should incorporate under the Companies Act of 1862; the lease would then be granted to a corporation and the Trustees would not be saddled with a large increase in personal liability. On 22 December the governors agreed to apply for incorporation naming themselves as the 'constituent members' of the School; an Executive Council of 15 members was to include five women and five ex officio members.[51]

On 13 January 1897 two Trustees, Norton and Mrs Thorne, refused to accept responsibility for signing the lease. Nor, by letter, would Jex-Blake who felt the School was in a transition stage and that expenditure on rebuilding was unnecessary.

Jex-Blake was potentially a fly in the ointment. On 13 April 1897 Council received a letter from Henderson (absent with influenza) recommending that it should – '*(1) authorise…two or more individuals to enter into the building contract on behalf of the School.* [52] *(2) decide in what order the various funds should be used up, e.g. subscriptions first, Pfeiffer Fund second etc. Then I think Miss Jex-Blake should at once be…asked to join the other Trustees in giving a Power of Attorney…to sell the Pfeiffer consols…for making the payment under the contract…If she refuses…we shall have to consider once for all how to compel her concurrence in the steps decided on. I also send herewith the provisional agreement asked for by the Foundling*'.

On 6 May Jex-Blake wrote to her old friend and colleague: *Dear Mrs Thorne,*

---

[50] The Dean, the Sub-dean, the Hon. Sec. & Henderson, the School's solicitor.

[51] The Dean, Sub-dean, Hon. Treasurer and Hon. Sec. of LSMW, and the Hon. Sec. of the RFH staff.

[52] The Dean and Hon. Sec. did so.

After mature consideration I feel that I have no alternative but to resign my position as one of the Trustees of the London School. I disapprove of the action taken as to expenditure without the money in hand and also to the incorporation of the school at this crisis; and as no attention has been paid to my suggestion that the question should be submitted to the whole Governing Body, I cannot but free myself from all responsibility in the matter. You will please report my resignation to the executive Council.[lxx]

Thus she severed her relations with the school she founded 25 years earlier.[53] In sympathy three of her Edinburgh friends (White Millar, Heron Watson, and Miss Du Pre) resigned as governors of LSMW, and Thomasson said he would not contribute to the Building Fund.

The building sub-committee report submitted to Council on 2 December 1896 gives the impression that LSMW considered joint incorporation with RFH, but that the Weekly Board considered 'the time had not yet come for a complete incorporation of the School with the Hospital'. LSMW wished to mark its close association with RFH and asked if the title of the incorporated School could be the 'Royal Free Hospital Medical School for Women'. RFH wanted time to consider the matter and its staff tried to use the discussions to wring concessions about the appointment of lecturers. Council retorted by asking for more say in the appointment of Hospital staff. However RFH won this particular battle. On 11 March Council accepted *'that in all future appointments of Lecturers…the Executive Council should consider the Medical Staff of the Royal Free Hospital before making such appointment and shall notify the Board of the Hospital the name of the person proposed to be appointed and give the Board an opportunity of making observations thereon. The Executive Council regretted the Weekly Board did not see its way to making this arrangement reciprocal.'*

Doubts arose about the wisdom of leaving 'London' out of the title – in case the School lost the legal right to the name 'London School of Medicine for Women'. Henderson proposed calling it 'The London and Royal Free Hospital School of Medicine for Women.' Mrs Thorne suggested the 'Royal Free Hospital London School of Medicine for Women'. However, in May 1897 someone suggested 'London (Royal Free Hospital) School of Medicine for Women', which proved acceptable to all parties.[lxxi]

LSMW applied for incorporation. Henderson, LSMW's solicitor, and Hon. Treasurer following Norton's resignation, heard on 28 July 1897 that the Board of Trade had amended the Memorandum and Articles of Association and stipulated

53 Jex-Blake remained on the Governing Body but the Annual Report for 1899 shows that after incorporation she was not listed as a Member of the Association.

that no member paid by the School could be involved in its management without incurring unlimited liability. Council objected to this so Henderson wrote asking if one-third of the new Executive Council might be School employees. On 16 March 1898 Council heard that the Board of Trade, advised by the Crown's Law Officers, would accept only one paid lecturer or officer on a new Council. Even so, incorporation was still thought desirable so it was agreed that two committees should run LSMW: 1) A small 'Executive Council', whose constitution conformed to the Board of Trade's conditions, to meet quarterly and have the final say in management and control of finance, and 2) A 'School Committee', composed as far as possible of members of the existing Executive Council, which would 'meet monthly, consider all points hitherto considered by the Executive Council and recommend procedure to the executive.'[lxxii]

The Articles of Association were signed on 3 August 1898. The institution incorporated was 'The London (Royal Free Hospital) School of Medicine for Women;[54] the word 'Limited' was omitted, because it was not run for profit. Incorporation changed the School's organisation. The 'Governing Body' was replaced by the newly-created body of 'Members of the School' (i.e. Members of the Association) which many governors joined. The financial liability incurred by members was limited to £1 in the event of the Association being wound up. [lxxiii]

The School's 'Officers' were to be a President, two or more Vice-Presidents, a Dean, a Vice-dean (a woman), an Hon. Secretary and an Hon. Treasurer, and such paid officers as Council might from time to time determine.

The new Council, which first met on 5 October 1898, consisted of the Dean, Vice-dean, Hon. Secretary and Hon. Treasurer, two representatives from RFH, and four lay members. At least four of the ten were to be women. RFH was represented by Charles Burt (Chairman of its Weekly Board) and Holroyd Chaplin.

Although the old Executive Council had held its last formal meeting on 20 July it met again on 28 October to choose the four lay members subject to election at the Association's annual meeting. The five names proposed were Professors Dunstan[55] and Halliburton, Mrs Fleming Baxter, Mrs Waller and Mrs Bernard Shaw; the last missed out. The new School Committee consisted of members of the new Council, the Hon. Sec. of the RFH staff, and ten other persons nominated by Council, of whom at least seven were to be teachers at LSMW; it first met on 12 October.[lxxiv]

LSMW had pressed ahead with expansion while awaiting incorporation. By December 1896 John McKean Brydon, the architect for the new New Hospital for Women, had made a sketch plan, based partly on EGA's views about the

[54] LSMW will remain the abbreviation for the School's name until the change of title in 1947.

[55] Later Sir Wyndham Rowland Dunstan, Director of the Imperial Institute.

accommodation needed for an annual entry of fifty, and partly on advice from the teachers of anatomy, physiology and chemistry. His plan, which would allow the School to function during building, was to erect a Wakefield Street block first, then a Handel Street block, and finally a block replacing the Hunter Street houses. The total cost was estimated as £20,000. It was thought the balance of the Oakes bequest (about £2900), the whole of the Pfeiffer fund (£3700) and Miss Payne-Townshend's gift of £1000 would cover the cost of the Wakefield Street block. More money was needed for the other two.[lxxv]

In the summer of 1897 building began on the site of the tennis court in the eastern part of the garden. For tennis players Mrs Thorne arranged the temporary use of a court in Regent's Park botanical gardens.

The new block came into use in June 1898. Its large laboratories for physics, chemistry, physiology and anatomy were as fine as those in any medical school in London. They had electric lighting throughout; the idea that gas lighting should be used to save money was rejected although gas was laid on for two of the laboratories.

The Prince and Princess of Wales performed the opening ceremony on 11 July.[56] The Princess declared the building open. The Prince then spoke of their joint interest in the education of women, particularly of medical women and their work in India. He thought medical men now sympathized with the women's movement, and hoped the money would soon be raised for the other two wings. A few days earlier he had visited the School to see the students at work, and had inspected the New Hospital for Women, whose foundation stone the Princess had laid in 1889.[lxxvi]

Council had not intended to start on the Handel Street wing in 1898. However, there was still money in the building fund, and neither the Oakes bequest nor money invested for scholarships had been needed to pay for the Wakefield Street block. When, in April 1898, the Princess agreed to open the new wing Council decided to press ahead with fund raising. The Dean appealed to past and present students, and to friends of the women's cause. Almost £4500 was raised in five weeks and, although another £2000 was needed, building of the second wing commenced soon after the Royal visit. A dog show held in the School garden in June 1899 raised £55. The Duchess of Newcastle acted as President and Kennel Club members as judges; 224 dogs were entered. The show was the brainchild of a clinical student, Lucy Wellburn.[57] A year earlier fellow students had given her a stethoscope and a case of instruments for being a good secretary of the Tea

[56] According to Jo Manton (p 307) EGA took a bottle of whisky so the Prince could have a drink before inspecting the new chemistry and anatomy laboratories.

[57] Lucy Wellburn married Dr A.E.Naish, former H.O. at RFH, and started a Naish dynasty at the School. For the Dog Show see Mag Oct 1899, pp 537, 564-566.

Club.[lxxvii]

The plans of the Handel Street wing were modified before building started. Instead of placing the library below two lecture theatres in a 'circular' section at the east end of the Handel Street wing it was to occupy a larger room in the Hunter Street wing; a clinical lecture theatre replaced it in the circular section. The Council Room was switched from the south end of the Hunter Street wing to the first floor of the Handel Street wing, which was also to hold a biological laboratory. A small research laboratory and dressing rooms were placed on the top floor; the ground floor contained cloakrooms, lavatories and a secretary's office, and there was a corridor connecting the Wakefield and Hunter Street blocks.[lxxviii]

The Handel Street wing was the south wing; lower than the other two it was to have a low pitched roof so that more sunshine would enter the central courtyard. (Fig 6.4) It was ready for occupation in October 1899. The building fund residue, Payne-Townshend's £1000 and the capital of the Helen Prideaux Scholarship Fund

Fig 6.4 LSMW quadrangle c 1922 to show low roof of the south wing

(£662),[58] were used to pay the £6300 cost, but a shortfall of £1000 remained.

Council had already decided to borrow money to expedite building of the third wing. It raised £8,000 by mortgaging the two new wings with the Equitable Life Assurance Society at a rate of 3¾%; the capital was to be repaid at £1000 a year beginning in 1902. Council was confident that with more fee-paying students,

[58] Both to be repaid later.

economies, and occasional windfalls from bequests and donations, it could meet annual expenditure. But help was needed to repay the capital over eight years. No public appeal was to be made until all building was finished, but Miss Douie prepared collecting cards and encouraged the students to help in fund-raising. Douie, an Edinburgh MA,[59] who graduated MB at LSMW in 1897, was elected School Secretary that June following Miss Heaton's retirement through illness.[lxxix]

Demolition of the Pavilion and the Hunter Street houses began in 1899. Again plans were changed, a fifth floor being added to this third new wing to provide students' residential chambers; even so building was finished by October 1900. (Fig 6.5) On thc ground floor there was a fine common room and a refectory for the students, and an anatomical museum. The kitchens, the housekeeper's rooms and a bicycle room were in the basement. The first floor held the materia medica room and the large library. The Magazine for January 1901 reported that the library was a large stately room, with a bow window overlooking the garden and two fireplaces with Teale grates; but it complained that it was '*not well lighted, and although the little electric lights are exceedingly pretty they are so few in number and so far above the tables that prolonged study in any part of the room is very trying*'.[lxxx]

The Hunter Street Chambers, on the top floors, were supervised by Miss Douie whose title was changed to 'Secretary and Warden'. They accommodated eighteen students and proved a success; by June 1901 rents received totalled £130 more than those from the Hunter Street houses. The *Express*, good-humouredly, suggested the gas ring provided would only allow preparation of tea and boiled eggs, hardly a suitable diet for working girls. Douie responded, more seriously, that luncheon was available from 12 noon to 2 p.m., dinner was served in the evening, and the resident housekeeper could prepare breakfast; a large gas stove made the gas ring unnecessary. Clinical students living in Chambers had other priorities. Their offer to pay five shillings a year each for a telephone link with RFH was accepted a few months later.[lxxxi]

Facilities also improved at RFH. A one-storied building had accommodated the post-mortem room and mortuary, along with a large room that housed all the Hospital pathological work and served as the museum. The large room became a well-equipped teaching laboratory fitted with water, gas, and electric lamps for working with microscopes. Another storey was added to provide a larger museum, a laboratory for the curator and medical staff, and a laboratory assistant's room. Mrs Webb paid for the alterations as her daughter Mabel, curator of the museum until her death in

[59] In 1893 Douie was one of the first eight women to graduate (MA) from the University of Edinburgh.

Fig 6.5 LSMW c 1900 after completion of Hunter Street Wing

October 1898, had planned to develop RFH's bacteriological and pathological work. Even before Mabel died Mrs Webb gave £1000 for School buildings and subsequently offered to pay for all the work on the pathology building, the new version of which was formally opened in February 1900.[lxxxii]

Increasing student numbers meant that the School was in need of more nearby residential accommodation – both before and after the construction of the Chambers. There had been a hall of residence at 1 Byng Place, Gordon Square since 1882. Soon known as College Hall it was founded by Mary Kilgour and the Browne sisters, Annie Leigh and Thomazina Mary, to accommodate ten women studying either at UCL or LSMW. Shaen was its solicitor. Its Principal was Eleanor Grove who until 1881 had been Lady Resident at Queen's College, Harley Street, where the Brownes had studied. Her brother, the famous musician Sir George Grove, compiled the *Dictionary of Music*.[lxxxiii]

The first two LSMW students at Byng Place, Mary Crawley and Margaret Smith, were followed by Isabella Macdonald, Helen Wilson (later Sheffield's first woman doctor), Louisa Aldrich-Blake, Ethel Vaughan (later Mrs. Vaughan-Sawyer), Frances Ivens, Louisa Martindale, Maud Chadburn, Elizabeth Courtauld (later a benefactor of College Hall) and the celebrated Indian medical student, Rakhmabai (see above).

After College Hall opened LSMW prospectuses also recommended other smaller establishments considered suitable accommodation for young women medical students. One, added in 1894-5, was 5 Endsleigh Street; its superintendent, Mrs Clarke Keer, taught Materia Medica at LSMW.

The new School buildings had cost over £35,000, far more than Brydon's original estimate of £20,000. When Louisa Aldrich-Blake, Britain's first woman Master of Surgery (1895), gave the inaugural address in October 1900 LSMW still owed £14,000. J. F. Turle,[60] there that day, gave £5,000 on condition no more debt was incurred until existing debts were repaid. The Hunter Street block became the Turle Wing, while the Handel Street block was the Oakes Wing after LSMW's first major benefactor. The Wakefield Street block, already called the Pfeiffer Wing, included a Payne-Townshend laboratory.

The splendid new buildings at Hunter Street resolved a problem. In 1892 the GMC's new guidelines suggested lengthening the curriculum to five years and laid greater emphasis on preliminary and pre-clinical subjects. Mental pathology, operative surgery and ophthalmic surgery were made compulsory. However the various examining boards had different requirements. To make curricular changes satisfying all of them LSMW's teaching needed a complete overhaul, as did the fees.

Chemistry and botany were taught from the beginning, but now the School decided to teach the elementary biology and physics needed for the LSA and the Scottish diplomas. Miss M.F. Ewart, B.Sc. (Mrs Ewart Macdonald from 1896) was appointed to cover both subjects. The revised fees were £125 as a lump sum. Paid in instalments they were: 1st yr £40 School; 2nd yr £25 School, £15 Hospital; 3rd yr £20 School, £15 Hospital; 4th yr £10 School, £10 Hospital; the 5th yr was free.

Durham agreed to admit LSMW students to its degrees in 1895,[61] but the standards it demanded for biology and physics could not then be reached at LSMW as it lacked the necessary laboratory facilities. LSMW's 'Durham' students therefore went to Bedford College or paid for private tuition. Similarly, before entering LSMW, students for the London MB paid other institutions for the necessary instruction on these subjects and on chemistry. However, with its new buildings LSMW could teach preliminary examination subjects to the level required at both London and Durham. It appointed Edith Stoney to teach physics, and GP Mudge to teach biology.

LSMW, supported by RFH staff, again asked London's Colleges of Surgeons

[60] Turle was a friend of the Dean; his father, James, was Westminster Abbey's organist from 1831 to 1882.

[61] The last year of the five-year course had to be spent at Durham. The first LSMW women to graduate MB Durham were Claudia Rowse, Grace Stewart and Margaret Joyce in 1898.

and Physicians to examine women. In October 1895 the physicians refused (voting 59 to 50). In December the Council of the Surgeons' College favoured granting the petition, but could not '*admit women to the conjoint examinations in face of the adverse vote of the meeting of fellows and members of this College and the expressed opinion of the Royal College of Physicians.*'[lxxxiv]

Clubs and Societies

There was more to LSMW students' life than work and examinations. Many participated in sports – perhaps because of the emphasis then placed on sports at North London Collegiate School, the model for subsequent girls' high schools, and at girls' public boarding schools such as Cheltenham Ladies' College, St Leonard's and Roedean. Women's sports also flourished at colleges in London, Oxford and Cambridge, and at provincial universities.

Tennis was an all year round game at LSMW after the court was laid in 1882. A Tennis Club was founded in 1888. When the court was tar-paved in June 1894 students and some Council members covered the cost. In 1896 Westfield College challenged the club to a contest; it was held on 4 November and LSMW won. By 1903 the club played against Westfield, Bedford College Old Students, KCL and UCL, but the annual highlight was the 'School' v 'Hospital' match. During building work at the School in the late 1890s the club played at Park Square Gardens; and in 1901 and 1902 the 'School' v 'Hospital' match was held at the Botanical Gardens, by courtesy of Isabel Thorne, herself a tennis enthusiast.[lxxxv]

After building finished a gravel tennis court was laid; it cost £130. Skelton Anderson paid £100 and Mrs Flemming Baxter £30. Fanny Wilkinson, a Garrett family friend and a landscape gardener with the Metropolitan Public Gardens Association, arranged the surrounding gardens.[lxxxvi] The reduced space around the court caused conflict between tennis players and the 'gardeners'. The Magazine of January 1901 noted '*there will be none too much space at either end for the taking of swift back-line balls*'. In June Council agreed to alter the Common room porch to reduce the danger to tennis players. In view of their continuing disputes with tennis players the 'gardeners' needed official recognition, and in June 1902 it was agreed that a committee of up to six members should supervise the garden.

The Tennis Club colours, initially an unpopular dark green, were changed in December 1894 to a broad band of black between narrow bands of light green. However, the hospital students wanted their own 'colours'. In 1895 they chose a hatband of bronze and blue with a narrow line of yellow, but switched in May 1896 to a black ribbon with a gold lion and a gold border for hats, and a black and gold stripe for ties. The whole School eventually adopted black and gold and the lion.[62]

Twenty-four students launched a Swimming Club in 1895. Its pool, in the Caledonian Road, was available only on Wednesday afternoons. A Bicycle Club was founded the following year; its members went off riding on Saturdays. Fencing and gymnasium classes were started in 1898.[lxxxvii]

From December 1897 there was a Hockey Club. Its first ground, at Wormholt Farm on the Uxbridge Road, was minutes by tram from Shepherd's Bush station. Two XIs were fielded in 1898-9 and that season the club moved to the nearby Columbines ground in East Acton Lane. In 1901 there were twice weekly practices at UCL's ground in Regent's Park; that season the first XI won 8 of 11 matches.[lxxxviii]

The increase in student numbers enriched the School's social life. The musical and dramatic societies organized entertainment for School parties, which were usually well supported and finished with dancing. They were certainly well attended;[63] 450 turned up for the one held in December 1901. Each Christmas a student choir sang carols in the wards at RFH and the New Hospital for Women, and patients received presents of old and new clothing.

In June 1895 a Common Room Committee was formed. It had five student members: one looked after the library, the others dealt with newspapers, the Tea Club, writing paper, and the distribution of pegs and lockers, etc. Each, in turn, kept the Common Room tidy for a week, and took the newspapers to RFH wards in the evening. The subscription, one shilling a term, entitled students to use the library books, newspapers and journals,[64] and paid for improvements to the Common Room. Louisa Stevenson continued sending shortbread and Scotch cake from Edinburgh. Gifts were solicited – the special needs being cushions, library books, and flowers. Two women from famous families were elected to the committee – Hilda Rowntree from York and Elizabeth Courtauld from Essex.[lxxxix]

A Medical Society founded in 1896-7 met twice monthly in the lecture room at RFH; students used the clinical notes for their presentations. All past and present students of LSMW and RFH were eligible for membership; RFH staff were honorary members. The first presidents were the medical and surgical registrars, Mrs. Percy Flemming and Aldrich-Blake.[xc]

The students' facilities at RFH were less comfortable than at Hunter Street. In

---

[62] From 1844 a lion adorned the front of the RFH building in GIR. There is no evidence it was there earlier. Queen Victoria granted RFH a Charter of Incorporation in 1892; that year an image of RFH's Official Seal, which included a lion, appeared on the cover of its Annual Report – perhaps explaining the lion adopted by the 'Hospital' tennis team.

[63] Particularly as the number of students entering in the previous five years varied between 25 & 38.

[64] Initially the *Daily Chronicle*, *Pall Mall Gazette*, *Punch*, *Nature*, and *Review of Reviews*.

1897 Hospital students agreed to contribute annually towards improving them. At a joint meeting with School students on 23 May 1900 the Students' Representative, Mabel Naylor, pointed out that fifty Hospital students lunched in space for sixteen, and that lavatories, sinks and hat-stands were near the dining tables. The students agreed to raise £1000 to implement Lucy Wellburn's[65] idea of a new lecture-room over the pathologists' room. RFH agreed and plans were drawn up. Each student was asked to raise five pounds; some contributed more generously. The Dean gave £100; £618 was raised by March 1902. Subsequently the Hospital withdrew its approval of the scheme – but the students continued raising money.[66, xci]

From March 1902 Hospital students each paid an extra shilling a term to employ a Mrs Surtees to supervise their common room; she served for many years. Initially she looked after only two rooms, as the dining-room also served as a dressing-room. Both were sparsely furnished and lacked cooking utensils, china, etc. She suggested that thank-offerings from the newly qualified should be much-needed articles, rather than cakes. Clocks, a notice board, a letter rack and dining-room utensils were acquired in this way.[xcii]

At a students' general meeting in March 1898 Emily Stuart was elected as the first 'School Representative'; she was to call formal meetings, open to all students, to discuss matters of general interest to them. Twenty-five students constituted a quorum. On 25 June discussion was limited to the opening of the new Wakefield Street block by the Princess of Wales, for which the students decided to wear a cap and gown to distinguish them from visitors.

On 13 July 1898, two days after the Royal visit, the Medical and Debating Societies held their first Conversazione. About 200 visitors, including representatives from similar societies at other London hospitals,[67] inspected the new laboratories and danced in the new chemical laboratory. In October the School Representative gave a welcoming tea at which various School officers explained their respective duties to newcomers. One School Representative seems to have upset some students as it was decided at a meeting on 6 May 1901 that their duties, clearly defined, should be those of delegates, not representatives with a free hand. Dorothy Hare, elected that year, worked untiringly for her fellow students.

In the Magazine for May 1901 the Dean announced that at RFH's Triennial Festival Dinner on 15 July she would be one of the stewards raising money for the Hospital. She suggested that to thank RFH for its support over many years, particularly as it

[65] Lucy Wellburn (of dog show fame).

[66] As a result major improvements were made in 1908.

[67] In 1896 LSMW students joined debates at Guy's Hospital Debating Society, and at KCL's Medical Society where the provocative motion – 'That women are unfitted to become medical practitioners' – was carried by 21 to 4!

now admitted women to resident posts, medical women collectively should fund two or three 'Students' Endowment Beds' by collecting about £500 before each Triennial Dinner. The scheme worked well.

The School held no annual School dinner. An old student, Eleanor Bond (LSA 1896), a practitioner in Bournemouth, wrote to the Magazine for May 1902 suggesting LSMW '*would do well to imitate the example of almost every other medical school in holding an Annual Dinner…it is a…personal loss that I have so few opportunities of meeting my fellow-students, many…, like myself, settled in country practices, and with whom – apart from…recalling old times – it would be helpful and stimulating to compare notes as to practice and prospects…Also to meet members of staff of the Hospital and School…Number of students is now large enough to make this scheme feasible.*'

Bond's suggestion was soon acted upon. The first 'Annual Dinner' of RFH and LSMW took place that December in the Holborn Restaurant (Fig 6.6); 385 attended. Norton, Ford Anderson, Halliburton, Starling and Sir Victor Horsley were among the many old teachers, students and friends present. The principal guests included Dr. Robertson, the University's Vice-Chancellor; Sir William Church, PRCP; David Ferrier, Dr. Horder, and Stephen Paget.[xciii] The dinner became an annual event (see later chapters).

About 660 students were admitted during EGA's time as Dean; about 490 of them subsequently qualified. Some gave up their studies owing to marriage, illness, death or failure in examinations. A number had already qualified in another country. Others either had no intention of practising, wished for some reason to study only one or two subjects, e.g. anatomy, physiology etc., or simply wanted to experience the life of a medical student. Lady Griselda Ogilvy, [68] keen to help the poor in her country district in Scotland, applied to attend classes in forensic medicine, clinical surgery and medicine having already worked in children's hospitals. She was admitted to the pathology class at the School but not to the Hospital.[xciv]

Staff Changes at School and Hospital

Garrett Anderson saw many changes in the School's staff during her time as dean. All the original lecturers were men. When she retired in 1903 half of the lecturers were women, although only one had a relatively senior appointment at RFH.[69]

Stanley Boyd (Fig 6.7) ran anatomy alone until 1904. Despite his duties at

[68] Probably the Lady Griselda who married James Cheape of Strathtyrum & Lathockar on 22 Dec 1897.

[69] Aldrich-Blake had been appointed anaesthetist at RFH in 1895.

Fig 6.6 1st Annual Dinner RFH & LSMW 1902

Charing Cross he played an important role in the management of LSMW, and was an advocate for medical women in the wider world. He was highly regarded as a teacher and in March 1888 the School increased his fees because his mock examinations were so thorough; the vivas, collectively, took 10 hours, and he corrected 35 sets of papers. A month earlier, concerned that students lacked enough individual attention, he suggested that two senior students, not one, should help as demonstrators on three days a week, summer and winter, and be paid £75. The first pair were Florence Longbottom and Mary Darby Sturge.[70] In July 1889 he married Florence Nightingale Toms, his first student demonstrator in 1882; she was renowned at LSMW for her dress sense and great charm.[xcv]

There were five physiology lecturers from 1883 to 1903 – all young, ambitious and highly talented research workers without clinical commitments; most continued working at UCL while lecturing at LSMW. Waller replaced Schäfer in 1883, but in July 1884 he left for St Mary's; there, in 1887, he was the first to record an electrocardiogram.[xcvi] In 1885 he married a former LSMW student, Alice Mary Palmer, daughter of George Palmer, Conservative MP for Eastbourne and

---

[70] Mary Sturge, granddaughter of Charles Sturge, mayor of Birmingham, was a leader in the Temperance Movement. She and Sir Victor Horsley co-authored *Alcohol and the Human Body* (1904). She was President of the Medical Women's Federation 1920-22.

Fig 6.7 Stanley Boyd (1856-1916) (from Lancet 1916,i,376)

co-founder of Huntley and Palmer's biscuit company. When he arrived for his next lecture at St Mary's he found 'Waller takes the biscuit' written on the blackboard; Waller quipped 'and the tin as well'. Alice gave up her studies but supported LSMW strongly until her death in 1922. Their daughter Mary taught physics at the School (see later).

Waller's successor, John Alexander McWilliam, lasted two years before moving to Aberdeen in 1886. His replacement, William Dobinson Halliburton, was a biochemist in today's terminology. Childhood poliomyelitis had rendered his right arm useless. He took the chair of physiology at KCL in 1890, but continued teaching at LSMW until 1898. Then for two years the women were taught by Ernest Henry Starling, a giant of physiology; he also lectured at Guy's, his own alma mater. In 1899, aged 33, he took the Jodrell chair at UCL when Schäfer moved to Edinburgh.

Thomas Gregor Brodie (1866-1916), Starling's successor, was also director of the ill-fated research laboratories of the Royal Colleges of Physicians and of Surgeons. When they closed in 1902 he became superintendent of the Brown Animal Sanitary Institution and professor of physiology at the Royal Veterinary College. In 1909, after ten years at LSMW, he moved to the chair of physiology at Toronto.

Heaton taught chemistry at LSMW from the beginning.[71] Illness forced his resignation in March 1893, six months before his death. When he asked for help with teaching in March 1891 Lucy Everest Boole[72] was made demonstrator in organic chemistry. Her father was the great mathematician George Boole, 'inventor' of Boolean algebra, and her mother and her sister Alicia were also gifted mathematicians. Lucy, essentially self-taught, was the first female Fellow of the Institute of Chemistry. She had begun studying chemistry in order to become a dispenser. She succeeded Heaton as lecturer. Six months before he resigned she fell ill while researching on croton oil, a highly toxic material. When she fell ill again in 1897 her doctor advised her to stop lecturing, but she continued teaching practical chemistry. She died in 1904 aged 42.

Boole's illness led to Clare de Brereton Evans's appointment as chemistry lecturer in 1897. She had taught at Cheltenham Ladies' College (then called Cheltenham College for Girls) for five and half years, and in 1889, while teaching there, obtained a B.Sc. before moving to the Technical Science College at South

---

[71] His sister, Emma Heaton, was the School's Secretary. Ill health caused her resignation in April 1897.

[72] Mt. Everest was named after her great uncle, Colonel Sir George Everest, Surveyor General of India.

Kensington. In 1897 she was the first woman awarded a D.Sc. in chemistry. In October 1898 she enrolled at LSMW as a student but abandoned medical studies and headed the chemistry department until 1912.

P. H. Stokoe of Guy's Hospital taught botany until 1900; it was then dropped from the curriculum. From 1892 physics and elementary biology (including zoology) were required for the LSA and LRCPSEd diplomas; Mary Ewart, who studied physiology at LSMW for her B.Sc, was made lecturer in biology and took a tutorial class for physics.

When EGA became Dean the physicians at RFH were Cockle and Buchanan Baxter, with Samuel West as assistant physician. Baxter fell ill in 1883 and died two years later, aged 41. Samuel West took over his beds and was made a physician; Harrington Sainsbury came from UCH as a locum to cover out-patient work and was soon made an assistant physician at RFH, where he also assumed West's role as pathologist. At that time the co-lecturers on Practice of Medicine were not RFH physicians but the Dean and Horatio Donkin, a physician at Westminster Hospital. Donkin taught Materia Medica initially but switched to Medicine when King Chambers retired in 1878.[73]

Over the years there were inevitably changes among the RFH physicians. Sainsbury joined West as physician when Cockle retired in 1888. The two recently appointed assistant physicians, Hector Mackenzie (1887) and James Calvert 1888) were joined by Frederick Andrewes in 1889. These physicians stayed together until 1893 when Mackenzie moved to his alma mater, St Thomas'. J. Walter Carr replaced him and after Calvert resigned in 1895 Raymond Crawfurd arrived. Andrewes's return to Bart's as pathologist in 1997 brought in Fawcett, but he soon left and Phear replaced him in 1899. West retired as physician in 1902 allowing the appointments of Crawfurd as physician and Farquhar Buzzard as assistant physician.[74]

Julia Cock replaced EGA as lecturer in 1897,[75] and when Donkin left in 1898, on becoming Commissioner of Prisons,[76] the assistant physician Walter Carr joined Cock as co-lecturer. Carr was appointed full physician in 1900 and when Samuel West retired in 1901 Crawfurd, replaced him as physician.

Until 1883 West lectured on Materia Medica – i.e. the source, composition, characteristics and preparation of drugs. West was also a Bart's physician, and in 1884 he had pleaded pressure of work, gave up the lectures, and resigned as

---

[73] For details of appointments, resignations etc see RFH Annual Reports & LSMW Prospectuses

[74] Andrewes, Mackenzie, Crawfurd & Farquhar Buzzard were all subsequently knighted.

[75] There are notes of EGA's lectures by Aldrich-Blake in the Wellcome Library. Ref 1889 MS.898

[76] Donkin was knighted in 1911.

pathologist at RFH. Harrington Sainsbury took over both roles and gave the Materia Medica lectures until 1903. Just before he started one of the university examiners implied that given the results in that subject LSMW's Materia Medica museum must be unsatisfactory! In April 1884 Sainsbury said the deficiencies could be corrected for £5. Within weeks a Mr. Martindale presented a catalogue of the drugs and articles in the museum. [77, xcvii]

For some years Mrs Clarke Keer, who lived in Endsleigh Street, taught practical pharmacy in her own home where some students were lodgers. In 1891, after 8 Hunter Street was connected to the Pavilion, her class moved to the newly created Materia Medica museum. That year Mary Sprigg, one of the students, gave £100 to improve the museum and Martindale reorganized it; three years later Sprigg presented the museum with a sample of all the drugs introduced into the British Pharmacopoeia in 1894.[xcviii]

Arrangements among the surgeons were similar those of the physicians at both RFH and the School. When EGA became dean Gant and Rose were RFH's senior surgeons. The lone assistant surgeon, Frederick Eve, soon left (see later). His replacement Boyce Barrow was promoted to surgeon in 1887, and that year Rose left to spend more time at KCH. That year two new assistant surgeons were appointed – James Berry and William Battle – and when Gant's long association with RFH came to an end in 1888 Berry replaced him as surgeon.[78]

In 1889 Edmund Roughton and Work Dodd joined Battle as assistant surgeons. So too, did Willmott Evans in 1895, but with the added responsibility of being Surgeon for Skin. Work Dodd was made ophthalmic surgeon in 1896; his senior colleague, Grosvenor Mackinlay, retired in 1899 and was not replaced. Battle was appointed as a third surgeon in 1896, and Roughton, who had dealt with ENT cases since 1895, was made a fourth surgeon in 1898. This left Willmott Evans as the only assistant surgeon. He was promoted to surgeon in 1902 (and remained Surgeon for Skin); his assistant surgeon's position went to Percy Legg. That was situation in surgery at RFH when EGA retired as Dean.

The teaching of surgery seems to have been less intensive that that for medicine – Practice of Surgery classes were held in alternate years, and classes on Operative Surgery (taught by Stanley Boyd) were arranged 'whenever a sufficient number of students present themselves'. After resigning as Dean in 1883 Norton taught Practice of Surgery instead of Cowell, the original lecturer on this subject; he had

[77] Probably the William Martindale who taught pharmacy at UCH, where Sainsbury studied. His '*The Extra Pharmacopoeia'* (1883) covered drugs not included in the 'latest' version of the British Pharmacopoeia. Ten editions appeared before Martindale died in 1902; the 37th came out in 2011.

[78] In 1891 Berry married Frances May Dickinson (MB Lond 1889), who was often his anaesthetist.

no co-lecturer until Boyce Barrow joined him in 1896. In 1897 Norton retired as Hon Treasurer and co-lecturer at LSMW, Berry taking the co-lectureship. Norton also left St Mary's (where he was Surgeon and Lecturer on Clinical Surgery). He moved to Ashampstead, Berkshire and in 1898, aged 57, married for the first and only time. During retirement he was active in the Worshipful Society of Apothecaries and was its Master in 1910-11. He died after surgery for appendicitis in 1912. Somewhat surprisingly the short biography marking Norton's retirement in the *St Mary's Hospital Gazette* made no mention of his involvement with LSMW.[xcix]

EGA's surgical practice was at the New Hospital for Women. Frances Hoggan's concern about EGA's surgical competence had led to the former's exodus from the New Hospital in 1877. (See Chapter 3) It remained an issue. Meredith, who helped in difficult cases, resigned in February 1888 as 'the record of Mrs Anderson's operations at which he had been present shewed too high a percentage of failures.'[79] [c] Louisa Atkins, who assisted EGA at operations, complained to the New Hospital's managing committee when EGA replaced Meredith with a clinical assistant (Mary Scharlieb) to help during operations. Atkins subsequently resigned over this issue in April 1888 as did Mary Dowson, pathologist and unofficial 'chloroformist'.[ci] Atkins, lecturer on diseases of women after Blackwell's resignation in 1877, now declined the post of teacher of practical gynaecology at the New Hospital, and in April 1889 resigned her lectureship.[80] Scharlieb took both positions, but transferred the practical gynaecology class to Helen Webb in 1894. Ford Anderson taught midwifery, the sister subject to diseases of women, from 1875 until 1893; when he resigned Scharlieb combined the two subjects.

There were longstanding problems with obstetrics teaching because RFH's staff could not practise midwifery on its premises. The 1901-2 prospectus states practical midwifery was learned '*by living in one of the lying-in hospitals for three to six months, and taking cases under the direction of the medical officers.*'[81] The School had lobbied RFH for a maternity department for years. In September 1902 Thies, RFH's Secretary, sought Council's approval for forming one. It opened in 1903 with Jane Turnbull (MB 1899) as the first Resident Obstetric Officer; soon it was clear a Junior Obstetric Officer was needed; Winifred Wigglesworth was selected. The New Hospital had opened a maternity department in 1901, but neither hospital had maternity beds – the patients were delivered at home.

In December 1896 the Dean suggested LSMW should hold lectures on tropical

---

79 William Appleton Meredith resigned in February but did not explain why he did so until June .

80 Atkins gave up hospital practice, but continued in private practice. She died in 1924, aged 82

81 The lying-in hospitals were Annie McCall's Clapham Maternity Hospital; Queen Charlotte's; the British Lying-in Hospital, Endell Street; City of London Lying-in Hospital; and Dublin's Rotunda.

diseases, as so many of its old students worked abroad. For 20 guineas Dr Patrick Manson (Sir Patrick from 1903) lectured at 6 p.m. on Mondays and Wednesdays from 3 May to 2 June. Doctors of either gender could attend the course for a guinea; students were admitted gratis. The Dean agreed to pay Manson's fee – if she could use any surplus earned by selling tickets to pay for future lectures by outsiders of distinction. Manson's course was a great success and continued, in alternate summers, until 1912. Occasionally he took students to see patients at the Seamen's Hospital.

August Dupré FRS, the last of LSMW's original group of lecturers, resigned as lecturer in forensic medicine in March 1901.[82] He had taught toxicology; his co-lecturers (Shewen, then Bond) taught medical jurisprudence. When Scharlieb, just back from India, replaced Bond in 1887 it was her first appointment at LSMW; Mary Dowson replaced her when Scharlieb switched to diseases of women in 1889. Hawthorne succeeded Dupré as co-lecturer in forensic medicine; Wilson Hake, who succeeded Dupré at Westminster Hospital, gave the toxicology lectures.

Jex-Blake and Pechey both taught hygiene from 1878 until 1883 when Pechey left for India; Jex-Blake carried on alone for another five or six years. From 1889 Scharlieb taught it within 'Forensic Medicine and Hygiene', the two subjects being dealt with in alternate years; Dowson covered the hygiene component from 1891. The approach to the subject changed when W. J. Simpson,[83] Professor of Hygiene at King's College, London, arrived as lecturer in 'Public Health' in 1899. He had been Medical Officer of Health in Calcutta and it was felt his appointment, like that of Manson in tropical medicine, would better prepare LSMW students intending to practise in India and elsewhere in the tropics.

Although Cowell was the first surgery lecturer the lectureship in his own specialty, ophthalmic surgery, was initially held by George Critchett, a founder of LSMW. Critchett died in December 1882, and owing to ill health his successor, James Adams of the London Hospital, resigned in May 1884. Grosvenor Mackinlay, RFH's ophthalmic surgeon, took over as lecturer. After he died in 1900 Work Dodd became RFH's ophthalmic surgeon, but the lectureship went to Charlotte Ellaby, MD Paris who, until she returned from India and joined the New Hospital, was Edith Pechey's colleague in Bombay. Dodd's colleagues at RFH were unhappy about Ellaby's appointment, but Dodd was satisfied that the School's Report and Prospectus recognized him as 'Lecturer on clinical ophthalmic medicine and surgery'.[cii]

Pathology at the end of the nineteenth century was not the wide ranging subject of

---

[82] Dupré was a Huguenot born at Frankfurt-am-Main & obtained his doctorate at Heidelberg in 1855. He was President of the Society of Public Analysts & founder member of the Institute of Chemistry.

[83] Sir William from 1923.

today. It was largely autopsy room pathology and the examination of surgical specimens. The 1883-4 prospectus divided it into 'general pathological anatomy' and the 'special anatomy of different organs'. Histology was beginning to play an important role and so students needed a microscope, but haematology, bacteriology and immunology were in their infancy. There were six 'pathological demonstrators' at RFH from 1878,[84] but the first to be designated 'pathologist' (in 1900) was Crawfurd (later Sir Raymond), assistant physician at RFH from 1896. At London hospitals and medical schools junior physicians and surgeons usually taught pathology as well as botany, physics and material medica and the relatively minor clinical specialties. Arthur Phear was pathologist after Crawfurd became full physician in 1903.

Although Sturge (see Chapter 5) left RFH in 1881 to move to Nice he did not resign the lectureship at LSMW until September 1884, The assistant surgeon, Frederick Eve, curator of the museums at both Bart's and the RCS, was to replace Sturge but he soon left RFH owing to his duties at the London Hospital. Quarry Silcock, pathology lecturer at St Mary's, taught pathology at LSMW in the summer of 1885 and then in alternate summers until 1897. Primarily a surgeon, he was one of the last to practise as both a general surgeon and an ophthalmic surgeon.[ciii]

In September 1897 Council was reminded that years earlier it had decided that, instead of a single course every other year, pathology should occupy two years, with 'elementary' pathology one year and 'advanced' pathology the next. This proved unsatisfactory and the original system was reinstated. When Silcock resigned in December 1897 pathology teaching was scrutinized, and Frederick W. Andrewes was appointed lecturer in pathology, a post he also held at Bart's. Andrewes, assistant physician at RFH since 1891, taught auscultation and physical signs at LSMW before becoming demonstrator in pathology. In 1895 he and the surgeon Roughton organised a bacteriological department at RFH. The following year Roughton ran a bacteriology class; up to 10 students were taught for six weeks on two afternoons a week.[85] In 1897 Andrewes succeeded Kanthack as pathology lecturer at Bart's but although he left RFH he lectured at LSMW until 1909.

Radiology – which was to prove as important as histology, haematology and bacteriology – was introduced at RFH in 1902. The Magazine for May 1902 noted '*an advance has been made...by the organisation of an electrical department. An X-Ray apparatus is now fitted up in Elizabeth Ward...Miss Stoney is appointed as electrician [with] two students as assistants, who will be initiated into*

[84] Sturge, Samuel West 1881; Sainsbury 1885; Mackenzie 1889; Andrewes 1892 and Crawfurd 1897.

[85] In 1896 Andrewes suffered a prolonged attack of erysipelas, which may have triggered his later interest in streptococcal infections. He became a distinguished pathologist & was knighted in 1920.

the mysteries. ...Miss Stoney attends on Wednesdays at 12.30 p.m. and on Fridays at 9 a.m.'. The choice of Stoney, who graduated MB Lond in 1885, and was also an anatomy demonstrator, was inspired; she became a pioneer of British radiology.[civ]

Only two people taught Mental Pathology during Garrett Anderson's term of office – William Henry Octavius Sankey,[cv] lecturer in mental health at UCH, who taught gratis, and Charles Arthur Mercier from Westminster Hospital.[cvi] Sankey taught until 1887 when the lectureship passed to Mercier, who wrote prolifically on the relationship between insanity and crime. In May 1894 the LCC made some asylums available for teaching and Mercier conducted demonstrations at the Colney Hatch asylum, later known as Friern Hospital.[86] He taught at LSMW until 1907.

One important appointment in 1895 was that of Mary Stewart (1862/3 – 1925) as the first hospital almoner. It was a post created jointly by RFH and the Charity Organisation Society because it was believed that some patients were abusing the system of free medical care provided at RFH. The almoner's role was to act as a gatekeeper, means-testing patients to decide if they were eligible to receive treatment at RFH (and, if so, whether they could contribute to their care), or whether they were better suited to treatment provided elsewhere. She found a large majority to be 'deserving' patients. While doing this she also took on the role of a medical social worker. Ill-health forced Stewart's retirement in 1899, but she had trained others to continue her work at RFH and at other voluntary hospitals. The Hospital Almoner's Committee, founded in 1903, became the Institute of Medical Social Work in 1964 and amalgamated with other groups in the 1970s to form the British Association of Social Workers.[cvii]

On 29 Jan 1903 the Dean wrote to the Hon. Sec.: *'Dear Mrs Thorne, I ask you to make it known to the Council that for personal reasons I wish to be relieved of my office of Dean. Miss Cock would be an excellent successor and some young person should be put upon the Council to get the training necessary to succeed Miss Cock at some future date. As the new Report is now being prepared, I think this is a good moment for making a change. With every good wish for the success of the school.'* The School Committee and Council agreed that Julia Cock should succeed her.

When Council wrote thanking EGA for her services to the School it asked if her name could go forward for election as its first President. She agreed. Students, past and present, contributed towards two gifts to remind her of her deanship.[87] One

[86] Friern Hospital later developed close links with LSMW and RFH.

was a silver cup by Messrs. Elkington and Co that was designed by Florence Steele.[88] The other was a copy of the Narcissus statuette in the Naples museum, where the copy was made. A book listing all contributors, bound in red Niger leather with gold tooling on either side, was designed and executed by Miss Stebbing – '*The scrollwork of leaves encloses the letters E. G. A. above and L.S.M.W. below, with the dates 1877-1903, being the period during which Mrs Garrett Anderson held the Deanship'*.[cviii] The 1877 was, of course, a mistake; she was not Dean until 1883. The same error appears on her plaque on the School's memorial wall, now situated in the Rowland Hill Street entrance to RFH in Hampstead. In December 1901 Sir Alan Anderson presented the Common Room with a copy of portrait of EGA by Sargent that had been exhibited in the New Gallery.[cix]

---

[87] The present students' subscription was limited to one shilling.

[88] The original was exhibited in the Academy of 1901.

CHAPTER 7

Julia Cock (1903-1914)

London's Royal Colleges open their doors to women – but not too wide!

LSMW's third Dean,[1] Julia Ann Hornblower Cock (Fig 7.1 Colour plate), was born in Shrewsbury in 1860. According to Scharlieb she was an orphan from her early years.[i] However the April 1871 census Cock records that she was living with her parents and three older brothers. Her father was a master tanner and currier. Little else is known about her early life.

Cock entered LSMW in October 1878 and spent a year, with Scharlieb and four others, preparing for the preliminary examination in science, a prerequisite for taking London University's MB courses and examinations. In the event she abandoned the MB, qualifying LRCPI in 1882. In April 1881 she lived at 79 Gower Street with four Bedford College students.[ii] After qualifying she fell ill and needed a long and complete rest.[iii] Her first post was as RMO at Sunnyfield Convalescent Home in Braintree in 1884,[iv] and in 1886 she worked at Braintree and Bocking Cottage Hospital. She joined the New Hospital for Women's out-patient staff in 1887, and its in-patient staff ten years later.

She added LRCS Edinburgh (1889) and MD Brussels (1890) to her qualifications. The latter was an odd degree; it was open to registered practitioners with British surgical and medical qualifications but did not allow its holders to practise in Belgium.[2] The examinations, held five times a year, lasted ten to twelve days; the three parts had to be passed sequentially but could be taken on separate occasions.

Thirteen examiners conducted sixteen separate viva voces – in French or English – in front of all the other candidates. Constance Colley (MD Brussels 1906) thought the degree was for 'foreigners' and the University coffers![3] '*Whether any Belgian ever took it, I could not find out...at the time of which I speak, the candidates were all English speaking, and consisted of American, Eurasian, English and Irish practitioners.*'[v] LSMW women taking the examination either wanted a degree, being dissatisfied with a diploma, or to be addressed as 'Doctor', a word not then

[1] The fourth if one counts Anstie who died before the School opened.

[2] Whereas foreigners with a British registrable qualification were allowed to practise in Britain.

[3] Colley paid the whole fee, £22, in advance.

used as a courtesy title for women practitioners.[vi] 'Brussels Sprouts' and 'London Pride' were sobriquets for LSMW women with either the Brussels or London MD.[vii] The first Brussels Sprouts graduated in 1888.[4] Although their MD was not rated highly at LSMW, and success in Brussels was not mentioned in the School's Annual Reports, at least fifty women with connections to LSMW had acquired this degree by 1899.

When Cock became Dean in 1903 the School Committee suggested the Vice-Deanship be in abeyance for a year but it was three years before Aldrich-Blake was appointed to the post. The delay may have been related to the fact that when Council received the Dean's resignation on 4 February 1903 it also received Aldrich-Blake's resignation from the School Committee.[5] At Thorne's request Aldrich-Blake withdrew it.[viii]

While Dean, Cock lived at 15 Nottingham Place off Marylebone Road. Isabel & May Thorne lived at No. 10; Samuel Garrett, EGA's brother, at No. 13; and Louisa Aldrich-Blake at No. 17.[ix]

Cock, like others, had professional interests outside LSMW and hospital practice. In 1885, while at Braintree, she succeeded Frances Hoggan as Medical Inspector at North London Collegiate School, then based in Camden. She wrote '*Medical Inspection of Secondary Schools for Girls*' for the fifth volume of the Report of the Royal Commission on Secondary Education published in 1894. Her views, then considered a counsel of perfection, later proved sensible when medical inspection of schools became widespread. She was a medical examiner for the Board of Education, and from 1887 'Medical Examiner to the Government Insurers and Annuities Fund for Women Proposers in the Metropolitan District' – another of the Government jobs for women doctors created by Henry Fawcett when Postmaster General.[x]

Cock's appointment as Dean coincided with new University regulations affecting medical degrees. She explained them in the Magazine for May 1903. Anatomy, physiology and pharmacology remained in the Intermediate MB exams; chemistry moved to the Preliminary Scientific Examination. The separate BS was abandoned, and from 1903 examinations for an MBBS degree gave more emphasis to surgery and pathology than the old MB. Outstanding candidates were still awarded honours in different subjects, but separate honours papers were abolished.

Graduates could subsequently sit for the higher qualification of MD – in Medicine, Pathology, Mental Diseases, Midwifery & Diseases of Women, or State

---

4 They included Florence Nightingale Toms, Waterston & Hunter.

5 In 1902 she attended only one meeting of the School Committee (later named 'Education Committee').

Medicine. The MD could also be awarded via a thesis or published work resulting from independent research, and original work could count towards the MS degree.

When Garrett Anderson was Dean an issue arose with serious implications for LSMW. The University of London Act 1898 suggested future amalgamation of schools for preclinical teaching, on the grounds that small premedical and preclinical departments could not provide good career opportunities for the scientists now being appointed as teachers, as they needed expensive laboratories for research. Furthermore, such teachers were often poorly paid in London and many left for Scottish or provincial schools. In some London schools expenditure increased as student numbers fell. While the large departments at UCL and KCL could cope without difficulty those at smaller schools struggled; not surprisingly some London schools wished to stop teaching preclinical subjects but were worried others would not follow suit.

In 1901 the Faculty of Medicine supported Senate's plan to create an 'Institute of Medical Sciences' at South Kensington for all pre-clinical teaching.[xi] A public appeal was set up to raise the £375,000 required. However, the issue was contentious and a potential threat to small schools. The Faculty had second thoughts and voted against the scheme in 1905, and in 1907 the University dropped it and returned to donors the £70,000 already raised. LSMW had well-equipped laboratories for all the subjects, but Westminster (in 1905), St George's (1908) and Charing Cross (1911) arranged for their students to go to KCL or UCL for preclinical teaching; most chose KCL.

Another reorganisation was under way. To reinforce the concept of a teaching university UCL offered to 'incorporate' itself into the University of London and agreed to cease existence as a separate legal entity. It proposed transfer of all its buildings and freehold to the University. Senate became its governing body. When the University College London (Transfer) Act 1905 took effect University College School (UCS) and University College Hospital Medical School (UCHMS) became separate bodies. In 1907 the new UCHMS was created on the UCH site on the west side of Gower Street. UCS moved to Hampstead, thus releasing space for development at UCL. Similarly when the King's College London (Transfer) Act 1908 took effect in 1910 Kings College School (KCS),[6] Kings College Hospital Medical School (KCHMS) and KCL's theological department became separate bodies. Although UCL and KCL were meant to work together – as parts of one great university run by committees of its Senate, the University College Committee and Kings College Delegacy – the necessary unity was not forthcoming.[xii]

[6] KCS had moved to Wimbledon in 1897.

LSMW, like other small colleges, considered incorporation but no recommendations subsequently emerged from the relevant Senate committee, and the issue became irrelevant in 1909 when a Royal Commission was appointed to consider University Education in London. London's hospital medical schools, Imperial College of Science and Technology, and the London School of Economic and Political Science retained their semi-detached status as 'schools of the University'.[xiii]

The Haldane Commission

The new Royal Commission, chaired by Richard Burdon Haldane (Viscount Haldane from 1911), was set up because of the constant conflict in Senate between those favouring external degrees and those wanting a teaching university with internal degrees. As a result issues were often decided by the votes of 'neutral' members ill-qualified to assess the arguments. Furthermore the award of a charter to Imperial College in 1907 revived controversy about a second university and the relationship of schools and colleges to the University.

In their final report in 1913 the Commissioners argued that one could not create a great university simply by attaching many independent institutions to a central degree-giving body which controlled only recognition of individual teachers, conduct of degree examinations, and approval of syllabuses. London's University had no proper academic relationship with its schools; it rarely visited them, had no financial control and no power over appointment of teachers or duplication of departments.

The Haldane Report made a number of sensible suggestions about reorganising the University but it met strong opposition. The President of the Board of Education set up a Departmental Committee, chaired by Sir George Murray,[7] to consider how to implement its recommendations but the task was abandoned when war broke out. A second Departmental Committee, the Hilton Young Committee, was set up in 1924. When it reported in 1926 it rejected the Haldane recommendations.

The Haldane Commission's discussions about London's medical schools make interesting reading and reflect the concerns of their staffs and students. The Commissioners concluded '*the University has signally failed to gain the sympathy and attachment of the London Medical Schools...Less than one third of their students are undergraduates of the University of London and the Medical Schools can scarcely be said to have any closer connection with the University of London than with the Universities of Oxford and Cambridge, or with the Conjoint Board of the Royal Colleges*'[xiv]

---

7 Murray was a former Permanent Secretary of the Treasury

The commissioners, none medically qualified, questioned the Dean of the Faculty of Medicine, representatives of its medical schools, the Royal Colleges of Physicians and Surgeons, the Society of Apothecaries, and the Asylums Committee of the LCC. Witnesses presented written statements before questioning. The Dean (Cock) and the Warden & Secretary (Brooks) represented LSMW.

Other schools complained about their students' problems in getting the London degree which had been introduced in 1839 (as MB initially, MBBS from 1903). For forty years only four to five per cent of London's students graduated MB, i.e. about twenty a year.[xv] More than fifty qualified MB in 1884 and about 100 in 1894. A much higher proportion of LSMW's students graduated, but this was partly through necessity. When the London MB opened to them in 1878 their only other way of qualifying was to sit an examination in Ireland; they could not take the London Conjoint until 1909. After 1900 about 75% of LSMW students qualified with the University degree; in 1911 about 130 students were reading for the London MBBS, only 15 just for a diploma. LSMW students had won the gold medal in every subject in which one was offered.

Many students, including some women, avoided London MB examinations as they were more demanding than those for the Conjoint diploma and the LSA. However matriculation was a barrier for many men. Lots of girls' schools prepared pupils for London matriculation; but most men's schools did not and many of their pupils going on to medical school realised too late that a degree was not an option if they had satisfied only the lower admission standards of the Conjoint Board and GMC. Haldane recommended that the subjects needed – physics, chemistry and biology – should be taught in secondary schools and included in the higher school examination, thus shortening the medical school course. Those taking arts at school would need to study those subjects elsewhere but would have to pass in the preliminary sciences before entering the Faculty of Medicine.

The Commissioners heard the concern of those who had qualified with a diploma or a bachelor's degree that although registered they had no right to the title 'Doctor'. The Commissioners thought the matter outwith their task, but pointed out that the profession could confer the legal right to use the title.[xvi] London's Royal College of Physicians changed its mind on the matter. In July 1912 it removed from its relevant by-law the stipulation that no diplomate 'shall assume the title of Doctor'.[xvii]

For many years LSMW continued to discourage old students from using the title 'Doctor' unless they also obtained a doctorate. This annoyed some old students. As late as 1950 Helen Dent (née Barnes, MBBS 1913) wrote to the School Secretary *'It may be that being a School of the University, you use the strictly correct procedures as to the use of 'Doctor'. I find that the male practitioners are more willing to give this courtesy title than are women. Some of us were too busy doing war medical work to take the MD. We were not so fortunate as the graduates of the last war who were often retained to take higher degrees. I was running a large obstetric department as well as doing supervising of unqualified residents when I might have been reading for MD. I have felt this for years that one's old school should not give the courtesy title when Societies such as the Hunterian Society do.'* Mrs Dent had been Vice Chairman of the Westminster & Holborn Division of the BMA.[xviii]

LSMW's written evidence[xix] indicated its concern about having to close if teaching of preliminary and intermediate subjects was centralized. It worried that even if women were accepted at men's schools they would be seriously disadvantaged, believing that co-education could be effective only if women had equal opportunities as undergraduates and postgraduates, plus representation on the governing body and teaching staff of schools. LSMW thought such concessions unlikely; it believed men's schools would not admit women unless they benefited financially. Its concern was unnecessary as 'Haldane' recommended that intermediate subjects should be taught close to the teaching hospitals. However, the hospital schools which had given up teaching anatomy, physiology and pharmacology did not re-open those departments.

The Haldane Commission is often credited with introducing into British medical schools 'clinical units' led by *full time* university professors, although its report stated '*it is not necessary or advisable to prohibit private practice altogether.*' The three men who influenced its views on clinical units were Ludwig von Muller of Munich;[xx] Abraham Flexner, the American who had studied medical education in Europe and the USA;[xxi] and Sir William Osler, the Canadian Regius Professor of Medicine at Oxford.[xxii] All argued for units led by professors supported by assistants, as in Germany and at Johns Hopkins,[8] which would promote research and provide students with a more scientific approach to medicine.[9] To some this was a welcome and logical extension of existing trends, but a larger, more conservative body of opinion criticized Flexner's doctrinaire approach and castigated Haldane's proposals as the 'attempted Germanization of London University'.[xxiii] Many worried that academically orientated teachers would produce doctors who would have little contact with patients, and that traditional bedside skills would therefore be lost.

The Commission's fourth report, in 1911, recommended moving the University's headquarters from the Imperial Institute buildings at South Kensington

---

8 Osler had been Professor of Medicine at the new Johns Hopkins Medical School in Baltimore.

9 The first such units were created from 1919 to 1921 at St. Bartholomew's, St. Thomas', St. Mary's, UCH & LSMW.

to a site closer to its main colleges; twenty-five years later the present Senate House was the outcome of this recommendation.

The London 'Conjoint'

In November 1906 LSMW again approached London's two Royal Colleges about access to their Conjoint examination, and 133 FRCPs, 380 FRCSs and 1500 MRCSs were among the 2800 signatories to a petition supporting the women (about 1000 from London, the rest from the provinces). Both colleges had to agree for the request to be granted. In February 1907 the RCS's Council, wishing to admit women to the MRCS exam, proposed polling fellows and members if the RCP agreed to open the LRCP to women. The RCP did not consider the petition until May, and in July its Comitia deferred discussion until a later meeting. The President's proposal that the RCP should poll its own licentiates was defeated by 27 votes to 24.[xxiv]

The RCP took counsel's opinion – which was that there was no bar to examining women for the LRCP. If they qualified that way, or graduated at a recognized university, they could sit for the MRCP and, if successful, be entitled to election to the Fellowship, which required a majority vote at the annual meeting of FRCPs.[xxv] Asked 'Can the College then make provision that a woman admitted to the Licence…shall be unable to proceed to the higher qualifications of Member or Fellow?' Counsel replied that although the College could adopt new by-laws to that effect its existing by-laws would be construed to apply to women as well as men; consequently a woman refused permission to proceed to the Membership or Fellowship could enforce her rights like a man. He also opined that if the College decided to admit women to one or more of its qualifications, it should enact new by-laws clearly defining the rights to be given to women and the limitations of such rights.

At a special RCP Comitia on 12 December 1907 Harrington Sainsbury, a physician at RFH, proposed the women's petition be granted. An amendment, suggesting admission to 'the LRCP only', was passed by 59 to 33 votes. On 17 January 1908 a large majority passed a second amendment omitting the word `only' and a further amendment opening all College examinations to women. The final resolution was `That it is desirable that such alterations be made in the Byelaws as to allow the admission of women to the Examinations of the College.' The Registrar (Edward Liveing) then proposed *`That it is not intended that any action should be taken under the Resolution just adopted inconsistent with the agreement between the two Royal Colleges under which the Licence of the one (LRCP) and the Membership of the other (MRCS) are only granted conjointly'*. Perhaps he felt the RCS would reject admission of women following a poll of its fellows and members.[xxvi]

The RCS reported on its poll in July 1908. Two-thirds of 1033 fellows voted to admit women as members, just over a half to admit them as fellows. Out of 8,256 members, most opposed admission of women as members (53%) and as fellows (57%). The RCS Council admitted women to examinations for the Conjoint diplomas, the fellowship, the diploma in public health, and the licence in dental surgery. But the women's success was incomplete. New by-laws rendered them ineligible for membership of the RCS Council, and prevented them voting in elections for Council, participating in meetings of fellows and members, and in taking part in the government, management, or proceedings of the College; nor were they eligible as examiners.[xxvii]

The RCP heeded Counsel's advice about by-laws and on 28 January 1909 passed one defining the women's rights. They were to be eligible for admission as licentiates and members, and for a Diploma in Public Health, on the same terms as men; in by-laws and regulations words implying males were to apply to females, and all proper alterations were to be made – '*Provided always* that women shall not be eligible for election as Fellows of the College, or…take any part in the government, management, or proceedings of the College.' Ernest Starling's attempt to have the words `*Provided always'* omitted was unsuccessful. It took sixteen years before women could be elected to the Fellowship, and a further nine before such an election took place.[xxviii]

The first woman MRCP, Ivy Woodward (MBBS 1903), was admitted in July 1909. LSMW and the Edinburgh Medical College for Women were recognized by England's Conjoint Examining Board in December and women became eligible for the RCP's scholarships and prizes – unless prohibited by the conditions of special trusts. In April 1910 Dossibhai Patell was the first female LRCP, MRCS; she graduated MBBS the same year and, after returning to India, became professor of obstetrics and gynaecology in Bombay. In December 1911 Eleanor Davies-Colley MD (MBBS 1907), surgical registrar at RFH and daughter of a Guy's surgeon, was the first woman FRCS.[xxix]

Financial Problems

When Cock took over from Garrett Anderson the School's financial situation was precarious, owing largely to the building debt, £2000 of which was owed to the scholarship fund. Mortgage repayment, £6000 over six years, was to start in 1904. Garrett Anderson bought £300 worth of stock from the School to help pay the first instalment – the rest coming from cash awaiting investment.[xxx] The sale of more stock paid for the second instalment in 1905. No purchaser could be found in 1906, so Aldrich-Blake and Stanley Boyd bought the requisite amount.[xxxi] The mortgage was fully discharged in 1909 and the deeds were transferred from the Equitable Life Assurance Company to Lloyds Bank.[xxxii] The remaining building debt, about £3700, was further reduced and in March 1912 anonymous donors gave £1500 to eradicate it.[xxxiii] LSMW, debt free for the first time in many years, heeded its auditors' warnings about covering the likely loss when the lease expired in 1977. It took out a capital redemption policy for £30,000, due in March 1977, for an annual premium of £150.[xxxiv]

There were other reasons for the financial difficulties. Changes in the London MB curriculum[xxxv] meant that extra classes were needed – and some optional classes, which had been charged to the students taking them, became compulsory. Council was reluctant to meet all the extra cost by increasing fees. In 1903 income exceeded expenditure by only £16 – despite Garrett Anderson's donation of £300 a year (for ten years) to cover the ground rent. From 1902, the £700 paid annually from a trust fund set up by Mrs Percy Sladen of Exeter in memory of her husband[10] supported four departments at LSMW. Sadly when Mrs Sladen died in January 1906 the payment lapsed.

According to the Annual Report the yearly deficit was £315 in September 1906, but by November it was £2000;[xxxvi] the increase was attributed to a small student entry and the fact that some students had paid their fees in advance the previous year. Fortunately before Mrs Sladen died she promised LSMW a large endowment. Her sister Ellen (Mrs Godfrey Walker, later Lady Granger) inherited the Sladen estate and honoured the promise in 1908. She gave the School £20,000 and a portrait of her sister.[11]

There were three other large bequests. In March 1907 Council heard that Henry Cullimore had died aged 28. Cullimore, son of an Irish physician, was an Oxford graduate who, from 1903, occupied the chair of English at Freiburg.[xxxvii] He left LSMW part of his estate, along with his brain and body and a portrait of himself; his skeleton still hangs at the new RFH in Hampstead. His mother and stepfather had a life interest in the bequest, worth about £10,000, so the School had to wait until 1926 for the money. (See Chapter 10) Louisa Lady Goldsmid,[12] who died in December 1908, left LSMW £3000 free of duty. Her bequest was also contingent on the life of an annuitant and was eventually received at about the same time as the Cullimore money.[13] The third bequest was more straightforward. In 1908

---

[10] Mrs Percy Sladen, née Constance Anderson, was the daughter of Dr William Anderson of York and a friend of Garrett Anderson. Percy Sladen, a distinguished and wealthy biologist, died in 1900.

[11] The portrait seems to be missing from the Royal Free collection. There are portraits of Mrs Constance Sladen and of Percy Sladen at the Royal Albert Memorial Museum, Exeter.

[12] Lady Goldsmid was a major benefactor of LSMW from its earliest days,

[13] In 1911 the Trustees of Lady Goldsmid's estate paid for improvements to RFH's quadrangle that included paving it with asphalt. Iron gratings were fitted round the trees, and large boxes of shrubs and flowering plants were introduced. For the patients' comfort a shelter, with seats, was erected. An inscription recording the gift was placed opposite the entrance.

LSMW received 100 Hudson Bay shares and other stock, worth in total about £9600, from the estate of the late James Robert Turle, who had given £5000 towards the new buildings in 1900.[xxxviii] His bequest covered deficits over the next few years.

LSMW had few scholarships. In September 1912 Council heard that the late Miss Mabel Sharman-Crawford, a travel writer, had left £2000 for a scholarship bearing her name. In June 1913 Mrs Richardson-Kuhlmann gave £635 for two annual prizes – one for the best student in clinical obstetrics, the other for the student with the highest aggregate mark for the class examinations in medicine, surgery, pathology and gynaecology.

In 1908, when St Mary's Hospital Medical School was in financial trouble, it applied for assistance to the Board of Education, set up in 1902 to control educational provision of local authorities. St Mary's received a grant in October 1909. LSMW applied for one in July 1909. The School, like St Mary's had to persuade the Board of Education that it was a technical Institute and so deserving of funding earmarked for such institutes.[xxxix]

However, such grants came at a price. Those awarding them felt empowered to influence the management of the schools receiving them, and the disadvantages of such influence were to become increasingly obvious over the next hundred years. In March 1910 the Board said it would provide funds for the teaching of 'professional' intermediate subjects (anatomy, physiology, etc) and final medical subjects (medicine, surgery etc), but not of 'preliminary' subjects, which it wished transferred to the University. To get the grant LSMW also had to negotiate a new agreement with RFH lasting 25 years; the School had to be represented on RFH's Committee of Management, and on sub-committees making appointments to the honorary visiting staff; in addition £100 per annum was to be paid to cover LSMW's accommodation at RFH in lieu of a percentage of student fees. The agreement was signed and sealed in September 1911. In December Council heard the grant for 1910-11 was £849.10s.[xl]

Thoughts turned to further building. The annual report for 1905 stated '*any appeal now made* [to clear the buildings debt] *would be a final one, as any extension of the School buildings is very unlikely to be required.*' This strikingly inaccurate prediction may explain why Council did not acquire the leases of 12 to 14 Hunter Street when offered them by the Foundling Hospital in January 1905 – and why, four years later, it did not bid for freehold property adjoining the School.

In June 1911, when finances had improved, the next door garden became available for a nominal rental of £1 a year; Council procrastinated, wishing to consult its Treasurer and to await the outcome of other negotiations. In September, for £125 a year, LSMW was offered a building lease, to run until Lady-Day 1977,[14] covering 2, 4, 6 & 8 Wakefield Street plus the garden ground. Again Council procrastinated. Not until December did it decide to acquire the garden and ask for first refusal on the building frontages.[15] Unfortunately the opportunity had been lost. In January 1912 the Foundling refused to grant tenancy of the adjoining garden; it now wished to let it with building frontage on Hunter Street and a Mr Davies acquired the lease.[xli]

Following completion of Garrett Anderson's building projects life at LSMW was relatively quiet. However, there were developments at RFH. In 1903 it opened a maternity department with Jane Turnbull (MB 1899) as the first Resident Obstetric Officer. It had no beds; confinements were conducted at patients' homes. There was also some expansion. When the Board decided the Sussex wing sanitary arrangements needed upgrading, it also decided to build two new operating theatres on top of the wing. By late 1905 each of its three wards had gained a kitchen and scullery, and radiators and electric light had been installed. Students' access to patients was reduced by the loss of the fifty Sussex wing beds during building. Subsequently the six wards in the central Calthorpe block and the Victoria wing were also renovated. The Calthorpe block and the Sussex wing were to house all surgical and gynaecological patients, and the Victoria Wing the medical cases.[xlii]

Princess Christian[16] opened the new operating theatre suite in December 1907. For thirty-seven years the only theatre at RFH was the one built in the central block in 1870, but the number of operations had increased tenfold. Access to the new theatres was by staircase or by an electric lift at the east end of the Sussex Wing. A sterilising room, an anaesthetic room, and rooms for surgeons and students served the theatres each of which had a gallery for students.[xliii]

The students' 'Lecture Theatre Fund', (see Chapter 8), plus contributions from Scharlieb and Garrett Anderson, paid to upgrade the RFH students' quarters. A cloakroom accommodating eighty students was built between the students' quarters and the mortuary alongside the south wall dividing the Hospital yard from Eley's. A covered way, with pegs for dressers' coats, led from the new cloak-room to the old one, now a luncheon room. The common room was re-painted and refurnished to provide a comfortable sitting room. The old operating theatre was available for

[14] Lady Day, the Christian festival of the Annunciation of the Virgin Mary, falls on 25 March. Until 1752 it began the legal year in England, and is still a quarter day (for the payment of quarterly rates or dues).

[15] That month it deferred the preparation of a scheme to extend the School's buildings. Aldrich-Blake offered to pay to link the adjoining garden with the School garden.

[16] Helena, Queen Victoria's 5th child & 3rd daughter, married Prince Christian of Schleswig-Holstein.

lectures and clinics, but lacked proper seats and was uncomfortable.[17] The old lecture room became a students' reading room & library. In November 1907, with upgrading complete, the students held a house-warming party for staff.[xliv]

RFH had not finished building. Its 'out-patients' department, which dealt with about 30,000 patients a year, was in a small, poorly lit and ill-ventilated basement beneath the Victoria wing.[xlv] In 1912 it paid the Calthorpe Estate £13,000 for one and a quarter acres behind RFH.[18] It was initially intended for a new out-patient department and chapel, but before construction started in December the plans had been amended to include the following: casualty; throat, eye and ear; massage; dental; X-ray and electrical departments; a complete maternity unit with operating theatres and physicians' and surgeons' rooms; students' quarters, and rooms for twenty-four nurses and resident ward maids. (Fig 7.2) On completion the building also contained a venereal disease department. The chapel went into space previously occupied by the original X-ray department and the operating theatre.[xlvi]

The Students' Chambers at Hunter Street were still a success. When one tenant's brother stayed with her in August 1912 all the tenants were reminded that male guests could not stay overnight. In March 1913 the Chambers Committee asked for authority over domestic matters. Council agreed, providing it became a properly elected body; the new committee was made up of three tenants, elected annually, and the Warden ex officio.[xlvii]

In December 1907 Isabel Thorne resigned after thirty years as Hon. Secretary.[19] Her daughter May succeeded her. May Thorne was a fine surgeon but in 1904 was accused of alleged negligence because a sponge was left in a patient's abdomen after surgery. The judge was pleased the jury made no imputation on Thorne's surgical skill, but refused its award of 'nominal' damages and awarded £25 for 'pain and suffering'. The LSMW Magazine for October 1904 claimed an important legal point was decided in this case, 'viz., that the surgeon must be responsible for any mistakes of his assistants'. The Medical Defence Union (MDU) paid for Thorne's defence; other doctors covered the damages and plaintiff's costs. The MDU had been established in 1885 as the world's first organisation to defend doctors' reputations. Its first female member was Elizabeth Margaret Pace (later Mrs A. Maitland Ramsey), who joined it as an LSMW student in 1889. She graduated MB Lond with honours in 1891 and MD in 1895.

After resigning Isabel kept in touch with the School and ran her usual tennis party in the summer of 1909. Later that year she recommended that the capital for

---

[17] According to RFH's Annual Report for 1909 it was also used for minor operations and massage.

[18] Occupied at the time by Messrs. Cubitt & Co.

[19] At the same meeting, (1907; 16 Dec) Louisa Garrett Anderson joined Council.

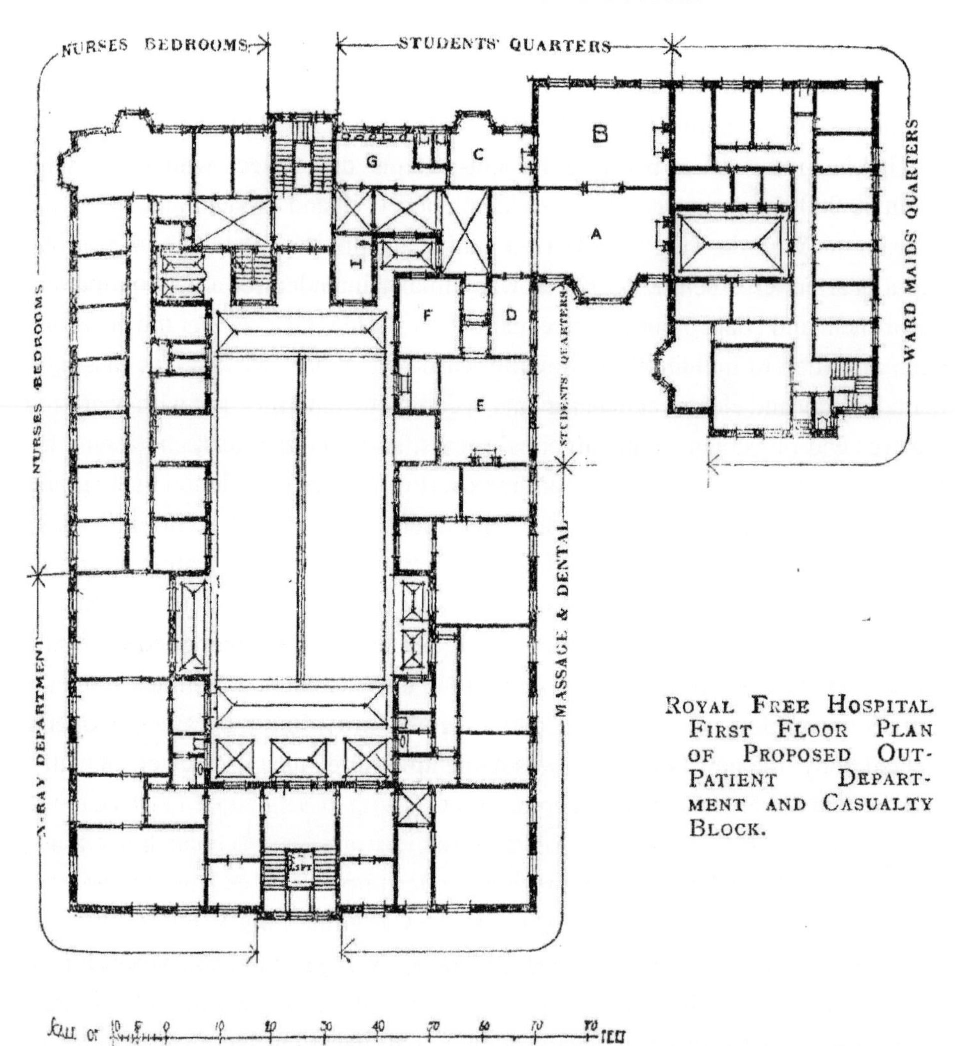

FIRST FLOOR PLAN.—Provision is here made for the Dental, Massage, X-Ray and Electrical Departments, Students' Quarters, and a suite of rooms for the Nursing Staff; these latter are connected by a private staircase with a similar suite on the floor above. Extending over the Casualty Block on this floor are the rooms allotted to the Resident Domestic Staff.

A Common Room.	*E* Dining Room.
B Reading Room.	*F* Kitchen.
C Writing Room.	*G* Cloak Room.
D Interview Room.	*H* Ward Coats.

Fig 7.2 First floor plan for Helena building (1913)

the Stuart Mill scholarship should pay for the tropical medicine lectures that helped students going to India; Indian women studying in England were to be admitted to them without fee.[xlviii]

Mrs Thorne died in October 1910. With Council's agreement a brass tablet, presented by May Thorne and bearing the words 'Isabel Thorne Common Room', was affixed to the door of the Students' Common Room in January 1913. The Thorne family founded a scholarship in her memory to be awarded annually on the result of the entrance scholarship examination. The first Isabel Thorne Scholarship of £30, awarded in 1913, was divided between Lena Adam and Muriel Landau.[xlix]

Isabel Thorne and Edith Pechey (Pechey-Phipson after her marriage in 1889) were Jex-Blake's first fellow students at Edinburgh. In 1891 Pechey became the first woman elected to the Senate of Bombay University. She retired as senior physician at Bombay's Cama Hospital in 1894 but continued in private practice and played a major role in a plague epidemic in 1896. She and her husband, a trader in wines and herbs, left India in 1905 to visit Australia and New Zealand where they had many friends and relatives.[l] Her sister Jennie had married Alfred Shewen, who taught forensic medicine at LSMW from 1874. The Shewens had moved to Sydney, where Alfred was a physician at the Royal Prince Alfred Hospital; he died on a visit to England in July 1900.[li]

The Phipsons returned to England in 1906. Edith joined the women's suffrage movement, and participated in the famous Mud March in February 1907. Before that May Thorne treated her for breast cancer. Edith died 14 April 1908, age 62. Her husband gave LSMW her books & bookshelves, and endowed a pharmacology prize (first awarded in 1911). A memorial fund set up in September 1910 led to the annual award of the Dr. Edith Pechey-Phipson Post-graduate Scholarship to assist with the cost of post-graduate study – open to all medical women but preferably for one from India or for one going to work in India.

Sophia Jex-Blake outlived Isabel and Edith. From 1899 she lived at 'Windydene', her small Sussex farm – with cows, a dairy and a fruit orchard. Each spring Agnes McLaren visited when returning to Scotland from her winter practice on the Riviera; the Phipsons visited frequently after returning to England. Sophia kept in touch with brother Thomas and his family,[20] and her sister Caroline was an occasional visitor, but it was Margaret Todd who was Sophia's main support in her declining years.[21]

True to form, Sophia became embroiled in another dispute in 1905 when a vacancy arose at Bruntsfield Hospital. The best applicant, Elsie Inglis, had triggered the demise of Sophia's medical school in Edinburgh and Sophia, still on

[20] Thomas, headmaster of Rugby School 1874-87 & Dean of Wells 1891-1911, had ten children: Henrietta became Principal of Lady Margaret Hall, Oxford & Katherine Mistress of Girton College, Cambridge. Bertha, (MBBCh 1903), studied initially at Sophia's school in Edinburgh but graduated from the Medical College for Women. She drowned near Whitby in 1915. Arthur, a physician, met his wife, daughter of the 14th Earl of Pembroke, at Boulogne during WW1; they settled in Kenya.

[21] Margaret Todd is buried with Sophia Jex-Blake.

the Hospital Board, said she would resign rather than acquiesce in Inglis's appointment. Inglis was appointed – and Jex-Blake's resignation was accepted, leaving her with no formal connection to the hospital and the two medical schools she founded.

From 1910 heart failure limited Sophia's activities. She died 7 January 1912, age 71. Her grave in Rotherfield churchyard (Fig 7.3) stands about 30 yards from that of Sir James Stansfeld.[22] Small memorials were placed later in St Giles's Cathedral, Edinburgh, and the Edinburgh Hospital for Women and Children. LSMW had already acknowledged its debt to her. In 1904, following a proposal by Garrett Anderson, a tablet was placed on the boardroom mantelpiece at LSMW stating '*The London School of Medicine for Women was established in August 1874 through the efforts of Miss Sophia Jex-Blake, MD*'.[lii]

For many years a student or recent graduate acted as librarian. However the post became more arduous. When, in March 1894, Council decided the librarian should attend for at least half an hour each day Mary Gordon (LRCPSEd 1890), the then librarian, could not cope. Her replacement Annie Piercy (MB 1893) married the RFH surgeon Willmott Evans in July 1895. When Piercy-Evans resigned in 1900 Douie, the Secretary and Warden, agreed to act as librarian for one year; she ended up serving for seven. Cullis took over in 1912. Council then decided to stop using students and staff and to appoint a librarian who would also assist in the office. The first of them, Miss Warner, appointed at £50 per annum, left a year later and her replacement, Miss Gadney, resigned within months to become a full-time librarian elsewhere. Ruth Edminson, who arrived in September 1913, had read modern languages at Oxford; she moved to a post with a higher salary in 1916.[liii]

Under Douie's guidance the library was upgraded. In October 1904 the Magazine reported the completion of the inner room bookshelves at a cost of £30. With shelf-holders on movable metal rods books of various sizes could be accommodated, and the shelves had handles which allowed dusting without disturbing the books. The inner room held about 1200 books,[23] and had a large desk for atlases. Subsequently, for £53, shelving was completed in the outer room.[24] Past and present students paid most of the cost.[liv] The Magazine for May 1910 reported that the library had been re-arranged, and re-catalogued.

---

[22] In July 1974 Council agreed to pay £200 to restore Sophia's grave plus an annual payment for maintenance.

[23] On biology, chemistry, physics, anatomy, physiology, materia medica, medicine, O & G, & forensic medicine.

[24] On surgery, pathology, bacteriology, hygiene, diseases of eye, ear and throat, & kindred subjects.

Fig 7.3 Jex-Blake grave at Rotherfield

On 16 December 1907 Council granted Mary Douie six months sick leave and accepted her resignation as librarian. Winifred Cullis stood in for her as librarian and Elizabeth Courtauld as Secretary and Warden.[25] Douie returned in September 1908 but was still unwell and resigned to go to India. Courtauld helped out again. Baines, the assistant secretary, declined promotion so the Vice-dean and Hon. Sec.[26] agreed to help with secretarial work. In December Louie Melita Brooks[27] was appointed as LSMW's Secretary (and later as Warden and Secretary). From 1913 Douie was Secretary of the South London Hospital for Women; before that she spent three years in Canada as secretary to Professor Brodie who had left LSMW for the chair of physiology in Toronto in November 1908.

On 29 January 1913 Council considered ways of improving the annual report and decided that, as well as an alphabetical list, it should include a topographical list of old students to make it easy for an alumna to find whether any others lived in a city or country which she might be visiting. The first such list appeared in 1914. Council also resolved that a list of original papers and other publications from School departments should henceforth be inserted in annual reports. In 1913 nine publications were listed (5 by Wood-Jones, 2 by Chambers, 1 by Cullis & Tribe, and 1 by Leetham, a B.Sc. research student). There were another nine in 1914, but only five in 1915.[lv]

Council And The School Committee

During Cock's deanship there were inevitably changes in the membership of Council, the School Committee and the 'Members of the School'. Two of LSMW's leading supporters – Sir Joshua Fitch[28] and Helen Prideaux's father – died in 1903. Two years later Henry Henderson, the School's solicitor, resigned after ten years as Hon. Treasurer; he died in 1906. His son Malcolm took his father's place on Council and as Hon. Treasurer, a position he held until called for military service in June 1916. Mrs Bernard Shaw joined the School Committee in February 1906, but within a year she resigned and also relinquished her place on Council.[lvi]

Although officially there was no 'Chairman of Council' after Stansfeld's retirement in 1891 Council agreed in February 1906 to elect a chairman annually.[29] Holroyd Chaplin[30] served until January 1913. Francis Dyke Acland then took over

---

[25] Courtauld was on prolonged leave from the Wesleyan Mission Hospital in Madras,

[26] Aldrich-Blake & Isabel Thorne.

[27] Assistant secretary to the Principal of Bedford College

[28] Fitch was a former Chief Inspector of Training Colleges, and a noted educationalist.

[29] From 1907 the Chairman was identified in the Annual Report.

[30] His sister, Matilda, studied with Isabel Thorne at the Female Medical College and at Edinburgh. His daughter Phyllis married EGA's nephew, Philip Cowell, an astronomer responsible for the Tide Tables.

as chairman, having been on Council only a year. He proved an ideal choice. Aged 39, he was MP for Cambourne and Under-Secretary of State for Foreign Affairs, Like his father,[31] he was interested in education and was well connected. From 1906-1908 he was Parliamentary Private Secretary to Haldane, who was to chair the Royal Commission on University Education in London (see earlier).

Council almost always approved the School Committee's recommendations but in September 1903 they disagreed over the award of the Mabel Webb research scholarship.[lvii] The Committee, by 6 to 5, favoured Monica Robertson over Janet Lane-Claypon. Robertson wanted to work on haematological changes in pulmonary tuberculosis – without supervision and away from scientific centres. Council pointed out that Lane-Claypon, a brilliant student and a gold medallist in physiology, wished to join Starling at UCL to study both the relationship of haemoglobin to oxygen and the action of ferments. The Committee gave way. Lane-Claypon's subsequent career, even as a student, fully justified Council's stand. In 1904 she won a BMA research scholarship, was awarded a D.Sc. in 1905, graduated MB in 1907 and MD in 1910. In 1912, in the first epidemiological study to use retrospective cohort design and the t-test, she established that breast fed babies gained more weight than those fed boiled cow's milk.[lviii]

School and Hospital Staff

In 1904 Stanley Boyd resigned his anatomy lectureship after 22 years; he remained active in School affairs and replaced Mrs Starling on Council in 1905. Frederick Guymer Parsons of St Thomas' Hospital taught anatomy at LSMW for seven years, and when he resigned in 1912 Frederic Wood-Jones became a whole time lecturer and head of the department.

In September 1903 Brodie was appointed Superintendent of the Brown Animal Sanatory Institution and Professor of Physiology at the Royal Veterinary College. He delegated a third of his work at LSMW to Winifred Cullis, a demonstrator since 1901. She succeeded him as lecturer when he left for Toronto in 1908, the year she was awarded a D.Sc.

Lucy Boole resigned her chemistry lectureship in 1897 but, despite poor health, continued to direct practical classes. After she died in December 1904, aged 42, her assistant, Sybil Widdows, ran them. Clare de Brereton Evans succeeded Boole as head of chemistry; and when she left in 1912 J. Addeyman Gardner took over. Mudge and Edith Stoney taught biology and physics respectively throughout Cock's time as dean. Mary Waller, Augustus Waller's daughter, was appointed demonstrator in physics in 1912.

[31] Sir Arthur Dyke Acland, 13th Baronet.

While Cock was Dean she and J. Walter Carr were co-lecturers on Principles & Practice of Medicine. Carr and Harrington Sainsbury co-lectured on Clinical Medicine but when the latter retired in 1913 all the physicians and assistant physicians shared the teaching of the subject. To mark Sainsbury's retirement students, past and present, gave him a 1481 edition of Dante's *Divina Commedia*![32,lix]

The physician Crawfurd (later Sir Raymond) left RFH in 1908 for KCH, then near Lincoln's Inn Fields, but he taught Materia Medica at LSMW until Frederick Ransom was appointed as 'Pharmacology' lecturer.[33] Ransom, unlike Crawfurd, needed a laboratory for research. Phear replaced Crawfurd as physician.[34] Branson replaced Phear as assistant physician. Farquhar Buzzard, an assistant physician/neurologist, moved to St Thomas' Hospital in December 1910; Frederick Langmead replaced him at RFH until 1913. [35, lx]

The surgeons Barrow and Berry were co-lecturers on both Practice of Surgery and Clinical Surgery. When Roughton replaced Barrow as surgeon and lecturer in 1904, Joseph Cunning joined Percy Legg as assistant surgeon. When Berry stopped teaching Clinical Surgery in 1911 Roughton carried on alone until November 1912 – seven months before his death from intestinal cancer. Roughton was also throat, nose and ear surgeon at RFH; John Gay French joined him as assistant surgeon in that specialty in 1911 and took his place in 1913. Louisa Aldrich-Blake and Wilmott Evans (who also taught dermatology)[36] then became co-lecturers for Practice of Surgery and, as with the physicians, all the surgeons and assistant surgeons lectured on Clinical Surgery. The assistant surgeon Percy Legg was promoted to surgeon in 1907 but resigned in 1913. Cunning was made fifth surgeon in 1911; Charles Pannett replaced him as assistant surgeon.[lxi]

No women were appointed as general physicians or surgeons during Cock's deanship but only women were appointed as anaesthetists, obstetricians and gynaecologists – with one exception. After Aldrich-Blake relinquished the post in 1904 Arthur Levy served as anaesthetist for a year or so, together with Mrs Dickinson-Berry.[lxii]

Mrs Ethel Vaughan-Sawyer[37] succeeded Scharlieb as physician for diseases of women at RFH in 1908, and lectured on gynaecology after Florence Nightingale

[32] How times have changed!

[33] The title 'Materia Medica' was changed to 'Pharmacology' in 1909.

[34] Phear was an assistant physician from 1901.

[35] Sir Farquhar Buzzard was Regius Professor of Medicine at Oxford from 1928. Langmead worked at several hospitals. From 1921 he was one of the first full time professors of medicine in England as head of the Professorial Medical Unit at St Mary's Hospital Medical School.

[36] In those days dermatology was considered as primarily a surgical specialty.

[37] Ethel Vaughan (MB 1896) married Captain Henry Sawyer (23rd Sikh Pioneers) in 1907; earlier he lost an arm after a struggle with a panther. Before marriage he became Vaughan-Sawyer by deed poll so Ethel would not lose her own identity. He was killed in action in October 1914.

Boyd's death in 1910. Scharlieb lectured on midwifery until 1913; her replacement, Mrs Florence Willey, had been assistant physician for diseases of women since 1908.

Charlotte Ellaby, lecturer in ophthalmic surgery, died in 1910 after a long illness. Her replacement Percy Flemming, like Ellaby, worked at the New Hospital where his wife, (Emily Wood, MB 1891) was a physician;[38] he also worked at UCH and Moorfields. The ophthalmic surgeon Henry Work Dodd retired in 1913; Malcolm Hepburn, his replacement at RFH, took Flemming's lectureship in 1914.

'Electricity' and X-Rays

Florence Stoney started the Electrical Department in April 1902, and in the Magazine for January 1903 she wrote that it had taken some time to get it into working order, '*but now the X-Rays are available twice a week,…and…patients are treated by electricity with the constant or interrupted current as required*'. Initially 'everyone' was meant to be able use the 'Roentgen Ray apparatus' but within days it was out of action; subsequently it was locked up and only those who understood how to work it had access to it. Stoney commented that with '*a delicate electrical instrument connected with an electric main with over 200 volts it does not do to blindly turn one handle after another and observe results.*'

In 1903 Stoney passed control of the department to the medical registrar, Miss Murrell, who took over the 'batteries', and to the surgical registrar, Florence Willey, who dealt with x-rays. In 1905 Adeline Roberts (MB 1898) replaced Murrell as Medical Registrar and Electrician, and Frances Ivens (MB 1900) took over as Surgical Registrar and Radiographer.[lxiii]

In 1904 Stoney resigned as anatomy demonstrator, owing to the claims of private practice, but continued as radiologist to the NHW, became a member of the Röntgen Society, and lectured on anatomy at Madame Osterberg's Physical Training College.

The two posts were combined again in 1906 when G. Harrison Orton was appointed 'Radiographer and Medical Electrician', thus unifying the posts held by Roberts and Ivens. Orton qualified in 1901; before joining RFH he had worked in the electrotherapeutic department at Bart's, and as radiographer at the National Hospital for Diseases of the Heart. He left in 1912 to head the radiology department at St Mary's. His replacement Ernest Ulysses Williams remained head of the X-ray department at RFH until 1947.

When Andrewes resigned as lecturer in Pathology in 1909, owing to pressure of work at Bart's, LSMW students presented him with Zeiss binoculars and antique

[38] Their son, Cecil, was later an orthopaedic surgeon at UCH.

silver. His replacement, Leonard Dudgeon of St Thomas', lasted a year or two and then Walter D'Este Emery, of KCH and Paddington Green, took over until 1917. None of the three worked at RFH where, from 1902 to 1912, the assistant physicians Phear, Buzzard and Langmead acted as 'pathologists'. They were assisted by LSMW graduates in the roles of clinical and/or assistant pathologist & curator of the museum. One of them, Helen Chambers became the 'pathologist' in 1913.[lxiv]

Mercier, lecturer on Mental Pathology for almost twenty years, resigned in 1907 and gave way to T. B. Hyslop, the Superintendent of Bethlem, where LSMW students attended classes. After about four years Hyslop was replaced as lecturer by William Stoddart, another Superintendent of Bethlem, who had married its Matron.

Throughout Cock's time as Dean the two components of 'Forensic Medicine and Toxicology' were taught, in alternate years, by Charles Hawthorne[39] (Forensic Medicine) and Wilson Hake (Toxicology). Tropical Medicine and Public Health lectures were also scheduled in alternate years. Sir Patrick Manson lectured on the former for fifteen years, resigning in 1912; his successor was Charles Daniels, a physician at the Hospital for Tropical Diseases. William Simpson continued to lecture on Public Health throughout Cock's deanship.

Student Matters

In December 1904 delegates from the University's various colleges formed a Students' Representative Council – to promote and represent the general interests of students, to liaise with University authorities, and to promote social and academic unity among colleges. The concomitant changes in student affairs at LSMW were described by Dorothy Hare in the Magazine of May 1905. A post called 'Students' Representative' had been introduced in 1898 to facilitate communication with the Dean, and the incumbent had worked closely with the School and Hospital 'Common Room' committees handling such matters as stationery and lockers. These committees were now given extended responsibilities; their members became proper representatives of their fellow students and worked even more closely with the Students' Representative. To match their new status the term 'Common Room' was dropped. The combined 'School' and 'Hospital' committees became the 'Students' Council', a representative parliament for discussion of school affairs, which organized the various clubs and societies and appointed LSMW's delegate to the University's Representative Council. The 'Students' Council', like the 'Students' Representative', was a brainchild of its President, the Dean, who wanted the students

[39] Hawthorne worked at several hospitals, including Hampstead General.

trained in citizenship. Dorothy Hare was a 'Students' Representative'; after graduating in 1905 she presented the Common Room with a grand piano, and for many years paid to maintain it.

In November 1905 students agreed that the person heading the poll for the six members of the School Committee should become its secretary. Two of the others would run the Tea Club, and the remaining three were to supervise the dressing-rooms and the Common Room library, and deal with newspapers. The system was not perfect; at the students' AGM in 1906 there were complaints about the Tea Club, and about untidiness and lack of cleanliness in the Common Room.[lxv]

The Debating Society flourished. Early in 1903 its 'political branch' met as 'L(RFH)SMW's Parliament' – with a constitution, 'Speaker' and 'Clerk of the House'. It debated the motion 'That popular control of Education as re-organised by the Education Bill does not tend to promote the intellectual progress of the country'. Miss Douie, 'MP for the University of Edinburgh', led for the Government, supported by the 'Home Secretary' (Miss Guest); Miss Tchaykowsky, 'MP for Battersea', led the opposition. The motion was rejected.

The subjects of some other debates remain topical. In a challenge debate in 1905 a Bedford College student proposed 'That Pauper Alien Immigration should be prohibited'. Constance Colley (LSMW) opposed the motion and prevailed by three votes. In March 1906 Miss Douie and Mary Parsons argued 'That the granting of the suffrage to women is both just and expedient'. Dr. Brodie, the token male, opposed the motion along with Hazel Cuthbert (later Mrs Chodak-Gregory); it was carried almost unanimously. In October 1912 'That the Nationalisation of the Medical Profession is highly desirable' was carried by eighteen votes.

In 1903 a Social Problems Society, founded at LSMW in 1901, listened to talks on 'Modern Hooliganism' and 'The Sanitary Aspect of the Housing Problem'. G. K. Chesterton and the educational reformer Margaret McMillan spoke at a lecture series on 'Socialism'. Meetings of the 'Social Problem and Debating Society' in the spring of 1908 suggest that the two groups merged for a while. On 13 February over 200 heard George Bernard Shaw speak on 'Socialism and the Medical Profession'. His disparaging comments about doctors upset some in the audience, but were hardly unexpected from the author of *The Doctor's Dilemma*. In March 1911 a 'suffrage meeting' discussed the women's movement; the speakers[40] were from the 'London Graduates' Union for Women's Suffrage' which participated in another meeting at LSMW in November 1912.

The Christian Union remained active. From 1903 its members visited patients in their homes but the Dean, while not objecting, thought their spare time would

[40] The speakers were Dr. Fraser (on legal aspects), Dr. Flora Murray (on the political situation) and Dr. Louisa Garrett Anderson, whose mother was vice-president of the Union.

be better spent in recreation. Many Magazine items indicated LSMW students' concern for the poor and disadvantaged. In May 1906 Sir John Gorst, a campaigner on behalf of children, discussed the formation of a 'Crèche Society' – to promote day nurseries for the children of women compelled to work to support their families. In May 1909 the Magazine suggested that students, although busy, might provide small local services to help those in need, e.g. reading to blind women or crippled children, or home visiting to check whether children took medicines ordered for them.

The Dramatic Society, founded in 1896, put on 'Theatricals' at parties, particularly at Xmas. It occasionally opted for grander productions such as Sheridan's 'The Rivals' (1904) and 'The Critic' (1907), and Beaumont's 'The Knight of the Burning Pestle' (1910); the profits from these went to the Students' Endowment Fund which, every three years, gave RFH a lump sum to support two or three beds.

A Royal Free Hospital Musical Society was first mentioned in the Magazine of May 1904 after its performance of 'Hiawatha's Wedding Feast' in March; men were recruited for tenor and bass parts. Its president was Arthur Phear, physician at RFH since 1901 and an outstanding pianist.[lxvi] It held concerts and 'At Homes', and sang carols at various hospitals at Christmas.

The Dance Club was founded in January 1911, mainly through the efforts of Mary Lucas (later Professor Lucas-Keene). At that year's prize giving Garrett Anderson expressed her delight about the club and expressed the wish it could meet nightly rather than monthly! Initially its twenty-five members brought partners, and sometimes other guests. Membership was later increased to twenty-eight, of whom five could be qualified if they had joined as students. A weekly class for Morris Country Dances was held in 1913; it is not clear how long it survived.

The Garden Society was active, but still in conflict with the Tennis Club over the area around the court. (Fig 7.4) In 1904 the 'gardeners' placed wire netting along borders damaged by tennis players and their balls, and provided special tools for reaching balls in the flower beds. From 1911 the Society gained representation on the Students' School Council. That year several keen gardeners arrived and many plants and bulbs were put in during the autumn; even so the Magazine of July 1912 stated the garden was in a bad way. To raise money for it a 'Box Social' was held. Each member brought a box that held supper for two and placed her name inside; the boxes were then auctioned and on opening them the purchasers found the names of their supper partners. The proceeds, over eight pounds, paid for new soil and garden feed. The flowers were better in 1913 and with a grant from Council many more plants were purchased.

Fig 7.4 Tennis in the Quadrangle

A Royal Free Hospital Medical Corps was formed in October 1912. It was to train officers capable of running Voluntary Aid Detachments of the St. John Ambulance Association; members were to be registered by the War Office and, if a war started, they would care for the sick and wounded and transport them between field ambulances and general hospitals. Only qualified women, clinical students, or pre-clinical students holding St. John First Aid and Home Nursing Certificates could enrol as full members; other students could attend and enrol on reaching Hospital. Initially the Corps had 19 full members (and 12 others) who had to sign on for a year and attend at least eighteen times. The Magazine of July 1913 described attendance as disgraceful and reminded members that theirs was the only corps receiving a grant from the St. John Ambulance Association for drill instruction. The Hon. Sec was Helen Mackay.[41]

'Parades' in the Territorial Hall in Handel Street usually involved a drill, followed by a lecture from Captain Humphreys, RAMC. Willmott Evans, an RFH surgeon, taught bandaging. Miss Ada Browne of Belsize Park, a former student who had been involved in forming the Corps, arranged riding classes at the Albany Street Barracks; six lessons cost 18 shillings. In June 1913 eleven members joined

[41] In 1934 the first woman elected FRCP.

Captain Humphreys and Miss Browne at the Welsh Harp to practise camp marking, tent pitching, and the collection of wounded on stretchers. By 1914 the group was called the Officers Voluntary Aid Training Corps. Membership increased markedly, but many senior members resigned before receiving the 'Commandant's certificate'. Mrs. Alton, a well-known shot, arranged firearms instruction with the College Hall Rifle Club.

One perk for LSMW students was the holiday home which Mrs. Garrett Anderson made available at Aldeburgh. In the Magazine of May 1909 Evelyn Constable described a holiday there – with boating, bathing, 'hunting for cornelians and amber' on the beach, delightful walks, and golf on Aldeburgh's excellent course (founded by EGA's husband Skelton Anderson). A year later no others had stayed there and Constable warned that while EGA welcomed student visitors she would not keep the house open if it was not used; students should repay her kindness by visiting Aldeburgh. Over the years the offer may have involved two different properties. Constable said it stood in its own grounds, five minutes from the sea, and had six bed-rooms and a palatial living room; but a single page 'flyer', offering use of a house rent free,[42] described two sitting rooms and three single bedrooms.

Sports Clubs

Sport flourished at LSMW during Cock's deanship although some clubs had problems. The Hockey Club lost its ground at Shepherd's Bush to builders in 1904. For seven years it tried other grounds. Some were unplayable in poor weather; one was prohibitively expensive: another became a building site. Money was a problem. Membership seldom exceeded 35 and in 1904 the subscription, 7s 6d, the highest for any LSMW club, just covered the ten guineas rent at Shepherd's Bush. Suitable grounds cost £15 to £35 a year. By 1909 the club could not raise two XIs, but for the 1911-12 season it used grounds at Hampstead and Regent's Park. More fixtures were arranged and the subscription was lowered to attract more players. Regent's Park was initially considered a great success but problems arose with its superintendent. The club yearned for a ground of its own.

Tennis players had the gravel court at Hunter Street for matches between School and Hospital students, and those between students and staff (which were primarily social occasions). However, the Tennis Club needed a grass court to host matches with other clubs. In 1904 it paid £2 a year for one at Regent's Park Square Gardens, but it was a poor court and was little used. The relaying of the gravel court in 1907 left the

[42] The house was mainly intended for weekends, or short holidays of up to 10 days. Applicants had to state whether 1, 2, or three ladies wished to come, the dates preferred and the length of stay. They had to supply their own food and (if a party of three) paid one shilling a day per head for service, breakages, lamp oil, candles, coals & household laundry.

club in debt for several years; membership had fallen and so subscriptions, at six shillings a year, did not cover expenditure. When re-gravelling was done again in 1911 the School paid for it. Membership rose and subscriptions were used to buy new netting.

The Swimming Club, founded in 1895, was dormant for some years but awoke in 1909. Members used Marylebone Baths on Friday evenings. The club soon had thirty members. The two club days were Fridays at Marylebone Baths, and Wednesdays at Highgate Pond. The club swam against UCL, and competed in London's Intercollegiate Championship (against Bedford, UCL, Holloway and King's). In June 1910 Miss Blandy won the Inter-Collegiate Championship Cup, while Forrester-Brown won the ladies' race at London University's Swimming Gala, Blandy coming second. Friday sessions switched to the Prince of Wales Road baths in 1911. In 1913 the great event at the club's annual gymkhana was a race between staff and Hospital and School students; Stoney, Waller, Blair, Davies-Colley and Gazdar represented the staff.

The Fencing Club started in 1903 with sixteen members.[43] M. Dreese of Stempel's Gymnasium taught them weekly. Because lessons were expensive there was no subscription; a small entrance fee paid for equipment. Standards improved and although there were only six members, including one from the Slade School of Art, two of them entered a competition for ladies in January 1907. Within three years fencing was one of the most important of the School clubs. In 1911 some classes took place in the garden instead of the physics laboratory. After the club's AGM in June past and present club members participated an open-air fencing display with a group of ladies from 'Bertrand's Fencing Academy' including two ex-champions of England. Aldrich Blake presented a challenge cup for annual competition between members. In 1912 a team competed in the Intersalle Ladies' Challenge Cup. Unfortunately they drew Bertrand's Academy in the first round and lost every bout. The following year they again drew the eventual winners!

The Boating Club started in 1904 with 18 members. The *Magazine* for October 1905 reported it was flourishing, had raced against pairs from Bedford College and UCL, and that energetic members could practise sculling in Regent's Park during the winter. It invited applications for a cox – '*the advantages offered being a cushioned seat, light work, and an opportunity to improve the vocabulary.*' There were 21 members in 1906 with two new racing boats on Regent's Park Lake. Enthusiasm then waned but revived in 1911.

A Chess Club and Badminton Club were founded during Cock's deanship. The former started in November 1904 with fourteen members and three boards; life-membership cost 1s. 6d. At its first match, held a year later at Miss Stoney's house,

[43] A fencing *class* had been introduced in 1898.

St. George's Hospital triumphed by two games to one. Badminton began in May 1906 with twenty members. The club soon lapsed; fortunately, to save money, it had borrowed the stands and net. It was revived in 1917.

Inaugural Addresses

Each academic year started with an opening ceremony at which a distinguished person gave an inaugural address. The speakers included former students (Mary Murdoch in 1904 & Jane Walker in 1912); past or present members of School or Hospital staff (Roughton 1910 & and Professor Schäfer 1913; members of the Association (Millicent Fawcett 1909); and prominent outsiders such as Professor Sir J. W. Byers of Belfast (1906) and Sir Charles Lukis, the Director General of the Indian Medical Service (1913). Byers, professor of midwifery at Queen's College, Belfast, had a personal interest in the problems facing medical women. His mother (née Annie Reay Barker) was at Edinburgh with Jex-Blake, graduated MD Paris in 1877, and registered with the KQCPI diploma in 1878.

Sir Henry Butlin's inaugural address in 1911 was read by the Dean. Butlin, then President of the Royal College of Surgeons, was suffering from laryngeal tuberculosis and died months later.[lxvii] Forty-six years earlier he led a campaign by fellow students to prevent Ellen Colborne's admission to Bart's.[lxviii] Now he bemoaned the dearth of women in medical research. The BMA allocated money annually to provide research workers with expenses. Julia Brinck (LSMW; LRCPI 1886) received such an award in 1890, but just three other women had benefited in that way and only about one per cent of the total amount allocated went to women. Lane-Claypon had been the sole recipient of a BMA research scholarship, but held it for just one year as she was still medically unqualified. Cambridge's Brown Scholarship went to a woman in 1909. Twelve women had applied for Beit Fellowships; three were successful – one in 1910 and two in 1911. But Butlin was optimistic; he thought more women were showing an interest in research and that committees and trustees looked favourably at their applications.

The other social event involving a formal speech was the annual prize-giving in June. A man usually gave the address if a woman presented the prizes, and when the Duchess of Marlborough did so in 1906 the speaker was Sir Benjamin Franklin, one of Lukis's predecessors as Director General of the IMS. The choice of Lukis and Franklin as speakers reflected the close links between LSMW and the medical system in India.

The national press usually covered the opening ceremony and the prize-giving – the space allocated depending on the stature of the speaker. There was wide coverage in July 1907 when William Osler, Oxford's Regius Professor of Medicine, presented the prizes. Given the difficulties many in his audience had faced when trying to establish themselves in the profession Osler's address was somewhat patronizing – especially his comment that medicine was a satisfactory profession for women if they realised it was not all roses and ice-cream and that they would not get a pecuniary return for everything they did. Osler suggested that the four principal avenues open to medical women were in sciences like bacteriology, histology and pathology; in institutions (e.g. working in asylums) or inspecting schoolchildren; in India and the mission field; and in general practice, especially in dealing with diseases of women and children. Apropos the last he suggested that while women did not believe much in male doctors they believed far less in women. His address hit the national press but received little coverage in the School's magazine and was not mentioned in Council's annual report. Osler, a Canadian, had opposed entry of women into the profession, both in Canada, and at Johns Hopkins University in Baltimore where women were admitted to its medical school from the start only because a gift from Mary Garrett (no relation to EGA) of over $300,000 was contingent on their admission on equal terms with men.[lxix]

Osler may have sensed his remarks went down badly. He invited ten LSMW students to spend a day with him at Oxford on 14 November 1907. He demonstrated patients at the Radcliffe Infirmary, and showed them his famous library at his home in 13 Norham Gardens. His guests were delighted.[lxx] Two years later the Oslers befriended Gertrude Flumerfelt, a young Canadian who studied at LSMW from 1907. In 1910, wishing to attend a co-educational school, she transferred to Manchester; there she met her future husband, a young anatomy demonstrator who was to became the outstanding neurosurgeon, Sir Geoffrey Jefferson. While at LSMW Gertrude was the 'Flower Secretary', responsible for the floral arrangements in the common room,[lxxi] and was one of the first women to pass the anatomy and physiology examinations of the Conjoint Examining Board of the Royal Colleges of Physicians and Surgeons.

Other items related to LSMW and RFH appeared in the national press. Sophia Hickman (LSMW, LRCPSEd 1902) disappeared in mid-August 1903 – the day after starting as a locum at RFH. Two boys found her body in the Sidmouth Plantation in Richmond Park on 18 October. Although apparently treated for 'heart weakness' no cause of death was forthcoming at the inquest.[lxxii] The death certificate stated 'poisoning by morphine sulphate, self-administered at a time when she was temporarily insane'. Before she was found, 'A Hospital Physician' wrote to *The Times* suggesting that the stress of working at RFH caused her to disappear and argued that women should not be appointed at general hospitals.[lxxiii] Women doctors obviously rejected his comments. Hickman may have been a locum for Katherine

Chamberlain,[44] whose appointment as house physician at RFH was announced in the *Daily News* of 3 April 1903. Katherine married a young ophthalmologist, Nathaniel Bishop Harman, later president of the BMA;[lxxiv] their elder daughter, Elizabeth Pakenham, Countess of Longford, was the mother of the author Antonia Fraser.

There was another bizarre death on 11 May 1910. Lyndall Rice, a first year student, died at home in High Wycombe from ingestion of prussic acid, which she was said to have acquired to kill a cat she wished to dissect. At the inquest an open verdict was reached, Mudge, the biology lecturer, having gone to great trouble to prevent a verdict of suicide.[lxxv]

While dead animals may have been dissected live animals were relatively safe at LSMW for forty years. Several of the School's strongest supporters were ardent anti-vivisectionists and their influence had led the physiologist Dupuy to resign within weeks of the opening of LSMW. (See Chapter 3) However, in 1912, following a Royal Commission report supporting vivisection subject to legal control,[lxxvi] the GMC encouraged teaching of 'experimental physiology' in medical schools. Council therefore decided, early in 1913, to convert the workshop into an animal house. Premises had to be registered with the Home Office for animal experiments, and someone licensed to conduct them. Mrs Enid Tribe, B.Sc., was granted a licence in January 1914.[lxxvii]

LSMW had another link with the anti-vivisection story. Two Swedish women, Emelie Augusta Louise (Lizzy) Lind af Hageby and Leisa Katarina Schartau, enrolled in 1902 to study physiology. This allowed them to attend animal experiments at UCL and at Waller's University Physiology laboratory. They were fervent anti-vivisectionists. In a book describing the experiments they claimed the first one they witnessed, conducted by Bayliss at UCL on 2 February 1903, was on an unanaesthetized brown dog struggling in agony.[lxxviii] Stephen Coleridge of the National Anti-vivisection Society read their account in public; Bayliss sued him for libel and won. Other LSMW students, who testified for Bayliss, said the dog was anaesthetized. Lind af Hageby and Schartau withdrew their book and removed the libellous paragraphs.[lxxix]

Gradually, if somewhat belatedly, new technology made the School staff's work a little easier. RFH used typewriters from 1902 but the first evidence of typewritten material generated within the School is an attachment accompanying the minutes of Council's meeting on 12 October 1910; the minutes themselves were not typed

[44] Katherine was the niece of the Colonial Secretary, Joseph Chamberlain.

until February 1934.[45] A Roneo duplicating machine was acquired in March 1912, and that December Alfred Langton, chairman of RFH's Weekly Board, gave the School £100 to buy an epidiascope. Other new technology was imported on special occasions. At the pathologists' evening reception, held at LSMW in February 1911, the highlight was an exhibition of Pathé Fréres' Scientific Cinematograph Films that included images of spirochaetes and trypanosomes moving and multiplying, and of stomach movements visualized by X-Rays.[lxxx]

Cock's Illness and Death

Julia Cock developed breast cancer. According to her former student Louisa Woodcock, who certified her death, it was first noticed in 1910. Cock continued working. She last attended Council in March 1913, and the School Committee in June. Aldrich-Blake had received correspondence as 'acting Dean' since September 1912, and two months later joined RFH's Weekly Board in place of Cock. The Magazine for November 1913 reported 'Miss Cock is resigning the lectureship in Medicine on account of ill health'. She died aged 53, at Upton Farm in Ockham, Surrey, on 7 February 1914. Aldrich-Blake was elected Dean on 18 March.[lxxxi]

Cock was commemorated in several ways. In 1913, close to death, she provided funds for an annual award for proficiency in clinical medicine. Miss Steele designed for her a beautiful bronze 'Dean's Medal for skill in the Eye, the Ear, and the Hand in clinical medicine'.[46] The first winner, in 1914, was Jessie Eva Hart. In September 1915 Cock's executrix presented Council with £200 to endow the medal.

In June 1914 Edith Garrod presented LSMW with a portrait of Cock. The artist, Horace Field, was almost certainly the architect who connected 7 & 8 Hunter Street to the Pavilion in the early 1890s, and who subsequently designed a terrace of three houses in Gainsborough Gardens, Hampstead for Edith's father, the physician Sir Alfred Baring Garrod.[47] At Cock's wish, as expressed by her to Miss Garrod, the School also received a portrait of Helen Prideaux,[48] painted by Edward Clifford, along with some of Cock's furniture.[lxxxii]

A Julia Cock Memorial Fund was set up in June 1914; the money went to the School Extension Fund. The first floor of the extension was named after Cock.[lxxxiii]

---

[45] Remington marketed its first typewriter in the USA in 1874.

[46] I have been unable to find an example of one of the early medals. The design was changed later.

[47] Edith's brother, Archibald, succeeded Osler as Regius Professor of Medicine at Oxford.

[48] The Prideaux portrait, painted in 1886, was listed as being at RFH in 2004 in British & Irish paintings in *Public Collections*, eds. Wright, C. et.al, Yale University Press, 2006. There is a photograph of Prideaux by Frederick Hollyer in the Wellcome Collection.

(See Chapter 8) In 1924 Edith Garrod bequeathed £800 to be devoted to the foundation of a scholarship in Cock's name.[lxxxiv] (See Chapter 9)

Advance of Medical Women

During Cock's deanship more provincial medical schools opened to women. The University of Liverpool decided in 1903 that women could take any degree or course of study, but the first to graduate MBChB there was Phoebe Mildred Powell in 1911; she added the MD in 1912. Leeds and Sheffield started admitting women just before WW1. Augusta Umanski graduated from Leeds in December 1915.[lxxxv] Sheffield registered its first women medical students in 1909; the first to qualify, in 1916, were Lydia Henry and Florence Elizabeth Millard.[lxxxvi] But the willingness of the provincial medical schools to admit women was not reflected in London. There, before the war, LSMW still stood alone in admitting them.

During EGA's time the School's annual reports drew particular attention to jobs given to LSMW alumnae that could have been given to a man. During Cock's time they tended to stress the number of *resident* appointments obtained each year. Between 1904 and 1912 the figure varied from thirty to fifty (with a gradual upward trend) and some of the posts had previously been held only by men.

More 'public' appointments were also being made. In 1903 Alice Vowe Johnson, MD, DPH, FRCSI (clearly well qualified!) was selected as Medical Officer to the Lambeth Poor Law Schools at Norwood. Three years later the LCC appointed two former students as Medical Inspectors to its Secondary Schools, and in 1908 Mary Louisa Gordon was made an HM Inspector of Prisons, the first such appointment for a medical woman; she was medical officer at Holloway Prison while suffragettes were held there.[lxxxvii]

When Edith Shove retired as female medical officer to the Post Office in 1908 Treasury officials, who had cavilled at her original appointment, (see Chapter 5) tried to deny her the addition of seven years service for pension purposes in recognition of her professional qualifications; such an addition was standard practice for professional men.[lxxxviii]

About the same time a younger medical woman ran into problems with the Civil Service. An Interdepartmental Committee recommended systematic medical inspection of elementary school children in 1903 and Janet Campbell, an LSMW alumna,[49] was appointed an assistant school medical officer in London. In 1907 she became the Board of Education's first full-time woman medical officer and the following year was employed on a temporary basis, at £600 a year without

[49] MB London 1901, MD 1904, MS 1905.

increments, as an assistant to George Newman, the Chief Medical Officer of the Board of Education. Attempts to make the position permanent in 1910 were unsuccessful but in 1912 the Board managed to persuade the Treasury that she should be paid the same as men of her standing – but it refused to provide the immediate increment requested.[lxxxix]

Within the Civil Service such restrictions were commonly enforced on women with 'real' professional qualifications as they undermined the appropriation of professional expertise by men. The few women doctors, educationalists, and other specialists employed in the Civil Service were considered the thin edge of the wedge. Such attitudes affected Campbell until the end. When, as Dame Janet Campbell, she married in 1934 she was forced to give up work despite her immense contributions to the public health of the nation.

In March 1904 there was widespread disapproval when the Western Dispensary failed to ratify the appointment of Dr Ethel Vernon who, having been employed on a temporary basis in November 1903, had subsequently acted as an attendant medical officer to the institution. Apparently one of the honoraries, Allchin (later Sir William), also a physician at Westminster Hospital, was abroad when the appointment was made and threatened to resign if she was allowed to continue her work.[xc] Commenting on the event a distinguished female Harley Street practitioner told a *Daily News* reporter that there was 'now no general ill-feeling in the profession against women'; there were 'some objections at hospitals in the country' usually because 'there is only one common sitting-room for the doctors, and an old bachelor has refused to have his habits disturbed by the presence of some strange woman'.

When three years later the County Asylum at Fulbourn stopped appointing women to its resident staff the *Observer* of 8 September 1907 ran an article discussing attitudes to women doctors. It pointed out that there were women doctors at several English provincial towns in addition to the 172 in London: Sheffield had 12, Liverpool 11, Hull and Manchester 9, Birmingham 7, Bristol 6, Leeds 5, Nottingham 4 and Newcastle 3. It sought the opinion of Miss Douie, LSMW's Secretary & Warden, who said a woman setting up in a provincial town '*usually has no competitor of her own sex to fear, and without buying a practice she is pretty sure,…, to earn about £200 a year…*[after two years…then] *her income increases more rapidly, for it is in earning the first £200 in fees that the medical practitioner has the hardest struggle of his life'*.

While some employers would not take women doctors some tried to get them on the cheap! At the AGM of the Association of Registered Medical Women on 1 March 1910 May Thorne reported that the Vigilance Sub-Committee was taking action when advertisements appeared asking for medical women to fill appointments (generally as school doctors) at salaries below the BMA's approved minimum. With the BMA's support the salary had been raised in every case. The BMJ also helped; it refused to insert such advertisements, and published warning notices about the appointments.[xci]

While women doctors, in general, encouraged young women to join the medical profession some lay writers discouraged them. In 'Woman at Work' (1911) Mostyn-Bird stated that a career in medicine was suited to few women, and that 'of the large number who enter, only 20 per cent get as far as the final examination'. This was clearly erroneous; Miss Brooks responded that of the 86 per cent of LSMW students who obtained a medical qualification, 75 per cent qualified with the University of London degrees.[xcii]

In 1913 the School's annual report included for the first time, a topographical listing of the School's alumnae – their addresses having, for many years, been printed in a separate list in the annual report. Initially it included all women on the medical register, whether or not they had been students at LSMW. With the growth in the number of registered women the list was amended to include only women who had been educated wholly or partially at LSMW and/or RFH, and was subsequently amended again to 'all former students'.

In the list for 1914, the year of Cock's death, information was provided for 531 alumnae; 28 did not supply an address. Of the 390 located in Britain there were 363 in England (with 203 in London), 10 in Scotland, 9 in Wales and 3 in Ireland (i.e. before partition). Of the alumnae in the provinces there were 6 in Nottingham, 5 in Cheltenham, Liverpool and Manchester, and four in Brighton, Leeds and Leicester; four of these cities/towns had an institution staffed by medical women. Proximity to the work place was most striking in London, where 48 lived in Marylebone, relatively close to RFH and the New Hospital for Women.

Of the 141 living abroad the majority (76) were in the old 'India'. Of these the large majority were distributed in about forty towns situated in present-day India; there were 11 living in seven places now in Pakistan, and one was in Bangladesh. There were 17 in China, four in Australia, the Malay Peninsula and what is now Iran, 3 in New Zealand and Burma, and 1 in Korea, Baghdad and Palestine.

Although many British women doctors were still going abroad, particularly as missionaries, it was clear, despite pessimism in some quarters, that the number of jobs available to them at home was increasing, albeit slowly. However in most of these posts their work was restricted to dealing with clinical problems affecting women and children. This was soon to change. After the start of the First World War it was realised that well trained women doctors could play a valuable role in the war effort. As a consequence young women were actually encouraged to enter medical school, and it soon became clear that as practitioners they could perform as well as men in almost any clinical situation.

CHAPTER 8

Aldrich-Blake (1914-1918)

Women Doctors at War – LSMW Students at St Mary's

Louisa Brandreth Aldrich-Blake (Fig 8.1) became Dean in March 1914; she died in December 1925. As the early years of her deanship were dominated by the events of the First World War it seems appropriate to deal with them separately. Chapter 9 describes her 'Years of Peace'.

Fig 8.1 Aldrich-Blake in 1912

Louisa was born at Chingford Rectory on 5 August 1865. Her father was an Aldrich – a Suffolk family whose pedigree went back 250 years. When curate of St Martin-in-the-Fields, Trafalgar Square, he met and married Louisa Blake Morrison, a Scottish heiress. Her uncle, Lt. Col. Thomas Blake of Demerara, had stipulated in his will that her future husband should take the additional name of Blake. So Frederick Aldrich became the Reverend Aldrich-Blake.[i]

Within months of Louisa's birth the family moved to Welsh Bicknor in Herefordshire and built a new rectory overlooking the Wye Valley. Four more children arrived. From 1881 to 1884 Louisa attended Oak Hill, Great Malvern where her schoolmates considered her 'manly'. She was subsequently educated at Neuchatel, where her father had taught English as a young man, and at St Hilda's, Cheltenham, where friends called her 'Harry' and admired her 'gentlemanly' appearance. She was a strong and skilful boxer and a capable cricketer.[ii]

After entering LSMW in 1887 she lived at College Hall, Byng Place until 1896,[iii] and then rented 17 Nottingham Place, W 1 – her home until she died. She graduated MB Lond in 1892, with first-class honours in medicine and obstetrics – and BS in 1893, again with first-class honours. She added London's MD (1894) and in 1895 became the University's first female Master of Surgery (MS).[iv]

After qualifying she worked at RFH (curator of the museum & assistant anaesthetist) and then at NHW where she was in turn clinical assistant to out-patients & RMO, assistant surgeon (1895), surgeon (1902) and senior surgeon (1910). From 1912 she taught gynaecology at LSMW and was joint lecturer in surgery. At RFH she was the first woman to hold the posts of anaesthetist (1895 to

1906), and surgical registrar (1896 to 1898). From 1897 to 1920 she served on the staff of the Canning Town Women's Settlement Dispensary and Hospital.

She had a flair for financial matters having been introduced to the pleasures of accountancy by her father; she took lessons in the subject in 1908 and her familiarity with bookkeeping and balance sheets served her well when Dean.[v]

In 1914 LSMW was concerned about the inadequacy of its facilities for clinical education;[vi] but the Hospital's funds were low, as a new block was under construction (see below), and it was reluctant to consider further expansion. In May Council discussed whether to raise money to increase the RFH bed number to 400, or to approach the Great Northern Central Hospital about amalgamation.[1,vii] Within weeks, Alfred Langton (Fig 8.2) promised to provide half of the £27,000 needed to acquire the Eley site to the south of RFH,[2] and Council promptly offered to lend RFH £12,000 to expedite the purchase.[viii]

The School and Hospital agreed in February 1915 that within two years they would need more patients for teaching – preferably by extending RFH.[ix] Two months later Langton announced a gift to RFH of the Eley site; it emerged later that he bought it himself.[3,x] However, the onset of war on 4 August 1914 meant development of the site had to wait.

To expedite it an appeal was launched in 1916 and over £25,000 was raised in two years. However the decision was then made to delay building until £200,000 had been raised, so the appeal committee stood down in 1918. Another eight years elapsed before firm plans were made to begin work on the Eley site.[xi]

The war exacerbated the difficulty of providing students with clinical experience. The day after war was declared RFH offered 30 beds to the War Office and 20 to the Admiralty.[4] The former requested admission of wounded soldiers. Forty arrived by early November; twenty more were to be admitted if necessary. Initially students could not enter the soldiers' wards unless accompanied by the visiting staff or the RMOs; but in January 1915 the students were allowed access for a one month trial period. The wards remained open to them.[xii]

---

1 The Medical Committee thought amalgamation with the Great Northern Hospital difficult if not unworkable and that enlarging RFH was the only satisfactory solution.

2 The Eley site occupied just over an acre,

3 Following Langton's death it was estimated he donated about £150,000 to RFH, much anonymously.

4 The Admiralty did not reply; the offer was withdrawn in September 1915 as the War Office occupied all available beds.

Fig 8.2 Alfred Langton (1842-1927)

The new Helena Building, containing improved out-patient facilities and maternity beds,[5] was due to open in the summer of 1914 but labour disputes delayed completion. The War Office commandeered it, unfinished, in January 1915. On 11 May it opened as a hospital for wounded officers – with thick carpets and palm trees. (Fig 8.3) Clinical care was provided by RFH staff who were denied military

[5] 'Out-patients' was in the basement under Moore Ward & the old Casualty in the Porter's Lodge at the entrance to GIR. See 'Sister Wynn remembers' Mag Jul 1939, p14

Fig 8.3 Officers' Ward in Helena building

rank even though it was a military unit.[6] 'Other ranks' (i.e. 'soldiers' not 'officers') were accommodated in Wynn Ellis and Hopgood wards; these were needed for civilian patients but because the Helena building provided only 200 beds, not the 250 intended originally, the War Office was allowed to keep the forty beds already occupied.[xiii]

The officers' block was unavailable for teaching. In June 1915 Acland complained about this to Keogh, Director-General of the Army Medical Service (DGAMS). It was suggested soldiers should also occupy the new block as the students had access to soldiers, but the Hospital deemed it too difficult to accommodate officers and other ranks in the same building.[xiv]

As the war drew to a close the patience of RFH's staff's was sorely tested. Carr told the Medical Committee that the War Office's occupation of the Helena Building and two other wards prevented RFH from meeting both clinical demand and the educational needs of students. More pointedly, Berry said accommodating convalescent patients was a waste of public money and of available medical and surgical skills. When the War Office asked for even more beds in January 1918 RFH refused, but its staff offered help with more serious cases.[xv]

---

6 Gertrude Dearnley was the RMO to the Military Block.

In June 1918 RFH rejected a War Office request that it should treat Army nurses and QMAAC women of non-officer status rather than the remaining forty soldiers. In December LSMW's Academic Staff Association (ASA) suggested asking the War Office to evacuate the soldiers' beds but Council was reluctant to do so. It is unclear when those beds returned to civilian use. The last officer left on 8 April 1919. The officers' block had received 4128 patients, its average daily bed occupancy rising from about 60 in 1915 to 115 in 1918. After tedious negotiations over its reinstatement, disposal of equipment and liability for dilapidations, the Helena Building was released in May 1919 and was in use as an out-patient department before the end of the year.[xvi]

Because many male doctors and potential medical students joined the armed forces the national press encouraged women to train as doctors. Staff at the School, Cullis in particular, went out recruiting at girls' schools. After her visit to Queen Anne's, Caversham, two of its pupils, Geraldine and Frances Barry, enrolled at LSMW. When they graduated in 1922 Geraldine won the University Gold Medal. Applications to LSMW increased strikingly. It admitted 49 students in 1913-4, 77 in 1914-5, 128 in 1915-6, and a peak of 135 in 1916-17.[xvii]

The shortage of beds for teaching at RFH led four students Marian Bostock, Hetty Claremont, Helen Ingleby and Lizzie O'Flynn (all visible in Fig. 8.4, a group photograph taken in 1913-14) to transfer to St George's Hospital.[7] On leaving RFH Ingleby wrote to Miss Brooks '*there is not sufficient opportunity for clinical work for the number of students at present at the Royal Free. It is however, with some regret that I take this step for I had hoped, even though doing a part of my work at another hospital, I might still remain a student at the Royal Free and could return there when it had expanded sufficiently to accommodate the increasing number of students. ... I should like to thank you personally for your kindness on many occasions…my loyalty & affection towards the School remains quite unaltered though the Royal Free* [Hospital] *was never able to rouse any such feelings.*'[xviii]

In May 1915 RFH's Medical Committee tried to prevent others moving elsewhere for their clinical course but Council pointed out that University regulations made it difficult to enforce such a stipulation, and that students could not be stopped moving somewhere else if that was their wish.[xix]

St George's Hospital (then at Hyde Park Corner) did not teach preclinical subjects. Its male students studied them at KCL, Oxford or Cambridge. Male preclinical students at KCL also went to King's College Hospital (which moved to

[7] Claremont (1909 entry) was secretary of LSMW's Fencing Club and a good tennis player; sadly she died in March 1924 aged about 32. O'Flynn joined LSMW from Edinburgh in 1914 to study for the primary FRCS.

Fig 8.4 Staff & Students c. 1913-14

Denmark Hill in 1913), Westminster Hospital, and Charing Cross Hospital (then near Trafalgar Square). When St George's accepted women for clinical training Halliburton, Dean of KCL's Medical Faculty, considered admitting them for preclinical subjects and asked for LSMW's views on the matter in June 1915.[8] Council replied that women's interests would be safeguarded only at a medical school open exclusively to women students.[xx]

In July 1916 Halliburton announced KCL would admit up to twenty women for preclinical studies in October.[xxi] It had amalgamated with King's College for Women in 1914 and almost all its classes were already open to women; anatomy was an exception only because its associated hospitals would not accept women. As St George's had broken ranks Halliburton hoped the other hospitals would follow suit; Charing Cross took women in 1916,[9] Westminster in 1917 and KCH in 1918.

These arrangements proved temporary, *The Lancet's* annual educational issue in 1916 stated that St George's was '*admitting a strictly limited number of women during the war; they would be allowed to continue their studies until qualification.*' The St George's entry for 1919 did not mention women students; it had stopped admitting them, as had other hospitals.

In December 1915 a Senate subcommittee was appointed to review London's facilities for women medical students. It found them inadequate and thought the

8 Halliburton had taught physiology at LSMW.

9 In July 1915 LSMW asked Charing Cross to admit women; it refused as did UCH, Guy's & Bart's.

problem acute and increasing. Urgent action was required but before making recommendations it wanted the opinion of people interested in the higher education of women or acquainted with provincial medical schools. In June 1916 LSMW was asked if it would provide clinical training for women studying pre-clinical subjects elsewhere in the University. It said 'yes', provided its own students had priority. Given RFH's inability to cope with students already at LSMW both the question and answer seem surprising, but the School's problems had just been eased – by help from an unexpected quarter.[xxii]

LSMW's Agreement with St Mary's

In February 1916 LSMW had asked RFH if, for teaching purposes, it could use beds at a hospital without a medical school, thinking it unlikely that any established teaching hospital other than St George's would take women students. It was mistaken. St Mary's Hospital Medical School was in desperate financial straits owing to the reduced student entry; young men were going to war – not to medical schools. Admitting women seemed the only remedy, but in December 1915 its Committee rejected that idea; instead it imposed a compulsory donation of £20 on members of staff – hardly a practical long term solution. A volte-face was inevitable and in February 1916 St Mary's offered to admit LSMW students.[xxiii]

At a meeting on 24 February St Mary's was represented by its Dean, Sir John Broadbent;[10] Austen Leigh, Chairman of the Hospital Board; Dr Wilfred Harris; a Mr Prideaux (not the Prideaux who helped LSMW); and Dr Graham Little, dermatologist and member of Senate. The School Secretary was in attendance. LSMW's representatives were Acland; the Dean; the Hon. Sec.; the Secretary; Mrs Waller (whose husband had worked at St Mary's); and the RFH physician J. Walter Carr. There was accord on the basics of the eventual legal agreement, which was to hold until September 1919; either side could terminate it then, or on 30 September in any year, by giving a year's notice. LSMW was not to send students to any other medical school; St Mary's would accept women only from LSMW. LSMW was to send ten students in May 1916, twenty by October, and a minimum of fifty by October 1917 – paying £21 per annum for each student (a fee raised to £23.16s within weeks following pressure from St Mary's). LSMW was to help pay for structural alterations needed to provide suitable quarters for women students. Its students were to be eligible for all prizes, medals, etc., awarded at St Mary's, which did not have to provide instruction in midwifery, vaccination or mental pathology, or lectures on gynaecology.[xxiv]

---

[10] Whose father helped LSMW to obtain teaching at the London Fever Hospital in 1878.

LSMW's School Committee wanted women to be eligible for resident appointments at St Mary's Hospital; Council did not demand this but sought assurance their applications would be considered. RFH's Medical Committee wanted students to attend St Mary's for the whole course, not just for clinical training. Council disagreed, but on approving the draft agreement on 5 April it showed solidarity with RFH by promising that if ever the Hospital wished to terminate the St Mary's agreement LSMW would join it in giving the notice required.[xxv]

The first women started at Paddington in May 1916. St Mary's soon wanted more money. In June it requested an annual payment for both its *Hospital Gazette* and for use of the common room and club refreshment room for which its male students paid five guineas; LSMW's Student's Union agreed to pay £10 per annum towards upkeep of the common room. In October a contribution for heating and lighting was requested; LSMW offered £20. Thus encouraged, St Mary's announced a pathological chemistry fee of one and a half guineas per student. LSMW contested this claim and won, but the relationship was now soured.[xxvi]

Transport between the two schools proved a problem, despite the underground railway connection between King's Cross and Paddington. In November 1916 it was agreed that students attending midwifery lectures at LSMW should return to St Mary's by bus or other suitable transport.

In December 1917 St Mary's complained that by October 1917 only 43 of the 50 students promised had turned up; three had already qualified; and one had abandoned her studies. LSMW sent an advance payment of £261, for eleven students due to transfer before September 1918. St Mary's then replied that there were 42 students during 1917 and that LSMW was £71 in credit.[xxvii]

In November 1917 Council, presumably concerned about rising student numbers, considered limiting LSMW's annual entry, but in March 1918 decided it should not fall below 128 – the average of the previous three years. This meant more clinical facilities were needed. St Mary's agreed LSMW could approach UCH, provided it received its own anticipated forty-five students. However, in June UCHMS was awaiting Senate's approval of clerkships and dresserships for male and female students at several specialist hospitals.[11] UCHMS admitted women that year, some coming from LSMW; so too did The London Hospital which became the most popular choice for students leaving LSMW.

Many LSMW women wanted to do their clinical training at St Mary's.[12] The autobiographies of Ida Mann[xxviii] and Octavia Wilberforce[xxix] describe their life

---

[11] In July LSMW also asked the University to recognise students' attachments to specialised hospitals.

[12] I found only one, Winifred Mary Jenkins, who asked to transfer back to RFH.[CM 1919: 25 Jun]

there. Marguerite Pam was one of the early transfers; Mann described her as '*South African provenance and related to Pressed Steel and Marmite and beer and in the money*'.[13] In 1918, the year she qualified, Pam married the brilliant young St Mary's pathologist, Edward Kettle. She became assistant editor of *The Lancet* the following year.[14]

Ida Mann, an expert on the comparative and pathological anatomy of the eye, had a glittering career. Appointed ophthalmologist to EGAH, RFH and Moorfields (where she was the first female senior surgeon), she moved in 1941 to Oxford and became its first woman professor the following year. Octavia Wilberforce, great-granddaughter of the anti-slavery campaigner, and friend of Leonard and Virginia Woolf, entered LSMW in 1913; on Pam's advice Wilberforce chose to go to St Mary's in October 1917.[15]

The increase in student numbers caused major problems at RFH but they had been anticipated at Hunter Street. Acland had pointed out in March 1914 that the unduly large entry expected that October would cause congestion in all departments in 1915, so Council decided to extend the School and began negotiations with the Foundling trustees. The lessee of the four Wakefield Street houses adjoining LSMW wanted £275 for his leases; the School offered £225 and settled for £335![xxx]

In June 1914 a School Extension Fund was set up with the Julia Cock Memorial Fund as its nidus. The first donation, £1000 from EGA, arrived within a day. The appeal went public in December and Sir Alan Anderson, Miss Adelaide Freeman, Lady Hall, Cullis, Scharlieb and a representative of RFH's medical committee joined its sub-committee (as later did Lady Cunard). The Duchess of Marlborough[16] was the fund's treasurer.

In February 1915 the Duchess ran an 'At Home' at Sunderland House, her London residence, with Sir Alfred Keogh as the main speaker. In June she held a reception at LSMW, and presided at a meeting at 133 Queens Gate, hosted by Miss Annabel Douglas; there the speaker was Sir Robert Morant, chairman of the National Health Insurance Commission.

The rich and famous followed the Duchess's example and raised funds at meetings all over the country. The Countess of Chichester and Mrs Arthur Wagg were hostesses at Hove. Sir Berkeley Moynihan addressed Dr Laura Veale's

13 Her brother Albert Pam was a rich man. Mann's 'South African' link may be misleading.

14 Pam committed suicide in 1939, three years after her husband died. Her only paper (as Kettle) was 'The fate of a population of women medical students' (Lancet 1936:2; 1370-4); it describes what happened to LSMW women who went to St Mary's.

15 Royal Free women apparently called each other by their surnames.

16 Born Consuela Vanderbilt of New York.

meeting at Harrogate. Miss Faithfull, Principal of Cheltenham Ladies' College spoke at the Duchess of Beaufort's meeting at Cheltenham. The Countess of Lytton (aunt of Ruth Balfour, an LSMW student) presided at 1 Fitzjohn's Avenue, Hampstead, home of the Debenhams (of department store fame). There the speakers were Sir William Osler and Acland, now Financial Secretary to the Treasury. Acland argued that as his department was spending £30 a second those present should spend their own money before the Government spent it for them. The meeting raised £300.[xxxi]

The Duchess of Marlborough, Lady Arthur Paget & Mr Alfred Butt (later Sir Alfred, head of the Theatre Royal, Drury Lane) organised a special matinée at the Palace Theatre in June. The famous vaudevillian Harry Lauder joined others to entertain a full house including the Queen and many wounded soldiers. Society ladies sold programmes, assisted by LSMW students dressed in gown and mortar-board. The event raised £1500.

Donations were solicited in a letter to the *Daily Telegraph* of 19 July 1915,[17] which read:

The War has constituted a turning-point in the position of medical women, and there are new openings and new opportunities for them in many directions.

Increasing numbers of women are desirous of entering the profession, and to provide for their adequate educational needs the London (Royal Free Hospital) School of Medicine for Women is now practically doubling its laboratory accommodation.

The Council of the School has already received £15,000 of the £30,000 required for the additional buildings and their equipment. We would direct your attention to the efforts started by a number of representative men and women to help to raise the remaining £15,000 by means of subscriptions of £1 each.'

The signatories were Prime Minister Asquith, former Prime Minister Balfour[18] and Lord Curzon.[19]

The letter was accompanied by a list of celebrities contributing £1 or more. A week later Dr and Mrs Beilby, Lady Cunard, Sir Algernon Firth and the Aga Khan headed a longer list. Lord Northcliffe published notices and lists of subscribers in *The Times*.[xxxii]

The appeal had its critics. In *The Hospital* of 13 November 1915 one claimed it served little purpose to try replacing men at war by expanding LSMW. The extra women students would not qualify for five years; by then the war would be over and the men back in civilian practice. He suggested that women students, who might later marry, should attend the men's schools that now lacked students.

---

[17] It also appeared later in other papers.

[18] Uncle of Ruth Balfour, an LSMW student.

[19] Former Viceroy of India.

The target of £30,000 for the extension was finally hit in June 1916 when Sir Arthur du Cros, head of the Dunlop Rubber Company, donated £7000.[xxxiii] He and his brothers pioneered the pneumatic tyre industry founded by their father in 1889, and were thus involved in the production of aeroplanes and ground transport (including ambulances). Sir Arthur, the Unionist MP for Hastings, was also active in recruiting and in the production of munitions.[xxxiv]

The architect put forward two schemes in July 1914; the one selected was costed at £15,000. In January 1916 Holliday & Greenwood, the builders, said they could not finish before October.[20] Further delay seemed inevitable; not only did a fire at the contractors' works destroy wooden laboratory fittings and many architect's drawings, but the Ministry of Munitions had to provide certificates authorising use of labour and materials.[xxxv]

The Queen opened the extension on 2 October 1916, six weeks before any part came into use; the contract was completed in August 1917.[21]

The opening ceremony was impressive.[xxxvi] By 2.30 p.m. there was a colourful display of academic dress in the long room. The procession of London University's Chancellor (Lord Rosebery) entered just before 3 p.m. Acland's young son carried the train of the Chancellor's gown.

The Dean, the Duchess of Marlborough, Acland and Miss Brooks received the Queen at the School's entrance. In the common room the Dean presented representatives from various groups;[22] they accompanied the Queen's procession to the long room where the audience joined a student chorus in singing the national anthem. Vanda Thomas, the Queen's Scholar,[23] presented Her Majesty with a bouquet and a beautiful key designed by Ashley, the architect.

The Dean outlined the School's history. Winifred Cullis spoke of the Queen's interest in medical women and singled out Mrs Garrett Anderson and Sir Arthur du Cros, as the first and last of the donors to the Extension Fund. Finally Acland read a telegram from May Thorne and 29 other former students then with the Royal Army Medical Corps in Malta. May Thorne was Hon. Sec. for almost all of Aldrich-Blake's time as Dean. Her absence on active service led her to submit her resignation in November 1917. It was not accepted and she remained in office until 1925.[xxxvii]

---

[20] As a result the new extension became the first at LSMW to be paid for before completion.

[21] The extension is described in *BMJ* 30 September 1916 & *Building News* 8 November 1916.

[22] Selected members of Council, the appeal committee, the student body and the medical staffs of RFH & St Mary's Hospital.

[23] The money for the Queen's Scholarship was part of a gift to the Queen from the wives of Freemasons wishing to help members of the professional classes in difficulty owing to the War.

Fig 8.5 North Wing

The new extension of 5250 sq. ft. formed the north side of the quadrangle. (Fig 8.5) Its basement contained the 'Consuela, Duchess of Marlborough, Physics Department', with laboratories, a lecture theatre and research rooms, together with a pathology research department complementing RFH's new pathology department. The ground floor held the "Maude du Cros" organic chemistry laboratory, a chemical research laboratory and the Students' Union room which, according to the Magazine of July 1917, served as smoking room, lounge, office, and committee room; it connected with the Hunter Street block common room via a colonnade, like that on the opposite south side of the quadrangle. (See Ch 6, Fig 6.4) The first floor of the extension, a memorial to Julia Cock, was devoted to physiology and contained a large laboratory, a demonstration theatre and lecturers' research and private rooms. The second floor extended the anatomical department. The 'long [dissection] room' was doubled in size, and there were also preparation rooms, a demonstration theatre and research laboratories. An animal house stood on the top floor.

The old part of the building running along Hunter Street was also modified. During the summer of 1916 Cubitts enlarged the biology laboratory and the top dressing-room was merged with the old physiology research room. The lower floor of the Students' Chambers was transformed into a beautiful library that retained the name 'Sladen-Walker Library'. The old library became a refectory seating 100 students and was the new home of the Tea Club.

According to the Magazine for July 1918, use of the garden increased following completion of the extension. Even in bad weather the northern colonnade provided an open-air luncheon place and on fine mornings it was a sun-trap. Miss Spencer Wigram, Aldrich-Blake's cohabitant at Nottingham Place from 1915, lent a large circular garden seat which was placed under the old ash tree – the one landmark still familiar to those who qualified before 1900.

Council considered the bill on 1 May 1918. Holliday & Greenwood claimed that building in wartime had increased the cost and that although the contract price was £28,090 they had spent £29,379. The architect confirmed their statement; Council paid an extra £642 – half the loss incurred.

The fact that LSMW had covered the cost of the extension by June 1916 did not mean it could stop fundraising. RFH needed money to develop the Eley site – an essential project if RFH was to cope with increasing student numbers. In May Thorne's absence Mrs Waller represented LSMW on the RFH appeal committee; the School allocated three rooms for use as appeal offices.[xxxviii] In 1919 it was agreed that there should be a joint appeal to raise £500,000 for the extension.

Early in Aldrich-Blake's deanship fee income rose with student numbers – but so did running costs, and the full-time teachers replacing part-timers were paid more and needed facilities for research. However, the School's financial situation gave little cause for alarm

With the dramatic increase in students numbers during the First World War demand grew for residential accommodation. Garrett Anderson's earlier building programme (1897-1900) created the chambers at Hunter Street, but some had been lost owing to wartime alterations. When, in March 1917, the Students' Union (see later) complained about the difficulty of finding suitable accommodation Council agreed to provide more chambers, but only if they were run as a proper business. The Dean offered to take a house in her name with Acland, Alan Anderson and Louisa Garrett Anderson as guarantors. In August the School acquired 36 Tavistock Square which provided ten sets of chambers, and before Christmas it purchased 25 Gordon Square. College Hall also expanded. The problem was eased.[xxxix]

Francis Acland chaired Council throughout Aldrich-Blake's time as Dean. Garrett Anderson's son, Alan, joined it following Stanley Boyd's death in February 1916 and acted as Treasurer when Henderson was called up for military service. During the war Anderson played an important public role. Appointed Vice-Chairman of the Royal Commission on Wheat Supplies in October 1916 he served on various committees of the new Ministry of Food; he was knighted in 1917.[xl]

Elizabeth Garrett Anderson died 17 December 1917. On 14 September 1914 she travelled to London to see her daughter Louisa leave with the first medical women's unit to serve in France (see later). Her memory was already impaired and, with dementia deepening, she spent the rest of her life in virtual isolation in Aldeburgh where she was buried. On 22 December, during the Christmas vacation, a memorial service was held at Christ Church, Endell Street. Travel was of course difficult and only forty people met at Hunter Street to walk to the church in academic dress to celebrate the life and mark the death of a remarkable woman – a great dean and LSMW's first president.[xli] Mary Scharlieb was elected as its second president in January 1918.

In 1912 the University started conferring the title 'Professor' or 'Reader' on teachers in London medical schools – if they deserved the title, were paid an appropriate salary, and had the time and facilities both for research and for teaching to a high standard.[xlii] Wood-Jones was made 'Professor of Anatomy' in March 1915. For much of the war he worked on treatment of nerve injuries at the Special Military Surgical Hospital at Shepherd's Bush.

When he was formally conscripted in June 1918 Council asked Mary Lucas-Keene (MBBS 1911) to run his department. As a student Mary Lucas was at the centre of LSMW's social and sporting life. Wishing to acquire the FRCS, she became an anatomy demonstrator in 1914. In July 1916 she married Captain Richard Keene. To support her as head of anatomy LSMW appointed several anatomy demonstrators – part-time and full-time – the latter being allowed time for research or clinical work.

During the war physiology was in safe hands with Cullis, a reader since 1912. A productive research worker she was, in 1915, one of the first women elected to the Physiological Society. Early in 1918 she lectured at the University of Toronto for four months, presumably to help fill the gap left following the death of Brodie, its Professor of Physiology, who moved to Toronto from LSMW in 1908. Brodie retained his house in Hampstead and spent his Canadian vacations working at LSMW. He died suddenly at his Hampstead home on 20 August 1916 while serving with the Canadian Army Medical Corps.[xliii]

Ransom, pharmacology lecturer from 1912, was made reader in 1915. An Edinburgh graduate (MRCS 1871, MD 1875) he had studied in Berlin, Halle, Marburg and Cambridge. He established a proper pharmacology department at LSMW, and was one of the earliest to provide a course of experimental instruction for students, thus stimulating interest in a subject previously taught in a perfunctory way.[xliv]

Chemistry caused problems. In 1915 Gardner, having been told it was unlikely he would be reappointed as head of department and lecturer in organic chemistry,[24] agreed to follow Council's suggestions about the organisation of the department. He thus kept his job. In May 1920 he was appointed reader in physiological chemistry.[xlv]

Edith Stoney, physics lecturer for almost sixteen years, left in May 1915 to join the Scottish Women's Hospital (see later) and her lectureship went to Mary Waller, a demonstrator since 1912. Edith worked in Serbia, Salonika and, in 1917, at Royaumont where she ran the X-ray department at Villers-Cotterets.[xlvi] In 1919 she was awarded the Croix de Guerre (with citation). After the war Edith was appointed lecturer in physics at KCL (Household and Domestic Science).[xlvii]

---

[24] The reason was not clear.

Edith's younger sister Florence[25] was an experienced radiologist. (See Chapter 7) In 1913 Florence visited the USA where she purchased her own newly developed Coolidge X-ray tube. At the onset of war her offer of her services, and of her portable X-ray machine, was declined by the British Red Cross, so in September 1914 she went to Antwerp and Cherbourg as Chief Medical Officer with Mrs St Clair Stobart's private medical unit. It ceased operations in March 1915 and Florence went on to run the X-ray department at Fulham Military Hospital until the war ended.[26] In 1919 she was awarded the OBE. She then moved out of London and worked as a radiologist at the Royal Victoria & West Hants Hospital in Bournemouth before retiring around 1927.[xlviii]

The staff lists in RFH's annual reports for 1914-19 do not reflect the impact the war had on the staffing of RFH. Three physicians (Carr, Phear & Branson), two assistant physicians (Saunders & Firth), three surgeons (Berry, Evans & Cunning) and two assistant surgeons (Pannett & Joll) were listed each year, but most spent periods away on military duty. Only Carr, Saunders and Cunning seemed to have remained at home – along with Evans, the surgeon to the RFH officers' ward. The ENT surgeon Gay French was a consultant to the War Office. Of the women, Helen Chambers, pathologist, and Mrs Handley-Read, the dentist, moved to Endell Street. (See below) Elizabeth Lepper, from the New Hospital and the South London Hospital for Women, replaced Chambers at RFH in October but did not stay long as she began working with the RAMC. Chambers took the general pathology lectureship at LSMW in September 1917 following Walter D'Este Emery's resignation.[27] The gynaecologists Vaughan-Sawyer and Willey remained in post.

At the start of the war Joll and Ulysses Williams, the radiologist, worked with the French Red Cross at the Hotel Majestic in Paris, while Branson was physician at the Duchess of Westminster's War Hospital at Le Touquet (and later a consultant for the 5th Army of the British Expeditionary Force). Doublas Firth's army service ended in illness. Pannett joined Lord Tredegar's luxury yacht *Liberty,* converted to a hospital ship, and subsequently served in Mesopotamia. In the Magazine of March 1915 he suggested women doctors should work at home to free men for the services – but if they wanted to go to France they should join a hospital recognised

[25] Their father was the Irish physicist George Johnstone Stoney (1826-1911). He coined the term 'electron', and was Secretary of Queen's University, Ireland which with KQCPI agreed in 1876 to examine women for medical diplomas on same terms as men.

[26] There she was assisted by Ida Mann who was a preclinical student at the time.

[27] When Endell Street closed in 1920 Chambers went to the Middlesex Hospital to continue studying th treatment of uterine cancer with radium, work that had started there some years earlier.

by the Army, Navy or Red Cross, as many private ventures were badly equipped and organised and the best surgical work was done near the front.[28, xlix]

In April 1917 the War Office called on all medical men of military age to serve in the Army. Joll joined the RAMC. As RFH's staff was already depleted Aldrich-Blake's offer to attend the surgical department on Monday and Thursday afternoons was gratefully accepted; she was subsequently allocated beds and in 1919 was listed as a Consulting Surgeon.[29] Boyce Barrow, who had retired in 1904, returned in September 1917, now aged 70, to look after Joll's beds.[l]

The war, which began on 4 August 1914, had been anticipated by LSMW students several years earlier, albeit humorously. In the January 1910 Magazine the Common Room committee reported '*the state of our finances is fat and flourishing. We think it advisable, however, in anticipation of the German invasion and the quartering of the more ornamental officers of the German army in the London School of Medicine for Women, to lay out our balance in arm-chairs and other furniture. (We understand that the residents in the flats will be coerced into the sausage-making service, the while they beat their brooms and brushes into beef-steak and black puddings.)*'

With war the tone changed. The November 1914 Magazine urged LSMW women to help by every means in their power, adding that 'A few lucky ones are now in Paris caring for the wounded.' With male doctors and medical students rushing to join the armed services there were fewer candidates for resident posts and many hospitals, including RFH, were left short-handed. Prejudice against medical women was put aside and more posts became open to them, including some at large provincial general hospitals.[li]

Former LSMW students played important roles during the war. There were two large suffrage organisations – the National Union of Women's Suffrage Societies (NUWSS) which favoured peaceful protests, and the Women's Social and Political Union (WSPU) which adopted more violent methods. Both wished to contribute to the war effort. WSPU's leaders, believing the Government would reject their help, set up a Women's Hospital Corps with the LSMW alumnae Flora Murray and Louisa Garrett Anderson (LGA) as director and chief surgeon. On 12 August 1914 they offered the French Red Cross a fully equipped hospital. Its staff left Victoria Station on 14 September, reached Paris two days later, and took over the Hotel Claridge – newly built and still unoccupied. With support from the London headquarters run by Dr Louisa Woodcock the hospital proved a great success,

[28] Pannett left RFH in 1922 to become full-time Professor and Director of the University Surgical Unit at St Mary's Hospital.

[29] The term 'Consulting Surgeon' here implies that she was no longer surgically active at RFH.

although senior British officers were unenthusiastic. Six other former LSMW students served there – Grace Judge, Rosalie Jobson,[30] Marjorie Blandy, Gertrude Gazdar, Irene Bastow and Hazel Cuthbert (later Mrs Chodak-Gregory).[lii]

When the fighting moved north the English hospitals in Paris sent staff to Boulogne, which was overwhelmed and needed another hospital.[31] In November Murray and LGA sought a suitable building and ended up with Château Mauricien, a small hotel at Wimereux three miles north of Boulogne. The British medical officer there accepted their offer of 100 surgical beds and the hospital was officially recognized by the War Office. The staff that had remained at Hotel Claridge moved to Wimereux on 18 January 1915.[liii]

At the end of 1914 the opposing armies became embedded in mud. As a result there were fewer casualties, and many were quickly evacuated to England. Sir Alfred Keogh asked Murray and LGA to return to London and take over the old workhouse of St Giles in Endell Street, which was to become a large hospital.[32] They did so on 22 March 1915 – quite unprepared for the obstruction and hostility encountered from many in the Army Medical Services. When the first patients arrived on 12 May the hospital had 180 staff. When it closed in October 1919 it had received 26,000 patients. Of the 570 beds about 60 were for medical cases; the rest were surgical. The women were denied commissions, honorary rank and badges of authority, but there were no problems with discipline until the war was over; even then the wounded soldiers accepted the authority of the hospital's officers.[liv]

Four of the seven women doctors who worked at the Hotel Claridge served at Endell Street;[33] many more were recruited. Louisa Woodcock, the physician, died of pneumonia, aged 53, in 1917. Her replacement, Margaret Thackrah, was joined by Ellen Pickard in 1919. Most of the rest were surgeons, led by LGA and Winifred Buckley; Amy Sheppard was the eye surgeon and Eva Handley-Read dental surgeon. Helen Chambers, RFH's pathologist, headed pathology at Endell Street from May 1915, and Ethel Magill was its radiologist from 1916.[lv] All trained at LSMW. In 1917 Murray, LGA & Chambers were appointed CBE, and Buckley, Sheppard & Magill OBE.[34] From 1 November 1915 there were six LSMW students

---

[30] Jobson represented Oxford at three sports and played hockey at international level. She married (Sir) Gordon Holmes in 1918.

[31] Jobson, Blandy & Gazdar moved to Wimereux from the Hotel Claridge; the RAMC then 'borrowed' Jobson and Blandy for 6 mths but they were maintained by the Women's Hospital Corps.

[32] A gloomy 5-storey building with bits dating from 1727, & allegedly the workhouse in *Oliver Twist.*

[33] Murray, Garrett Anderson, Gazdar & Jobson.

[34] The Order of the British Empire was created during the War. Women's services to the country were so loudly acclaimed that the Government, unwilling to award them a recognised man's honour, had to find them a decoration; the Order of the British Empire was established mainly for that purpose.

at a time at Endell Street, each spending three months as clerks or dressers; other LSMW students helped during vacations.[lvi]

The NUWSS's contribution to the war effort was organised by Dr Elsie Inglis.[35] Having tried to join the Women's Hospital Corps, which had its full complement of surgeons,[lvii] she suggested to Millicent Fawcett that women doctors, nurses and ambulance workers should staff well-equipped NUWSS hospitals. The first such unit, the 'Scottish Women's Hospital',[36] was established in October 1914 at the Abbaye de Royaumont, 35 km north of Paris, under the direction of Frances Ivens, a former LSMW student.[37] More than thirty women doctors worked there, including three other former LSMW students – Elizabeth Courtauld (the oldest member); Mrs Berry (née Jessie Augusta Lewin – the longest serving member, who came out of retirement to join her friend Ivens), and Marjorie Martland, a recent graduate. Other LSMW women spent short spells at Royaumont. Aldrich-Blake 'vacationed' there in 1915 & 1916; and Louisa Martindale and Mary Lucas-Keene also helped out, as did Vera Foley and Margaret Joyce, both practitioners in Liverpool where Ivens was the first woman consultant. Joyce triggered Ivens's choice of medicine as a career.[lviii]

After the war Ivens was awarded the Legion d'Honneur and the Croix de Guerre with Palm. The Croix de Guerre (for service in face of the enemy) was also awarded to Berry, Courtauld and Martland, and to the student Ruth Plimsoll, who went on to qualify in 1923.[lix]

Other Scottish Women's Hospital units went subsequently to Belgium, Serbia, Russia and Corsica. Inglis initially ran things from home, but in May 1915 she took over as head of the first Serbian unit. After one of their attacks was repulsed by Serbia the retreating Austrians left behind 60,000 prisoners and dirty, overcrowded hospitals. Typhus raged for three months. Subsequently the Serbian army, and the hospital, retreated to Krushievatz. The inevitable defeat followed; Inglis and her staff stayed to tend their patients. In February 1916 the Austrians closed the hospital and transferred the unit to Zurich. Inglis returned home, but in October, despite resigning from the SWH, she took a unit to south Russia to help the Serbians fighting with the Russians. When Russia withdrew from the war after its revolution in March 1917 the Foreign Office proposed repatriation of the SWH staff but Inglis demanded that Serbians who so wished should leave with them. She got her way, but sadly died of cancer two days after reaching England.[lx]

---

[35] Inglis was secretary of its Edinburgh branch.

[36] It was linked with the French Red Cross.

[37] In 1917 Ivens received the Cross of the Legion d'Honneur from the President of the French Republic.

James Berry and his wife (Frances May Dickinson), surgeon and anaesthetist at RFH, had spent pre-war holidays bicycling in southeast Europe. He spoke fluent French, German, Magyar and Serbian. Early in 1915, through the British Red Cross, they set up an Anglo-Serbian hospital unit, with six hospitals and 360 beds, at the sulphur springs of Vrnjatchka Banja. The main task of its staff, largely from RFH,[38] was not surgery, but the promotion of hygiene among refugees. A typhus epidemic was controlled by strict individual de-lousing. The Austria-Hungarian Army over-ran the hospitals in 1916 but treated their staff courteously. The Berrys described their adventures in an 'At Home' at LSMW in May 1916.[lxi] Berry subsequently led a Red Cross unit in Romania and linked up with the Serbian army again at Odessa in South Russia; he returned to London in 1917.

Ulysses Williams, RFH's radiologist, accompanied the Berrys to Serbia along with two students soon to qualify at LSMW – Dorothy Chick and Kathleen Parkinson. When the students left in May 1915 Helen Boyle (LRCPSEd 1893) arrived for three months. So too did another LSMW student, Mabel Ingram, who acted as a dresser and radiographer for nine months; she qualified in 1919. After Berry's first wife died in 1934 Mabel became the second Lady Berry (Berry was knighted in 1925).[lxii]

One LSMW graduate played an unusual part in the Serbian story. Ella Scarlett Synge, who had settled in Canada, was Colonel of a Vancouver Women's Voluntary Reserve group which travelled to Serbia. There her sister, Evelina Haverfield, was a transport officer with the Scottish Women's Hospital. Ella was at Balochina when the Germans invaded. She remained with the wounded and was impressed by the good conduct of the German Red Cross doctors and by the German soldiers' attitude to the Serbians. She asked their commander if she could return home via Germany to inspect the prisoners of war camps there, wondering '*if as many lies had been told about them as about the conduct of the troops*'.[39] She visited camps at Wittenberg, Gottingen, Rubleben and Giessen and after the first camp was allowed to talk to British prisoners without an inspector being present. In England she submitted her 'Report of visits to English Prisoners-of War camps in Germany' to Lord Robert Cecil, hoping to lessen ill feeling between Britain and Germany. On 4 November 1916 the *Daily Sketch* reported it as a pro-German whitewash.

In 1916 the War Office invited women doctors to serve with the armed forces and many LSMW alumnae volunteered. Some, like May Thorne, replaced men at hospitals in Malta. Unlike the Endell Street staff they received a flat rate without

---

[38] On 30 Dec 1914 Berry asked the RFH Weekly Board for permission to attach the Hospital's name to his team. It refused.

[39] In 1901 she was with Millicent Fawcett's commission investigating conditions in British concentration camps in South Africa.

an allowance for seniority. They wore uniform but, as civilians, were denied rank.[40] This created problems as some RAMC privates refused to take their orders, except through NCOs.[41] They were sometimes denied access to officers' messes and could not travel in army motorcars. Refused the first-class rail travel available to nurses and RAMC officers they travelled third class as 'soldiers' families'.[lxiii]

In March 1917 the Army established the Women's Auxiliary Army Corps (WAAC).[42] The first 'WAACs' went to France on 31 March; about 6,000 were there early in 1918. They were used for cooking and catering, storekeeping, clerical work, telephony and motor vehicle maintenance. The Army now needed female doctors. Dr Chalmers Watson (née Geddes), one of Edinburgh University's first two women medical graduates, was Controller of the WAAC.[43] Although not then working as a doctor, she welcomed other medical women to her service. She made Jane Turnbull (MB Lond 1899) medical officer and adviser to the War Office on matters concerning the women.

After the Air Ministry was formed in January 1918 women working at aerodromes and other air force formations were incorporated into the Women's Royal Air Force (WRAF). In June Letitia Fairfield, another Edinburgh graduate, transferred from the RAMC to run a medical service for the WRAF.[44] Although they lacked commissions WRAF medical women were spared the problems faced by those in RAMC hospitals. Chalmers Watson, profiting from her WAAC experience, secured for them a better defined status and more favourable conditions of service. Dorothy Hare served with the Army in Malta in 1916-17, but from April 1918 to October 1919 she was chief medical officer, ranked as assistant, in the Women's Royal Naval Service.[lxiv]

Female doctors in army hospitals and casualty clearing stations did not get the recognition appropriate to their professional status. Demand therefore arose for a new female medical society – one which would promote greater union, social and professional, between medical women, and which could voice their views as a whole. In 1917 the various associations of medical women in Scotland and England amalgamated as the Medical Women's Federation (MWF). The November 1917 issue of LSMW's Magazine announced its formation and listed its officers: President, Jane Walker; Vice Presidents, Scharlieb and Chalmers Watson; Hon.

---

[40] RAMC badges of rank were denied to women doctors until 1939.

[41] NCO = Non-commissioned officer, e.g. sergeant or corporal.

[42] 57,000 volunteers were eventually employed by the Women's Auxiliary Army Corps.

[43] Chalmers Watson (née Geddes) was EGA's niece; her brother, Acland Campbell Geddes (later Baron Geddes), also a doctor, was Director of Recruiting at the War Office..

[44] Fairfield also served during the Second World War.

Treasurer, Aldrich Blake; and Hon. Secretary, Frances Huxley.[45] The MWF, with offices at 9, Clifford Street, New Bond Street, differed substantially from its predecessor, the Association of Registered Medical Women, as it functioned primarily as a pressure group capable of influencing public policy relating to medical women. Although initially only 190 of the 1200 registered medical women were members, there were 385 in 1918; and 1347 in 1930, i.e. about 40% of the women then active in medical practice in Britain. Female medical students also joined.

In 1916 LSMW's students set up a branch of the War Savings Association; they also volunteered to work on the land in the summer vacation but relatively few were chosen that year. In 1917 most of LSMW's thirty volunteers found employment. They pulled flax in Somerset, picked plums in Hertfordshire, and engaged in haymaking, hoeing, pea-pulling and fruit-picking. They earned about 15 shillings a week, and lived in cottages, farms or tents. Forty-five LSMW students took to the land in 1918. They planted potatoes, picked fruit and cut timber, but most pulled flax in Somerset, Ilchester or Peterborough. Flax was used in making aeroplane cloth; machine-gun belts and breech covers for guns; nose-bags, harness and saddlery for horses; canvas covers for wagons and cars; tents and marquees; and Army boots – and Germany controlled the large flax producing areas in Belgium and Russia.[lxv]

LSMW's students also made a more unusual contribution to the war. Writing on 'Self Experiment' in the magazine of the Research Defence Society for April 1922 Major-General Sir David Bruce[46] described 'self experiments' with anti-tetanic serum (ATS) done early in the war to ascertain its durability in the blood. About a dozen LSMW student volunteers were inoculated with ATS; their blood antitoxin levels were then measured and after 10 to 14 days antitoxin levels in the blood fell markedly – so more than one dose of ATS was recommended.[lxvi]

The Students' Union

In 1912 and 1913 the students discussed amalgamating all their clubs into a single body – to facilitate collection of subscriptions, centralize administration, and improve interaction between School and Hospital students. Council approved the formation of a Students' Union in March 1914; in May seventy-seven students (School and Hospital) voted for it and only two against. The Union's rules appeared in the Magazine for November 1914.[lxvii]

---

[45] Huxley graduated in Manchester in 1908; the others trained at LSMW.

[46] Bruce identified the cause of Malta fever (Brucellosis) and of 'sleeping sickness' (caused by Trypanasoma brucei).

Almost all clubs and societies were affiliated with the Union, including the Magazine, the Christmas Party Committee and the Hospital Entertainment Committee. Only the Christian Union, Dance Club, Training Corps and Suffrage Society were excluded. Finding a suitable sports ground was to be a major priority. Student membership was compulsory on entry to LSMW; subscriptions were collected with fees. Former students and post-graduates were eligible for membership. Students paid 2 guineas a year, or £10 for the whole course; past students and staff paid half a guinea a year, or three guineas for life membership. All subscribers received the Magazine.[lxviii]

Miss Douie, then Secretary of the South London Hospital for Women, presided over the Union's first AGM on 14 October 1914 (reported in the July 1915 Magazine). Dr Phear was the treasurer, Alice Lloyd-Williams the secretary. May Thorne represented Council. Mrs Willey spoke on the advantages of a Students' Union and Dorothy Chick about the affiliated clubs. Two student vice-presidents[47] and ten other students were elected to the committee and the secretaries of the various clubs then enrolled members. The Committee was to meet monthly and hold a general meeting each term. Initially the Union office was in Flat No. 1 in the Hunter Street Chambers, but when the new extension opened in 1917 it moved to a room in the colonnade on the north side of the quadrangle.

A tie in the colours of LSMW – half 'old gold' and half black – was chosen for those representing its sports teams. Standing orders were drawn up for selection of teams and for the organization of Christmas entertainments, including those for in-patients. Christmas parties were cancelled until the war ended, and in 1915 it was decided that money usually allocated for them, about £25, should go to students in financial difficulty owing to the war.

In November 1914 the Union asked Council to increase the wages of Mrs Surtees, who had run the students' quarters at RFH for 14 years.[48] Poor health led her to retire in 1915. Past and present students were asked to raise at least £80, to provide her with five shillings a week before she received her old age pension in 1921. Uncharacteristically, the response was poor; a year later £40 was still required.[lxix]

At the Union's second AGM in October 1915, Noel Olivier[49] and Octavia Wilberforce joined the committee. A year later the AGM for the election of officers

---

47 One 'Hospital' (Florence Edwards), the other 'School' (Doris Howard).

48 See Chapter 6.

49 Noel Olivier (MB 1917) had been secretly engaged to Rupert Brooke – see "*Song of Love – The letters of Rupert Brooke and Noel Olivier*" ed. Pippa Harris. New York, Crown Publishers Inc. 1991. Noel's father Sir Sydney Olivier (later Baron Olivier) was Governor of Jamaica. Noel married William Arthur Richards (MBBS) in 1920.

was moved to January to improve the method of representation of first year students.[lxx]

In February 1916 the students requested a telephone at Hunter Street.[50] Asked to pay the wages of a uniformed messenger to attend to it the Union suggested an under-porteress could perform that and other duties. Council agreed and the students contributed five shillings a week to her salary. The following year Council approved a telephone line between the maternity hospital in Endsleigh Street and 24 Mecklenburg Square.[lxxi]

At the AGM on 17 January 1917 'St Mary's women' were granted representation on the Union committee. After a heated argument about introducing a School blazer in wartime a small majority voted in favour. The initial preference was for one with narrow yellow stripes on a black background – but the Magazine for July 1920 noted an agreement 'to investigate the price of striped blazers since many students thought these would be preferable to the plain back ones'. In 1925 it was decided to retain the 'Colours' blazer, which presumably had a striped design, and to introduce an ordinary blazer – plain black, with a lion rampant on the pocket and L.S.M.W. embroidered above the lion in old English letters.[lxxii]

A suggestion that the students should adopt academic dress, to reinforce the professional atmosphere of collegiate life, was rejected almost unanimously in October 1917, as was the idea of spending £76.10s on an application to the College of Heraldry for a coat of arms; such expenditure was deemed inappropriate in wartime.[lxxiii]

In December 1917 the Students' Union asked Council if the office of Vice-Dean (in abeyance since Aldrich-Blake became dean) could be reinstated. Many students wished to consult a suitable medically qualified person about future careers, current work problems, examinations, hospital posts etc. The increase in student numbers meant that the two hours a week the Dean allowed for such interviews did not meet the demand. However, instead of a Vice-Dean, three tutors were appointed to liaise with students already in their first, second and third years; new students were allocated to them on admission to the School.[lxxiv]

The first three tutors were Elizabeth Bolton, assistant surgeon at the Elizabeth Garrett Anderson Hospital (EGAH);[51] Margaret Fraser, physician at South London Hospital for Women; and Hazel Chodak-Gregory, acting assistant physician at RFH (and in 1919 the first woman appointed assistant physician there).

[50] The rental, £20 a year, allowed an unlimited number of free calls.

[51] The New Hospital for Women was renamed 'Elizabeth Garrett Anderson Hospital' in 1917.

Hospital students were provided with tutors in March 1918. Chodak-Gregory was made medical tutor, Gertrude Dearnley gynaecological tutor, and Lionel Norbury surgical tutor; each was to give four courses of ten classes a year.[lxxv]

The expansion of student numbers during the war boosted membership of existing clubs and societies at LSMW and stimulated the formation of new ones. Although some had their activities curtailed by the war almost all clubs flourished after it ended in November 1918.

When the Students' Union was founded it adopted the Tea Club, the oldest of the School's clubs. It had been run for almost 40 years by a student secretary, but in 1916 increasing student numbers led the Union to ask if the housekeeper, appointed in 1912 to manage both School and Chambers, could also take over the Tea Club. Council said 'No' – so a committee was set up to run it.[52] After the extension opened it met in the new refectory.[lxxvi]

When bread became scarce in 1916 a weekly 'breadless day' was introduced. The oat scones which replaced bread proved so popular that two days were made breadless; on the other three weekdays 2 oz of bread and butter were served, or 1½ oz of bread and a small bun. To comply with the rationing introduced by the Government in 1918,[53] which lasted three years, buns had to have a standard weight of 2ozs. In the autumn of 1919 the committee established a canteen so that students could buy extra cakes. Membership of the Tea Club cost a guinea a year (about 6d. per week).[lxxvii]

During the war the Debating Society held its own debates and also competed against other colleges. In 1918 it hosted the London Intercollegiate Debate where the motion 'That the League of Nations is necessary for the maintenance of universal peace' was carried by 11 votes.[lxxviii]

The Socialist Society formed in 1915 initially had 13 full members – and 11 associates who were not convinced socialists. Its first three meetings covered the principles of socialism, 'English Industry before the Industrial Revolution', and 'The Munitions of War Act'. Subsequently members studied the British Labour movement and the formation of large craft unions. Speakers included the economic historian G.H.D. Cole, Dr Lawson Dodd and Aylmer Maude, an authority on Tolstoy.[lxxix]

In the winter of 1917-8 the Dramatic Society celebrated its 'resuscitation' by performing W.W. Jacobs's 'The Monkey's Paw', and Gertrude Jennings's 1915

[52] The secretary and four others.

[53] Rationing was not due to a shortage of food but to a widespread panic about its distribution.

play 'Five Birds in a Cage' set in a London Tube lift (or elevator). Within months it had about a hundred members. During the summer term Mrs Lucas-Keene invited them to a party in the Common Room at which three short plays were performed.[lxxx]

The Magazine first mentioned the Choral Society's wartime activities in its July 1917 issue, which reported a Students' Social held in March. After a piano solo by Miss Sansom, songs from Miss Aitken and the Choral Society, and a duet for violin and piano, Doris Odium gave two amusing recitations – the first a skit on British aloofness and the absurdity of social conventions, and the second on truth and the dire consequences befalling those who lie. Everyone then enjoyed an impromptu dance – '*notwithstanding that in a somewhat crowded room, the steering of those who filled the gap, in the absence of males, left room for improvement, and shows that even medical students in some things, have something to learn from the male element!*' At Christmas the Society sang carols at RFH and several other hospitals.

The sports clubs benefited from the wartime influx of students. Before becoming Dean Aldrich-Blake had helped the Hockey Club to rent playing facilities in Hampstead, but in 1915 an excellent ground was found at Edmonton. Even though access was difficult, particularly for practice, it was used for about ten years.

With the formation of the University Fencing Club in 1913 LSMW's own club grew in importance, if not membership, as it was the only women's college with a fencing club. Its members represented the University in the Inter-salle competition that December but subsequently the club's fortunes fluctuated.

The Swimming Club held life-saving classes at Highgate Ponds in 1914. The following year its Gymkhana included a 'dressing-up race' (the most popular event), 'diving for plates', and a 'music race' in which no one managed more than one note before choking on ingested water; the students defeated the staff in two team races. By 1918 the club had over 100 members.[lxxxi]

In 1915 the Tennis Club played its matches at the Royal Botanical Gardens, Regent's Park, and for the next few years used hard courts at Belsize Park, and the court at Mary Waller's home in St John's Wood. Waller was a fine sportswoman who played hockey for Middlesex. The Tennis Club won all its matches in 1916, 1917 and 1918, and by winning the intercollegiate competition three years running kept the cup.

The Boating Club, active during the early years of Cock's deanship, went through a fallow period, and although it had been reactivated in 1912 it suffered during the war. Most of its competitions were restricted to sculling, usually as coxed pairs.

The Gymnastic Club started in the autumn of 1914 and held a weekly class at the Regent Square Institute gymnasium.[lxxxii] The Badminton and Netball Clubs, both formed in 1917, used the court in the quadrangle which became available again after work was completed on the new extension. The Netball Club soon had 60 members and in its first full season its first-team won five matches and drew one. Both clubs played home matches in the quadrangle.[lxxxiii]

After the 1914-18 war life gradually returned to some semblance of normality. Fortunately LSMW and RFH had suffered nothing like the disruption that they were to experience during the 1939-45 war. (See Chapter 12). However, the war had a marked effect on women's place in society at large and in the medical profession in particular. Women doctors found it relatively easy to find work during the war because so many male doctors, medical students and potential students had enlisted. But there was concern that problems of employment for women would recur or get worse with demobilization – when male doctors returned to their practices, students who had been diverted from their studies re-entered medical school, and young men applied for admission to medical school rather than join the armed services. However one thing now in the women's favour was that during the war they had shown their competence in almost all types of clinical practice.

CHAPTER 9

Aldrich-Blake (1919-1925)

Peace, the O & G Unit and the Jubilee

The First World War changed the life of British women. Parliament recognized the important role they played in it and introduced several pieces of legislation that affected women in general and women doctors in particular. In 1918 the Representation of the People Act enfranchised all women over 30 who were on the local government register or married to registered men – and the House of Commons voted to allow women to stand for Parliament. Three women doctors stood in October 1924; all unsuccessfully. Two LSMW alumnae, Ethel Bentham and Stella Churchill, were Labour candidates for London constituencies – Bentham having also stood in 1922 and 1923.[i] In 1919 the Sex Disqualification (Removal) Act allowed women to hold public office and civil and judicial posts. More than 190 women became magistrates the following year; two LSMW graduates, Mary Scharlieb and Janet Lane-Claypon, were among them.

In October 1919 the School's inaugural address was given by the Minister of Health, Dr Christopher Addison, a Bart's graduate and previously professor of anatomy at Sheffield. He had just appointed four LSMW alumnae – Janet Campbell, Florence Barrie Lambert, Jane Holland Turnbull & Irene Eaton – to newly created posts in the Ministry of Health. Campbell became a Senior Medical Officer and remained Chief Woman Medical Adviser to the Board of Education (see Chapter 7). Barrie Lambert took charge of 'Remedial Treatment', but resigned in 1921 to enter politics. Turnbull worked with Campbell in Maternity and Child Welfare and headed that division when Campbell (now Dame Janet) retired in 1933. Eaton, who had served in Malta during the war, died unexpectedly in 1920 aged 38.[ii]

When men returned from the war unemployment rose and women faced pressure to give up their wartime jobs.[iii] Few had had the opportunity of a fulfilling career in public office, and those who had found that if they wanted to marry they were expected to retire to their 'proper' place in the home. The first women to hold senior posts in the Civil Service were not subject to this bar, but in 1894 the Treasury had made it a condition of employment for the rest of the Civil Service. Not all departments complied, but in 1918, despite the passage of the Sex

Disqualification Act, which should have prevented such action, the Treasury made the marriage bar absolute, but not retrospective.[iv]

Dr Eileen Hewitt was appointed the first female Medical Inspector of Factories in 1921. She was forced to resign when she married in 1923. Sybil Gertrude Overton, another LSMW alumna, succeeded her as Medical Inspector of Factories in October 1924; somehow she avoided Hewitt's fate when she married Captain Bernard Horner in 1931.

The Medical Women's Federation wrote to *The Times* of 6 December 1921 to complain about the refusal of Glasgow Corporation and St Pancras Borough Council to employ medical women whose husbands were employed. The latter dismissed Dr Gladys Miall-Smith after she married another doctor, and gave her job to Dr Stella Campbell, a well qualified widow.[1] Such discrimination against married women doctors persisted for many years.[v]

In 1919 the pound's purchasing power was a third of its 1914 value. Wages had lagged behind the cost of living; they almost caught up again in 1917 but slipped back during the post-war boom. LSMW's staff received a much-needed pay increase in 1919 but – despite an increase in both student numbers and the Board of Education's annual grant – the School anticipated a shortfall of about £2000.[vi]

When the deficit rose the following year prospects seemed gloomy. A conference of London medical schools recommended that all should increase fees by at least a third. At LSMW they rose to £240 for new students. Existing students (or their parents) were asked to pay a surtax of £10 per annum for the rest of the course; this raised £3520 in its first year and Lady Beilby gave £400 to assist those who could not afford it. Income just covered expenditure in 1920-21.[vii]

Council was worried that fees might have to rise again but, as the only all-women school, it was reluctant to charge more than men's schools. It therefore opened an appeal for money to endow chairs – which would reduce future expenditure on salaries – and for a bursary fund to assist good students unable to pay the full fees.

Income narrowly exceeded expenditure in 1922, thanks again to the surtax which raised £2760 – less than in 1921 because many students paying it had left. Council considered savings that reduced efficiency as a false economy; if as a result the student intake fell income might drop faster and further than expenditure. LSMW saved £1800 in 1922-23 while maintaining efficiency. More drastic economy, demanded from all departments in May 1923, led to a surplus of £413

---

1 Miall-Smith entered general practice. After retiring she worked in different parts of Africa until she was 80. She celebrated her 100th birthday on 1 May 1988.

in 1923-24, but the following year there was a deficit of £2519, and several lean years were anticipated until there was a full recovery from the effects of the war.[viii]

The main problem post-war was the striking fall in the admission of new students – from a peak of 134 in 1916 to 62 in 1922-23, 43 in 1923-24 and 45 in 1924-25. Even so the deficit was only £346 in 1925-26 and Council thanked staff for making every pound tell, the Treasury for increasing the grant, and donors to the new Jubilee Endowment Fund for their generosity. Income from fees, although still low, was considered stable at £10,500 – about a third of total expenditure – and there was optimism about future student numbers.[ix]

In May 1919 the Foundling Hospital suggested the School should purchase adjacent property in Compton and Wakefield Streets. It offered a 58 year lease on 7-19 Compton Street at an annual rent of £270. The leaseholder of the site at the corner of Compton and Hunter Streets also offered to sell. Council procrastinated and no further negotiations took place about Compton Street until 1926.[x]

In May 1919 the School's residential accommodation (Hunter Street Chambers plus the Tavistock Square & Gordon Square houses) was thought inadequate for the autumn intake. Qualified women living at Hunter Street were asked to leave before October. The School acquired two more houses – Nos. 15 & 16 Brunswick Square – and it pressed the University to increase the number of women's hostels.[xi]

In October 1919 Sir Alan Anderson suggested incorporating the chambers as a Friendly Society. 'Students' Chambers, Ltd' was inaugurated early in 1920 and took over the leases and obligations for the four houses. The sale of £1 shares and £100 Loan Stock to students, past students and friends raised £4432 to buy more houses. Interest was limited to 6%; profits were to be spent in the tenants' interests. In November 1920 the society acquired 5 Mecklenburgh Square which would hold thirteen students or, if required, places for eight students from India. 'Students' Chambers, Ltd', with F.R.S. Balfour as chairman, then housed over fifty students.[xii]

From September 1918 RFH could no longer provide luncheon facilities for the greatly increased number of clinical students and so an early lunch for hospital students was served at the new refectory at Hunter Street which seated 100 students. To improve the situation Council decided to acquire 27 Mecklenburgh Square. Although primarily a luncheon club it had two unfurnished chambers for rental to hospital students. It opened in December. Clinical students could enter the rear of the house via a passageway opening from Gray's Inn Road opposite the main entrance to RFH.[xiii]

The first tenancy agreement expired in September 1920. The Foundling offered a seven-year lease, with the proviso that the right of way to Gray's Inn Road could be closed at short notice; Council, unenthusiastic, agreed another single year tenancy. A year later it again rejected a long term lease owing to clauses covering dilapidation. In October 1922 a more satisfactory seven-year lease was accepted. The house was then redecorated but the arrangement proved short-lived. In April 1925 RFH opened a new students' dining-room; 27 Mecklenburgh Square was no longer needed and the staff went, along with the student accommodation.[xiv]

In November 1918 Ransom, ASA's Chairman, reported students' dissatisfaction with the availability of patients at RFH and predicted that some of the best would leave. Between 1917 and 1923 at least fifty students transferred to a medical school other than St Mary's. The London Hospital was easily the most popular choice (24 or more), with UCH and KCH as runners-up.[xv]

St Mary's provided more places than the other schools, but by October 1919 its financial situation had improved and its arrangement with LSMW was now a hindrance, as it prevented admission of women either from another medical school or to its own preclinical course. It gave notice to terminate the agreement on 1 October 1920, but in November 1919 its Dean wrote that LSMW could still send students there. Six months later LSMW rejected a draft new agreement. Some financial clauses affected it adversely, and St Mary's did not guarantee to take all the students it wished to send. A new agreement was eventually hammered out, but in July 1920 St Mary's asked LSMW's permission to admit a woman student directly to St Mary's Hospital.[xvi]

St Mary's had a record intake of 84 in 1920; 37 were women. But old problems re-surfaced with an influx of ex-servicemen hostile to the women, some of whom were now demonstrators and house officers. The poor attendance of men at clinical teaching was attributed to their fear of appearing ignorant in front of women. The women's position, already under attack, weakened when Charles McMoran Wilson (later Lord Moran), away in France during the war, succeeded Broadbent as Dean in December 1920. According to Garner, Wilson distrusted intelligence, but enthused about team sports and valued the attitudes towards service, duty and loyalty exemplified in public school-educated rugby players; he sought such recruits for St Mary's.[xvii]

The pathologist, Sir Almroth Wright, who had also been in France, shared Wilson's views. In January 1889 he had married Jane Georgina Mackay Wilson who came from a wealthy Irish family. Their union seemed doomed from the start. He was a notorious misogynist and anti-suffragist, while she subscribed to the National Society for Women's Suffrage before marriage.[2] She supported LSMW generously, endowed the Mackay prizes, and started the School's Repayment of Debt fund.[xviii]

---

[2] The Wrights did not divorce but separated in late 1914. A facial tumour caused her death in 1926.

Discontent grew at St Mary's. On 1 April 1924 the Medical School Committee discussed a request from 96 male students to stop admission of women students. It began 'the recent, but apparently habitual defeat of St Mary's in the Rugger Cup-tie, calls for serious consideration'. The men claimed women reduced St Mary's institutional virility, as evidenced by its results on the rugby field, and concluded: 'the men do not want the women, they had no wish to be friends, or to cooperate with them in any way'. The rugby argument was flawed. Garner calculated that from 1910 to 1914 St Mary's (minus women) won 35% of its matches; from 1919 to 1923 (with women) it won 60%, and in 1923 it won the prestigious Hospitals Cup for only the second time in its history.[xix]

After an inconclusive debate the matter was referred to the hospital staff, perhaps to circumvent the premedical teachers who supported the women. The clinicians' recommendation to exclude women then went to the hospital board. Initially it demurred, but on 12 May decided no new women students would be accepted after 1925. Lady Harris and Mrs Harben objected but an old regulation prevented women governors from voting on school matters. Earlier the hospital's secretary had estimated that excluding women would cost the school £8,400 over the first three years; he thought it could 'just meet this financially' but warned that reserves would be severely depleted and that long-term building plans might be irreparably damaged.[xx]

In May Council asked LSMW's School Committee for how long clinical facilities would be needed at St Mary's. It replied that as student numbers were falling the arrangement should cease. So Council would not have been unduly concerned to receive the St Mary's letter of 23 June 1924 terminating the October 1920 agreement.[xxi]

St George's (1919) and The London (1921) had given up admitting women several years earlier, and Charing Cross, Westminster & King's stopped admitting them in 1928. (See Chapter 10).

UCHMS admitted women from 1918. In October 1920 male students urged its Committee to refuse them admission in future and in November the entry of women for 1921-22 was reduced to twelve. This created a problem as UCL had admitted 44 women to its preclinical course in October 1920. One affected was Gwen Hill (later Mrs Hilton), then working for a B.Sc. in physiology. Her father M. J. M. Hill, a mathematics professor at UC, was a former Vice-Chancellor – and a member of the sub-committee of the Academic Council set up in December 1915 to consider facilities for the Medical Education of Women in London.[3]

[3] The Hills were a distinguished family. Gwen's uncle George was Director of the British Museum. One brother, Sir Roderic Hill, was an Air Chief Marshal, Rector of Imperial College and Vice-Chancellor of London University; her other brother, Geoffrey, was Professor of Engineering at UCL.

Hill consulted her father and fellow students and, with a lawyer, prepared a strong case urging continued admission to UCHMS for UCL women. On 9 December 1920 the Dean read a letter from UCL's Provost urging that women who had passed 2nd MB before July 1920 should enter the Medical School; its Committee agreed. Subsequently the future entry of the regular, though small, entry of women students applying for entry to UCHMS was assured. From 1921 it admitted 12 a year, with four nominated by UCL and four by examination.[xxii]

Although LSMW wished to expand and improve educational facilities at RFH it occasionally sought access to other general hospitals, particularly during the First World War. It used at least one LCC hospital from 1920 – the Magazine noting that *'St Pancras Infirmary — or Hospital as it is now called — will eventually allow us…its medical and gynaecological as well as its surgical beds. …, our students are…dressers in the surgical wards…[with] sixty beds, [supervised by] the Medical Superintendent…Mr Norbury, makes a weekly round there. This opening up of Poor Law Institution beds and clinical material for teaching is a new development — the only precedent being the taking over of the Paddington Infirmary beds by St Mary's Hospital staff during the war — and it is being watched with much interest.'* LSMW agreed to provide clerical help for RFH's medical and surgical registrars so that they could also teach at St Pancras Hospital.[4, xxiii]

The Obstetrics and Gynaecology Unit

On 14 January 1914, just before Aldrich-Blake became Dean, the Board of Education wrote asking for LSMW's views on the Haldane Commission's proposal that there should be university clinical units with a large bed allocation – to be run by professors with some whole time clinical assistants. With the onset of war planning for such units was put on hold.

Discussions resumed in 1918. In November LSMW was asked to co-operate with the extension of RFH. Before committing itself Council studied a sketch plan of the proposed building, as it wished to promote the most advanced methods of teaching and research with a view to LSMW becoming a 'University Unit' in the forthcoming reconstruction of the University. It sought help from Sir George Newman, Medical Adviser to the Board of Education, who met Council members in December. The March 1919 Magazine pointed out that Newman's ideas on clinical teaching (set out in *Some Notes on Medical Education in England)*[xxiv] now had added relevance because the Board of Education intended to spend more on universities.

[4] In 1929 Hadfield involved RFH staff in post-mortems at St Pancras thus increasing the pathological material available to LSMW's students (see Chapter 10)

Carried away by its enthusiasm for a proposed extension of RFH by over 200 beds LSMW conceived grandiose plans for a 'Clinical Unit' with medical, surgical and gynaecological elements, each with a professor and 70-100 beds. Following an unsuccessful application for funds the idea was abandoned.[5] Instead, in October 1919, LSMW corresponded with the Board of Education about an Obstetrics and Gynaecology (O & G) unit.[xxv]

Even though the Free and the New Hospital for Women had no maternity beds,[6] facilities for obstetric training of LSMW's students had improved. Before the war the Duchess of Marlborough bought two houses in Endsleigh Street, off Tavistock Square, as a home for prisoner's wives. However, during the war, she found *'labour wards were…being given over to…caring for the wounded and…there was an increased demand for a lying-in hospital. I decided…to [close] my Home for Prisoner's Wives…with eighteen beds, it became an annexe to the Royal Free Hospital. Lady Barrett and Dr Aldrich-Blake, two prominent gynaecologists, headed the staff of women doctors and students.'*[xxvi] The Marlborough Maternity Unit accepted unmarried mothers, who were not always welcome at other hospitals. The unit was handed over to RFH in 1918 and the Duchess, herself American, persuaded the American Red Cross to help endow it and to donate £10,000 towards extending it into neighbouring houses in Endsleigh Street. By the end of 1919 it held 37 maternity beds

This was the situation when negotiations started about a professorial O & G Unit. In December 1919 the Weekly Board agreed to support it with fifty-five O & G beds. In 1920 twelve maternity beds became available when Washington Ward opened in the Helena Building; it eventually housed twenty-three beds. Sir Alan Anderson gave £1000 to equip it; Aldrich-Blake and May Thorne each provided £1000 for structural alterations. The American Women's Club also supported it.

The UGC visitors came in March 1920 to discuss the proposed unit; approval came two months later – but its director had to be appointed as a professor. LSMW wanted Lady Barrett to head the unit but neither the University nor the UGC would countenance a part-time professorship. Barrett agreed, reluctantly, to accept a whole time post but it seems clear she was not deemed a suitable candidate.[xxvii]

In February 1921 the University's board of advisers' chose Anne Louise McIlroy (Fig 9.1) to be the first professor and head of an O & G Unit of the type envisaged by the Haldane Commission – and the first woman appointed as a clinical professor at any British medical school. Lady Barrett resigned her lectureship in midwifery

[5] The application was to a foundation set up by Sir Ernest Cassel.

[6] Somewhat prematurely LSMW's 1917-18 prospectus claimed 'Special Lying-in-Wards, with 8 beds, plus a labour-ward of 3 beds and an operating theatre. All students…take duty in the Midwifery Department for two months, during which time they reside in the special quarters at Hospital.'

Fig 9.1 Louise McIlroy (1874-1968)

and her appointment at RFH and in May she joined Council when Mrs Waller resigned after 23 years. Mrs Vaughan-Sawyer remained as gynaecologist.[xxviii]

The Magazine of March 1921 welcomed the appointment of McIlroy, who had trained in Glasgow, London, Birmingham, Vienna and Paris and held the midwifery diploma of the Rotunda Hospital, Dublin. Before the war she was senior assistant to Munro Kerr, Muirhead Professor of O & G at Glasgow's Royal Infirmary. From 1915 to 1919 she was Surgeon-in Charge of the Girton & Newnham unit of the Scottish Women's Hospital in Salonika and Belgrade, and from 1919 gynaecological specialist to the 82nd General Hospital at Constantinople.[xxix]

RFH agreed that McIlroy's first assistant, Gertrude Dearnley, could continue working at Queen Charlotte's Hospital. Charlotte Houlton, of the Women's Medical Service, India, was appointed second assistant and Muriel Landau[7] registrar pathologist. Dearnley replaced Vaughan-Sawyer as gynaecologist at RFH in 1925.

The Unit, which started up in April 1921, was formally opened by the Queen on 11 May. After the dedication service she visited the Unit's wards, subsequently known as the 'Queen Mary' Wards, before joining people for tea.[xxx]

[7] The first Jewish woman to qualify FRCS, and mother of the psychiatrist/author Oliver Sacks.

Alfred Langton's gift of £6500 in 1914 allowed RFH to purchase the freehold of Nos. 1 to 11 Cubitt Street, where a nurses' home could be built after the leases expired in 1922.[xxxi] In 1915 the local council made another part of Cubitt Street available.[xxxii] RFH started building the new nurses' home in August 1923 in anticipation of the termination of the tenancy of Nos. 20 & 21 Endsleigh Street in 1925. After the opening of the Alfred Langton Nurses' Home[8] in April 1925 the Marlborough Maternity Section moved from Endsleigh Street to the old nurses' quarters. In 1924 work also started on two new wards over the casualty block – to take venereal and septic obstetric cases. They were called the Consuela Marlborough Block in honour of the Duchess.[9]

In October 1924 the School Committee supported McIlroy's idea of opening a maternity hostel in north Islington or north St Pancras. The HRH Duchess of York Maternity Centre was established at 434 Essex Road and 1 Dorset Street, Islington, which had tram and bus connections to RFH. Lord Riddell (Fig 9.2) bought and equipped it; the Scottish Women's Hospitals Association gave £1000 a year for running costs. The formal opening in October 1925 was by Dame Janet Campbell, an LSMW alumna, then in charge of Maternity and Child Welfare at the Ministry of Health.[xxxiii]

Gynaecology was taught at RFH and at the Elizabeth Garrett Anderson Hospital (EGAH),[10] but in January 1922 the University threatened withdrawal of recognition of EGAH unless it established separate wards for gynaecological cases within the year. Its delay in complying meant it was not formally recognised for gynaecology until early in 1924.[xxxiv]

Louise McIlroy's time as director of the Unit was not plain sailing. In October 1925 the UGC, before recommending continuation of the Unit's grant, sought assurance that her tenure as director, and as a university professor, would extend beyond the five year probationary period ending in February 1926. However, Medical Committee members,[11] profoundly dissatisfied with McIlroy, recommended the appointment of a new director. Langton (the Weekly Board's Chairman), Lord Riddell and the Dean (now 'Dame' Louisa) interviewed the Committee's chairman (Phear), secretary (Hare), and Norbury to discuss the Committee's report.[xxxv]

McIlroy and her solicitor had made it clear she would remain a candidate for the directorship and would court the fullest possible inquiry into the matter. The

[8] The new nurses' home housed 80 nurses and maids and had a large dining room for students and hospital staff.

[9] She had divorced the Duke and was now Mrs Jacques Balsan, having remarried in July 1921.

[10] The name of the 'New Hospital for Women' was changed to EGAH after Garrett Anderson's death.

[11] The Meeting on 12 October was attended by 4 women (the Dean, Chodak-Gregory, Lewis & Hare) & 8 men (Phear, Joll, Dible, Norbury, Ulysses Williams, Gay French, Hepburn & Shattuck).

Fig 9.2 Lord Riddell (1865-1934)

Weekly Board wrote to Council, agreeing the Unit should continue and setting out the views of the Medical Committee.[12] The last met again on 26 October[13] and discussed a letter from the Board explaining why the recommendation that McIlroy should be replaced had been rejected. The Committee expressed surprise that more weight had been attached to a board of inspection, held two years earlier, than to the considered opinion of individual members of the Committee which took into account the whole of the Unit's existence. Stress had been laid on good

[12] There is no indication in Council minutes of the dissatisfaction of the Medical Committee.

[13] Apart from the Dean, all present at the first meeting attended, plus Mrs Vaughan Sawyer, Mant, Haldin Davies, Branson & Jenner Hoskin.

examination results, but the Board had to realise that many taught O & G, and credit for examination results could not go just to a single individual.[xxxvi]

The Board asked why the Medical Committee had not made its views known earlier; it retorted that criticism was more appropriate at the end rather than during the course of a probationary period, and while spontaneous criticism might be difficult, criticism in response to a request for an expression of opinion was a duty. The Committee felt the Board's decision indicated a lack of confidence in its judgement and members questioned whether they could continue meeting their present responsibilities to the Weekly Board. They did so only for the sake of the Hospital and School! [14, xxxvii]

Following a request from LSMW the University wrote on 19 November 1925 that McIlroy had been reappointed to the university chair of O & G without time-limit up to the age set for retirement. She continued as director and the UGC renewed the grant. On 30 November McIlroy, responding to a letter from the Weekly Board's chairman, wrote that she would not press for an inquiry about recent matters.[xxxviii]

Changes in Administrative and Teaching Staff

Acland was Chairman of Council throughout Aldrich-Blake's time as Dean. Henderson, the Treasurer, returned from war service early in 1919 and suggested that Sir Alan Anderson, who acted during his absence, remain as Treasurer. This meant Henderson, also the School's solicitor, had to be co-opted on to Council. Dorothy Hare also joined Council in 1919. In January 1921 she pointed out that her employment as RFH's medical registrar contravened article 6 of the School's Memorandum of Association allowing only one Council member to hold at the School 'any salaried office or any office paid by fees'. To resolve the issue Henderson relinquished all payment accruing to him as solicitor, and Hare became the Council member eligible to receive fees from the School. [15, xxxix]

In November 1925 May Thorne resigned as Hon. Secretary – explaining that she had, for several years, found herself unable to maintain close enough contact with the students. Janet Aitken, a relatively recent graduate, replaced her.

Poor health led Miss Baines, the assistant secretary, to resign in March 1921. Agneta Beauchamp took her place.[16] Miss E. M. Jukes BA, appointed as LSMW's first registrar in 1918, resigned in March 1923 to become private secretary to the Provost of UCL. The general office took over her work, and the post of registrar lapsed until 1953. Outside school hours Jukes had worked for the Executive

[14] The Medical Committee minutes give no views of individual members or details of the discussions.

[15] Hare served in Malta 1916-7 & was Medical Director of the Woman's Royal Naval Service in 1918-9.

[16] There were 215 applicants for the job

Committee of the UK Branch of the Dufferin Fund, of which Miss Brooks was Honorary Secretary. The general office also took over that work, for which the Dufferin committee paid a fee of £50 per annum.

Winifred Leyshon, appointed demonstrator of physics in 1917, left in 1918, at the request of the Signals Experimental Establishment (Royal Engineers) to work on short distance radio telephony, a field in which she was a pioneer. She returned to LSMW in 1920 and was made head of physics in 1947.[xl]

Wood-Jones, then LSMW's only professor, resigned in December 1918 to take the chair of anatomy at Adelaide; as a leaving gift the students gave him a microscope. Council considered appointing another professor, but instead made Lucas-Keene lecturer in anatomy and promoted her to reader in May 1920. In November 1924 Senate agreed to confer the title of professor upon her when her salary was raised to £800 per annum; this Council did without delay.[xli]

In November 1919 the University conferred the title of professor on Winifred Cullis. She was the first woman appointed to a chair in a British medical school – and the second in any British university[17] – so when she lectured at Vassar College, New York, in March 1920 she really was a 'visiting professor'.

The University refused Ransom a chair in pharmacology in 1919 and again in 1923, the year he resigned owing to poor health. Eleanor Scarborough, his demonstrator since 1919, took over the department and was promoted to reader in 1924.

In December 1919 Dr George Scott Williamson MC was appointed pathologist and director of pathological studies at RFH. He replaced Mary Schofield, the acting pathologist following Elizabeth Lepper's departure to the RAMC. He was made Reader in Pathology at LSMW in May 1920. From March 1922 he had help from Iris Fox, a clinical pathologist and assistant director of pathological studies.[18] Sadly she died of septicaemia four weeks after an accident in the post-mortem room on Christmas Eve 1925.[xlii]

Scott Williamson proved a disappointment. Council reproached him in May 1922 for acting, without permission, as pathologist to the London Throat, Nose and Ear Hospital, and for unauthorized expenditure. In October 1924 the Dean reviewed his departmental accounts with him. Shortly afterwards LSMW applied to the University for a chair in pathology linked with RFH. It was not intended for Scott Williamson. He was sacked in December.[19, xliii]

---

[17] Caroline Spurgeon assumed the chair of English literature at Bedford College in 1913.

[18] Her brother, later Sir Theodore Fox, was editor of *The Lancet* from 1944 to 1964.

[19] With Innes Hope Pearse (1890-1979), the first female medical registrar at the London Hospital and his assistant in thyroid studies, George Scott Williamson later started the famous 'Peckham experiment', i.e. the Pioneer Health Centre, a unique experiment in community health.

James Henry Dible, who took the chair in April 1925, aged thirty-five, proved a great success. After graduating in Glasgow in 1912 he was a pathology demonstrator in Sheffield and during the war commanded an RAMC mobile laboratory. He joined LSMW from Manchester Royal Infirmary, having published eleven papers. In October Lucy Wills, honorary chemical pathologist to RFH, arrived as demonstrator in pathological chemistry. Dible moved to Cardiff after three years.[xliv]

Berry and Cunning were left as surgeons after Willmott Evans retired in 1919. RFH did not appoint another 'Surgeon for Diseases of the Skin' to replace Evans. Instead it chose to appoint Haldin-Davis as 'Dermatologist'. James Berry (Sir James from 1925), retired as senior surgeon in 1920 and Cecil Joll replaced him as surgeon. Aldrich-Blake and Willmott Evans relinquished the joint Lectureship in Surgery in May 1921; Joll replaced them and unified the appointment.[xlv]

However, when Walter Carr resigned the lectureship in medicine six months later Council decided all of RFH's physicians and assistant physicians should contribute to the two-year course of 40 lectures. Carr also resigned as physician at RFH. His replacement Percy Whittington Saunders was a Toronto graduate (MB with gold medal), and assistant physician at RFH for ten years before joining Phear and Branson as a full physician in 1923; he was also assistant physician at the National Hospital, Queen Square. Within months of being appointed physician he succumbed to an obscure malignant disease.[xlvi] He was not replaced. Jenner Hoskin was appointed as an extra assistant physician, joining Mrs Chodak-Gregory and Dorothy Hare. He remained an assistant physician for some time but from 1924 also served as Physician to the Cardiographic Department.

In 1921 Charles Brehmer Heald, now an MRCP, was appointed 'Medical Officer of Electro-therapeutics and Massage' at RFH. Ten years earlier he was RMO at Bart's where he qualified in 1909. During WW1 he served with the Navy, the RAMC and the Royal Flying Corps. He was the first medical officer attached to an active service flying unit and earned his pilot's wings. In 1920 he became Chief Medical Adviser to the Civil Aviation authority. He was to become a pioneer of rheumatology.[xlvii]

There was continuity in some of the senior appointments at RFH towards the end of Aldrich-Blake's deanship. Hepburn was ophthalmic surgeon, Ulysses Williams radiologist, Mrs Harwood dentist, and Gay French ENT surgeon (with Harold Mant as assistant surgeon from 1923). Mrs Gilliatt (née Kann, MB 1910) was an anaesthetist throughout Aldrich-Blake's time as dean;[20] most of her fellow senior anaesthetists were also LSMW alumnae, including Mrs Dickinson-Berry (MB

---

[20] Her husband (Sir) William Gilliatt of KCH was the gynaecologist who delivered Prince Charles & Princess Ann.

1889), the wife of (Sir) James Berry, and Mrs Sprott (née Broster, MBBS 1911) who had an early Daimler built for her. A male anaesthetist, Vivian Orr, served from 1911-1917, and another two males, Claude W. Morris (in 1919) & N. MacDonald (1920), later joined Gilliatt, Sprott and Dickinson-Berry; the last retired in 1921.

In July 1919 Dr Bernard Spilsbury became lecturer in forensic medicine and toxicology, and from November 1920 Sir Leonard Rogers held the Stuart Mill lectureship in tropical medicine.

Clubs and Societies

Most of LSMW's clubs and societies flourished just before and after the end of the war. Christmas parties were held in December 1918, and LSMW's annual dinners resumed on 13 March 1920. The Magazine for March 1918 reported that the Medical Society 'after some years of obscurity…has taken on a new lease of life'. It usually met at the Hospital, but in December 1921 members viewed 'cinematographic bacteriological films' in the Hunter Street Common room. The Society was well supported by students but few staff attended meetings.[xlviii]

The Dramatic Society was resurrected in 1917. To celebrate the war's end it performed 'As You Like It' in Regent's Park on Gala Day – 19 July 1919 – the nation's official 'Peace Day'. Subsequent productions raised money for the RFH appeal fund. When, in March 1925, the Students' Union requested money to buy a proper stage for the Dramatic Society Council provided half the estimated cost of £40.[xlix]

The Choral Society got going again at the end of 1917. It sang the customary carols at RFH and other hospitals, and performed at Students' Union events. By Christmas 1918 the membership had risen to fifty. The following year it put on a good show at the Students' Social. Its conductor, Janet Aitken, an outstanding musician, resigned some months later and a fellow student, Mary Swann, took over the baton. At a concert in 1923 Dr Phear played the piano, and accompanied Marjorie Hayward, a student who played the viola, and R.G.K. Lempfert, a violinist who became a distinguished meteorologist. The Society performed 'Trial by Jury' in 1925.[l]

Dance classes began again in the autumn of 1918, and the club was re-activated the following spring. Initially classes and practice sessions were held fortnightly (in alternate weeks). Membership grew and there were soon twice-weekly classes, except in summer. In May 1921 a poor attendance, owing to the miners' strike, meant the annual big dance lost money. Fortunately the profit on the first dance of the Christmas term cleared the deficit, and an increase in the Dance Club's grant allowed for a considerable reduction in the subscription.[li]

The Debating Society's fifty members joined with staff in December 1919 to consider the motion 'That the sale of intoxicating liquors should be prohibited in the British Isles'. The following year the motion 'That co-education among medical students is advisable' was carried by 33 to 20, while 'That a uniform style dress should be adopted by medical women' was rejected by 14 votes. The Magazine carried no reports about the Debating Society for some years after 1922.[lii]

In 1919 Miss Llewelyn Davies addressed the Socialist Society on 'Care of Maternity from a Socialist Standpoint', and Dr Lawson Dodd on 'A National Medical Service'. By 1921 it had metamorphosed into a Social and Political Society which, without political affiliation, kept members in touch with current events; its 60 to 70 members chose the subjects and outside speakers. After a meeting on 'The Coal Crisis', Lady Rhondda's talk on 'The Six Point Group', considered the role of women in political life. The society was short-lived.[liii]

The Literary Society, formed early in 1919, soon had about 80 members and the following year ran competitions, with prizes for poems and essays. It held weekly poetry readings in 1921-22. The first outsider to give one, Alfred Noyes, read from his own poetry. [liv]

Sport was important at LSMW, and the various clubs flourished with the wartime influx of students. For the 1919-20 season the Hockey Club had 57 players and fielded three XIs; two years later it had 75 members and for the following season it hired a charabanc to reach the ground in Edmonton, even for mid-week practices.

Fencing prospered in 1919 and 1920 and, at Professor Tassart's Salle d'Armes, club members fought for the LSMW Challenge cup presented by Miss Cullis, herself a keen fencer; Miss Walker, the Ladies amateur champion, was a judge. Doris Odlum reached the semi-finals of the Ladies' Amateur Fencing Championship in 1920, but four years later the club had only ten members, mostly beginners.

In 1921 the coal strikes caused many baths to close, but the Swimming Club's 77 members could still use St Marylebone Baths on Tuesdays and those at St Pancras on Wednesdays. In 1923 the club competed against Somerville College, Oxford, the Inter-Hospital Nurses Swimming Club and London's women's colleges.

The Tennis Club, victorious in the three previous intercollegiate competitions, won the cup again in 1919 even though the LSMW women at St Mary's entered their own team for the new trophy. The purple patch did not continue. In 1920 the new courts at Cricklewood were difficult to reach and members were grateful for their access to Miss Waller's court. It was a wet summer; most matches were cancelled and some were played in testing conditions. In 1921 the club used courts at Belsize Park, but despite a membership of over 100 it struggled to raise teams and lost half its matches.

The Boating Club's race against Newnham College, Cambridge at Marlow on 14 June 1919 was a historic event – the first ladies' eight-oar boat race on the Thames. Newnham won by 1¾ lengths, but LSMW had not rowed as an VIII until the previous day; it had trained as two IVs! The boats were lent by Marlow Rowing Club. That year Doris Odlum, LSMW's stroke, was one of the first seven women to receive an Oxford MA.[21] A member of the Women's Volunteer Reserve, she had suspended her medical studies during the war, and for two years ran a large government forage depot.[lv]

Newnham won by four feet in 1920. In 1921 there was a dead heat! That year Margaret Geddes, an LSMW student,[22] ran a Boat Club dance. The proceeds provided the club with its own eight-oar boat, and her mother presented a silver cup for the annual Newnham race. Oddly the LSMW Magazine did not cover the race on 23 June 1922; the *Westminster Gazette* of 11 May carried a photograph of the LSMW crew, and the *Daily Telegraph* reported Newnham's victory by four lengths. LSMW won in 1923, 1924 and 1925. In 1923, just before the University of London formed a Women's Rowing Club, a Rowing Club split off from the Boating Club.[lvi]

Early in 1921 a few cricket enthusiasts undertook 'with some trepidation' to raise a team to play at other colleges' grounds. Soon there was a Cricket Club affiliated to the Union. It won three of its first five matches, lost one and tied one. Bedford College provided a practice net on two evenings a week. Lloyd-Williams, a future Dean of LSMW, was the first captain. In 1922 the club found a ground at Wembley Park, and five of its members turned out for the newly formed ULAU Cricket Club. Photographs of the team that played Bedford College at Harrow in 1922 appeared in the *Sunday Express* (14 May) and *Daily Sketch* (15 May).[lvii]

Because LSMW lacked its own playing fields the different sports clubs had to rent separate and widely scattered grounds. This was uneconomical and inconvenient so efforts began to acquire a ground. The Magazine for December 1923 announced: *Wanted – a Playing Field by LSMW. Will any member of the School, past or present, who can suggest a suitable neighbourhood or site within reasonable reach of the School, kindly communicate with Miss Partridge at 39 Weymouth Street.*[23]

Partridge, then President of the Students' Union, found one at Sudbury in April 1925. Costing £3000 it occupied six and a half acres of rough land on the main road

---

[21] Odlum took her honours degree in 1912, when women were not allowed the title Bachelor of Arts.

[22] Geddes abandoned her studies.

[23] Joyce Partridge FRCS studied joints as an anatomy demonstrator. After 15 yrs of surgery & anatomy she took up psychiatry and worked at the Tavistock Clinic before moving to Devon.

between Wembley and Harrow, and was bounded to the south by a railway cutting. The Students' Union could not legally hold freehold land, so the School bought it. Council did not charge the Union rent but asked it to find £2000 to develop the site as a sports ground for hockey, cricket, lacrosse and tennis and then to maintain it. Sadly the Dean died before it came into use in October 1926.

The Jubilee [lviii]

One of the great events of Aldrich-Blake's deanship was LSMW's Jubilee; detailed planning for it began in October 1923. Dean Inge offered the use of St Paul's Cathedral on Saturday 25 October 1924 – for a service of thanksgiving for the opportunities for training, work and service opened to women during the fifty years of the School's existence. A Jubilee committee [24] dealt with the main celebrations – including the service, a dinner and a special meeting at the School.[lix]

The occasion was also considered an excellent opportunity for increasing the endowment of LSMW. In June 1924 the Appeal Committee suggested that a fund of £60,000 be raised to endow three chairs, in anatomy, physiology and pathology, bearing the names of Elizabeth Blackwell, Sophia Jex-Blake and Elizabeth Garrett Anderson respectively. An organising secretary was appointed. Gifts and promises amounting to £7,518 had already been made, including £50 from the Queen and £1000 from Dr Scharlieb. However, a month later it was realised that a direct appeal for funds had already been made to past students in connection with RFH's jubilee in 1928, and Council felt it would be improper for the Appeal Committee to approach them again on behalf of the School's endowment fund.[lx]

The celebrations on 24 and 25 October 1924 were grand affairs. They received wide coverage in the national press – and on Thursday evening, 23 October, Professor Cullis broadcast from radio station 2LO,[25] and spoke about the lives of Blackwell, Jex-Blake & Garrett Anderson. [lxi]

On 24 October 467 people dined at the Guildhall; they paid 30 shillings (£1.50) for a nine course meal,[26] accompanied by sherry, Graves, champagne (G H Mumm, Cordon Rouge 1913), port (Cockburn's) and soft drinks. The Band of the Royal Regiment of Artillery played before and during the meal.

---

[24] The School's honorary officials plus Lady Barrett, Mrs Scharlieb, Dr Louisa Garrett Anderson, Dr Jane Walker, Dr Chadburn, Dr Lucas-Keene, Dr Janet Aitken, Miss Henrietta Jex-Blake, Mr James Berry, Dr Walter Carr, Mr Reginald Smith and representatives of the Academic Staff Association, Medical Committee and Students' Union.

[25] 2LO was the call sign of a radio station & transmitter at Marconi House in the Strand, London. In 1922 the newly formed British Broadcasting Company took over the call sign and transmitter.

[26] Hors s'Oeuvres, Tortue Claire, Filets de Sole, Ouefs Dauphine, Noisettes d'Agneau à la Bouquetière, Faisans en Cocotte, Charlotte Russe, Glacé Praline, and Dessert followed by coffee.

Dame Mary Scharlieb toasted 'Our Most Illustrious Doctor, His Majesty the King' and the Royal Family. Dean Inge toasted 'Women's Work' and, lauding their achievements during the war, noted they could now vote and work in almost every field open to men – except the Church. He thought they should enter the ministry, that women should confess to women, and that the disparity of the sexes in the churches, often regretted by clergy, might be redressed if there was a young and attractive 'vicaress' in the pulpit. Dean Inge's remarks offended many newspaper readers the next morning. Lady Barrett and Mrs Fawcett replied on behalf of women.[lxii]

Professor Ernest Gardner, the Vice-Chancellor, proposed a toast to 'The London (RFH) School of Medicine for Women'. When the Dean got up to respond everyone rose to sing 'For she's a jolly good fellow'. She presented Langton, the Hospital's Chairman, with a list of new subscribers and donors to RFH who had been recruited during Jubilee Year by past and present students. Finally, Professor Cullis toasted 'The Chairman' – Dame Mary Scharlieb, the School's President – who received a bouquet from the Students' Representative.

At 2:30 p.m. on Saturday a Service of Thanksgiving was held at St Paul's. Princess Beatrice and Princess Arthur of Connaught represented the Royal family. The procession, headed by a student, included distinguished former students, past and present members of staff, three nieces of Sophia Jex-Blake, and representatives of RFH, the Royal Colleges, the Ministry of Health, and many women's organisations. The Dean and the President of the School brought up the rear.

The organist of St Paul's, Dr Charles MacPherson, conducted members of the London Symphony Orchestra who played Sullivan's overture 'In Memoriam', the larghetto from Beethoven's second symphony, and Mackenzie's Benedictus. The service included the 103rd Psalm; Matthew v, 1-15, as the lesson; and the Magnificat, set to music by Sir Charles Stanford. After the hymn 'For all the saints who from their labours rest, …' the Archdeacon of London announced: *'Through the ages there have been women in spirit born before their time. They had vision and faith, and by their toil and sacrifice, by their persistence and courage, opportunities for women in training, work and service have been won. Three Pioneers opened the doors of Medicine to Women – Elizabeth Blackwell, Elizabeth Garrett Anderson, Sophia Jex-Blake. With love and reverence our hearts turn to them.'*

The theme of the Bishop of Lichfield's sermon was from Paul's Epistle to the Ephesians (4:1) – 'I beseech you that ye may walk worthy of the vocation wherewith ye are called'. William Blakes's 'A Vision of Jerusalem', sung to the music of Sir Hubert Parry, preceded the sermon, which was followed by the hymn 'Now thank we all our God'. Elgar's Imperial March followed the Blessing and

National Anthem. A collection covered the expenses of the service and the balance was given to RFH.

On Saturday evening there was a party at Hunter Street. The Dean received guests in the students' common room from 8 until 9.15 p.m. Scientific exhibits were on view in several departments – demonstrations involving liquid air in the Physiology Theatre, and electromotive response demonstrations in the Physics Theatre. There were Dramatic Society performances in the Long Room, Choral Society concerts in the common room, and refreshments in the marquee in the quadrangle and in the Union room.

On 5 November Council thanked Louisa Garrett Anderson and Lucas-Keene for their untiring devotion in organising the service and the dinner, and expressed their appreciation for the work of the office staff: Miss Brooks was given £25 and a fortnight's holiday (because she had been unwell); Miss Beauchamp and Miss Culverwell got £10 each, and Miss Burt three guineas.

In the New Year's honours published on 30 December 1924 Aldrich-Blake was appointed a Dame Commander of the British Empire. She was the second woman doctor to receive the honour – Dame Janet Campbell was the first, earlier in the year.

About a year before the centenary celebrations Aldrich-Blake fell ill, but despite the progression of her cancer she continued working until days before her death. She last visited the School, for a Council meeting, on 18 November 1925 and on 16 December chaired Council at her home, 17 Nottingham Place, where she died 28 December 1925.

A fine portrait of Aldrich-Blake, painted by Sir William Orpen in 1921, (Fig 9.3 Colour plate) was displayed at the Royal Academy in 1923. It was presented to the School by those who raised the funds for it. From 1924 it hung in the School's library.

In her will Dame Louisa left about £38,000 (c £1,500,000 today). LSMW, RFH & EGAH each received £1000, and her secretary and maid were both left £500; her chauffeur got six months' wages. To Rosamund Wigram, who lived with her, she left £2000, all household and personal effects not otherwise bequeathed, the use of 17 Nottingham Place for 12 months, and the income for life from a trust fund of £6000. The rest went to relatives and friends.[lxiii]

At Council on 27 January 1926 Acland stated it was now customary for the School Committee to nominate the Dean and he proposed letting it do so at its meeting on 3 February. Council agreed unanimously with its nomination of Lady Barrett.

Aldrich-Blake was not forgotten. Lord Riddell soon wrote her biography,[lxiv] and a memorial fund committee decided to commemorate her – with a public monument, by hanging replicas of Sir William Orpen's portrait of her at RFH and EGAH, and by providing a travelling scholarship open to women graduates from United Kingdom medical schools. (See Chapter 10.)

CHAPTER 10

Lady Barrett (1925-1931)

Midwifery and Mysticism

Lady Barrett (Fig 10.1) was arguably the most colourful of the School's deans. At fifty-nine she was the oldest on taking up the post; her five year term of office was the shortest.

She was born Florence Elizabeth Perry at Compton Greenfield, Gloucestershire in 1867. Fourteen years later the family lived at Avonleigh, Stoke Bishop.[i] Her father, Benjamin, was a railway agent and wharfinger.[1] He and his wife had five children and employed a governess and three servants.

In 1891 Florence was the first woman to enter the Bristol Medical School which could not then award degrees. She graduated B.Sc. (Lond) as an external student in 1895 and the following year married Frederick Willey, an Australian fellow student at Bristol.[ii] He qualified MBBS Durham in 1894. They moved to London and Florence entered LSMW in October 1896. She graduated MB London in 1900 (with honours in obstetrics) and later BS (1901), MS (1904) and MD (1906). In 1901 the Willeys lived at 8 Avenue Road, Hornsey – with a cook, housemaid, coachman & page.[iii]

After qualifying Florence held several junior posts at RFH – assistant anaesthetist; ophthalmic assistant; surgical house officer & clinical pathologist; surgical & gynæcological registrar (with responsibility for the new Xray department); and gynæcological assistant & anaesthetist). Appointed Assistant Physician for diseases of women in 1908, she succeeded Scharlieb as Lecturer in Midwifery in 1913. Ahead of her time, she organized ante-natal clinics at RFH and emphasized the importance of an adequate diet for expectant and nursing mothers. She was also senior surgeon at the Salvation Army Maternity Hospital in Clapton, and ran a large private practice.[iv]

The Willeys divorced in 1909.[v] In 1916, by special licence,[2] Florence married the 72 year-old bachelor Sir William Fletcher Barrett FRS, Professor of Physics at Dublin's Royal College of Science from 1873 to 1910. He left Ireland to join her in London. In 1917 Willey, now Lady Barrett, was appointed CBE and in 1929,

---

1 Owner or keeper of a wharf.

2 Special licences were rarely granted when the former spouse of a divorced person was still alive – and Frederick Willey outlived his ex-wife.

while Dean, she was appointed a Companion of Honour. Sir William died in May 1925, shortly before she became Dean.

In 1882 Sir William, with Gurney, Myers and Sidgwick, founded the Society for Psychical Research (SPR), which encouraged scientific investigations into telepathy, mesmerism, mediums, apparitions and physical phenomena associated with séances. It had the support of authors (Alfred Lord Tennyson, Mark Twain, Lewis Carroll & Arthur Conan Doyle); scientists (Lord Rayleigh, Sir Oliver Lodge & Sir Joseph J. Thompson); philosophers (Jung and William James); and politicians (Gladstone, and the Balfour brothers, Arthur and Gerald, whose sisters married Sidgwick and Rayleigh). Florence shared her husband's interest in psychic research; her book *Personality Survives Death; Messages from Sir William Barrett, edited by his Wife* appeared in 1937.[vi]

Fig 10.1 Lady Barrett (1865-1947)

In 1916 Lady Barrett served, along with Mudge, LSMW's biology lecturer, on the Eugenics Education Society's Council. Although an advocate of birth control she expressed concern in *Conception Control* (1922)[vii] that it was practised mainly by intelligent people – '*For the birth-rate amongst the least intelligent, least efficient and the mentally deficient will be unaffected…After…such weeding out of the best, with the continuous multiplication of the worst type of citizen, the general standard of efficiency, enterprise and executive skill of the nation would be seriously impaired.*' Scharlieb held similar views about the consequences of contraception but, unlike Barrett, was opposed to it. Barrett was also involved with the temperance movement. From 1931 to 1933 she was president of the Society for the Study of Addiction, as Scharlieb had been twenty years earlier.

Barrett remained on RFH's honorary staff while Dean and in May 1926, with McIlroy's agreement, was given three beds in the O & G Unit, an arrangement approved by the Board of Education and the UGC, providing the beds remained within the Unit. Her link with the Unit ended when she resigned as Dean.[viii]

The teaching staff still complained about inadequate representation on Council and so in June 1925 Council asked the Board of Trade if it could increase its membership to fourteen – and if three members, rather than one, could be paid a salary or fees by the School. The Board did not object but said only teachers could join Council and receive remuneration, and that changes had to conform to the Companies Act 1908.[ix]

Henderson advised against changing the Memorandum and Articles of Association which would be expensive and difficult. Instead Council considered applying to the Privy Council for a Royal Charter. Acland, himself a Privy Councillor, was to make preliminary inquiries.[x]

Council discussed a draft charter in March 1926 but before it could examine a revised version on 14 July Sir Alan Anderson resigned as Treasurer.[3] He objected to certain proposals in the draft, and questioned the legality of handing over trusts created to promote the interest of medical women to a Council not primarily appointed for that purpose. Acland forecast difficulties if Anderson's objections were raised before the Privy Council, and so application for a charter was deferred indefinitely. Sir Alan agreed to continue as Treasurer. Council reconsidered the matter on 17 December 1930, when Acland[4] placed on the table the draft charter abandoned in 1926. Two days later Sir Alan wrote again questioning the wisdom of the proposed changes and the matter was dropped until 1936.[xi]

In July 1926 Council considered appointing a Vice-Dean.[5] As only one Council member could receive fees from the School Dorothy Hare,[6] then Assistant Physician, offered to relinquish her emoluments from School funds to facilitate the appointment of a Vice-Dean. In the event Lucas Keene took the post without payment.

In November Council, unable to add more salaried members, discussed with the School Committee how teachers might be more involved with School policy and organisation. They agreed that while the School Committee would provide the nominations for the offices of Dean, Vice Dean and Honorary Secretary Council would have to approve them. The Vice Dean and Hon. Sec. were to be eligible for annual reappointment for up to four years, a term to be exceeded only under exceptional circumstances. The Vice-Dean was to vacate office if a new Dean was appointed.[xii]

Lucas-Keene, affected by these new rules, stepped down as Vice-Dean in 1930 and was replaced by Janet Aitken, The latter had been Hon. Sec. following May

---

[3] And therefore his seat on Council.

[4] Now Sir Francis Acland. He succeeded his father and became the 14th baronet in October 1926.

[5] The post lapsed with Aldrich-Blake's election as Dean; it is unclear whether this was to save money.

[6] Hare held some hospital posts before entering general practice in Cambridge in 1910. She served with the RAMC in Malta from 1916, and in 1918 was Medical Director of the new Women's Royal Naval Service. Later medical registrar at RFH, she passed the MRCP in 1920 and was the 3rd woman FRCP.

Thorne's resignation in 1925, but Cullis took over the post in 1928. Aitken, born in Buenos Aires in 1886, was a talented musician who had studied in Paris and at the Manchester College of Music.[7] While training as a masseuse during the First World War she decided to study medicine. She entered LSMW in 1916, aged thirty, and qualified in 1922. When Barrett's term as dean ended in January 1931 Aitken, following the rules, stepped down as Vice-Dean; she was re-elected and served until October 1933.[xiii]

There were relatively few changes among the teaching staff during Barrett's deanship, and no changes among premedical teachers[8] who, in 1928, became eligible for appointment as professors or readers. The University rejected applications for readerships for Widdows, Mudge and Waller.[xiv] The last certainly had the interests of LSMW at heart. To save it money she had became a 'part-time' lecturer in June 1923, resuming full time status in 1927. Although head of physics from 1915 she was not a 'recognized teacher' of the University until 1927, the year after she published her textbook on physics for medical students.[xv]

The preclinical teachers had no promotion problems. Cullis (physiology) and Lucas-Keene (anatomy) were already professors when Barrett became dean; Gardner, nominally head of chemistry, was made reader in physiological chemistry in 1920, and Eleanor Scarborough reader in pharmacology in 1927.

Cullis and Lucas-Keene held personal not established chairs. The Jubilee appeal for funds to endow chairs named after Blackwell, Jex-Blake and Garrett Anderson had proved disappointing. By March 1926, £18,880 had been raised for the Jex-Blake chair, £2015 (plus a £10,000 reversionary gift) for the Garrett Anderson chair, and £93 for the Blackwell chair. Council earmarked £20,000 for the first chair and Winifred Cullis was appointed as the 'Sophia Jex-Blake Professor of Physiology' in June. Her salary had already been raised to £1000 per annum, the University having announced that professors and readers should have minimum salaries of £1000 and £500 p.a. respectively; those of Professors Dible (pathology) and Lucas-Keene (anatomy) were raised to £900 p.a., and then to £1000 in October 1927.[xvi]

A fundraiser, Mrs Balfour Duffus, was sent to the USA to persuade Americans to support the Elizabeth Blackwell Chair in Anatomy. She returned in July 1926, having raised only £910, claiming little interest there in the work of medical women. By January 1927 the Blackwell fund held £2004, but the idea of the Blackwell & Garrett Anderson chairs had been abandoned.[xvii]

---

[7] Aitken won the gold medal for singing at the Manchester College in 1912.

[8] i.e. Teachers of chemistry, physics, biology etc, not preclinical teachers of anatomy, physiology etc.

Cullis played a key role at LSMW, particularly during the 1920s and 30s when there were prolonged discussions with RFH and the University on the medical education of women. She also had many outside interests. In March 1930 the BBC asked her staff to broadcast weekly lectures on physiology, and that summer, at Sir George Newman's request, she supervised physiology teaching at Dartford Training College. In 1931 she visited Massachusetts' Wellesley College for a meeting of the International Federation of University Women (IFUW), of which she was president from 1929-32.[9,xviii]

The only senior academic staff at RFH worked in pathology and O & G. Funding of pathology was contentious and the Hospital refused to contribute to the professor's salary in 1927 and 1930. Dible moved to Cardiff in January 1928. His replacement, Geoffrey Hadfield, a Bart's product, had been an RAMC pathologist in France, Gallipoli and Mesopotamia during the war, and was a clinical pathologist at Bristol General Hospital before joining LSMW.

The pathology department was clearly too small and Hadfield, like Dible, tried to improve its facilities. There was limited teaching space at RFH, and from 1914 the pathology research room and workshop were accommodated in a Hunter Street basement. In 1928, during planning for the Eastman Dental Clinic (see later) it was decided part of the clinic's basement should house a pathology extension.[xix]

In January 1926 Iris Fox, senior assistant pathologist and assistant director of pathological studies, died from septicaemia following a post-mortem room accident on Christmas Eve.[10,xx] In her memory friends raised £350 towards extending the pathological laboratory. Her replacement was Joan Ross, assistant pathologist at St. Mary's Hospital, where Ross had been an LSMW clinical student. Her book *Post Mortem Appearances*, a classic text, ran to six editions between 1925 and 1963. In January 1929 she sought permission to act as consulting pathologist to St Pancras South Hospital, a post paying £100 a year. Hadfield agreed, as involving LSMW staff in St Pancras's post-mortems would enhance the students' pathology experience. Council, however, created a new post of 'assistant morbid anatomist & curator of the museum'; it involved work at St Pancras, payment for which contributed to the salary. Gertrude Harre, the first appointee, was replaced after a year by Florence Louis. The latter announced within months that she was to marry but the terms of her appointment were not affected.[xxi]

In 1928 Lucy Wills (MBBS 1920), a demonstrator in pathological chemistry from 1925, went to India to study macrocytic anaemia of pregnancy. She

---

[9] The IFUW was founded by Virginia Gildersleeve (Barnard College USA), Caroline Spurgeon (Bedford College) & Rose Sidgwick (Birmingham University) in 1919. Sidgwick died in the 1919 influenza pandemic. Spurgeon, Britain's first woman professor, was the first president (1920-1922).

[10] Iris was the sister of Theodore Fox (later Sir Theodore), editor of *The Lancet* from 1944 to 1964.

discovered that yeast and the yeast extract Marmite cured it – a finding that led to the discovery of folic acid. The Marmite Company was run by the brother of Marguerite Pam, a fellow LSMW student.

Although RFH's Medical Committee had tried to remove Louise McIlroy the O & G Unit prospered under her guidance – and she was appointed DBE in 1929. Her first 'first assistant', Gertrude Dearnley, became gynaecologist at RFH in 1926 when Ethel Vaughan-Sawyer retired,[11] and later replaced the latter as lecturer in gynaecology.

In 1924 Helen Chambers, then a radium research officer at the Middlesex, recruited several LSMW trained surgeons (Lady Barrett, Lady Briscoe, Maud Chadburn and Louisa Martindale) for a trial of the effects of radium therapy on uterine carcinoma; McIlroy and Elizabeth Bolton became involved later. During the first three years of the study over 300 patients were treated at RFH, EGAH, the South London Hospital and the New Sussex Hospital at Brighton. The good results led to the foundation of the Marie Curie Hospital in Hampstead.[xxii]

There were few changes in RFH's senior staff during Barrett's deanship. Ill health caused Branson to resign in November 1926.[12] His general medical beds went to Lancelot Burrell, a chest physician. Hazel Chodak-Gregory, an assistant physician, took charge of the new Riddell children's wards.[13] After they opened the School Committee thought all the students should attend the children's post at RFH (under Gregory and Phear) and that a month at Great Ormond Street was superfluous. However the students were keen to retain that link so it was agreed that if final year students still wished to spend a month at 'Ormond Street' after taking the RFH course the School would pay for it. With the opening of the children's department RFH had to have an orthopaedic surgeon in order to comply with new University requirements. Jenner Verrall was appointed.[xxiii]

Neill Hobhouse, assistant physician from 1927 and full physician from 1934, was the first RFH physician with a special interest in neurology. Arthur Phear, who should have retired in 1927, was persuaded to stay for another year. In 1897 he had married Ellen Frances, daughter of Arthur Lister FRS, an eminent botanist and younger brother of Lord Lister. An outstanding pianist, Phear presided over the Choral Society and conducted many of its performances.[14] At his retirement tea party in July 1928 the students gave him a Chesterfield couch, two Persian Bokara

---

[11] The students gave Vaughan-Sawyer an electric steriliser for her consulting rooms & a fur car rug. [Mag Nov 1926.]

[12] He lived until 1950.

[13] The new wards were opened formally by the Queen in 1927.

[14] Phear died in 1959. He presented an organ to the chapel at RFH in 1958, and gave his own piano to the Nurses' Home in 1959. (see Obit, *Lancet* 1959, 7 Mar)

rugs and a gold fountain pen. When his replacement, Harold Gardiner-Hill, left for St Thomas' Hospital in 1930 Daniel Davies was appointed assistant physician. Dorothy Hare, already a full physician, took over Gardiner-Hill's lectures.[xxiv]

The assistant general surgeons Lionel Norbury, Clement Shattock and Catherine Lewis became full surgeons in 1927 and all served many more years. Malcolm Hepburn retired as ophthalmic surgeon in 1928 and was replaced by the brilliant young LSMW graduate Ida Mann, already an honorary at the famous eye hospital Moorfields.

Alexander Foulerton lectured on public health for 16 years. Asked to replace him in March 1930 Professor Jameson said his staff at the London School of Hygiene and Tropical Medicine (LSHTM) would teach public health and preventive medicine at LSMW; he would give demonstrations at LSHTM's museum. At his suggestion his assistant, Colonel G.S. Parkinson, took the lectureship.[xxv]

Horton Mental Hospital, Epsom, had 2000 beds, and in December 1927 Colonel Lord, its medical superintendent, requested affiliation and reciprocity with LSMW/RFH. Arrangements to transfer teaching of psychiatry to Horton were finalized in October 1928. Lord became an honorary lecturer in clinical psychiatry; Porter Phillips remained lecturer in mental diseases.[xxvi]

From July 1919 Dr B. H. Spilsbury lectured on forensic medicine and toxicology, and from 1927 he was (as Sir Bernard) appointed a recognized teacher in medical jurisprudence.[xxvii]

Financial Matters

During Lady Barrett's first year as Dean (1925-6) the School's deficit was only £346 – £2000 less than the previous year. Things were looking up – costs were kept down, the Treasury grant increased, and student numbers were expected to rise. Furthermore the deaths occurred of two people who had a life interest in large bequests made to the School many years earlier (see Chapter 7). The value of the Goldsmid bequest had fallen from £3000 to £2490 owing to duty and taxation; the first instalment, £1500, was paid in June 1926 and the rest a year later. To realise the Cullimore bequest Council had to sell a house in Torquay worth about £8,000.[xxviii]

There was no major building at Hunter Street while Barrett was dean, but there were issues relating to property. After Students' Chambers Ltd acquired Nos. 9 & 10 Brunswick Square in 1928 there were over seventy students living in its seven houses, and another six on the School premises.

In June 1926 Foundling Estates, Ltd, the purchasers of the Foundling Hospital, asked LSMW if it wanted to buy the freehold of Hunter Street, and that of seven derelict houses in Compton Street. Prolonged negotiations followed and in May 1927 Foundling Estates Ltd accepted '29 years purchase' (£11,020) for the freehold of LSMW, but refused £7,500 for the Compton Street houses and freehold. Negotiations about Compton Street began again six years later.[xxix]

It was the realisation of the Goldsmid and Cullimore bequests that enabled LSMW to purchase its freehold – along with £4160 raised by redeeming the insurance policies covering termination of the lease in 1977. It was thus freed from annual expenditure of £685 for the policies and ground rent and from potential problems at the end of the lease.

In 1926 Beecham Estates and Pills Ltd, the purchasers of Foundling Hospital Estates, planned to move Covent Garden market, owned by the Beecham family, to the Foundling estate. Such a move would have greatly altered the character of Bloomsbury, where many students lived and/or worked, by changing a primarily residential area into a commercial one intersected by new roads carrying heavy traffic. Fortunately the plan was abandoned.[xxx]

The way in which LSMW received its government grant changed in 1929. Five years earlier the short lived Labour government (with Haldane as Lord Chancellor) appointed a new committee to review London University's constitution. Its chairman was Hilton Young (later Lord Kennet) whose father, Sir George Young, had campaigned for a teaching University in London forty years earlier. Changes were needed because the Senate, as constituted in 1900, could no longer control the University's large, complex organisation.

The Hilton Young report of 1926 proposed a smaller Senate, with more members from constituent schools. A 'University Council' (later named the 'University Court') was to control finances and have the authority to negotiate with grant-giving bodies and allocate funds. The University, recognised as a federal university, was to retain its 'external' side, unrestricted and undiminished.

Senate and Convocation rejected the report but the Government acted promptly and, within a year, despite opposition from the University's MP, Dr Ernest Graham-Little, it passed the University of London Act 1926. The new statutes came into effect in March 1929.[xxxi]

Government grants, previously distributed directly to colleges, now went as one sum to the University Court, which made allocations to colleges. In 1930 LSMW's annual grant was £13,100, with the promise that it would be £14,250 for the next four years, £500 being earmarked for the pathology department. By then students' fees covered only forty percent of the cost of maintaining the School so grants from state and county exchequers were essential.[xxxii]

In the mid-1920s entry to British medical schools fell after an end-of-war boost. The press implied that this would reduce employment prospects for women doctors. In response LSMW circulated the 224 alumna who qualified in 1923, '24, & '25 to ask about work undertaken since qualification ; 216 replied. Only 33 who desired paid work were without it; of those 18 had held resident appointments, and most of the rest were doing unpaid medical work. Sixty-six were in practice or assistant practice; 53 worked in hospitals, twelve in public health and 19 in the mission field; ten held government appointments abroad; seven were reading for higher degrees, six travelling abroad, and ten, for marriage or other reasons, had given up practice. Although it hoped these findings would encourage women to take up medicine Council did not altogether deplore public arguments against women entering medical school, arguing that potential applicants put off by them would not make the best women doctors, and that weeding out less committed candidates might be a good thing.[xxxiii]

Seven men's medical schools had accepted women during the war, when there was a dearth of male students, but within six years of the armistice St George's, the London and St Mary's excluded women. Early in 1928 KCL was concerned that Charing Cross, Westminster and KCH, which took its students for clinical studies, would also exclude women (as they did later that year).[15] The only other London schools taking them as clinical students were LSMW and UCHMS, the latter admitting only twelve a year. In March Council was asked how many clinical places it could give KCL over the next three years. Although preferring students to pursue pre-clinical studies at LSMW it agreed, given the exceptional circumstances, to admit students from other places – including Oxford and Cambridge – but for clinical studies only.[xxxiv]

At that March meeting a former student, Dr Adeline Roberts (MB 1898), sought Council's opinion about a resolution that Graham-Little[16] intended placing before Senate that afternoon -one demanding that all London's medical schools be opened to men and women. Miss Brooks had already responded – pointing out that Senate's power over London's general hospitals was limited and, while the resolution would affect all medical schools and hospitals, LSMW's Memorandum and Articles of Association forbade acceptance of men, and funds held in trust for women could not be diverted from that purpose. She thought Graham-Little's suggestion unhelpful; if women formed a small minority in eleven schools their interests were unlikely to be protected. LSMW considered the status quo satisfactory; potential women medical students could choose co-education – or entry to the only women's school.

[15] Two years later KCHMS agreed to admit ten women a year for clinical studies.

[16] Graham-Little was a dermatologist at St Mary's, and London University's MP from 1924-1950.

'CMEWU'

Graham-Little's resolution was not discussed that day. Instead Senate was persuaded to set up a **C**ommittee 'To consider the question of the limitations placed on the **M**edical **E**ducation of **W**omen **U**ndergraduates (CMEWU) and to report to the Senate thereon'.[xxxv]

CMEWU first met on 23 March with the then Vice-Chancellor, Sir William Beveridge, in the chair. On 4 May the Academic Registrar outlined the history of women's admission to the men's schools and noted that Statute 22 {e}, stipulating that 'no disability should be imposed on the ground of sex', was in the University's Charter of 1878, which provided that all regulations relating to the granting of degrees should apply to women as well as men. However, he stressed that this merely limited Senate's powers in making statutes etc.; it did not give the University any legal powers over the schools, some of which were, by their instruments of government, restricted to men while one was restricted to women. Before that second meeting CMEWU received letters from the Six Point Group,[17] the National Council of Women of Great Britain, and the Women's Freedom League, all deploring further closure of schools to women. Women's groups continued to send such letters.[xxxvi]

By 15 June 1928 CMEWU had interviewed representatives (mainly Deans) of all the men's schools. As representatives of LSMW, Lucas-Keene & Miss Brooks were interviewed on 14 May and Lady Barrett & Miss Brooks on 21 May. They argued that women and men should have equally good training and subsequent opportunities. They did not think every school should be co-educational, but thought it essential that women's growing role in medicine should not be hindered by a male monopoly of teaching or postgraduate experience. Demand for women trained at LSMW had increased steadily, and most maintained themselves by their work and enjoyed normal health.

The statements presented to CMEWU by the men's schools showed some uniformity. They argued that many men, particularly those from 'Oxbridge',[18] would not attend hospital schools taking women, and that some old students of such schools would not allow their sons to follow in their footsteps. Schools that had admitted women believed they lost male students as a result; those which subsequently excluded them claimed the intake of men then increased. Several schools therefore agreed to take women only if all the men's schools did so.

Hospital consultants were called 'honoraries' because they received no income from their hospital practice. Their old students referred private patients to them

---

[17] A feminist campaign group, founded by Lady Rhondda in 1921 to press for changes in the law in six areas related to the status of women.

[18] A word used as shorthand for 'Oxford **and** Cambridge'.

and so most disliked co-education; men had larger practices and were perceived as staying in practice longer, so 'honoraries' thought their future income would suffer if women displaced male students.

Several schools suggested lecturers felt uncomfortable teaching mixed classes, particularly on certain topics. They believed men were less serious in the presence of women, and suffered because they held back in class and let women take the best places. Concern about sporting prowess was also an issue. The fewer the men the less choice there was in selecting teams, and providing sports grounds and pavilions able to accommodate both men and women was costly.

Tellingly, no hospital that had admitted women students complained about their competence or behaviour. However, some refused them resident appointments because suitable accommodation was lacking and the cost of providing it prohibitive. Others were concerned that women residents might give up medicine and waste their training. Some disliked denying resident appointments to men – '*who remained cool and collected and had the gift of conveying confidence*' – in favour of women who might prove less capable despite a better academic record. And, of course, it would be unfair to admit women students if they could not subsequently compete equally for resident appointments!

There seemed no easy solution. Lady Barrett was blunt in her assessment of the problem. She said the schools then taking women were not the most popular ones. The older, more favoured schools would always have first choice and so schools now planning to exclude women would not experience the hoped-for influx of men.[19] Provincial schools were co-educational but it was not true that student relationships there were not as close as in London's men's schools; at Bristol (where she started studying medicine) students were just as much a corporate body in relation to its social life as in the London hospitals. The claim that women might give up practice prematurely was exaggerated; a Medical Women's Federation survey had found wastage of only about 9% in recent years.

Barrett predicted, correctly, that there might be no single-sex medical schools when the public accepted the benefits of co-education – but argued that while there were men-only schools there should also be one just for women. She thought schools that had admitted women and then excluded them had incurred by their original action a responsibility to their women students; if they would not return to co-education LSMW should try to accommodate all London's women medical students. Starting another new and inevitably weak school admitting women only would be disastrous.

[19] Medical student numbers were falling nationally at that time.

Beveridge, and the new Vice-Chancellor, Sir Gregory Foster, met the deans of medical schools (excluding LSMW)[20] to review the situation on 9 July. They did not report to CMEWU until 19 December when the minutes record starkly 'The result of the meeting [i.e. with the deans] was negative'. CMEWU approved its draft report to Senate on 15 January 1929. However, on 23 January the penultimate paragraph was amended[21] to read '*Co-education must be voluntary. It will only come about if there is agreement between the University and the schools, and with an arrangement whereby several schools would agree to a certain proportion of women students.*' The first sentence of the original final paragraph, suggesting that Senate with its present powers was in no position to take any further action, had been omitted. The University's new control over funding through its Court clearly provided it with the power over its medical schools; it simply chose not to exercise it.

CMEWU's report stated *inter alia* that '*the position created is in no degree due to the women students themselves, and the Committee see no valid reason against the provision of co-education in Medicine... The university cannot, however, make admission of both sexes a condition of recognition for admission to University degrees of students from any Medical School. Were such a principle applied it would have to refer to all the Schools of the University in all faculties ... Nor could the power of the Court and Senate over grants be used to compel any School of the University to become co-educational against its will... Co-education, if it is to succeed, must be voluntary.*'

Senate sent the report, with a questionnaire, to all London's medical schools. On 14 March 1930 CMEWU reflected on the replies. Statistical tables showed that the fall in the number of medical students since the peak years of 1920-22 was proportionately greater for women, particularly in London, although the absolute number of women had risen in some provincial schools and in Edinburgh and Glasgow. The inference was that some women who would have come to London had gone to the provinces. A motion to dismiss CMEWU was lost, but no further action was recommended and it did not meet again until 11 November 1931, after Lady Barrett had retired as dean. (See Chapter 11)

As the report evoked no action the main responsibility for the medical education of women in London rested again on LSMW and RFH. Enlargement of the latter was therefore essential, and Council beseeched those who liked fair play, and those who wanted women to study medicine, to support RFH's appeal for funds.

---

[20] This exclusion did not go down well at LSMW.

[21] At the suggestion of Lord Dawson of Penn.

The appeal was launched in 1926 in the hope that RFH could celebrate its centenary (1928) by erecting a children's block, the Queen Mary's Wing, to complement the recently opened Riddell children's wards. Albert Levy, chairman of the Appeal Committee, provided office space at 170 Piccadilly. However, in December the architect, H. V. Ashley, was asked to prepare plans embodying 'the requirements of the Hospital as discussed at various times in recent years'. They included completion of the Alfred Langton Home for Nurses, a 'septic ward' for casualty cases, private wards, a Hospital Chapel, new quarters for the female VD department, and an extension to the pathological department including a chemical pathology laboratory. The new buildings, to be erected on the Eley site, were to cost about £200,000. Council discussed how LSMW might support the appeal; suggestions included entertainments by staff and students, a two-day summer fête in June 1927, and a course of public lectures.[xxxvii]

Circumstances changed dramatically in January 1927 when RFH heard that George Eastman, founder of the Eastman Kodak company, contemplated creating in London a dental dispensary like the one he had built at Rochester, N.Y.[22] On a visit to London in March he agreed to link it with RFH – if the Hospital provided both the land and an endowment of £100,000 to maintain the clinic. The obvious land was the Eley site, donated in 1915 by Langton, who died aged 85 on 12 May – just six days before Riddell presented details of Eastman's offer to Council. At a meeting with Riddell and Levy in Paris in December Eastman ordered the transfer of £200,000 to the dental clinic trustees (Riddell, Levy & Mattison; the last worked for Kodak in London). Council saw the likely benefits for LSMW students and the possibility of opening a women's dental school linked with RFH.[xxxviii]

The Hospital also considered other ways of improving facilities for LSMW students. In December 1927 Council heard of plans for a new O & G unit behind the dental institute,[23] together with a new X-ray department and more space for pathology – but to pay for them the Centenary appeal would have to raise another £110,000. The School focused on raising the £15,000 needed to extend the pathology department, so donations to the general appeal fund went to Albert Levy and those marked 'pathology extension' to Sir Alan Anderson. [xxxix]

Riddell wanted to start a women's dental school in the Eastman building but Acland, who had a major interest in dentistry,[24] stressed London's need for

---

[22] In 1914 Burkhart (New York State's best dentist) supplied Eastman with dentures that improved his appearance & self-confidence. Told of the serious after-effects of poor dental care in childhood Eastman built the Rochester Dental Dispensary; it opened in 1917 with Burkhart as director.

[23] The old 'O & G' unit was to re-house the venereal disease department and provide private beds.

[24] Acland, involved in dental reform from 1917, chaired the UK Dental Board after its formation in 1921.

postgraduate teaching and research in that field. Following discussions about the teaching role of the Eastman Dental Clinic, Senate approved in principle the establishment of a dental school on the lines proposed. In March 1930, a memorandum supporting LSMW's grant application for the 1930-35 quinquennium noted that the Eastman was designed to accommodate a dental school admitting thirty students a year; it also mentioned that LSMW already had eight dental students, with four in their third year attending the Royal Dental Hospital.[xl]

When Eastman visited RFH in June 1928 Albert Levy stated that he and Riddell would each provide £50,000 to endow the clinic so that RFH could proceed with other planned developments. Work began in October on the dental clinic's basement floor – which was initially to provide space for the new maternity unit, the pathology department extension, and for some other groups.[xli]

The Prince of Wales laid the foundation stone of the Eastman building on 1 May 1929, in the presence of the Prime Minister (Stanley Baldwin), Neville Chamberlain and the American ambassador; Dr Burkhart represented Eastman. A casket containing the day's programme, a copy of *The Times*, some current coins, and the latest RFH annual report, was placed in the foundation stone by Sir Albert Levy.[25] The Prince sent to Eastman the presentation trowel and mallet used to perform the ceremony. The clinic, which cost £124,000, was completed in May 1930. (Fig 10.2) The first patients were treated on 17 November.[xlii]

Early in 1929 Levy (Fig 10.3) gave RFH another £50,000 to re-house the O & G Unit in an Albert Levy Wing, which was to occupy the last land available for a major building at RFH – the site between the dental clinic and the main outpatients block at the rear of the Hospital. Initially there were to be two floors – accommodating a new boiler and powerhouse; the dietetic, diabetic and central kitchens; the electro-therapy department; resident medical officers' quarters, and an Albert Levy Hall. Construction started in 1930. This 'Queen Mary Building' was intended eventually to be seven storeys high but £150,000 more was needed before work on the other floors could be authorised. Earlier plans for extending RFH were now abandoned, including those for the much needed extension of the pathology unit which had been sent to the University for approval.[xliii]

The Dean invited representatives of women's organisations to a meeting on 21 March 1929. Those present appointed a committee to appeal for funds for the 'RFH

---

[25] Levy's company made State Express cigarettes. His knighthood was announced 1 March 1929 (not 1 January) because the King's illness delayed the announcement of that year's New Year's Honours List – which also included Lady Barrett's CH, McIlroy's DBE, & CBEs for Cullis & Frances Ivens.

Fig 10.2 Eastman Dental Clinic

Extension to Ensure Medical Education for Women'. Mrs Gertrude Kinnell was its chairperson;[26] the Marchioness of Hartington was President of the Young People's Group.

When, early in 1930, Kinnell's committee announced that the RFH appeal still needed £100,000, it became known as the 'Last Hundred Thousand Appeal'.[27] In May a concert at the Royal Opera House featured the soprano Elizabeth Schumann and the tenor Heddle Nash; it raised £1200. The following week John Masefield, the new Poet Laureate, read his own poems to a packed common room at LSMW; he subsequently gave six more readings for the appeal.[xliv]

In the summer of 1929 evacuation of more Cubitt street houses allowed enlargement of the Alfred Langton Nurses Home – but it was a year before the

---

[26] Gertrude Kinnell, daughter of Sir John Cass of Bradford was a pianist & patron of Covent Garden. After marriage she lived in Russia & Mexico where there were family jute mills. As chairperson of the Society for Women's Suffrage she pledged its services to the Government at the onset of WWI. From 1937 she chaired RFH's Weekly Board – the first woman chairperson at a London teaching hospital. Her sister, Viscountess Cowdray, later chaired the South London Hospital for Women. Kinnell died in 1952.

[27] By 1 August 1931 it had raised £20,262 & £14,000 had been transferred to the RFH building account.

plans were made for an extension costing about £68,000.[28] There was already accommodation for 146 nurses; 60 in the Nurses Home, 70 at Mecklenburg Square, and 16 in the Hospital. As more nurses were needed to staff the Albert Levy wing and the Dental Clinic RFH wanted to extend the Nurses' Home quickly but, owing to the Great Depression, it was 1932 before the building contract was placed.[xlv]

Fig 10.3 Sir Albert Levy (1864-1937)

Council accepted trusteeship of the travelling scholarship fund (about £540) set up by the Aldrich-Blake memorial fund committee; it was to be open to medical women throughout the United Kingdom. The Dean, the Hon. Treasurer, the President of the Medical Women's Federation, and EGAH's senior surgeon were to advise on the award of the scholarship.[xlvi]

There was also a public monument erected to Aldrich-Blake's memory. The bronze double bust on a plinth above a corner seating arrangement at the south-east corner of Tavistock Square Gardens (Fig 10.4) was designed by Sir Edward Lutyens; A.G.Walker was the sculptor. It was unveiled on 4 July 1927 by Beveridge, the University's Vice-Chancellor. Dame Louisa's brother, the Rev F.H. Aldrich-Blake, pronounced the benediction. The Magazine thought the monument's situation highly appropriate – *'...from the corner of Tavistock Square she will watch present and future medical students trudging past on their way to the School.'* Council accepted responsibility for a fund for the upkeep of the memorial.[xlvii]

Later that year another method was introduced for commemorating LSMW worthies. Winifred Secretan Patch, a GP in the Holloway Road, died in 1924 after colliding with a lorry while cycling to visit her patients. As a member of the Women's Freedom League and the Tax Resistance League she had participated in a picket of the House of Commons from July to October 1909, and in the Census protest of 1911. Her refusal to pay taxes from 1908 led to occasional seizure and sale of her goods. Many suffragists attended the public hearing in 1917 when the Inland Revenue proceeded against her in the Bankruptcy Buildings.[xlviii]

[28] Dr Elizabeth Courtauld contributed £10,000 for this purpose.

Fig 10.4 Aldrich-Blake monument Tavistock Sq

A memorial fund for her raised £500. In November 1927 Council agreed that £400 would endow a Winifred Secretan Patch cot in the Riddell wards and an anatomy prize bearing her name. In addition a small memorial tablet was to be placed in a panel on the right hand wall of the porch leading to the School's north wing, with similar tablets commemorating other past students. (Fig 10.5) Louisa Garrett Anderson paid for the initial panel and for tablets memorializing her mother and Julia Cock. In March 1928 she offered to pay to convert the whole of the north porch into a memorial. Acland then suggested six panels, with the central one reserved for those with a direct official and/or teaching connection with LSMW. The porch, designed by Laurence A. Turner, was unveiled after the 1928 prize-giving. [29, xlix]

[29] The tablets are now on display in the Rowland Hill Street entrance of the new RFH in Hampstead.

Fig 10.5 Memorial plaques

In the same year Council decided to pave the quadrangle rather than re-gravel it. The loss of the uncomfortable gravel surface was hailed with joy, but many lamented the loss of the old ash tree: *'To preserve this, lecture theatres in the 1897 building were placed at a special angle and now it has disappeared! All who have sat in the shade, had tea under it, attended classes under it, and even those who in former times lost points at tennis through the spread of its trailing branches, will be sad at the loss of an old friend... The surround of rectangular Derby stone in shades of brown and green is beautiful in tone. The utilitarian centre of tar macadam will be appreciated by the net-ball and ring-tennis*[30] *section of the community. Two long beds opposite the administrative offices will, we hope, be filled with a succession of flowers. The Quadrangle and Memorial Porch now make a complete and dignified centre to the School life.'* Sir Alan and Lady Anderson, Sir Francis Acland, Mr Balfour and Mr Henderson paid for the resurfacing.[l]

Unfortunately the tar macadam centre was poorly laid. In 1931 Henderson took legal advice about the liability of the contractors. Two independent contractors were asked if the job had been done properly; they gave private opinions but would not testify in court. Resurfacing was delayed until Easter 1933 when contractors laid a new surface with hot tar and fine ragstone grit, rolled it and re-painted the lines.[li]

The Sports Ground

The committee set up to run the new sports ground at Sudbury had members from Council, the Students' Union and the sports clubs; Miss Bond[31] was its Honorary Steward. To improve the property £275 was later paid for an adjoining acre of land, including an access road, and £1270 of the Cullimore bequest was used to purchase a pavilion. F.R.S. Balfour gave 80 young trees for planting and £20 to develop the ground.[lii]

The sports ground came into use in October 1926. The pavilion had a club-room, cloakrooms and service kitchen on the ground floor, and a flat for a full-time caretaker-groundsman above. To facilitate use of the ground during the winter there were no classes on Wednesday afternoons, and on Wednesday 27 October LSMW, for the first time, held its Sports Day on its own ground. About 75 turned up, including School and Hospital staff. The third year triumphed in the field events and won the cup donated by Miss Partridge, the Athletic Club's President. Fun

---

30 Ring-tennis involves tossing a rubber ring back and forth across a net. It originated from 'Deck Tennis' played on passenger ships in the early 1900s. This quote suggests the ordinary tennis court had gone.

31 Assistant lecturer in physiology.

events included potato & egg and spoon races, an obstacle race, a three-legged race, and a staff and visitors race. At Sports Day the following June the Dean presented the prizes. New cups were donated and the staff promised to provide small replicas of trophies to be retained by winners; Miss Partridge's cup went again to the Third Year.[liii]

Sudbury was acquired mainly for the cricket, lacrosse, tennis & hockey clubs, but none made best use of its facilities. The journey from LSMW took 70 minutes; access by rail was difficult. The Cricket Club, inactive through lack of members, played only a few games there in 1927. The Lacrosse Club, despite boasting several members of the ULAU team, was struggling when the ground was acquired, but many keen freshers joined in October 1929 and LSMW won the inter-collegiate cup in 1930.[liv]

Bad weather and difficulty in raising teams meant that despite a full fixture list the Hockey Club played few matches at Sudbury in 1926-7. After the pitch was moved to higher ground near the pavilion it proved less wet than most London hockey fields,[32] and more matches and practice games were held there. The first XI won only six of sixteen matches in 1927-8, and the poor state of the ground meant fewer matches were played subsequently. In 1930-1 the club, now lacking its own ground, started the season on LCC pitches – often unfit for play and without pavilion accommodation. Despite these difficulties the first XI won most of its matches and for the second half of the season used the Civil Service Ground at Chiswick.[lv]

The Tennis Club had considered itself fortunate to have three new hard courts but few matches were played in 1927; many were cancelled owing to bad weather and to apathy; the club had forty members but struggled to raise six players on weekdays. Post-Sudbury it practised on courts at Cartwright Gardens and played matches at Regent's Park.[lvi]

By June 1929 the pavilion and ground were in poor condition and the Union could not afford proper maintenance. Council asked Dr Aitken, Mr Balfour and Lady Anderson to look into the matter but they could find no satisfactory solution. The ground could be retained only if each student paid 25 shillings a year to maintain it. The Union balloted its members; 123 voted to sell the ground, and 102 to raise the subscription by £1 to keep it. But the Great Depression was not the ideal time to sell; the ground realised only £6825 in May 1930, having cost about £7500. The Union received £2457; the balance was invested. A search began for a new ground, and for temporary facilities within reach of the School.[lvii]

---

[32] The lower part was let to the Wembley Church Lads Brigade for Saturday afternoon football.

The other sporting clubs, relatively unaffected by events at Sudbury, had mixed fortunes. In 1927 the only members of the Fencing Club were qualified women and outsiders. Five fencing 'freshers' arrived in 1929 but no 'events' were organised until 1932.The Gymnastic Club's members trained fortnightly in the Handel Street Drill Hall but its activities were restricted by a low membership and a consequent lack of funds.[lviii]

Before Sudbury was sold the Netball Club raised funds for a court there, but instead it had to continue playing matches on the Hunter Street court, which was improved by the resurfacing in 1929.[33] Many freshers joined in 1929 and in 1930 the club turned out two VIIs; the following year the 1st VII reached the semi-finals of the intercollegiate cup.[lix]

The Rowing Club prospered. The Newnham race was cancelled in 1926, owing to the General Strike,[34] and again in 1927 when many of the Newnham crew had examinations. In 1928 LSMW won by two lengths, won nearly all its other races, and triumphed in the UL VIIIs. (Fig 10.6) That year 21 new members signed up; even so, the club performed poorly for several years and lost the next three Newnham races.[lx]

Although the Boating Club competed against other colleges and participated in the inter-collegiate bumps it was primarily a social club with many members. There was sculling year-round at the Regent's Park Lake, but punting, canoeing and dongoling were confined to the summer term. The annual 'strawberry breakfast' was popular; during the one in 1930 '*the barge "Have a Ride" was taken all around the lake by means of every available punt pole and paddle, and a couple of sculls were towed for part of the way by an energetic member in a tub.*' [lxi]

The Swimming Club remained active. Its annual 'Sports', with staff participation, took place in the St Paul's Girls School pool at Brook Green, Hammersmith. Although it had almost fifty members it fared poorly in competitions, and lost all seven matches in 1928. Concern expressed then about its future was justified; it received no mention in the Magazine between November 1930 and July 1944.[lxii]

LSMW had no Golf Club but, for many years, Lord Riddell ran a Staff v Students match at the famous Walton Heath Golf Club of which he was the proprietor; [lxiii] it was the venue of the 1981 Ryder Cup – the first between Europe (not GB&I) and the USA to be held in Europe.

---

[33] The court had to be re-laid in 1931 (see earlier)

[34] During the May 1926 General Strike men at other London schools acted as transport workers & special constables. Some LSMW students used their own cars to transport patients and thus allowed hospitals to continue working. The July 1926 Magazine commented on the potential value, even in normal times, of using cars to transport disabled patients who had difficulty in getting to hospital.

Fig 10.6 Rowing VIII 1928

Non-sporting Clubs & Societies

The Medical Society's meetings usually involved a talk, or presentations by students about cases encountered and/or pathological specimens. In 1931, however, it debated Arthur Hugh Clough's well-known lines 'Thou shalt not kill, but need'st not strive officiously to keep alive'; Dr Burrell proposed the motion, Dame Louise McIlroy opposed it. [lxiv]

In 1926 Walter de la Mare spoke to the Literary Society on 'Atmosphere in Fiction'. The following year John Galsworthy read from his stories. Some of the Society's meetings had a medical flavour. Hugh Crichton-Miller, founder of the Tavistock Clinic, talked on 'The Psychology of Dreams' in 1929, and the following year Letitia Fairfield, the LCC's Senior Medical Officer, described her work with mentally deficient children. But the major event in 1930, one linked with the RFH appeal (see above), was the visit of John Masefield.[lxv]

The Dramatic and Choral societies flourished. The former's productions raised money to add a carpet and a roller drop screen to the stage properties. The Choral Society continued its Christmas carolling at RFH and EGAH. Its three performances of 'Ruddigore' in March 1926 provided £90 for the Games Ground Fund, and 'The Gondoliers' raised £167 for the pathology fund in 1928. In 1930, at the Countess of Dufferin and Ava's invitation, the Choral Society entertained members of the Round Table Conference of Indian politicians being held at the Eastman Dental Clinic. It put on the two short operas 'Trial by Jury' and 'Cox and Box' in 1931.[lxvi]

In 1929 LSMW's recently founded Folk Dance Club was coached by an instructress from the English Folk Dance Society. It entered two teams for the country dancing section at the Bromley Musical Festival; they came second and third. The following year it won a second place at the Guildhouse Musical Festival and again did well at Bromley.[lxvii]

The Political and Debating Society was revived just before Easter 1929 and at a mock election in May the Conservative candidate won by 31 votes. However, there is no record of another meeting. The Magazine for March 1931 reported that 'the mortality rate among the school's societies is at present unduly high' and, in particular, regretted the demise of the Debating Society.[lxviii]

An annual corporate subscription meant all LSMW students belonged to the National Union of Students (NUS). Founded in 1922 to promote friendship between British students, it also had close links with French and German student bodies. It ran holiday tours, had a hospitality section and a debating society, and held an annual congress.[lxix]

The School's branch of the League of Nations Union was active from 1925 to 1930. It recruited outside speakers and held lunch-hour study circles, as did the branch of the Student Christian Movement (SCM). The latter had about forty members but according to its rapporteur in the July 1928 Magazine few took part in study and prayer. The LSMW branch of the London Inter-faculty Christian Union (LIFCU) organised a club for neighbourhood girls in 1926.

Old Students Association

In July 1928 the Magazine reported that the Students' Union wished for the formation of an Old Students Association – to include staff and students, past and present, of School and Hospital. No time was wasted. Professor Cullis promoted the idea of the Association at the School's annual dinner on 6 December at which Colonel John Buchan MP [35] was the main speaker. It was attended by over 400.[lxx]

At a general meeting of past students on 7 March 1929 seventy enrolled in the new association and elected Lady Barrett president, Gertrude Dearnley chairman, E.M. Rooke treasurer, and E. M. Hall and E.M. Scarborough as secretaries. The Students' Union's vice presidents (J. Healy and Ursula Shelley), H.M. Harris, J.M. Oldaker, and F.M. Mackenzie Shattock completed the executive committee. Within months membership was 285 and again over 400 attended that year's LSMW dinner.[lxxi]

[35] Buchan(later Lord Tweedsmuir) is best remembered as the author of *The Thirty-nine Steps.*

At the Association's first AGM in May 1930 Sir James Berry was elected president for 1930-31. In October 1930 he spoke on 'Reminiscences of the School and Hospital'.[36] During his talk he presented the Association with an original portrait of Frederick Gant – drawn in 1889, when Gant was senior surgeon, by his house surgeon Henry Tonks. Tonks, although an FRCS, gave up medicine for art; from 1917 he was Slade Professor of Fine Art at London University.[lxxii]

During Barrett's deanship the prospects for women doctors improved somewhat. In 1929 Ethel Bentham, a general practitioner, was at her fourth attempt elected to Parliament as Labour MP for Islington East. She was the first woman doctor (and the fifteenth woman) to take her seat there. She had become a prominent politician after the Labour Party absorbed the Women's Labour League in 1918. One of the early women magistrates, she served on the Labour Party's national executive and, at age 70, was the first woman to die while sitting as an MP.

In 1930 women doctors achieved several firsts. One was made Commissioner to the Board of Control (for Lunacy and Mental Deficiency), another Chief Medical Officer of a London Borough, and a third was appointed Regional Medical Officer under the National Health Insurance Acts. A further breakthrough was that London County Council, one of the largest employing authorities, decreed that all its medical appointments would be open to both women and men.[lxxiii]

However medical women in the Civil Service still faced problems. Janet Lane-Claypon, a brilliant student (see Chapter 7), distinguished herself as a physiologist and epidemiologist before becoming Dean of King's College for Women in 1916. Faced with hostility from some on its executive committee she moved to the Department of Health in 1923.[lxxiv] Her work on stillbirths and neonatal deaths, and on risk factors and treatment for a variety of cancers, was outstanding – and included a classic study on the epidemiology of breast cancer. In August 1929 she married Sir Edward Rodolph Forber (1878–1960), then Deputy Secretary, Ministry of Health, and, despite her pre-eminence, had to retire from the Civil Service because of its restrictive policies regarding employment of married women.

In November Lady Barrett announced her resignation as Dean, with effect from 31 January 1931, and at its next meeting Council accepted the School Committee's recommendation that Elizabeth Bolton be elected Dean. In March 1931 Barrett was promptly elected as the third President of the School – the second, Mary Scharlieb, having died in November 1930.[lxxv]

[36] The Magazine for November 1930 carried a detailed account of the talk.

Barrett continued in practice after retiring as Dean, and worked at the Marie Curie Hospital in Hampstead and the Salvation Army Maternity Hospital in Clapton. She died at Maidenhead on 7 August 1945.

In 1929, towards the end of Barrett's deanship a global economic depression began but it did not really impinge on either School or Hospital. British exports fell by about 50% – and so unemployment rose markedly – but their price did not fall. And while there was little change in the volume of imports their cost fell dramatically so, while there was suffering among those unfortunate enough to become unemployed, those in work were actually better off. A secondary economic crisis developed in 1931, because the balanced budget needed to maintain the pound on the Gold Standard was unachievable if, while revenue was falling, large amounts had to be spent to assist an increasing number of poor and unemployed. This affected events at School and Hospital for some years after 1931.[lxxvi]

CHAPTER 11

Elizabeth Bolton (1931-1939)

The Lull before the Storm – Strange Happenings in O & G

The Dean of LSMW from 1 February 1931 was Elizabeth Bolton, (Fig 11.1), the daughter of a Congregational minister. Born in Leeds in 1878 she attended Stoneygate College, Leicester, and London's Bedford College before entering LSMW in October 1899. She graduated MBBS in 1904 (MD 1907) and, before becoming a surgeon at EGAH in 1910, held several posts at RFH, including a surgical registrarship. When Bolton retired in 1945 Chodak-Gregory wrote that her appointment as Dean was viewed with doubt and misgiving but '... *she tackled the situation with her characteristic honesty and simplicity and...the first people to acknowledge the success of the appointment were the clinicians...* [she] *gave her whole attention to everybody's problems, whether it was* [arranging] *lectures to suit some member of the honorary staff, or advice to a newly qualified graduate or the personal affairs of a student.*'[i]

Three months after she took office there was a new agreement with RFH, one meant to last 50 years. LSMW was to continue sending clinical students to RFH, which was to admit them only from LSMW. There would be cross-representation on School and Hospital committees, but nothing authorizing interference by one in the affairs of the other. If LSMW stopped sending students to RFH then 'Royal Free Hospital' was to be omitted from the School's name.[1] On 1 July the 'School Committee' became the 'Education Committee'; new by-laws were agreed in October.[2, ii]

In 1932, after a by-election, Sir Francis Acland re-entered Parliament as Liberal MP for North Cornwall. That October he left Council, both as chairman and as a member – probably owing to his wife's poor health rather than his return to the Commons. She died in December 1933; Acland died six years later.[iii]

Sir Alan Anderson, Acland's replacement as chairman, resigned in July 1934 before a long trip to Australia. Henderson, deputy chairman and LSMW's legal adviser, succeeded him. Following Riddell's death in December 1934 Sir Alan chaired RFH's Committee of Management, and in 1935 was elected MP for the City of London. He remained on Council but the Hon. Francis Rodd took over as

[1] The official name then was 'London Royal Free Hospital School of Medicine for Women'.

[2] The new by-laws governed the constitution & powers of Council's Education & Finance Committees.

Fig 11.1 Elizabeth Bolton (1878-1961)

Hon. Treasurer.[3] The School wanted Anderson's sons, Colin (b. 1904) and Donald (b. 1906) to join the Finance Committee in 1936, but their father thought them too heavily involved with their own business affairs.[iv]

Lady Barrett, elected President of the School in March 1931 in place of Scharlieb, was quickly co-opted back onto Council and, with Chodak-Gregory and Joll, became a full member in July. In July 1931 Lady Bingham was elected to Council and was chosen to represent it on RFH's Weekly Board. In October 1933 she replaced Winifred Cullis as Hon. Secretary, and Chodak-Gregory replaced Janet Aitken as Vice-dean. Bingham seems to have been a student at the School.[4] In December 1929 she had married George Bingham, who became the 6th Earl of Lucan in 1949. One of her daughters, Jane Bingham, graduated MBBS at RFHSM in 1957. Lady Lucan's son, Richard Bingham, was the Lord Lucan who disappeared in 1974, suspected of the murder of Sandra Rivett, his children's nanny.

One long-standing issue – the dissatisfaction of teachers with their representation on Council – still needed addressing. When LSMW incorporated in 1898 the Board of Trade insisted only one Council member could hold a salaried office with the School or receive fees from it. To resolve this problem Council had considered petitioning the Privy Council for a charter in 1925 and again in 1930; each time Sir Alan Anderson opposed it for reasons unrelated to the representation of teachers.[v] (See Chapter 10)

Council finally decided to seek a charter in December 1936. The following July the Association approved a draft version under which the School's officers were to be a President (without time limit); the Dean (a Member of Council, appointed annually and eligible for re-election); the Hon. Treasurer; and a paid Secretary, who might also be appointed Warden.[5] From its members Council could appoint a Vice-Dean – eligible for re-election for a second year, and for subsequent re-election if a year had elapsed since her previous term of office. A petition was sent to the Privy Council. The King approved the Charter Statutes on 4 November 1938; Letters Patent under the Great Seal were received in March 1939. The post of Honorary Secretary was abolished. Its last incumbent, Lady Lucan, remained on Council until 1962.[vi]

---

3 A post Anderson had held for eighteen years,

4 The Magazine for July 1931 noted that Lady Bingham 'known to her fellow students as Miss Kaitilin Dawson' had joined LSMW's Appeal Committee as vice-chairman – but her name is not listed as having been admitted to LSMW.

5 Council members elected a chairman annually; he was not an 'officer of the School'. Although women occasionally chaired Council meetings no woman was ever elected or appointed chairman.

Apart from the President and Honorary Treasurer the new Council included two from the Committee of Management of RFH (F.R.S. Balfour & Sir Frank Newnes); four teachers – two pre-clinical (Cullis & Lucas Keene) and two clinicians (Joll & Catherine Lewis); two from the University of London's Senate;[6] and six elected by Members of the School.[7] Council was to elect the Dean annually from among its members. Chodak-Gregory remained Vice-Dean. No more than five members were to receive a salary or be paid fees from School funds, and no more than four were to be teachers at LSMW. In March 1937 Bolton became the first Dean to be paid. [8, vii]

Louie Brooks, the paid Secretary and Warden, retired in 1937 after twenty-five years distinguished service.[9] Her successor had to be younger than forty and a woman graduate of a British university. Nancy Moller was appointed from 1 September. Catherine Lewis became Vice-Dean in June 1939, but this post became somewhat irrelevant during the war; no Vice-Dean was appointed for 1942-3. Katherine Lloyd-Williams was elected Vice-Dean in October 1944.[viii]

Throughout Bolton's deanship LSMW was the only London school able to guarantee women a complete medical education. KCL struggled to place its female preclinical students – except for KCH's quota of ten – and UCL limited its own intake because UCHMS would only admit twelve women a year (some of whom came from 'Oxbridge'). Hoping to find a solution to this problem CMEWU met again in November 1931 and was reminded of past problems in finding clinical places for women. Halliday, KCL's Principal, reported increasing demand and said that if KCL's women could not attend KCH or RFH they would have to go to the provinces – even though most were from London.[ix]

In February 1932 CMEWU saw no prospect of accommodating all KCL and UC women and asked the men's schools to help. The London agreed '*to admit women students on a quota basis, but only if and when the other Schools…agree to do the same'*. CMEWU approached the Royal Northern Hospital but its buildings, especially for pathology and outpatients, were considered inadequate. It could not afford to improve them as it was £100,000 in debt.[x]

When the University Court visited LSMW in April Bolton said that LSMW and RFH would take ten extra women to work for a degree, not a diploma – but with

[6] Sir William Girling Ball & Dr. A. M. H. Gray

[7] Janet Aitken, Sir Alan Anderson, Lady Bingham, the Dean, Henderson & the Hon. John Mulholland.

[8] The Finance Committee was to consider the matter but its deliberations are not recorded in its minutes.

[9] At Sir Alan Anderson's house on 13 March Council presented Brooks with a Mazer Bowl created by Omar Ramsden. Old students gave her an antique ruby diamond ring engraved 'LSMW.1909-1937', plus £250 to spend during a round the world voyage. [Mag Nov 1937] She received an OBE in the 1938 New Year's Honours List.

no guarantee of extending this concession (see later). Despite this Senate would not provide any funds to improve facilities at RFH. Kirk, a sub-dean at UCL, thought such places of little help to UCL women, who favoured co-education; denied a place at UCHMS they would attend a provincial hospital rather than RFH. In June CMEWU informed Senate that lack of clinical facilities for women in London was a serious gap, but it could suggest no way of plugging it.[xi]

LSMW heard in August that a women's undergraduate clinical school might open at the West London Hospital, which already had a co-educational college, founded in 1893, that provided medical training for postgraduates. On 2 October Bolton met its dean, Dr Sinclair, and a year later the University asked if LSMW would admit, for certain preclinical subjects, students who would go to the West London for clinical studies; however, Council was reluctant to take them just for anatomy (and possibly for physiology).[xii]

The West London Hospital Medical School opened in October 1937. Although primarily a women's school men were not barred. It came within the purview of London University's Council for External Students, although not as one of its schools, and was recognised for clinical training by Oxford and Cambridge and other licensing bodies. It lasted fifteen years.

The Local Government Act 1929 allowed authorities to convert poor law institutions into modern hospitals and the LCC planned to place some on a par with the London teaching hospitals.[10] In March 1932 the Medical Committee approved LSMW's temporary cooperation with an LCC hospital – but without enthusiasm, believing that only LCC medical officers would be allowed to treat patients there. They thought clinical instruction excluding discussion of treatment to be of little value, and suggested LCC hospitals be used only to extend the system of short case classes already in place at St Pancras Hospital.

RFH's physicians decided twelve more medical beds should open at RFH as soon as possible, and that a third medical post – with 14 beds and supervised by a full physician – should be introduced in November 1932.[11] A new assistant physician was to have two outpatient days a week, and cover beds when a full physician was on leave.[12,xiii]

---

[10] In 1875 the School asked the President of the Local Government Board to admit women students to its new hospital in Cleveland Street, but the Metropolitan Poor Act 1867 prevented use of such asylums for medical instruction. The Poor Law Act 1889 allowed Metropolitan Asylums Board isolation hospitals to admit patients with infectious diseases from all social classes, allowing greater use for teaching students – see Ayers, GM, 'England's First State Hospitals' 1971, p. 89.

[11] The full physician seems to have been Jenner Hoskin as Burrell & Hare gave up beds for the new post.

[12] Assistant physicians did not have beds.

On 26 July 1932 RFH's Committee of Management appointed Una Garvin Ledingham as the new assistant physician. This caused a crisis. Lord Riddell wrote: '*In view of what took place yesterday, I have decided to sever my connection with the hospital. Will you please therefore, as soon as possible, announce to the Weekly Board my resignation as President'*. The reason for Riddell's reaction is not clear but it appears related to the voting power exercised by Medical Committee delegates at the Committee of Management and Weekly Board.[xiv]

School and Hospital united to persuade him to withdraw his resignation. The Medical Committee voluntarily reduced its voting power from three to one in August, and in October unanimously accepted Riddell's suggestion that Ledingham's appointment should be made permanent only if, after twelve months, Sir Thomas Horder and Dr Robert Young considered her healthy.[13] Riddell was mollified. From 11 October he again chaired the Weekly Board; in July 1933 it confirmed Ledingham's appointment as assistant physician. [14,xv]

In 1933 the LCC agreed that LSMW could use St Mary's Hospital (Islington) and Highgate Hospital for undergraduate teaching, and St Pancras Hospital for postgraduates. From November Ledingham took Jenner Hoskins's students on a weekly round at Highgate. A year later she complained about teaching without holidays, so Council agreed quarterly posts should run for ten weeks, the other three weeks being scheduled around the usual holiday seasons. If Ledingham wanted a longer leave the medical registrar had to cover for her.[xvi]

In November 1935 Council heard from a Sheffield solicitor of an anonymous donor (later identified as Joseph Rawlins, Mus. Bac.) who wished to give £11,000 to found, for women only, a 'Free Woman's Chair' of medicine.[15] The money paid for bedside teaching at RFH and associated hospitals, and for a woman medical registrar to teach on the wards. Alice Stewart, later famous for her pioneering work on the biological effects of radiation, was the first registrar so appointed.[xvii]

In February 1936 Ledingham was offered a part-time appointment as the 'Free Woman Lecturer in Clinical Medicine'.[16] For 40 weeks a year she was to give three clinical lectures a week in the wards of affiliated LCC institutions. She accepted, but then complained that the stipend of £260 per annum was inadequate given her increased status and responsibility. It was increased to £306. She sought a further increase in February 1937, for extra time required over and above the thrice weekly

[13] Her son John Ledingham, a physician, is convinced she suffered from anorexia nervosa, complicated by thyroid surgery.

[14] Riddell must have known Ledingham's father J. L. Garvin, the famous editor of the *Observer.*

[15] Rawlins died the following April.

[16] Renewable yearly until the age of 60.

sessions. Payment was raised to £350. Weeks later she complained this did not cover the fourth half day she gave each week; Council allowed this letter to 'lie on the table'.[xviii]

When Dorothy Hare, the third female FRCP, retired in July 1937 Lee Lander was appointed assistant physician; and after the senior physician, Lancelot Burrell, died in September 1938, aged 55, Thompson Hancock was also made assistant physician.

Reginald Brain took over as dermatologist when Harold Haldin-Davis retired in 1935. Soon afterwards Ursula Shelley became assistant physician to Chodak-Gregory in the Children's Department, which Margaret Price joined as first assistant in 1936. Frank Howitt, Heald's assistant in the Physical Medicine department, left in 1937 to run a similar department at the Middlesex Hospital.[17] His replacement, Ernest Tertius Decimus Fletcher,[18] became director of the rhematology unit when Heald retired in 1948.

In 1931 RFH had two venereal disease departments; one for women run by Margaret Rorke, and Horace Winsbury-White's clinic for men. Mary Shaw joined Rorke in 1935 and took over the department in 1937. The male V.D. department closed in 1934 when the LCC concentrated such work at larger centres.

Lectures on psychiatry and tropical medicine were given at LSMW. Students were also taught on psychiatric patients at Horton Mental Hospital from 1928. Its superintendent, Colonel John Lord, was an honorary lecturer at the School. He died in 1931 and was replaced at Horton by his colleague William D. Nicol who later played a key role in the development of psychiatry at RFH. Major-General Sir Leonard Rogers resigned as the Stuart Mill lecturer in Tropical Medicine in 1937; Hamilton Fairley, Rogers's own choice as his replacement, took over from 1938.

When Cecil Joll replaced Cunning as senior surgeon in 1931 Gwendoline Barry was appointed assistant surgeon. Although no further general surgical appointments were made before the Second World War, changes were needed in the surgical specialties. The ENT surgeon Mildred Warde[19] married and moved to Nigeria in 1931. Her replacement Douglas McLaggan took Nielson's slot as ENT lecturer in 1932. When McLaggan succeeded John Gay French as head of the department in 1933 Scott-Brown was appointed assistant surgeon as was Dorothy Collier in 1934.

From 1934 the ophthalmologist Ida Mann was assisted first by Marcelli Shaw and Alison Collie, each serving for a year. When Collie left, Hugh Keoch joined Mann for about two years. Julia Fleming followed him and stayed until 1940.

---

[17] Howitt, like Heald, was also a pilot. See Munk's Roll V, p. 202

[18] So called as a third son and tenth child.

[19] At her MS exam in 1926 Warde won the University gold medal– the first awarded for ENT.

In 1933-4 Gwendoline Smith, who trained at UCHMS, became the first to assist Jenner Verrall in the department of orthopaedics. Smith moved in 1940 to the South London Hospital for Women and Children where, despite her prolonged exposure to orthopaedics, she practised general surgery. Charles Gray replaced her at RFH and worked there for thirty-three years, retiring in 1973.[xix]

During Bolton's deanship staffing of the X-ray and anesthetic departments changed little until the onset of war in 1939. Gordon Calthrop joined the radiologists Ulysses Williams and Dulcie Staveley in 1938, and Phyllis Simon (soon to be Mrs Daplyn) replaced the anaesthetist Barbara Sprott. The other four anaesthetists – Claude Morris, Enid Browne, Stanley Rowbotham and Katherine Lloyd-Williams – served throughout Bolton's years of peace.[xx]

After the Eastman Clinic opened RFH's senior dental establishment also increased, because when Lily Harwood retired in November 1936, after twenty years service, two men, Alan Deverell and M.P. Hudson. joined her assistant Eric Wookey. Claremont, the Eastman's first director, resigned in May 1932 and was replaced by C. L. Endicott.[xxi]

There were extraordinary happenings in the O & G Unit. In December 1933 Louise McIlroy announced she would retire in September 1934 to enter consulting practice. Amy Fleming was appointed professor and director from 1 October. Four years later RFH's Medical Committee objected to her reappointment in 1939, a situation similar to that faced by McIlroy in 1926. This time other School and Hospital committees, including Council, supported the Medical Committee, but Council wanted to keep the professorial unit. The University demanded an explanation for such goings-on, and after meeting School representatives on 2 December it informed Fleming her appointment would lapse on 30 September 1939. It still wanted to hear what plans LSMW had for the O & G chair.[xxii]

The Medical Committee favoured its abolition, but in February, a joint meeting of Council and the Weekly Board '*having heard...* [the Medical Committee's]*...criticism of the Unit System remain of opinion that the Unit of Obstetrics and Gynaecology should be continued and...recommend...the continuance of the chair of obstetrics and gynaecology.*' [xxiii]

On 30 May the University's Board of Advisers unanimously recommended the appointment of Meave Kenney – a decision based on her contributions by research to the advancement of gynaecology and obstetrics, her known powers as a teacher, and her distinction in her subject. The Medical Committee unanimously disagreed – she was too young, clinically inexperienced, lacked the FRCS, and had graduated

[20] She trained at Lady Hardinge Medical College, graduating MBBS Punjab in 1931, but subsequently studied at LSMW to obtain a registrable qualification in 1934.

at a 'lesser known' university.[20] It would not accept the appointment. Council concurred and asked the University to defer things until the autumn. The Medical Committee instructed its representatives not to meet the Board of Advisers to reconsider the matter, but Council, despite considering Gladys Hill and Jocelyn Moore[21] acceptable candidates, rejected an interim appointment. A subcommittee appointed to facilitate the Unit's work asked Gertrude Dearnley to take charge until an appointment was made – with Moore as her assistant. However, when the war started discussion about the chair gave way to more important matters. LSMW, which had the first such appointment in Britain in 1921, did not have another professor of O & G until 1965.[xxiv]

Obstetrics was taught at RFH, EGAH and at the Essex Road Clinic. During its first ten years the last dealt with over 5,500 ante-natal patients. About a half that number were delivered at home (the students benefiting from the 'on the district' training), and about a third in the GIR maternity beds. The Scottish Women's Hospital Association gave Essex Road £1.000 per annum, and for some years supervised its domestic arrangements.[xxv]

Initially the Essex Road Clinic was a great success, but a students' report on the curriculum in 1938 was scathing about it, and compared it unfavourably with the experience at EGAH – *'students attend ...[about] five cases each... representing the obstetric experience...from one month...in residence...[involving] considerable discomfort and inconvenience.'* Its unpleasantness for patients explained why fewer used it; '*the maximum discomfort, lack of space...complete lack of privacy...squalid appearance of the clinic and the deafening noise of the trams,...make [it] so unattractive that women will...engage midwives for their confinements, thereby avoiding the necessity for attending ante-natal clinics at all...everything possible should be done to make [it] less unattractive to the patient'*.[xxvi]

During the 1930s pathology experienced major changes in staff and accommodation. In the late 1920s plans were made to extend the department but the project was delayed – partly for financial reasons and partly because work had begun on the Eastman Clinic and the Albert Levy Wing, (see Chapter 10) both potential homes for pathology. When in May 1931 the University postponed a decision on a capital grant for pathology further delay seemed inevitable. In June Bolton asked if pathology might move into the lower ground floor of the dental clinic, as the Eastman had agreed to let 10,000 sq.ft. for £1000 p.a. She told the University the scheme was essential and that LSMW would pay the rent from the pathology department's joint funds if given adequate financial support.[xxvii]

---

[21] First assistant on the O & G Unit from November 1935.

A School/Hospital committee set up to supervise the transfer of pathology to space in the Eastman building metamorphosed within weeks into a more permanent management group – the Pathology Unit Joint Committee (PUJC). On 10 July 1931 it approved the Eastman move -but by August the scheme was abandoned, ostensibly because the dental clinic now needed the space! Addition of a further half floor to the Sir Albert Levy wing was considered. The architect, Ashley, submitted two plans; the cheaper, at £8,000-9,000, was adopted. As the University Court had said a promised grant (£500 annually for four years) could go towards the scheme PUJC thought £10,525 was available, but by November the figure had fallen to £5000.[22] Ashley said that would pay only for a shell; PUJC recommended building the shell.[xxviii]

However, the 'Great Depression' of the early 1930s was beginning to bite. In mid-1931 RFH was £45,000 overdrawn, and running costs were bound to increase when the new buildings came into use. In November it provided only £2750 of the £6450 needed annually to maintain the pathology department; a year later it contributed £2475.[xxix]

In January 1932 PUJC told Ashley that the proposed extension, for which £8,405 was now available, had to have a large laboratory for 52 students, with water at every bench, and that windows facing the central courtyard had to be enlarged. Council considered the tenders in March. [xxx]

The Levy Wing of the Queen Mary Building, under construction since early 1930, was handed over by the contractors in March 1932. A beautiful building, its lower ground floor housed a boiler house and heating installation serving the Hospital and Eastman Clinic. There was also a new central kitchen able to feed 600 people a day and to provide the many different special diets needed; it also allowed the clinical students' dining room service to be transferred back from the medical school to hospital management.

There were handsome quarters for the resident medical officers. The rooms of the maternity, ante-natal and post-natal department opened off a large central waiting hall, and the students' section included a library and a lecture hall. The entrance to the Queen Mary Building from the body of the Hospital was in a small inner court. (Fig 11.2) From there a flight of white stone stairs led to a beautifully paved and pillared hall bearing Sir Albert Levy's name. (Fig 11.3) His portrait hung in a recess at one end. In the wide central quadrangle around which the wing was built a hard tennis court was laid for staff use. The Levy Wing was officially opened on 8 June 1932. The hall was used for LSMW's prize-giving for the next

[22] PUJC decided to include only the first tranche of £500 from the University and RFH had removed £4000 which it claimed was already allocated to other building projects.

Fig 11.2 Levy Entrance

Fig 11.3 Albert Levy Hall

three years and for the inaugural address in 1936 and 1937. In 1938 the address was switched to the Lecture Hall of the Eastman building.[xxxi]

When the University Court visited in April Riddell suggested twelve medical beds might be available in the Eastman building by October 1932, albeit as a temporary measure. On this basis Bolton told the University that LSMW would admit ten extra students for the clinical course (see earlier). Riddell also offered £10,000 towards a *complete* extra floor on the Albert Levy wing (to house 24 obstetric beds and the pathology extension) for which the total cost, with equipment, would be over £30,000; 40 new medical and surgical beds could then be placed in the existing obstetric wards.[xxxii]

Ashley was instructed to plan for a whole extra floor, and to indicate if it could be in shell form, permitting ready conversion at an appropriate time. The Weekly Board, arguing that the extra floor would benefit medical education, asked if LSMW could raise money for it over and above that already available for the pathology extension. Council offered to assist in raising the £9,000 needed, but the University, considering the new floor all hospital accommodation and not predominantly educational in purpose, refused to help. [xxxiii]

The Weekly Board now asked Ashley about the additional cost of building the pathology extension separately from the rest of the extra floor, and whether subsequent building of wards would interfere with the pathology department's work. On 5 July it approved the construction of the extra floor, as did the King Edward's Hospital Fund.[xxxiv]

On 20 July Council heard Riddell had temporarily withdrawn his offer of £10,000 towards the floor.[23] The Weekly Board, already facing high expenditure on the Albert Levy wing and the new Nurses' Home, decided on 26 July it could not take risks with the pathology extension. It told LSMW that before it would sign the contract the School had to provide £10,000, and a legal guarantee to provide the balance, plus £1000 to cover the extra cost of constructing the floor in two separate sections. That effectively destroyed the plans made for pathology in the Levy Wing, and ended the dream that the wing would eventually have seven storeys.[xxxv]

On 27 September Sir Albert wrote to the Weekly Board that the financial situation was grave,[24] and emphasized the need to economize and curtail further capital expenditure. He contemplated resigning as Hon. Treasurer but decided not to withdraw while RFH was faced with serious financial problems.[xxxvi]

In 1932 there were plans to reorganize pathology teaching, with practical classes

---

[23] Riddell appears to have withdrawn his offer before the appointment of Ledingham as assistant physician led him to resign as President (see earlier in this Chapter)

[24] There was an overdraft of £55,000 and £12,500 was owed in respect of the Albert Levy Wing contract.

involving 40 to 60 students. The larger laboratory needed could be provided within nine months – either by taking over a room in the Eastman clinic or by using the physiology department at Hunter Street. Hadfield said neither was a long term solution as the existing department had to be enlarged. Because renting and fitting up an Eastman room would cost about £1000 PUJC accepted Cullis's offer of the physiology department.[xxxvii]

In late November a small fire broke out in the pathology technicians' room at GIR. In January the Weekly Board told Council the existing pathology department was seriously overcrowded and that fewer students should work there; Riddell said threat of fire called for immediate action. There were two possibilities – the plan to build the new extension over the Levy wing (now costed at £12,000) could be reactivated, or pathology could be housed in the whole of the lower ground floor of the Eastman dental clinic, at a moderate rent and for at least two years.[xxxviii]

Sir Alan Anderson inspected the existing pathology department and the Eastman building and wrote to PUJC before it met on 13 February 1933 stating that it would reflect badly on RFH if the Eastman building was not fully used. He added – '*I don't know how [RFH] will use the empty space in the Eastman building if it is not wanted for the clinic or for Pathology but... the use would be benevolent and will add to the annual expense of the hospital. ...one must remember not only the £12,000 cost of the new building, as against £2000 cost of adapting Eastman, but the extra annual cost of operating which the hospital will probably incur if it does not use these Eastman rooms for pathology.*' It was apparently necessary to retain the mortuary floor of the existing department, and the floor below it from which there was access to the north wing of the Eastman clinic.

Sir Alan suggested two possible sites in the Eastman building – its north wing or the sub-ground floor. The latter was further from the mortuary but there was room for further growth and its quiet and well-lit east facing rooms were suitable for delicate work while those facing Gray's Inn Road could provide cloakrooms and other necessary accommodation.[xxxix]

The Weekly Board agreed LSMW could have the sub-ground floor for 10 years for £400 per annum and that the pathology unit could retain its existing quarters. The pathology extension fund would cover alterations and equipment. The deal was conditional on RFH being able, if required by George Eastman's executors,[25] to give the pathology department two years notice to vacate; in this event RFH would reimburse the School for its original outlay. Council agreed and asked for an early move of pathology into the Eastman Clinic.[xl]

[25] Eastman was plagued by progressive disability owing to lower spine problems. Increasingly frustrated by his inability to live an active life he died by his own hand on 14 March 1932 aged 77.

Hadfield did not lead his department into its new accommodation. He resigned in June to take the chair of pathology at Bristol. Robert Alexander Webb, his successor, was a 42-year-old American who trained at Johns Hopkins. He came to Europe with the American Red Cross during the First World War, was attached to the RAMC and served with the British Expeditionary Force in 1917-8. Subsequently he worked in Manchester and Cambridge before joining LSMW. In 1926 he established the importance of having optimal proportions of antigen and antibody in serum precipitation reactions and in the same year discovered *Listeria monocytogenes,* a bacterium subsequently identified as a cause of severe human infections.[xli]

The new department contained a large practical classroom accommodating 60 students – with adjoining rooms for lecturers and technicians, for preparation of media and class material, and for cleaning and storage of apparatus. The surgical histology technician's room was next to the Iris Fox Memorial Library facing the professor's room. The other wing housed a small lecture theatre (with a larger one upstairs) and a chemical pathology laboratory occupied by the resident pathologist dealing with routine clinical pathology, the A M Bird research scholar, and the senior students spending a month there. The bacteriology lecturer also had a room. On 2 November Sir Alan and Lady Anderson hosted an evening party in the laboratories at which the guests met the newly appointed professor.[xlii]

The post-mortem rooms and the museum remained in RFH's main block; the floor below, allocated to the sub-department of chemical pathology, contained two biochemical laboratories, rooms for the chemical pathologist and biochemistry lecturer, a waiting room for patients and a room for basal metabolic rate estimations. The new unit was accessible via basement corridors or over the roof of the Levy wing. Tests for venereal diseases were done in a special laboratory next to the V.D. clinic.

Facilities for pathology continued to improve. In December 1933 Council heard that LSMW's animal house was inadequate and, being separate from RFH, inconvenient for the O & G and pathology units. Money from the pathology extension fund paid for a second one to be built above RFH's museum, and for larger windows and improved artificial lighting in the museum. In November 1935 the Magazine reported that there was now a clinical inoculation laboratory and increased laboratory accommodation for ward clinical testing.[xliii]

With the expansion of the Hospital the need for isolation facilities became clear – for septic surgical patients requiring exclusion from the main wards, acute septic cases admitted from Casually Department, medical problems such as pulmonary abscess or diabetes with gangrene, delirious or noisy, restless cases, or those requiring extreme quiet.

An Isolation Ward, costing about £12,000, was obtained by building a third floor, on top of the Casualty and Marlborough wards in the rear of the Hospital. General surgical and medical cases were isolated in two double wards, each with a separate bathroom and WC, and two soundproofed single wards; there was also an operating theatre suite and a kitchen and sluice room. Obstetric cases were housed at the other end of the floor – in a completely separate unit of two wards (with two and three beds respectively), a small soundproofed labour room, a kitchen and toilet facilities.

Behind each bed was an electric light point, an electric bell 'button' which also activated a luminous dial in the corridor and a wireless point. The wards had a power point for the X-ray apparatus and a dimmer for night-time.

The obstetric wards opened onto a wide covered balcony facing west, on which beds could be wheeled, with one end protected from the weather by glazing. This end of the new floor projected beyond the line of the lower floors so detached piers were needed to run direct to the ground, and these allowed a balcony to be provided on the existing second floor.[xliv] (Fig 11.4)

The Hospital's Annual Report for 1936 pointed out that as a result of the financial depression, 'from which the nation is now emerging', the Queen Mary building had remained incomplete and temporarily roofed for six years. But RFH remained optimistic, and the report outlined a scheme of development involving the addition of 50 surgical and 50 medical beds; re-housing of an obstetric unit of 41 beds; improved accommodation for resident medical officers; additional theatre accommodation; rearrangement of existing wards to house all medical wards in the extension and surgical wards in the old part of the hospital; and improvement of administrative offices. The bed complement was to rise to 424.[xlv]

These plans did not come to fruition. Even if they had Sir Albert Levy would not have seen the buildings. He died after a long illness on 5 September 1937.

The great advances being made in bacteriology and chemical pathology had made it essential to increase the staffing of the pathology department. When Elizabeth White (MBBS 1929), RFH's resident pathologist and 'routine' bacteriologist, was appointed bacteriologist at Queen Charlotte's Hospital in 1931 RFH recognized its own need for such a post. Cicely Weatherall (MBBS 1923), the first to hold it, moved to Cardiff in 1933;[26] her replacement, Joan Taylor, had trained at UCL and UCH.[27] Joan Ross, the morbid anatomist, was promoted reader in pathology in 1933.[xlvi]

---

[26] In Cardiff she was Mrs Waters.

[27] Taylor eventually became director of the Salmonella reference laboratory at Colindale.

Fig 11.4 Isolation Block 1936

In October 1931 RFH decided to appoint two half-time 'biochemists' and the School provided a quarter of their salaries. Lucy Wills, just back from India where she carried out her classical studies on macrocytic anaemia of pregnancy, became lecturer in chemical pathology. She visited India again in 1932 and 1937. The other 'biochemist' Mrs Pillman-Williams, wife of the radiologist Ulysses Williams, covered while Wills was away.[xlvii]

In March 1935 Sybil Widdows questioned the title and status which Council had accorded to Addeyman Gardner and queried her own status. Gardner became 'lecturer in organic chemistry and head of the chemistry department' in 1912, just

Fig 1.1 Elizabeth Blackwell Statue by A.E. Ted Aub = Hobart and William Smith Colleges, N.Y.

Fig 7.1 Julia Cock (1860-1914) by Horace Field

Fig 9.3 Dame Louisa Aldrich-Blake (1865–1925) by Sir William Orpen

Fig 13.6 RFHSM Coat of Arms

The Arms are blazoned *Quarterly per fess indented and per pale Sable and Or in the firth and fourth quarters a Lion rampant Gold and in the second and third a Rod of Aesculapius also Sable*. The Crest is On a Wreath of the Colours [here gold and black], *Within two branches of Rose Tree flowered Gules barbed seeded and leaved an open Book proper bound and clasped Or*. [Coll Arm Ms Grants 116/301].

Fig 14.1 Dame Frances Gardner (1913-1989) Portrait (by Shephard)

Fig 15.4 Queen at RFH 1978

Fig 15.5a 'No Flowers' car windscreen sticker

Fig 15.5b 'No Flowers' car windscreen sticker

Fig 15.7 Dame Sheila Sherlock (1918–2001) (by Ruskin Spear)

Fig 15.9 Mural by Utermuhlen

KEY TO MURAL

1. *RFH, Hampstead*
2. *RFH, Gray's Inn Road*
3. *Gates and steps of St. Andrew's Church, Holborn*
4. *RFH Medical School for women*
5. *RFH nurses, circa 1889*
6. *Florence Nightingale*
7. *Princess Christian of Schleswig-Holstein*
8. *Nurse and patient in wheelchair, 1985*
9. *Queen Victoria commanded that the "Free Hospital" be the "RFH", 1837*
10. *Medical students receiving clinical instruction in cholera wards*
11. *RFH was the only hospital to admit cholera patients, 1832*
12. *William Marsden, Founder of the Free Hospital*
13. *William Frederick, Duke of Gloucester first President of the Free Hospital*
14. *King George IV first Royal Patron of the Free Hospital*
15. *Destitute girl found by William Marsden on the steps of St. Andrews, Holborn*
16. *Occupational Therapist and patient, 1985*
17. *RFH Houseman, 1985*
18. *Nurse and child, 1985*
19. *RFH Medical student, 1985*
20. *Elizabeth Garrett Anderson*
21. *Patient using a Zimmer frame, 1985*
22. *Duchess of Gloucester, President of the RFH circa 1944*
23. *Mary Stewart, RFH was the first hospital to appoint a lady "Almoner", 1895*
24. *George Qvist, Consultant Surgeon*
25. *RFH Sister, 1985*

Fig 15.11 MacGillivray Portrait (1927–2010) (by William Bowyer)

Fig 16.2 Arie Zuckerman Portrait by Susan Ryder

before Widdows arrived as lecturer in inorganic chemistry. In 1915 Council, probably responding to student complaints, intimated that it might not reappoint him, but when he was made reader in physiological chemistry in 1920 his original designation was not changed, which explained why he was still 'head of chemistry' in 1935. Widdows had run the department for years and so Council confirmed her as lecturer in inorganic chemistry *'in charge of'* the department of chemistry'.[xlviii]

Although Gardner was then sixty-eight he was reluctant to retire and suggested longer notice should be given for termination of appointment. Cullis told Council that London, and other universities, usually extended appointments until the end of the academic year in which a professor or reader reached sixty-five. Council, wanting a retirement age of sixty, decided Gardner had to go in September. In June it agreed senior staff should retire at sixty, but with the possibility of extension to sixty-five; other staff members were to retire at sixty.[xlix]

Pharmacology and histology were sub-units of the physiology department. Eleanor Scarborough, the pharmacologist, was a reader from 1924 but her salary, £500 p.a., had not changed subsequently. In view of the financial situation in 1932 Council, feeling unable to increase it, tried designating her 'part-time' so that she could undertake other paid work; but the University blocked the conversion of a full-time post to a part-time one at the same salary. Offered a part-time salary of £400 p.a. she reluctantly opted to remain full time, but complained that £500 p.a. should not be the maximum earning capacity of an LSMW graduate. The histologist, Evelyn Hewer (D.Sc. 1924), not medically qualified, was promoted to reader in 1932. Her *'Textbook of histology for medical students'*, first published in 1938, ran into many editions.[l]

In 1935 the University recognised Mary Waller as a 'teacher of physics'.[28] A wealthy woman, she wrote in 1936 expressing regret at her impending absence owing to her need to undergo surgery. Her offer to meet the expenses incurred for carrying on the department was reminiscent of her time spent voluntarily as a part-time teacher from 1923 to 1927 so that the School could save money. (see Chapter 10) The new offer was refused![li]

The School's social life was active during the 1930s. In 1932 the Choral Society performances of 'An Elizabethan Revel', an original programme, raised £73 for the RFH extension fund. In order to incorporate a newly formed orchestra with ten members, but short of viola, cello and woodwind players, it was renamed the 'Musical Society'[29] in February 1934. The orchestra may have been short-lived –

---

[28] In this context 'Teacher' is a title conferred by the University to indicate a degree of seniority.

[29] Although the Magazine for March 1935 still referred to a 'Choral Society'.

as the Magazine for November 1939 noted that a new 'orchestra (string)' had played at the Union Garden Party in 1938. It also provided the incidental music for a production of 'Back to Methuselah' by the Dramatic Society, which was busy during the 1930s but inactive after the outbreak of war.[lii]

A Folk Dance Club, inaugurated in 1929, saw many of its competitions cancelled in 1931 owing to the financial crisis. By suspending activities in the summer of 1932 it saved enough to employ an accompanist for practices during the winter term – at the end of which it won first place at the Kingston Musical Festival, plus the Mayor's Cup for the highest marks given in any section of the festival.[liii]

The Medical Society held clinical meetings, occasional debates, and heard lectures from staff and distinguished visitors. In November 1938 Josephine Collier, an ENT surgeon at RFH, talked on 'Aspects of Nutrition in Republican Spain'. She had visited Catalonia during the Civil War and commented on the hardship endured there by many children, their diet being barely sufficient for survival.[30] Owing to the war the famous Spanish neuro-anatomist, del Rio Hortega, whose Madrid laboratory was in ruins, was working at Oxford. In February 1939 he described the brain cells he discovered in a talk to the Society on 'Microglia at rest and in physiological activity'.[liv]

The Debating Society had ceased activities in 1922. Ten years later the Students' Union re-introduced debates and in November the motion 'That the rising generation should be taught not how to earn its living but how to spend its leisure' was lost by 26 votes to 28. Poor attendance led the Magazine for November 1935 to stress that debates were a Union activity in which all students should participate. However, the Magazine did not mention debates again until it referred to those held by ULU in 1945.[lv]

Politically motivated societies seemed ephemeral. At a Political Studies Society's meeting in May 1934 Dr Kershaw, Ealing's Assistant Medical Officer of Health, explained 'Why medical students should study politics'. No further meetings were reported, but the group may have been subsumed in the short-lived League of Nations Union started in 1934.

After the creation of the National Union of Students (NUS) in 1922 Britain's student body was gradually politicized. Initially this had little impact at the School but fifteen years later LSMW, the Middlesex and UCHMS were the only three London schools to send delegates to Liverpool for a national conference of medical students that asked the NUS to start a medical subsection.[lvi]

---

[30] Collier was instrumental in bringing the Catalan surgeon Josep Trueta and his family to England. He became Professor of Orthopaedics at Oxford.

The resulting Medical Students' Committee met in LSMW's common room in July 1938 to discuss 'The Training of the Doctor'. The Middlesex and UCHMS helped with organization. All British and Irish medical schools were represented except Bristol. Sir Henry Brackenbury (BMA)[31] spoke on the curriculum, Professor Lovatt Evans (Jodrell Professor of Physiology at UCL) on teaching methods, and Pearce Gould (a Middlesex surgeon) on examinations. Professor Jameson (LSHTM) dealt with public health issues; he taught at LSMW from 1930 and was subsequently a key planner for the NHS.[lvii]

The meeting carried four resolutions: i) Medical students should discuss their curricula – and either inform teachers of their findings or set up a staff-student committee. ii) The primary object of the medical curriculum was to produce an efficient doctor; although a wider culture was necessary no compulsory steps should be taken to that end. iii) The committee was to ascertain whether recruitment to the medical profession of this country could be adequately met by British subjects; if so, entry of foreigners should be severely restricted.[32] iv) Enquiries were to be made about using local municipal hospitals for clinical instruction.

LSMW followed up on the first resolution. In November 1938 the Magazine published the Students' Union report '*Some Aspects of the Medical Curriculum and Conditions of Work at the Royal Free Hospital*'. Addressing only 'weak' aspects, it pleaded that appointment committees should consider candidates' teaching skills as well as their clinical ability, and that tutorials and demonstrations should replace formal lectures, except for those on Public Health and Forensic Medicine. Surgical teaching involved too much time in theatre, where only the 'assisting' student saw much of the operation. Finally it suggested abolishing the three months Casualty post or shortening it to a month, as about 90% of it was nursing work. Several suggestions were made for improving the midwifery post.

At the Union General Meeting at which the document was finalized other points, outwith its scope, were also raised. Students wanted more residents (and particularly a third casualty officer); a voluntary system of district visiting; and two months at Great Ormond Street. They also asked that a Staff-Student Committee be set up.

In the Magazine for March 1939 Lucas-Keene accepted some points but complained that releasing it via the Magazine was discourteous, and implied mistrust of the Education Committee's members for whom it was intended. She deplored the tone of resentment, and the suggestion that senior staff cared little for the real needs of the students, and thought some phrases deliberately rude.

[31] Sir Henry Britten Brackenbury (1866-1942) was a medical politician, and involved in 'local and national government' with the BMA, Ministry of Health, etc.,etc.

[32] An issue which remains a matter of debate over seventy years later.

However, in the same issue, Muriel Bond, the physiologist, congratulated the Union for a thoughtful, critical report providing constructive suggestions.

In May 1939 the Education Committee approved many of the report's recommendations. Attendance at lectures was made voluntary, except for Public Health and Forensic Medicine; so too was attendance at operations, except for the students who were to 'scrub up'. It made no changes in the Casualty Post, believing that the students' presence was of real assistance. The comments on midwifery training 'were to be investigated'.

The Education Committee emphasized that staffing at RFH was outside its jurisdiction, but was satisfied that teaching facilities at RFH were adequate. A system of district visiting was deemed unfeasible. It considered it impossible to cover the ground-work on paediatrics in less than two months, and that this was better accomplished at RFH than at Great Ormond Street. It thought a Staff-Student Committee would serve no useful purpose; the Dean met students every week and seniors on posts could always discuss difficulties with staff.[33]

Sports

In 1932 the Students' Union officially adopted a lion[34] as the School badge, as it was believed that one had 'adorned the front of the original RFH building when it served as a barracks for the Light Horse Volunteers'. This may explain why, in 1896, the hospital students' own Tennis Club 'colours' were switched so that hats had a black ribbon with a gold lion and a gold border, and ties a black and gold stripe (see Chapter 6). There seems no evidence that there was a lion on the barracks when the Light Horse Volunteers occupied it, but there was one there in 1844 after the frontage had been altered to indicate it was now the Royal Free Hospital. However, the lion may well have been chosen by the Hospital tennis players in 1896 because in 1892, when RFH received a Royal Charter of Incorporation, its annual report, for the first time, displayed on the cover an official seal including a lion. (See Chapters 6 & 13). [35, lviii]

The Rowing Club's main opponents in London were UCL and KCL, but it also raced against other universities and colleges including Reading, Edinburgh, Armstrong College, Newcastle, Bristol and of course Newnham. The Newnham race was for VIIIs; IVs were used for most other competitions. LSMW was usually well represented in the University's boat and often provided its president, captain and/or secretary.

---

33 At this time 1st & 3rd year clinical students at LSMW were taught together on medical and surgical firms, a practice which continued until 1970 (see Chapter 14).

34 Sable [black], lion rampant or [gold], langued gules [red tongue].

35 See Ch 4 Fig 4.4. See also the story of the lion in the RFH's Maltese Cross logo in Chapter 13.

The March 1939 Magazine reported that Rowing Club members travelled by train from Waterloo to Chiswick, where the new boathouse was a five minute walk from the station. It had a comfortable lounge, changing rooms, a cloakroom with showers, and an indoor tank for practice. There was rowing on Wednesday afternoons, and Saturday morning practices were not cancelled unless fog obscured the far bank of the river; rain, snow and winds were ignored. The Union paid half the fares for away races. All members underwent a yearly medical examination by Dr. Shelley (a former oarswoman).

During the winter term the Boating Club, a less serious outfit, sculled on Regent's Park Lake; in the summer there was also punting, canoeing and dongolling. The Club competed against other colleges but the Magazine for March 1934 reported that all fixtures were lost in late 1933, and there were no further entries about the club during Bolton's deanship.

The Lacrosse Club was strong in 1931 but missed its four 'purples' when its matches clashed with those of the University. Following the sale of Sudbury it played only away games until it shared Paddington Recreation Ground with Southern Ladies. One member, Franklin-Adams, played for England in the early 1930s.[lix]

The Hockey Club, also homeless, used LCC pitches; they lacked pavilion accommodation and were often unfit for play in bad weather. Even so the first XI won most of its matches in 1930-1, but lost the cup final against UCL. For the second half of the season Wednesday practices were at the Civil Service ground at Chiswick. The following year they used Bedford College's ground at Headstone Lane, and in November 1931 received coaching from England's hockey captain, Mildred Knott. Mary Waller stepped down as President. Miss Higgins, her successor, who worked at RFH, was secretary of Eastern Counties hockey team, and coached the LSMW team.[lx]

After several years of inactivity the Cricket Club was revived in 1933. Twenty members practised hard at the Bedford College ground, and the team won all its ten matches. Edith Gilchrist, to whom this book is dedicated, received her colours for cricket in 1935, a year marred by bad weather and cancellation of many matches.[lxi]

The Netball Club still had its court at Hunter Street and practised once or twice a week. It fielded two teams on Wednesdays and Saturdays, but its large membership meant many who were keen to play in matches were disappointed.

In 1931 the Tennis Club played home matches at Regent's Park and practised at Cartwright Gardens. It too had a large membership but received no mention in the Magazine between July 1932 and July 1943.

Late in 1936 two squash courts became available at Clare Court, a nearby block of flats, and the School soon had a Squash Club with thirty members. Sadly the

Clare Court arrangement was a temporary one. A more satisfactory and permanent arrangement was sought, but the Magazine carried no further entries about squash until 1946.[lxii]

In the early 1930s the Fencing Club had a small membership, few attended lessons, and no events were held. In 1933 the ULAU refused it a grant, so the club raised funds to pay for lessons at the Tassart-Parkins School of Fencing. In 1936-7 the club won the Inter-Collegiate Cup, recently presented by Professor Cullis, and two members represented the University. The club remained active. In 1939 two teams competed within London and at other Universities, and Thurlow, LSMW's captain, also captained the University.[lxiii]

In 1937 a 'Keep-Fit' Club met on Tuesdays in the Drill Hall, Handel Street, and performed exercises set to music. The classes were taken by the future dean, Katherine Lloyd-Williams, a physiotherapist before entering LSMW in 1920. An all-round sportswoman as a student, she was president of the UL Athletic Union (Women) in 1922-3.[lxiv]

The first mention of an Ice-skating Club was in LSMW's Magazine for March 1939. For a reduced rate, of 2s.6d. per session, members used Queen's Ice Skating Club, Bayswater where famous skaters practised. There was no subscription, the club paid for lessons and gave members sixpence every time they skated!

In 1928, 1929 and 1930 the Old Students Association held annual dinners ending with dancing. There was no dinner in 1931 & 1932, presumably because of the Great Depression. When the dinners restarted in 1933 they were linked with a week-end postgraduate course for old students, an arrangement that proved successful. However the dinner lost money in December 1938, attendance having fallen from 432 in 1932 to 292. The 1939 dinner was cancelled – not because the war had started but because neither the treasurer (Jenner Verrall) nor the committee would guarantee a £17 deficit. Owing to the war no more such dinners were arranged until 1947.[lxv]

The Continued (but slow) Advance of Women Doctors

In September 1933 Christine Murrell was the first woman elected to the General Medical Council; sadly she died, aged 59, before she could take up her seat. In 1924, she had become the first woman on the BMA's Central Council, having previously served on some of its other committees. A practitioner in Bayswater, she had a particular interest in infant welfare, was an active crusader for women's rights, and was the fifth president of the Medical Women's Federation.

London's Royal College of Physicians was more reluctant to open its examinations to women than any other examining body. When the College eventually allowed women to sit for the LRCP & MRCP in 1909 it passed a by-law stopping them becoming Fellows. (See Chapter 7) It also ignored the Sex Disqualification (Removal) Act 1919 that made such discrimination illegal. In 1924 a proposal by Drs John Fawcett and Farquhar Buzzard to alter the by-law was carried by 20 votes to 12; both had taught women at RFH. As the official history of the College puts it – 'After a decent interval of nine years [i.e. in 1933] the first woman fellow was elected, Dr Helen Mackay, an eminent paediatrician'. The next two female FRCPs were Hazel Chodak-Gregory (1935) and Dorothy Hare (1936).[lxvi]

Women still had problems within the Civil Service and with other public bodies, including the armed forces. Dame Janet Campbell's reports on maternal care and on neonatal & infant mortality from 1923 to 1932 helped to reduce mortality & morbidity rates in women and children. Even so, in order to be able to marry Michael Heseltine, the GMC's registrar, in 1934 she had to relinquish her position at the Ministry of Health. Parliament eventually lifted the 'marriage bar' for women holding senior positions in the Home Civil Service at the end of 1946; their counterparts in the Foreign Office had to wait until 1973. The other longstanding problem was that women earned less than men doing the same job. It was 1956 before the principle of 'equal pay' was brought in for civil servants and women teachers.[lxvii]

Far more serious problems began emerging during the 1930s. Concerns about the deteriorating political situation in Europe first impinged on LSMW in 1933 when it was asked to help fifteen women doctors or medical students who had left Germany for political reasons and wished to study in London. Council, while sympathetic, felt unable to help because of the large number of applications already received.[lxviii]

The refugee situation worsened. In June 1938 John Ryle, Regius Professor of Physic at Cambridge and an adviser to the Ministry of Health, asked medical schools to follow the London Hospital's example and accept one Austrian student for the whole medical course without charge. Bolton replied that LSMW, with limited accommodation, could not offer Austrians facilities unavailable to many British applicants. In November, the Coordinating Committee for Refugees requested a free clinical place for Helene Weyr, an Austrian doctor who hoped to qualify in Britain. She was the only woman among fifty refugee practitioners accepted by the Home Office. Bolton said she could enter when her English had improved. She appears to have started in April 1939 but there is nothing to suggest she subsequently attended RFH or qualified from LSMW.[lxix]

In December 1938 the Students' Union offered to maintain an Austrian student at LSMW if Council would provide her with a free place. From the many applicants the Dean selected Elizabeth Szabo of Vienna University for a full Conjoint course. In March 1939 the Students' Union outlined plans to raise money and to house her for all vacations. She arrived in Britain and in October joined the LSMW students evacuated to Aberdeen. In May 1939 Council offered a free place for a two year clinical course to enable a Dr Gerda Sgalitzer to gain British qualifications so that she could take up a post offered to her in India. However Sgalitzer left Liverpool for Boston on the SS Nova Scotia on 13 December 1939.

As the threat of war increased, universities and medical schools took action. In 1936 Scarborough, the pharmacologist, and Agnes Kelynack, then RMO at RFH, attended a fortnight's course at the Civilian Anti-Gas School in Gloucestershire. Subsequently they taught LSMW students about anti-gas measures using equipment provided by the Home Office. Kelynack went on to work in the Home Office's air-raid precautions department, and in 1944 was the first medically qualified woman appointed to the staff of the BMA – as its Assistant Secretary.[lxx]

In June 1938 London University, fearful of the anticipated bombing, began discussing the disposition of its medical students in the event of war. In May 1939, with war now seeming inevitable, it began planning the evacuation of preclinical students. Schools were asked not to approach provincial universities and colleges directly. Although clinical students were not to be evacuated en masse their education was bound to be seriously disrupted, as the Emergency Medical Service (EMS) was to take control of London's hospitals. Even before the war LSMW students considered themselves either 'School' or 'Hospital' students; this perception was reinforced by their separation during the war years.[lxxi]

CHAPTER 12

Elizabeth Bolton

The War – Dispersal, Disruption & Devastation (1939-1945)

After war was declared on 3 September 1939 RFH sandbagged the quadrangle windows (Fig 12.1) and the School began evacuating its preclinical students. LSMW rejected London University's idea of sending them to Birmingham, considering it as vulnerable to bombing as London. Instead it accepted offers from Aberdeen and St Andrews. Second and third year students began at Aberdeen on 2 October; the first-year premedicals joined St Andrews the following day. Aberdeen charged £7.17s.6d a year per student, St Andrews cost twice as much. All LSMW's full-time teachers went to Scotland and some part-time staff (Mrs Mills & Mrs Hughes in biology) and (Miss Airs, chemistry) accepted temporary full-time appointments at St Andrews. Bolton remained Dean throughout the war; Lucas-Keene acted for her in Aberdeen. [1, i]

Ironically, Aberdeen proved a more attractive initial target for German bombers than London. In February 1940 parents objected when told their offspring would remain there until the June exams and so the students at Aberdeen returned to Hunter Street after Easter. St Andrews was not bombed and the 'first-years' remained there the whole academic year.[ii]

As London appeared relatively safe for much of 1940 the students were due to return to LSMW in the autumn, re-evacuation remaining a possibility. In June Dr John Murray, Principal of Exeter's University College of the South West of England (UCSWE), offered to accommodate all preclinical departments (including the 'first-years') for £12.10s. per student per session, with places for some in halls of residence.[iii]

The 'Blitz', the eight-month period of intensive bombing of London and other cities, began on 7 September 1940.[2] On 23 September LSMW accepted Murray's offer. The students started at Exeter on 22 October. The Dean and Assistant Secretary stayed in London to support the clinical students; most of administration,

---

1 Catherine Lewis was elected Vice Dean in June 1939 but the war made the position redundant. There was no Vice-Dean for 1941-42. Lucas-Keene acted as Dean at Exeter, and Chodak-Gregory at Arlesey.

2 It lasted until 16 May 1941. Hitler then moved his bombers east to prepare for the invasion of Russia.

Fig 12.1 Sandbags in the RFH quadrangle in 1939

including the Students' Union office, went to Exeter. Earlier in October a 'Molotov basket'[3] ignited the dissecting room roof at Hunter Street; the flames were soon controlled but water from firemen's hoses exacerbated the damage. On 15 October the blast from a nearby explosion blew out windows and skylights at the School.

During this period two old students of LSMW, Hannah Billig and Alison McNairn, were awarded the George Medal for bravery; even though injured themselves they continued treating people injured by bombing – Billig in Wapping, and McNairn at the City General Hospital in Plymouth. Billig joined the Indian Army Medical Corps in 1942, and three years later was awarded an MBE for her work in Assam. She returned to her general practice in the East End.

Council met throughout the war with Henderson as Chairman. As regular attendance was difficult for everyone the University announced in February 1940 that during the war Council's quorum could be five instead of eight. When his father died in July 1941, the Treasurer, Francis Rodd, became the second Baron Rennell. He had served in the First World War and was a Major-General throughout the Second. Although officially Treasurer to the end of Bolton's deanship he left the country on duty in 1942; Sir Alan Anderson acted in his place.[iv]

The war disrupted the teaching staff. The University had agreed a year's extension for Winifred Cullis, due to retire in September 1940. A further extension was to be sought, but in July the Ministry of Information asked her to tour the Far

3 A landmine containing many incendiary bombs that scattered over a large area when the mine exploded.

East publicizing the activities of British women during wartime. The School granted her six months' leave and extended it until April 1941. The Ministry's American Division then recruited her to head the Women's Section of the British Information Services in the USA for two years. Cullis, recognizing the problems created, offered to resign in March 1941 and the School accepted.[v]

Cullis was thus only the nominal head of the physiology department in Exeter. Her senior colleagues, both readers, were Evelyn Hewer (histology) and Eleanor Scarborough (pharmacology). Her father's poor health led Hewer to offer to resign in January 1941; instead she received a prolonged leave of absence. After he died in the summer of 1944 she returned to LSMW but did not work full-time until the spring term of 1945.[vi]

Scarborough resigned in January 1941; the reason is unclear. Council, perhaps anticipating her return, sought outside help and Woolley, pharmacology lecturer at St Thomas' Hospital, gave the autumn lectures. In February 1942 LSMW offered Scarborough a senior lectureship and she was reinstated as a reader from 1 October.

Bond acted as head of department following Cullis's resignation, having run physiology teaching in her absence. She certainly had problems. In October 1940 Miss Yang, due to help cover for Cullis, decided not go to Exeter. Her replacement, Miss Sikes, had her appendix removed in March 1941 and then missed four weeks of the summer term. Furthermore after Scarborough resigned Bond had to give the anti-gas training to the preclinical students. She attended a three week training course during the 1941 summer vacation, and qualified as a special instructor and examiner in all branches of air raid precaution work; after the return to London in 1943 she was made LSMW's senior fire guard.[vii]

In October 1941 Esther Margaret Killick replaced Cullis as Sophia Jex-Blake Professor of Physiology.[4] In 1924, while a medical student at Leeds, she had taken a B.Sc. in physiology, and then spent two years in Sheffield as a research fellow with May Mellanby[5] before returning to Leeds for clinical studies. She graduated MBChB in 1929 and began her life long study of carbon monoxide toxicity.[viii]

Most LSMW students at Exeter lived in halls of residence. Thomas Hall (Fig 12.2) which accommodated about thirty-five was allocated exclusively to LSMW and was the social centre for its staff and students. Miss Moller was warden, Miss Stott matron,[6] and George Knight, the Hunter Street hall porter, the 'houseman'. Moller,

---

4 Killick was married to A.StG.J.M. Huggett, Professor of Physiology at St Mary's Hospital Medical School. Their first daughter was born in 1940. Killick missed the start of the autumn term 1945 while expecting their second child.

5 The wife of (Sir) Edward Mellanby,

6 Stott resigned at Easter 1941.

Fig 12.2 Thomas Hall, Exeter

unhappy about the domestic arrangements, wanted LSMW to rent Thomas Hall and take control of it but UCSWE's terms proved unacceptable. In October 1941 seven of the School's portraits were moved to Thomas Hall, including those of Jex-Blake, Garrett Anderson and Aldrich-Blake.[ix]

Fifteen LSMW students lived in Reed Hall, and twenty in Lopes Hall, which also had five students 'attached' to it;[7] thirty-two were 'attached' to Hope Hall. Some students 'attached' to halls wanted to move into lodgings in the city, but the Principal objected and contacted their parents directly. Council 'regretted' his approach to the control of LSMW students.[x]

When Bolton and Henderson, Council's chairman, visited Exeter in December 1940 to discuss the matter with Murray he agreed students 'attached' to halls might take lodgings. However he demanded final authority over those living in halls and insisted such students, except those at Thomas Hall, paid five shillings a term for medical attendance.[8] Although LSMW expected a large entry in October 1941 Moller heard in July that no extra space was available in halls of residence; she had to arrange lodgings for about 130 students.[xi]

At Hunter Street there was further war damage. On 27 October an anti-aircraft shell damaged the lower cloakroom, the biology demonstrators' room and the

---

[7] 'Attached' students presumably slept nearby but took their meals in the hall.

[8] Presumably medically qualified LSMW staff cared for those at Thomas Hall.

entrance hall, and on 29 December an incendiary bomb breached the west wall of the Dean's room, burnt a hole in the carpet and singed the floorboard. On 16 April 1941 three similar bombs fell into the quadrangle; another went through the roof and down the lift shaft in the extension that had been opened on the north side of the quadrangle in 1916. Fortunately they did little harm.[xii]

The Hospital escaped serious damage during the Blitz but disaster was avoided only through good fortune and the great skill of a bomb disposal team. In early October 1940 an incendiary bomb hit the workshop of Kelvinator Ltd., adjoining the north-west corner of RFH. The fire was soon extinguished but the top storey was left open to the air.

On 15 October blast from a nearby bomb damaged the north and west wings of RFH. There were few injuries as they were almost empty – and students and staff slept in the air raid shelter under the main quadrangle. Forty minutes later a magnetic mine loaded with 2000lbs of TNT – which would have demolished most of RFH – floated down by parachute, passed through the open roof of the Kelvinator building; and remained suspended about 18 inches above the ground, perilously close to RFH's north wall. All patients, except those too ill to move, were evacuated to Bart's or EGAH. With great difficulty a naval squad led by Lieutenant John Miller, RNVR,[9] defused and removed the mine on 20 October. Later he wrote '*I do not recall any other mine…which imposed so great a strain upon the will*'.[xiii] Within a day or two RFH reopened as a casualty clearing station, ran a full outpatient service and serviced 265 beds in the Eastman Clinic wing.[xiv]

Unexpectedly, Exeter suffered a massive air attack on 4 May 1942; [10] 10,000 incendiary bombs and 75 tons of high explosives destroyed much of its centre and hit the college. Students assisted civil defence and other services,[11] and helped Ernest Williams, LSMW's anatomy technician, to salvage tables and other equipment from a dissecting room while its roof burned. LSMW people suffered no casualties but some, made homeless, spent the rest of term at the Teignmouth home of Dr. Mules,[12] an LSMW alumna. The American Women's Hospitals Fund gave £175 to assist twelve students who lost all their possessions.[13] Council, although alarmed, decided the pre-clinical departments should stay in Exeter for 1942-3.[xv]

---

[9] Miller received the George Cross for bomb disposal work during the Blitz.

[10] Hitler, enraged by bombing of the cathedral city of Lubeck launched reprisal raids on beautiful, but strategically unimportant, English towns. Exeter was the first hit. (*www.exetermemories.co.uk*)

[11] Lucas-Keene asked if LSMW's medically qualified staff could serve part-time in the EMS in a crisis, Council agreed providing it was voluntary service only (with training being done in their own time).

[12] The 1942 *Medical Directory* notes that Bertha Mules & daughter Annie (also LSMW) lived at Cliffden, Teignmouth, and ran a private mental hospital at Court Hall, Kenton, Exeter.

[13] The money was given through the Medical Women's Federation.

Clubs and societies struggled during the war owing to the evacuation of the preclinical students and the separation of students in the different clinical years. The Students' Union affiliated to the local Guild of Undergraduates at Exeter and during the first year launched Scientific and Architectural societies and tried to get rowing started again.

The Scientific Society usually had outside speakers, but some were LSMW students experienced in other areas – e.g. Dr. Frankl, a Viennese psychology graduate, spoke on 'The value of psychology to the medical student', while Townsend spoke on 'Radioactivity and the artificial disintegration of atoms'.[14] During its second year three students – Bush, Anderson and Cook – spoke on 'Guinea Pigs at War Work', having spent a summer vacation loading shells in a Lancashire factory for a study on TNT poisoning headed by Alice Stewart, a former LSMW student. The study changed the way shells were made. In March 1943 Stewart herself spoke on the haematological effects of TNT poisoning.[15, xvi]

The Architectural Society had no rules or subscription. It just organised expeditions and on fine summer days members benefited from the wartime introduction of 'Double Summer Time'.[16] They visited ancient churches, manor houses and farms, and rambled in Old Exeter, visited the cathedral or listened to each other's talks on architecture. Mary Waller detailed places visited, including Walter Raleigh's birthplace, in the Magazine for January 1942.

Because the new London University boathouse was commandeered as a mortuary in the summer of 1940, the rowers who came back from Aberdeen used Tom Green's Boathouse, one of the Rowing Club's old haunts. UCSWE had no rowing club so, when LSMW began rowing in Exeter, Miss Parker, the only student who had rowed in London, coached the novices in boats hired from Exeter's Port Royal Boat Club. Dalley and Mitchell, two club stalwarts, came from London for the weekend in June 1942 to help her. The only other active sports club at Exeter was the Netball Club which, for two seasons, played 1st & 2nd team matches against local sides including UCSWE, Bishop Blackall and Maynard schools, and against KCL, which was evacuated to Bristol.[xvii]

In October 1941 the Students' Union revived the Dramatic Society, and started Contemporary and 'National Effort' societies. The last may have metamorphosed into the 'Produce Club' which 'knitted for victory'; by July 1942 it had produced fourteen helmets, four pullovers, seven pairs of gloves, and eight pairs of socks. It kept rabbits at Thomas Hall to ensure a supply of rabbit pie.[xviii]

---

[14] Townsend had worked at the Cavendish Laboratory at Cambridge.

[15] Stewart first described the damaging effects on the fetus of X-raying the abdomen of pregnant women.

[16] Double summer time was two hrs ahead of GMT; the usual summer time was one hr ahead.

The Contemporary Society, which promoted 'interest in the trend of contemporary thought and achievement', soon had a hundred members. In November 1941 a Dr. Stengel talked on 'Medical Education and Research in Vienna'. Early in 1942 John Coatman, then BBC's Regional Controller in Manchester, described 'The Present Situation in India' and the writer L. A. G. Strong talked on 'Broadcasting'. In May Gustav Holst's daughter, Imogen, spoke on 'Listening to Music'.[xix]

LSMW had had a 'Musical Society' from 1904 to 1917. It was then called the 'Choral Society' until 1934, when it became the 'Musical Society' again for eight years. 'Re-founded' as the Choral Society in Exeter in June 1942, it gave its 'first' concert in December in Reed Hall.[17] Dr Wilcock, Exeter Cathedral's organist, was the conductor, and Miss Narrish of UCSWE the accompanist.[xx]

The preclinicals returned to London in October 1943. When they left Exeter in June UCSWE presented LSMW with a silver rose bowl inscribed *L.S.M.W. d.d.*[18] *U.C.S.W.E. Exeter 1943*. To reciprocate, the School wished to give UCSWE some teak seats but they were unobtainable during the war. Instead F.R.S. Balfour found a 1770 mahogany bracket clock, costing £35, and had a gold plate engraved *'To the University College of the South West of England from the London (Royal Free Hospital) School of Medicine for Women to commemorate the three years spent by members of the School at Exeter as guests of the College'*.[xxi]

The war and the resulting evacuation of the students had a disruptive effect on the School's special occasions. The inaugural address scheduled for 2 October 1939 was cancelled and the next one was held in Exeter in 1943 shortly before the return to Hunter Street. UCSWE's Principal was to give the address in London on 29 September 1944, with his wife presenting the prizes. Owing to air raids the joint event was delayed until 17 January 1945. Poor health then prevented Mrs Murray's attendance; her husband performed both functions. The official 1945 prize-giving, held in the Great Hall of BMA House on Thursday, 21 June, was a very special occasion, as Her Royal Highness Princess Elizabeth, resplendent in her ATS uniform, presented the students with their prizes and addressed them afterwards.[xxii]

Clinical Education during the War

The Emergency Medical Service (EMS) controlled both voluntary and municipal hospitals during the war, so the fate of London's clinical students was determined by which hospitals were allocated to their individual schools. London was divided into ten sectors, each based on one or more teaching hospitals; nine sectors radiated

[17] The madrigal from 'The Mikado', the Barcarolle from the 'Tales of Hoffman', Mozart's 'Alleluia', and 'The Death of Minnehaha' from Coleridge Taylor's 'Hiawatha'.

[18] d.d. – *dono dedit* (gave as a gift)

from the centre into the Home Counties. First-aid and casualty sorting centres provided immediate treatment in danger areas and prepared casualties for transfer to advance base hospitals. More distant hospitals received patients for after-care; less well equipped hospitals dealt with convalescent and chronic cases.[xxiii]

Initially patients were discharged or evacuated from central London hospitals in anticipation of a large wave of air-raid casualties but, despite casualties from Dunkirk and the London Blitz, there was not the avalanche of injuries for which the EMS was created. Base hospital staffs had relatively little to do, and beds lay empty in central London until limited services resumed.

Although clinical students were not 'evacuated' they left Gray's Inn Road for much of their training. RFH, like Bart's, was a Sector 3 casualty clearing station unsuitable for general medical training of undergraduates. In July 1939 Sir Girling Ball,[19] the head of Sector 3, decided LSMW's first and third clinical year students would receive general training at the Three Counties Hospital at Arlesey in Bedfordshire; second year students would remain at RFH. Ball was a member of LSMW's Council from 1939 to 1944.[xxiv]

On 26 August 1939 the Dean heard that accommodation at Arlesey would not be ready for several months and that the billets[20] promised through the EMS were unavailable (but see below). Sadly there were only about 65 beds at Arlesey and little prospect of more, but it seemed unlikely that better accommodation would be found elsewhere.[xxv]

Within weeks of the onset of war forty students went to Arlesey. One described their early experiences in the Magazine. Their accommodation was comfortable. The newly built hospital, Fairfield, had light, sunny wards and a well equipped theatre. Cycles were the main form of transport. Patients travelled from London by 'ambulance bus' twice a week and the Friday 'bus' returned to town full of students. Desks and tables were dotted about the large recreation hall which contained the pathology department; a pile of mattresses concealed Professor Webb's corner 'office'.[xxvi]

Sporting pursuits at Arlesey included 'hockey, golf, riding, squash, and shooting rats at the sewage farm'. Some students there, as at Exeter, felt the call of the footlights. By the summer of 1943 the 'Three Counties Emergency Hospital Dramatic Society' had over a hundred members and had joined the Drama League. With seven productions it raised over £84 for charities. Its meetings included a

[19] Sir Girling Ball was dean of Bart's medical school, and chairman of the group officers from the different sectors. He was immortalised in Richard Gordon's 'Doctor' books, as the irascible surgeon Sir Lancelot Spratt who was played by James Robertson Justice in the films that followed.

[20] 'Billets' usually refers to civilian houses where soldiers are lodged.

'balloon debate', two poetry readings, and a piano recital by the young surgeon Peter Essex-Lopresti who was also a gifted musician.[21, xxvii]

In January 1940 Ledingham and Shattock took charge of the medical and surgical divisions at Arlesey. The Medical Committee agreed all should share the work there. The RFH physicians and surgeons prepared rotas; those stationed at Arlesey did the routine visits, everyone else was on call one day a week for emergencies.[xxviii]

After the initial evacuation patients gradually drifted back to RFH, and for the first year of the war most junior clinical students actually remained at RFH. But patients were evacuated again during the Blitz, and in September 1940 there was insufficient clinical material for the 170 students attending RFH. The RMO needed thirty volunteers to assist with casualties; for them sufficient 'general work' could be provided. Most others went to Arlesey, but other places used for clinical training included Oster House, St. Albans (run by EGAH staff); Wellhouse Hospital, Barnet; Carshalton (for children's diseases); and various specialist hospitals. Out-patient numbers fell sharply at hospitals in and around London during the Blitz, so the Dean arranged for some second clinical year students to attend a small three-month outpatient post at Royal Devon and Exeter Hospital from April 1941.[xxix]

During the academic year 1941-2 more evacuated residents returned to London and the number of patients at RFH steadily increased. The Ministry of Health cut its requirement for emergency beds and even more beds became available for students at GIR the following year.[xxx]

The first LSMW student to die through enemy action was L. J. Gregory, a third year clinical student, killed in October 1940 at the Imbeciles Asylum, Leavesden, near Watford – a Great Ormond Street Base Hospital in Sector 4, whose teaching hospitals were UCH and Charing Cross.[xxxi]

The work of RFH's clinical staff was seriously disrupted – by the demands of the EMS, which dictated how and where they functioned, and by loss of some to the armed forces. In LSMW's list of Lecturers, Teachers and Demonstrators for the academic year 1943-4 those 'absent for duration' included two physicians (Lee Lander & Rendel), the three orthopaedic surgeons (Jenner Verrall, Gray & Jebons), a dentist (Deverell), three gynaecologists (Hill & Sharpe with the EMS, Moore with the RAMC), two pathologists (Taylor & Louis), an ENT surgeon (Collier), a radiologist (Staveley), and two anaesthetists (Rowbotham & Claude Morris). In anticipation of the early release of some individuals after hostilities ceased in Europe, LSMW was asked In December 1944 which of them were deemed essential for teaching. The Dean named Collier, Lee Lander, Rowbotham and Staveley.

[21] He died in 1951, aged 35, when a consultant at Birmingham Accident Hospital.

Ledingham subsequently asked Council to petition for her husband's early release – stating that she might otherwise have to resign or take a prolonged leave of absence – but the Central Medical War Committee proved unsympathetic![22,xxxii]

When the war started Qvist was a surgical registrar at RFH and from 1941 he worked there with the EMS. In 1944 he joined the RAMC and served in Europe & Middle East as a Lieutenant-Colonel. He was appointed surgeon at RFH on leaving the Army.

About a year after joining RFH as a consultant neurosurgeon in 1943 Diana Kinloch Beck (MB 1925) was moved to Chase Farm Hospital to satisfy the EMS, and then to Bristol as regional consultant adviser in neurosurgery for the West Country.[23] In February 1944 she asked about keeping dogs at LSMW for work she and Dorothy Russell, a neuropathologist, were doing for the MRC's 'war wounds committee'. Her request was turned down because the animal house was near residential flats. In 1947 she was appointed consultant neurosurgeon at the Middlesex Hospital.[xxxiii]

Although Ida Mann was an 'honorary' at RFH she seems to have spent relatively little time there.[24] In May 1941 she was appointed Margaret Ogilvie's Reader in Ophthalmology in the University of Oxford. In 1945 she was given the title of Professor, but Oxford's annual report for 1947-8 emphasized that its first 'full' woman professor was Agnes Headlam-Morley who assumed the Montague Burton Chair of International Relations in 1948. Jean Fleming had left RFH's ophthalmology department in 1940. Her replacement, Jean Dollar, was appointed as an assistant surgeon but ran the department more or less single-handedly until after the war.[xxxiv]

After Webb moved to Arlesey, along with most of his pathology department, Lucy Wills, a chemical pathologist, acted as head of pathology at RFH. Dorothy Vaux,[25] who taught morbid anatomy, resigned in 1944 to become pathologist to the Ludhiana Women's Christian Medical College in the Punjab.[xxxv]

In October 1941 Council asked Hadfield,[26] then professor of pathology at Bart's, to allocate at least half the practical post-mortem experience at Oster House Hospital, St Alban's, to the LSMW students studying there. There was also pathology teaching at the Archway Hospital, Highgate, and in October 1943 LSMW asked the LCC if this could continue.[xxxvi]

---

[22] While her husband was away Ledingham not only worked at RFH but also ran his general practice.

[23] Sir Geoffrey Jefferson said there was then no other woman neurosurgeon in Western Europe or North America (*The Times* 6 Mar 1956).

[24] Ida Mann has a 'blue plaque' at 13 Minster Road, West Hampstead (her home from 1902-1934).

[25] From December 1932 Vaux was demonstrator in morbid anatomy & curator of the museum.

[26] Hadfield (Webb's predecessor) moved to Bristol in 1933 and in 1935 was appointed Professor of Pathology at Bart's.

The RFH pathology department was seriously hampered by lack of space. A subcommittee appointed to consider the eventual return from Arlesey of the pathology & x-ray departments suggested that annexes of Queen Mary Ward, including Washington Ward, might serve to enlarge the pathology department. It cost about £432 to convert them; the School paid half.[xxxvii]

The threat of bacterial warfare, or of epidemics resulting from movement of large numbers of people, led to the creation in 1938 of an Emergency Public Health Laboratory Service (EPHLS) administered by the MRC. The bacteriologist Joan Taylor joined it in October 1939, expecting to return to RFH and LSMW after the war. However, in October 1945 she left LSMW having been offered a permanent position in the Public Health Laboratory Service (PHLS – which replaced the EPHLS in 1946). From June 1943 Nuala Crowley was lecturer in clinical pathology, with some responsibilities at RFH; she remained bacteriologist at RFH and was promoted to senior lecturer in 1947.[xxxviii]

As Hamilton Fairley was serving overseas Philip Manson-Bahr, Director of Tropical Medicine at LSHTM, lectured on tropical medicine at LSMW in 1941.[27] Dr A.L. Gregg of Westminster Hospital Medical School was then lecturer until Fairley's post-war return. Colonel Parkinson, the lecturer in public health, was conscripted when the war started; Maitland Radford, St Pancras's Medical Officer of Health, gave the lectures from October 1939. When Radford died in January 1944 Pritchard, his deputy at St Pancras, took over until Parkinson returned briefly (as a Brigadier). When the last relinquished the lectureship in October 1945 it went to Herbert Chalke. Sir Bernard Spilsbury, lecturer in forensic medicine and toxicology from 1919, was too old for active service; he continued in post at LSMW until 1947, four years past the usual retirement age.[xxxix]

Provision of adequate midwifery experience was a major problem. Following the rejection of Kenney's appointment as professor in 1939 the O & G Unit had no director. Dearnley took charge on 1 October 1939, with Jocelyn Moore as her assistant (see Chapter 11), but for some reason Moore was allocated to EMS Sector 8 (based on St Thomas' Hospital);[28] she was therefore unavailable to teach at LSMW. In January 1941 Moore joined the RAMC. [xl]

During the war women doctors entering the armed services were initially commissioned on a 'wartime basis'. Two early ones, Mrs Ethel Whitby and Miss Muriel Boycott, were given the 'relative rank' of Lieutenant RAMC on 4 November 1939. Subsequent lady medical officers had the 'proper rank' of

[27] Manson-Bahr, knighted in 1941, was the son-in-law of Sir Patrick Manson, who gave the first lectures on tropical medicine at LSMW when Garrett Anderson was Dean.

[28] According to the Medical Committee's minutes for 10 July 1940 she tried to transfer to Sector 3. Her father, a Major-General, had been head of the Army Veterinary Service.

Lieutenant. Ethel's husband, Lionel Whitby, previously a pathologist at the Middlesex Hospital, was Brigadier in charge of the Army's Blood Transfusion Service, in which his wife also served. In 1945 he was knighted and appointed Regius Professor of Physic at Cambridge; she became an acting Major![xli]

Mary M. Munro joined the RAMC in August 1943 and became an Army pathologist. She kept extending her short service commissions and in 1962 was the first woman granted a 'Regular Commission' in the RAMC.[xlii]

In September 1939 the EMS took over all O & G Unit beds for casualties, and only four were released quickly. Home deliveries continued playing a major role in midwifery training; they took place in the large district covered by EGAH and the Essex Road maternity clinic, both of which also had beds. The EMS posted Dearnley to Arlesey, which lacked maternity beds, but she went on lecturing at RFH. In November Gladys Hill was asked to supervise maternity work at RFH, but Dearnley, now only half time with the EMS, returned to RFH by December and was given ten beds.[xliii]

During the academic year 1940-1 the students also learned midwifery at the Mothers' Hospital, Clapton, at Woking Hospital and the City Hospital, Exeter, and in January 1941 the Ministry of Health announced they could go to Shardeloes Maternity Hospital at Amersham, if RFH staff supervised the teaching.[29] However, Bucks County Council would not provide accommodation or meals and insisted that staff already at Shardeloes, or subsequently appointed there, must do the teaching; RFH was also to replace any nurses who resigned because Shardeloes taught medical students. The Ministry pressed LSMW to agree to these conditions. In 1942 thirty obstetrical beds were re-opened at RFH.[xliv]

When the pre-clinicals returned to Hunter Street in October 1943 life at LSMW began returning to normal. The Students' Union created a single Sports Club with a committee including a President, Secretary and Treasurer, and representatives from the main sports clubs. It coordinated financial and other aspects of all the individual clubs, i.e. gymnastic, hockey, lacrosse, netball, rowing, sailing,[30] swimming, table tennis and tennis clubs. The Union also hoped to revive the dramatic and orchestral societies.[xlv]

The activities of a new Social Club ranged widely. It ran weekly ballroom dancing classes and was invited to dances at other institutions. There were two dances at Hunter Street during the Easter term of 1944 but the number that could

[29] Shardeloes was a beautiful country house; it was requisitioned at the start of the war to allow London women to have their babies in a gentler environment than wartime London. My wife, an RFHSM graduate, was born there in 1942.

[30] Students could only join the sailing club if their parents gave permission in writing.

be held there was limited by the shortage of domestic staff. There were theatre parties, and lunchtime pursuits included gramophone recitals, debates, spelling bees, sing-songs, an obstacle race, and a 'tenniquoit' tournament.[xlvi]

The Scientific Society, founded in Exeter, still met regularly. The dormant Medical Society[31] awoke in 1944 and one speaker was Margaret Jennings, an LSMW alumna, who described her work on penicillin with Florey's team at Oxford. [32, xlvii]

The Orchestral Society, reborn in the autumn of 1943, needed more instruments, more members, and particularly a viola player. The Choral Society practised for its traditional carol singing. The Dramatic Society eschewed a major production in 1944 in favour of sorting out its props and costumes, but did present a one-act Victorian comedy as a curtain-raiser to the Topical in March.

The Socialist Society, active in the 1920s, was re-activated in 1939 as an *'independent, progressive, political club*...[that] *aims at placing before students a variety of different opinions and facilities for discussion'*. In its first term there were two meetings on social (nutritional)[33] and industrial (silicotic) diseases, and two political ones – on Russia and on the position of students. With UCL's Conservative Association it debated the motion 'That this house could have no faith in any form of Socialist Government at the present time'; the motion was lost. For most of the war the society was inactive.[xlviii]

In 1942 a newly formed Socialist Medical Association met at RFH and at Arlesey to discuss 'The British Medical Services', 'Social Security in New Zealand', 'Medicine in the USSR', and 'National Health Insurance'. A student usually led the discussion. The attendance was about twenty at Arlesey and ten at RFH, but fifty heard Philip D'Arcy Harte [34] from the MRC speak on 'Tuberculosis and the War'. In 1944 there were lunch-hour readings (from the works of Bernard Shaw, Marx and the Dean of Canterbury, etc.), weekly discussions on current events, and sittings of a 'Controversial Brains Trust' to which various outside 'brains' were invited.[xlix]

In 1944 the Rowing and Sailing clubs started up again. The former had forty members but Saturday afternoon turnouts were poor. The 'sailors' were pleased

---

[31] In April 1942 it debated 'That state control of general practitioners and hospitals would be of benefit'; the motion was lost by 45 votes to 5.

[32] Born Margaret Fremantle 1904, daughter of 3rd Baron Cottesloe. Graduated BMBCh Oxon 1933 as Hon. Margaret Augusta (Mrs) Jennings). The Oxford team established penicillin was non-toxic to man, but that allergy was a problem. She was then Florey's mistress, and became the second Lady Florey in 1967.

[33] The speaker, Wilfred Le Gros Clark, was Oxford's charismatic Professor of Anatomy. Blinded in WW1 he led the medico–political Committee against Malnutrition.

[34] D'Arcy Hart died in 2006, aged 106 and still publishing! He held an MRC grant until 1993.

that most of the club's dinghies had returned from the repair yards ready for use.[l]

The Swimming Club was neglected by the Magazine between November 1930 and July 1944. Re-activated in October 1943 it met only twice that winter. From May 1944 members swam at the Marshall Street baths. When they closed early in 1945 the club returned to the Buckingham Palace Road baths.[li]

In July 1943 the Tennis Club was revived but the following year its activities were restricted owing to a shortage of balls, and problems with booking public courts at requisite times. Reconditioned balls were obtained in 1945 and practice courts became available again in Regent's Park.

The Table Tennis Club formed in March 1944 had two tables – so 1st and 2nd team matches could be played simultaneously. In October the club joined the London University Table Tennis League, the only women's team granted this privilege. Not surprisingly it did poorly against the men's teams, but competed well against women's or mixed teams.[lii]

Doodlebug Damage at RFH

At 10:10 p.m. on Wednesday 5 July 1944 a V1 flying bomb hit the south east-corner of the RFH quadrangle, at the top of the lift between the Private and Riddell wards. The south wing of the old central block and half of the east wing were destroyed and the north wing was damaged. The electro-therapeutic department, post-mortem room, museum, pathology department, chapel, temporary theatres and the residents' quarters all suffered severely. (Figs 12.3 & 12.4) The cost of repair was estimated at £250,000. Ninety-seven beds were totally lost and others put out of action. St Bartholomew's Hospital, EGAH, the National Hospital for Nervous Diseases, the Hospital for Sick Children, and UCH took all the patients within an hour.[liii]

Eight persons, including six patients, were killed; most were in the dental clinic. Ten, mostly nursing staff, were seriously injured. The matron, Miss Cockayne, had a narrow escape; buried by debris in her quarters she was soon extricated and conducted a roll-call. None of the sixty students on posts at RFH was hurt; forty-one moved to Arlesey on 10 July. The twelve casualty students remained at RFH,[35] and some senior students accepted 'unqualified' house appointments elsewhere. Three midwifery students moved to EGAH, two subsequently transferring to Pednor House, Chesham, which Bucks County Council brought back into use as a maternity home; EGAH took maternity cases not considered suitable for transfer to Chesham.[liv]

[35] One student in Casualty at the time described the bomb's impact in the Magazine (1945 Jan-Mar).

Fig 12.3 Bomb damage SE corner of RFH

By Monday 16 July 1944 all outpatient clinics were working, but on a reduced scale. In late September 93 beds were available at RFH; and the Central London Ophthalmic Hospital, then in nearby Judd Street, placed an additional 22 beds at RFH's disposal until May 1945. By 2 June 1945, 219 beds were in commission but that day fifteen bedrooms (remnants of the devastated private wards) were gutted

Fig 12.4 RFH Bomb damage to RFH seen from South-east.

by a fire which delayed the return to use of other beds. Gertrude Kinnell ward subsequently occupied the site of the private wards.[lv]

After the bomb RFH struggled even more to meet the needs of clinical students. The dearth of patients suitable for training was exacerbated because the V1 flying bomb attacks, which started 13 June 1944, caused about 1,500,000 people to leave London, and patients were also evacuated from London hospitals. The Dean arranged for clinical students, except for the twelve on RFH's Casualty Post, to work elsewhere, mainly at Arlesey. Preclinicals were not affected.

The annual entry to LSMW, 60 in 1939, was just over 100 in 1945. The optimum bed number for such an intake was calculated at 800 to 1000; by the autumn of 1945 RFH would have about 260. The Ministry of Health suggested it take over the 200 beds at the London Fever Hospital, Liverpool Road (Fig 12.5),[36] but the City of London Maternity Hospital was using some of them. As an interim arrangement RFH rented 100 of the beds, mainly for paediatric and gynaecological patients; this relieved the pressure on beds at GIR. The Ministry allowed RFH to retain 300 beds at Arlesey and bore the entire cost;[37] the RFH nurses there returned to staff the Liverpool Road Annexe. More beds could also have been placed in the huts that had been erected on the GIR tennis court to house physiotherapy after the V1 strike in July, if and when the physiotherapy department returned to its old quarters.[lvi]

After RFH was hit Miss Moller asked whether plans were needed to accommodate the School elsewhere if LSMW's own building was damaged, or if working in London became impossible. The idea of leaving Hunter Street was rejected. However, from 8 September, London was attacked by V2 rockets. They

[36] This suggestion eventually had major consequences for RFH and LSMW.

[37] Initially unable to house all students the Arlesey Billeting Officer, for a nominal rent, acquired 'Arlesey Bury', a large manor house previously used by the Army. [CM 1944: 31 Aug]

Fig 12.5 London Fever Hospital Liverpool Rd

were much more dangerous than V1s and at 4.07 p.m.[38] on Friday 9 February 1945 one struck close to the School's new wing. (Fig 12.6) It was tea time; many had already gone home so there were few serious injuries and no fatalities.[39] Staff and students attended casualties, extinguished a fire in the organic chemistry laboratory, and carried out valuable salvage work. No usable laboratories remained and some were completely wrecked. Much valuable equipment was lost. The Dean recuperated from head and shoulder injuries in a Brighton nursing home. Owing to censorship the Magazine could not mention the damage to the School until its July-September 1945 issue, which was produced after the war with Japan ended on 15 August.[lvii]

Other London medical schools, the BMA and London's Conjoint Examining Board came to the rescue. On Monday 12 February Guy's welcomed students for organic chemistry and physiology. From 13 February classes for March examinees were held at Guy's and the Queen Square Examination Halls;[40] anatomy was taught at the Halls and in a lecture theatre at the National Hospital, Queen Square. First year students started at St. Mary's on 19 February. Repair work began at Hunter Street but there were difficulties about obtaining a licence to re-build the most damaged block, without which laboratory space was inadequate. Before the 'first

[38] Phyllis George noted in her diary that all the clocks in the lecture theatres stopped at that time.

[39] Six people had bruises & cuts needing hospital care; a 2nd year student suffered severe acid burns.

[40] They began work there on Tuesday 13 February.

Fig 12.6 LSMW Bomb damage 1945

years' and the preclinicals returned (see Chapter 13) LSMW had a new dean as Bolton retired at the end of September 1945.[lviii]

The serious bomb damage sustained by LSMW and RFH raised concerns about their joint future. The EMS's coordination of the efforts of voluntary and municipal hospitals had sown the seeds of a national post-war hospital policy. In 1941 a central committee debated which hospitals should close – and which should be kept and developed after the war. Some regionalisation was felt necessary, given the difficulty of providing a full health service within small local authority areas; however, arrangements suitable for the provinces seemed inappropriate for a city with twelve large voluntary teaching hospitals and the world's largest municipal hospital service. It was suggested that, as in the EMS, groups of hospitals might serve London and much of the Home Counties; teaching could then be decentralised and peripheral hospitals improved. If bomb damaged teaching hospitals were simply allowed to rebuild in the city's centre an opportunity for rational planning would be lost.[lix]

The Minister of Health's post-war policy, announced on 9 October 1941, proposed a service organised by local authorities and involving cooperation between voluntary and municipal hospitals. At the time some clinical teachers and students were working at municipal hospitals run by the EMS. To provide a basis for planning there was a national hospital survey to review available hospitals, clinical conditions treated, geographical origins of patients, and supply and demand for hospital facilities. It was hoped the survey would indicate which hospitals appeared redundant and where new ones were required. Although London's survey was not made public until April 1945 its findings were made available to an important committee that had been set up after the post-war hospital policy was announced. Its official name was 'The Interdepartmental Committee on Medical Schools' but it was soon better known as 'Goodenough' after its chairman William Goodenough, Deputy Chairman of Barclays Bank and Chairman of the Nuffield Provincial Hospitals Trust.[41].

'Goodenough' was to consider, *inter alia,* what financial help teaching hospitals might need. It first met on 14 April 1942. According to Rivett its membership reflected the Government's preconceived views and seemed likely to suggest greater admission of women to medical schools; cultivation of professorial units, particularly in London; and abolition of non-university medical education.[42] The Goodenough Report (also usually referred to simply as 'Goodenough') was published in June 1944, and was the most important statement on British medical education since Sir George Newman's 'Notes on Medical Education' in 1918. Many of its recommendations were acted upon.[lx]

The committee took evidence, consulted widely, and visited LCC hospitals to explore their educational potential. LCC officers, who received covert copies of its papers, wished the LCC to play a larger part in undergraduate medical education, perhaps by establishing a municipal teaching hospital,[43] and hoped LSMW might leave RFH and attach itself to the Highgate group of hospitals. 'Goodenough' saw no reason why a municipal hospital should not support a medical school but was opposed to creating a new one in London which already had too many schools; it recommended closure within five years of the West London Hospital Medical School, which had provided clinical training for women since 1937. The LCC was to cooperate by providing teaching facilities – not by pushing for its own teaching hospital.[lxi]

'Goodenough' agreed with a BMA memorandum suggesting that a school admitting 100 clinical students a year needed access to about 1000 beds, excluding

[41] In October 1939 Lord Nuffield wrote to the Minister of Health to introduce Goodenough, who advised Nuffield on his financial support for several Oxford hospitals. Goodenough established the Nuffield Provincial Hospitals Trust to which Nuffield gave £1,250,000 to encourage regionalisation and the coordination of municipal and voluntary hospitals.

[42] It included the haematologist Janet Vaughan, Principal of Somerville College, Oxford, who had strong views on women in medicine, and there were two members from UCH, which had a highly developed professorial system.

[43] It already supported the Postgraduate Medical School at Hammersmith,

those for tuberculosis, infectious and mental diseases, and for highly specialised functions like radiotherapy. By this standard ten London schools were short of medical beds, and seven also of surgical beds.

The Interdepartmental Committee wanted medical education to be more educational and less vocational – and properly planned and conducted within a comprehensive health service. It proposed 'university medical schools' as integral parts of a university, but the London schools, except for Bart's[44] and LSMW, were subsidiaries of their teaching hospitals. Instead of university-managed teaching hospitals 'Goodenough' advocated 'university teaching centres' – each having a medical school with a 'parent' hospital providing much of the teaching, and local hospitals and clinics as teaching facilities. Medical schools and their teaching hospitals liked the concept of grouped facilities, which would increase the number of beds available for teaching, and had experienced linkage with other geographically-related hospitals under the EMS. However, some were a long way away, and experience of coping with such dispersal convinced most deans that decentralised schools were to be avoided.[lxii]

'Goodenough' made many recommendations about the curriculum and its management. It called for whole-time professors of medicine, surgery, and O & G at every medical school. One crucial recommendation was that admission of newly qualified doctors to the Medical Register, and their entry into independent medical practice, should occur only after they had served twelve months as a junior house officer in approved hospitals. This came into effect on 1 January 1953.

However, the report's main consequences for LSMW and RFH came from its proposals on co-education and on the siting of London's medical schools and hospitals. 'Goodenough' thought all medical schools should be co-educational, and should receive Exchequer grants only if they admitted a reasonable proportion of women students (or men in the case of LSMW).

Goodenough considered the geographical distribution of London hospitals and schools unsatisfactory. While educational purposes might well have been served by concentrating schools in central London, local needs did not justify the continued existence of all the teaching hospitals. Amalgamation of smaller schools was considered but there was more support for transferring entire institutions to the periphery. Outward movement seemed inevitable and educationally advantageous. The committee therefore proposed that Charing Cross Hospital and its school should move to a site in Middlesex, St George's to another outer suburb, possibly in south London, and RFH to a northern suburb such as Highbury.

[44] Bart's obtained its charter as the independent 'Medical College of St Batholomew's Hospital in the City of London' in 1921.

In its 'Memorandum on the Report of the Inter-Departmental Committee on Medical Schools, 1944' LSMW's Council saw no advantage in moving RFH to Highbury. If it remained in Gray's Inn Road the close relationship between the University, medical school and hospitals advocated by Goodenough would be preserved, as would the easy access of students & staff to university libraries and museums; furthermore segregation from students in other faculties would be avoided. The proximity of RFH to three major railway termini meant that getting there was relatively easy for most patients, students and staff.[lxiii]

LSMW and RFH suggested retention of parts of the old buildings, construction of a new RFH on the site to the east of LSMW fronting on to Gray's Inn Road and Heathcote Street, and acquisition of a bomb site adjoining LSMW.[lxiv]

War and the Magazine

For reasons that were not entirely clear the page size of the Magazine was increased to 23.4 cm x 15 cm in July 1937 and returned to its former size, 21.2 cm x 14 cm, in 1945 (July-September). During the war fewer issues were produced each year and they tended to come out much later than the date on the cover. The issue for November 1939 described the dramatic changes at Gray's Inn Road where *'The theatres are underground, the symmetry of the furnace windows is ruined by piles of coke, and the...Unit wards [O & G], now dormitories for students'... 'There has been an epidemic of matrimony, almost a pandemic, spreading from the House even to students' quarters'*. The March 1940 issue mentioned the return of the students from Aberdeen, the Government's decision to conscript doctors and the effect this might have on the prospects of women doctors and students.

The Magazine could not continue reporting in this vein. In the next issue – dated July 1941 – there was a letter from Edward Mellanby, Secretary of the MRC, written a year earlier (on 29 July 1940), that explained the delay in its publication. Also sent to other journals it asked that no information be published which would be of value to the enemy. Two copies of every paper to be published were to be submitted to the Press and Censorship Bureau and marked for the attention of the Technical Section. On the advice of Reuters, which controlled the Magazine's advertising, it was decided to cut the number of issues to two a year because of the difficulty of distributing it to old students. It could not of course comment on the bomb and rocket attacks on the Hospital and School (see above).

The March 1940 Magazine noted that in May the National Union of Students (NUS) was holding a meeting on medical education in Manchester – one organised by the London Committee. An NUS Council meeting followed in November 1940, also in Manchester, at which LSMW was the only London medical school represented. The medical faculty of NUS was now the British Medical Students

Association (BMSA), with LSMW's Cicely Tinker as secretary. It was asked by the BMA's Planning Committee to submit evidence on medical education. The three individuals that directed this work were Rosemary Biggs, a mature student at LSMW (and later a distinguished haematologist at Oxford), and students from UCH and the Middlesex. The outcome was an 'Outline for Discussion on the Reform of the Medical Curriculum'. LSMW students then produced a set of comments relating to the situation at their own School, as did the Education Committee and individual department heads. The BMSA declared its independence from NUS in 1942, and held its first AGM in July 1943.[lxv]

On 16 March 1944 Bolton suggested a younger person should become Dean. That October she accepted re-election for the ensuing year but stated firmly she would not stand again. The anaesthetist Katherine Lloyd-Williams was elected to serve as Vice-dean for Bolton's final year. As the Vice-dean had to be a member of Council Lloyd-Williams took the place of Chodak-Gregory, Vice-Dean since October 1942. The latter continued acting as Dean at Arlesey, and re-joined Council as an 'assessor' in March 1945. No voting was necessary to elect a new Dean as Lloyd-Williams was the only nomination; she took office in October.[lxvi]

The ASA thought a 'clinical' Dean should have a 'pre-clinical' Vice Dean, and vice versa. It also wanted the latter to have specific duties and responsibilities – such as attendance at all important committees – so that she would be fully informed and ready to act for the Dean if circumstances demanded. Council subsequently decided, in keeping with the statute in the School's Charter, that there should be no restriction on the choice of a Vice Dean other than Council membership; but that the Dean's views would be sought about appointing a Vice Dean.[lxvii]

Council lost some longstanding members before Bolton left office. In March 1944, owing to the important decisions to be taken in the near future, Janet Aitken, a member since 1929, resigned in favour of a younger person; she died age 96 in 1982! In February 1945 F. R. S. Balfour died after twenty-nine years on Council. Lady Barrett died six months later and Bolton replaced her as President of LSMW as soon as she finished as dean.

In 1937 Bolton had become the first dean to be paid by the School. Her honorarium was increased to £330 per annum in May 1942, and to £385 in August 1944. Following her retirement she received a testimonial and £1100 in appreciation of her services as Dean.[lxviii]

Elizabeth Bolton was elected President of the School after the death of Lady Barrett on 7 August 1945. Illness forced her to resign in 1957 and Lucas-Keene succeeded her as President. Bolton left her flat in St. John's Wood and took up residence at the Mansion Hotel in Eastbourne where she died on 25 May 1961.[lxix]

CHAPTER 13

Katherine Lloyd-Williams (1945–1962)

The Men Appear...as a Trickle not a Flood

Katharine ('Kitty') Georgina Lloyd-Williams was born 14 February 1896 in the Welsh parish of Nantcwnlle, near Lampeter. Her father was headmaster of Carmarthen Grammar School, and later of Oswestry Grammar School. Educated at Queen Anne's School, Caversham [1] and Bedford Physical Training College, Lloyd-Williams taught at Newland High School in Hull and worked as a physiotherapist in London before entering LSMW in 1920 (not 1921 as sometimes quoted). A fine all-round sportswoman, she was president of the University of London Athletic Union (Women) in 1922-3.[i]

She graduated MB BS in 1926 and proceeded MD in 1929. She was an anaesthetist with the professorial O & G Unit before becoming anaesthetist to RFH in 1934; that year her book 'Anaesthesia and Analgesia in Labour' was published. Obstetric anaesthesia remained her major clinical interest. From 1928 to 1935 she lived at 48 Gordon Square and subsequently at 6 Endsleigh Place, Gordon Square, where, with her friend Enid Clarke (Mrs Smith), she combined general practice with her anaesthetic work at RFH and EGAH. Clarke was married with small children and after the war started she moved to the country and the combined practice folded. Lloyd-Williams resumed full time hospital work. She was RFH's only consultant anaesthetist during the war – being helped by a registrar and two junior residents; Stanley Rowbotham visited weekly while stationed at Aldershot.

Her deanship began in October 1945. It was to prove a busy one. In addition to her expected duties as Dean she had, almost immediately, to plan for admission of men to a School that had taught only women. School and Hospital also had to be readied for the introduction of the National Health Service (NHS) and subsequently to be re-housed, ideally within a single complex.

Fortunately Lloyd-Williams was supported by experienced officers – especially Henderson, Council's chairman. At her first Council meeting on 24 October 1945 Lord Rennell resigned as Hon. Treasurer (but remained on Council).[2] The Hon. John Mulholland replaced him and when he died in March 1948 Sir Alan

1 Where, age 13, she played in the lacrosse first XII. (Mag March 1956]
2 When Lord Rennell, a major-general, was away at war Alan Anderson acted as Hon. Treasurer.

Anderson's son, Donald, became Treasurer. Sir Arnold Overton, Permanent Secretary to the Ministry of Civil Aviation, joined Council after Sir Alan died on 4 May 1952.[ii]

The Fishmongers' Company supported the School for many years. In 1950 Sir Alan, one of its former Prime Wardens, gave it a large sum of money to be used, charitably, in the interests of women and thus to commemorate his mother. The Company decided to award 'Elizabeth Garrett Anderson Scholarships' to female medical students at RFHSM; Sir Alan's son, Sir Colin Anderson, also a Prime Warden, augmented the fund in 1956.

In May 1951 Henderson thought he should give way for a younger, more 'prominent' chairman.[3] When he needed surgery in February 1952 Sir Harold Claughton covered for him but would not replace him. Henderson recovered and agreed to continue until a successor was found. In February 1953 Francis Lascelles was elected chairman.[4, iii]

Henderson died in March 1954. He had acted for the School in all legal matters since the death in 1906 of his father, Henry, who took over as legal adviser when his senior partner, Shaen, died in 1877.[5] According to Lascelles the School had never formally appointed a firm of solicitors. Henderson's firm, Shaen Roscoe and Co, was duly employed and Roscoe, its senior partner, became RFHSM's solicitor.[iv]

Lloyd-Williams had no Vice-Dean until Beatrice Turner's appointment in October 1952. Council chose both Dean and Vice-Dean. There was no mechanism for involving others, but Lloyd-Williams suggested that from October 1953 the Education Committee chairman (elected biennially, and alternately a preclinical and a clinical teacher) should be Vice-Dean ex officio. The first thus chosen was Alexander Lawson (1954 & 1955). He was followed by the physician, Lee Lander; the physiologist, Killick, and the physician, Frances Gardner.[v]

Nancy Moller resigned in May 1949 to become principal of the Lady Mabel College of Physical Education at Wentworth Woodhouse, a former stately home near Rotherham.[6] Joan Beale, Registrar of Royal Holloway College, replaced her as Warden and Secretary but in 1956 the combined post was deemed too onerous for a single person. Pauline McCormick, Assistant Secretary from March 1949, and Registrar following the creation of that post in 1954, took over the Warden's office (which dealt with grants, and offered general help to students). When Beale

---

3 He had been Chairman since 1934, and a Council member since 1907.

4 Lascelles Clerk Assistant to the House of Lords, was later Clerk of the Parliaments. Created KCB in 1954 he also chaired the committee of the Westminster branch of Moorfields, Westminster & Central Eye hospitals. Donald Anderson was knighted earlier in 1954.

5 Malcolm Henderson was also Hon. Treasurer from 1906 to 1916.

6 Moller died October 1960 when warden of the University of Khartoum's women's hall of residence.

moved to Bristol's Institute of Education in 1960 she was replaced as Secretary by Mrs Stephanie Robinson, Secretary and Treasurer of St Hilda's College, Oxford, and a former general secretary of the Family Planning Association.[vi]

The School's financial situation was relatively stable during Lloyd-Williams's deanship, although rising costs were a problem in 1955-6. The quinquennium was drawing to a close, and it was increasingly difficult to meet wage increases and costs that had not been anticipated when the estimates were prepared several years earlier. From October 1952 all students paid a composition fee of £55 a year that covered tuition fees, subscription to the Students' Union, the use of the library, and laboratory apparatus. In 1956 it was increased to £65 – still a nominal amount given the cost of medical training. Although the annual report for 1956-7 hinted at some new development in 1959, the following year's report emphasized the financial stringency needed in the new quinquennium, and the resulting difficulty in planning long-term research. Fortunately a grant increase in 1958/9 ensured current research was unaffected.[vii]

Council, at Lloyd-Williams's first meeting as Dean, agreed to the University's request – made in response to the Goodenough Committee's recommendation – to admit men as 15% or more of the total entry.[7] The School's Charter therefore needed amendment – to allow admission of men, and to change the School's name, thus signalling it was no longer for women only. The changes were approved in June 1947 and LSMW[8] became the 'Royal Free Hospital School of Medicine' (RFHSM).[viii] Male nurses were not accepted at RFH until 1974!

The Men Arrive

The first two men, Brian Hanbury Day and Mikolaj Lubinski, entered in October 1947. Day had come over from Australia in 1937. After working at a city desk he served in the Signals Corps from 1941 to 1946 and took 1st MB from the Northern Polytechnic. On qualifying MBBS in April 1952 he was RFHSM's first male graduate and became an orthopaedic surgeon at St Helier Hospital, Carshalton. He died November 2005. Lubinski, whose father was a major in the Polish army, failed his first year exams and left the School.[ix]

While awaiting the admission of men the *Magazine of the London (Royal Free Hospital) School of Medicine for Women*[9] commented on 'changes which threatened the School and Hospital'. However, the editorial in the July-December 1947 issue, the first under its new name – *Magazine of the Royal Free Hospital School of Medicine* – hinted that the women were underwhelmed by the first two

---

7 Men's schools were asked to admit women.

8 Strictly speaking 'L(RFH)SMW'.

9 Abbreviated to R.F.H.L.S.M.W. at the top of individual pages

men, stating 'The changes have been nominal rather than real, for while the women have disappeared from the title of the school, the men can hardly be said to have appeared in the school. If the idea suggested in our last number had been adopted by the authorities, the title would now be *LONDON (ROYAL FREE HOSPITAL) SCHOOL OF MEDICINE FOR WOMEN and two men.*'

In 1948 four men joined the first year course; three of them qualified (Hargreaves, Tecwyn Jones & Reeves). Of the ten or so entering in 1949 two, Robert Danbury and Thomas Dormandy, had studied elsewhere and so completed their 2nd MB (normally a five term course) in March 1950.[10] A similar number arrived in 1950, and there were 23 male students in a photograph of preclinical staff and students taken in October 1950.[x]

Initially the men were denied scholarships and bursaries but three men gained certificates in individual subjects in 1949 and in 1950.[11] The following year Peter Scheuer, later professor of histopathology at RFHSM, won prizes in organic chemistry, practical anatomy and practical physiology, and Michael Day won second prize in practical anatomy.[xi]

Council agreed to a Students' Union request that from October 1952 scholarships would be open to men unless restricted to women by trust deed; the disposition of restricted scholarships was to be reconsidered when there were many more male students. In 1952 Michael Charlesworth got an A. M. Bird Entrance Scholarship and Robert Danbury a Flora Murray Bursary, while in 1953 Brian Philip Day[12] got an Elizabeth Bolton Scholarship (from the Students' Union); Thomas Lloyd James won the Sarah Holborn Scholarship; and Peter Scheuer was awarded a Flora Murray Bursary.[xii]

Traditionally the prize-giving was in June and the inaugural address in October. From 1945 the Great Hall at BMA House was used five times for such celebrations and St Pancras Town Hall once (1954); but from 1948 the main venue was the Beveridge Hall of the Senate House. When Lilian Penson addressed the School in September 1950 she also presented the prizes.[13] Lady Newnes presented the prizes in June 1951 but because the Queen opened the new extension on 24 October (see below) there was no inaugural address that year. In October 1952 Sir Henry Dale gave the address and Lady Dale presented the prizes at a combined ceremony.

Lloyd-Williams's task on becoming Dean was daunting. The preclinicals could not return until the Hunter Street bomb-damage was repaired, and the clinical

---

[10] Danbury had studied medicine in Vienna, Dormandy in Geneva.

[11] In the Magazine for July-December 1949 Day is shown shaking hands with the Duchess of Gloucester at the June 1949 prize-giving. The caption suggests he won a prize; in fact he got two certificates.

[12] Not to be confused with Brian Hanbury Day – see above..

[13] Lilian Penson was then the first (and only) woman Vice-Chancellor of London University.

students were still widely scattered. Beds for clinical training were needed much closer to the School as RFH was also bomb-damaged. Matters would have been further complicated had the Government accepted the suggestion of 'Goodenough' (and of the London Hospital Survey) that LSMW and RFH should move together to a northern suburb such as Highbury; it would then have been reluctant to spend much money on repairing Gray's Inn Road and Hunter Street. The Dean wrote a memorandum stressing the need for a hospital of 800-1000 beds; RFH and LSMW wanted it built at nearby Mecklenburgh Square, a site unacceptable to the powers that be. The other possibilities were the Caledonian market, derelict for seven years, and a site in Canonbury, near the Liverpool Road annexe.[xiii]

The plight of clinical students working at distant hospitals was eased somewhat by the renting of beds at the London Fever Hospital and continued use of Eastman Dental Clinic wards. The London Hospital Survey of 1945 had suggested amalgamating the Fever Hospital with RFH; formal approval from the Charity Commissioners was unnecessary as both were to transfer to the Ministry of Health and the Fever Hospital soon became an RFH annexe in Liverpool Road.[xiv]

Students' access to beds also improved through the creation of an RFH/LSMW 'teaching group' *à la* Goodenough. The Royal Northern Hospital (RNH) offered to join in August 1945. It took two posts of ten students, one surgical and one medical, and had a representative on LSMW's Education Committee. Further negotiations foundered when it requested equal status with RFH; the School considered that inappropriate. In May 1946 EGAH, long associated with LSMW, asked for official recognition as part of an RFH teaching group; University approval came in July 1947.[xv]

In May 1946, pending rebuilding, RFH's Medical Committee suggested taking over 300 beds in the Archway group of municipal hospitals – to accommodate medical, surgical and O & G units; a junior medicine post was established in October and in January 1947 the LCC's Sir Allen Daley and Archway's medical superintendent Dr Coyle offered 200 beds there. More importantly Daley suggested beds might be available at the North Western Fever Hospital (NWFH) in Hampstead; there, in April, RFH was allocated about 150 beds plus facilities for students. Forty-eight beds were handed over quickly as Heald's British Legion rheumatology unit had to move from Arlesey.[14] The LCC remained responsible for the NWFH beds; RFH met the cost of changing their function.[xvi]

---

[14] In 1922 Heald joined RFH as a physician interested in physical medicine & rheumatology. He was a founder of the Red Cross Rheumatism Clinic in 1930. In 1946 he set up the British Legion Rheumatology Unit, the first bedded arthritis unit associated with a London teaching hospital. This helped to create rheumatology as a separate specialty. [Munk's Roll VI, p231, BMJ 29 June 1946]

Two medical wards opened at NWFH in October, and patients, staff, students and equipment moved from Arlesey to 'Lawn Road', the name by which NWFH was soon widely known.[15] Surgeons stayed at Arlesey until operating theatres were available at Hampstead. The quest for beds at Archway was abandoned, but its medical post was retained until Lawn Road could accommodate the extra students.[xvii]

Somewhat surprisingly James Henderson, the University's Academic Registrar, announced in July 1947 that RFH's teaching group would include the London Fever Hospital, EGAH and the Royal Northern group of hospitals (including the Royal Chest Hospital and Grovelands Hospital, Southgate). The Dean responded that RFH was already associated with EGAH and the London Fever Hospital, and queried whether negotiations with the LCC about 300 beds[16] at NWFH might conflict with arrangements with the Royal Northern group.

On 9 October she wrote again, with copies to the Ministry of Health and the North Western Metropolitan Regional Board (NWMRHB), proposing – 'That the site now occupied by the North Western Fever Hospital should be the future site of the new Royal Free Hospital and Medical School' She emphasized ease of access to the University area, the size and suitability of the site, and the benefit that infectious diseases beds would bring to a modern teaching hospital as reasons for suggesting that RFH's sphere of influence should switch to the north-west rather than the north.[xviii]

Hampstead General Hospital (HGH), within spitting distance of NWFH, was unhappy. Hoping to become a postgraduate medical centre it wanted a hundred of its neighbour's beds. Aware of this, the Dean wrote to Frederick Messer MP, Chairman of NWMRHB, seeking sympathetic consideration of the RFH proposal and, if it was unacceptable, his suggestion of a different site for an 800-1000 bedded hospital and medical school.[xix]

After meeting Royal Free representatives on 5 February 1948 the Vice-Chancellor, David Hughes Parry, recommended to the Ministry of Health that RFH&SM's future should be on the NWFH site, and that NWFH, HGH and Hampstead Children's Hospital, rather than RNH, should join the teaching group.[17] Sir William Douglas, Permanent Secretary at the MoH, agreed; he informed Messer and on 1 March wrote to Hughes Parry — '*... the right course would be to designate the Royal Free Hospital and the Elizabeth Garrett Anderson Hospital,*

[15] The London Fever Hospital was already being called 'Liverpool Road'.

[16] Changed later to 200 beds.

[17] In 1882 Dr William Heath Strange founded the Hampstead Home Hospital and Nursing Institute for paying patients in South Hill Park Road. From 1894 it was Hampstead Hospital. In 1902 work began on Hampstead General and North-West London Hospital on Haverstock Hill. In 1912 a new out-patients was built at Bayham Street, Camden, in the house in which Charles Dickens lived as a boy.

together with the North Western Fever Hospital, the Hampstead General Hospital and the Hampstead Children's Hospital, as the new teaching hospital under one Board of Governors. The New End Hospital would not be included in this group, but the Fever Hospital in Liverpool Road would be included, until such time as it is possible to release the premises for the use of the Regional Board.'[18] The University's Academic Council hoped *'amalgamation with Hampstead General Hospital would ...not produce the conflict of views which...made ...amalgamation with the Royal Northern Group of Hospitals out of the question.'* The Dean met representatives of HGH and assured them of cooperation on the friendliest terms.[xx]

The proposal that the NWFH should be the future site of RFH & SM proved inspired. Planning soon started but it was almost 25 years before the idea became a reality. During that time both Hospital and School had to continue functioning and they could not do so satisfactorily unless much of the damage done at GIR and Hunter Street was remedied.

Early repairs allowed the staggered return of the preclinical 'evacuees' after the bombing in 1945. Those at St Mary's and Queen Square came back in January 1946 when biology, physics, inorganic chemistry, anatomy and organic chemistry started functioning again at LSMW. Part of physiology returned in April; biochemistry stayed at Guy's until October. However, valuable space had been lost and the buildings, despite the repairs, became overcrowded.[xxi]

It was possible to extend Hunter Street on the adjoining site of 68-84 Tavistock Place (originally 7-19 Compton Street). Council had procrastinated when the Foundling Hospital offered a 58-year lease on it in May 1919; it would not meet the asking price in 1926, and when it expressed an interest in 1933 was told the site had been sold. Further fruitless enquiries were made in 1938 and 1940. [xxii]

Negotiations resumed in 1945; 72-84 Tavistock Place was now a bomb site [19] and LSMW's property advisers thought £700 p.a. a reasonable ground rent for a 99-year building lease. In February 1946 the University agreed to the inclusion of an extension on this site in an application for building licences for 1945-6. The Foundling eventually agreed to a 99-year lease for £720 p.a.[xxiii]

The architect, Ayrton,[20] said constructing part of the final building would be cheaper than using temporary huts, and in February 1947 the University approved

[18] The MoH notified RFHSM officially on 23 April 1948. [CM 1948, 12 May] James Stansfeld would have been delighted; he helped to develop NWFH while President of the Local Government Board in the early 1870s.

[19] As a result of the V2 rocket that hit the School in February 1945. (Mag Jul-Dec 1945, p 55)

[20] Maxwell Ayrton, who trained with Lutyens, was an expert with reinforced concrete. He worked on the Wembley Stadium (1924), the National 'Epileptic'Hospital Queen Square and many bridges.

expenditure of £30,000 on the ground floor and a semi-basement. The Ministry of Works agreed building could start In March 1948.[xxiv]

Ayrton favoured using a big contractor, believing that smaller firms like Price, the School's usual builders, had poorer access to materials and labour. Persuaded by Ayrton and by Mais, the quantity surveyor, Council agreed to employ Trollope and Colls. However, Sir Alan Anderson intervened and Price was chosen – probably because Donald Anderson[21] had learned Mais was likely to become a director of Trollope and Colls. He suggested employing independent quantity surveyors, but Ayrton persuaded Council to stick with Mais's firm, a decision with unfortunate consequences (see below).[xxv]

The University now agreed that the School could build all seven floors, and supplied the necessary steel from its own allocation. The new wing was to accommodate pharmacology and biology; a new biochemistry teaching laboratory; a museum and lecture theatre for anatomy; additional research laboratories and preparation rooms for all departments; a new animal house and conservatory; cloakrooms and meeting rooms for the students, and similar facilities for the technicians. The layout of the basement, ground, first, second, third & fifth floors was approved in May 1949.[xxvi]

In November 1949, at the Students' Union's request, fourth floor space was earmarked for a general common room, a room for male students, a kitchen and a bar. For three years the bar lost money. Few students used it and in May 1954 the Union requested its closure, with the option of reopening it in the autumn; Council stipulated that if it reopened the Union must cover any deficit.[xxvii]

In July 1948 Mais costed the new wing at £143,655; the University allocated £152,325. In May 1950 his revised estimate was over £200,000 and RFHSM had to request another £71,000 plus an interest-free loan to cover current debts. The University Court allowed building to proceed only to a total expenditure of £160,000, and RFHSM waited until October for news of additional funding.[xxviii]

Problems continued. On 11 December 1950 Ayrton announced that taps for the new wing, already overdue, would not arrive for weeks; until the taps were fitted it was impossible to install sinks or complete decorations. Work was suspended – the delay cost thousands of pounds.[22, xxix]

Departments moved to the new wing at Easter 1951. For the Queen's official opening in October the Long Room was used as the 'Assembly Hall' and the junior common room as a reception room; lecture theatres were robing rooms and the senior common room provided an overflow hall, with loudspeakers, for those not

---

21 The School's Hon. Treasurer since March 1948.

22 This matter occupied four and a half pages of the minutes for Council's meeting on 13 December 1950.

allocated a place in the Long Room. In June 1954 the extension was named the Henderson Wing to mark Malcolm Henderson's long service as legal adviser, Hon. Treasurer and Chairman of Council. Memorial plaques to him were placed in the main hall of the new wing, and on the connecting door from the old building.[xxx]

The School now had to pay for the extension. The contractors offered to close for £245,000 in June 1951. Mais considered this excessive and went on 'measuring' but the University demanded a final costing, and an explanation for the original inaccuracy before determining the School's grant. Based on a new figure of £248,822 from Mais the UGC allocated an extra £90,000 – as a final grant. Mais then calculated the extra cost as £100,505 leaving the School, already heavily overdrawn, to contribute £10,505 in addition to £4000 already spent. In March 1952 the 'final' cost was estimated at around £262,000, £14,000 more than the estimate used to determine the UGC's final grant, leaving RFHSM's contribution as £29,900.[xxxi]

Council met with the contractor, architect and quantity surveyors on 27 March. Mais now anticipated final agreement within three months at only £235,000. Clutching at this straw, Council agreed to further measurements and pricing. Although promised by July it was February 1953 before Ayrton reported a 'final' account of £249,720, which annoyed Council, given Mais's refusal to settle for £245,000 in June 1951. So too did his suggestion of an exact figure of £239,732 in December 1952, when he also said extending the contract would cost no more than £2000, a figure which was almost £10,000 two months later. The 'very final' account revealed that RFHSM had to find £13,453 from reserves! [xxxii]

Other changes were made at Hunter Street. The move of the senior common room into the old biology department created space for a 'Council and Committee Room' (the Sir Alan Anderson Room). Re-housing the accountant and departmental clerks freed space for the library and for domestic use. The old pharmacology department became a porter's lodge, waiting room and office. An electric lift was installed in the new wing, and an electric motor was fitted to the anatomy lift, previously operated by hand. The 1915 wing was re-decorated, as were the Junior Common Room and refectory. The old black and white tiles in the main entrance hall gave place to grey and green terrazzo, and staircase colour schemes were changed there and in the 1915 wing.[xxxiii]

The pathology department, situated at the southeast corner of the main hospital building, had been severely damaged by the V1 flying bomb in July 1944. While most of the pathologists were at Arlesey those left at RFH needed new quarters. As pathology was to be re-housed as part of a major building scheme it seemed sensible to minimise expenditure on what would be temporary buildings. The 1931 agreement allowed pathology to use the lower ground floor of the Eastman dental clinic. However the EMS commandeered part of the floor in 1939 for use as wards (called Unit 4). But when the EMS released Unit 4 the Eastman would not renew the 1931 agreement, which had lapsed in 1943, as it wanted to use the whole floor to accommodate post-graduate dental students. Pathology staff moved to Washington ward in the Helena building (see Chapter 12). In November 1945 the medical committee wanted that reopened as a medical ward and suggested pathology return to the Eastman until late 1946. However, the reconditioning of Unit 4 was deemed uneconomic, as it was soon to return to the dental clinic, so the pathologists remained in Washington ward.[xxxiv]

In the summer of 1945 discussions began about ameliorating the situation resulting from the damage to the pathology block. The immediate requirements were to restore the old post-mortem room, chemical laboratory, animal house and lift-shaft, and to provide a new morbid anatomy department plus accommodation for media preparation. The architect, O'Rorke, suggested a brick structure would be cheaper and more permanent than Nissen huts. On 14 February the senior pathologists met on the roof of the damaged Levy Wing, and O'Rorke indicated an area that would provide space for morbid anatomy and a small lecture room, and meet the pathology's unit's requirements for several years.[xxxv]

He drew up two schemes. The one chosen, costing £11,700, was to stand on the Levy Wing roof, close to the old pathology block, and extend over the damaged part of the wing. As delay would be unavoidable pathology had to remain at Arlesey.[xxxvi]

In September 1946 plans for the new block went to Sir Arthur Rucker,[23] with an urgent request for a licence; financial support was sought from the King's Fund. A year later it was found that the licence for the new block did not cover work on the old pathology block; a revised application was needed. Fortunately the Iron and Steel Board brought forward the allocation of steel for the new block to early 1948.[xxxvii]

In September 1947 Webb reported that pathology had to leave Arlesey. His suggestion that RFH's pathology work should go to the LCC laboratory at Lawn Road was agreed as a temporary solution. However the Medical Committee wanted pathology housed at RFH and suggested erecting a temporary hut on the roof of the Queen Mary wing or the roof of the rebuilt post-mortem room. By November work on the old block was well advanced and application was made for a licence to complete it and to convert the previous post-mortem room into a laboratory.[xxxviii]

The old pathology block was ready for occupation in August 1949, although building continued there for three more years. As all teaching could again take

[23] Deputy Secretary at the Ministry of Health.

place at RFH, students no longer needed to attend Archway Hospital, where pathology had been taught since early in the war. Progress on the new block was slow, but in July 1951 the RFH Committee was assured of completion within six months.[xxxix]

In June 1956 Kenneth Hill was appointed to the chair of pathology. Before arriving on 12 November he sent detailed proposals for enlarging the department. He suggested halving the height of the museum in the old pathology block to provide an extra floor – into which the animal house could transfer from the top of the building; a new post-mortem room could then occupy the former animal house. He also advocated another floor on the new pathology block to house the professor and the teaching laboratory. The existing 'Basal Metabolic Rate' room was to be removed and three 'half floors' joined on to the existing old building.[xl]

The architect, unimpressed by Hill's ideas, did not want to touch the old block. Instead he suggested adding three floors to the existing pathology block at a cost of up to £150,000. However the Ministry of Health, having decided in August 1957 to rebuild RFH&SM at Hampstead, was understandably reluctant to spend money altering existing buildings. So Hill agreed on a modified plan that enlarged the existing PM room by incorporating the viewing chapel; a new viewing chapel was created in a small hut outside the PM room. Hill was happy to expand into two new huts – one on the roof over the general offices, linking with the existing pathology department, and a larger one on top of the south wing of the Levy building, which was next to the chimney and overlooked St Andrew's gardens. This was the arrangement for pathology until the eventual move to Hampstead.[xli] (Fig 13.1)

In 1948 School, Hospital and University were enthusiastic about moving to Hampstead, but eight years later the first two seemed to have a change of heart, wishing instead to expand at Gray's Inn Road, Liverpool Road and Hunter Street. Following discussions with the Board of Governors the Ministry of Health said any such joint policy required University support. In June 1956, with Lascelles's approval, Peter Samuel, the Board's chairman, wrote to Logan, the University's Principal, to explain why Hospital and School now wished to remain on their present sites – and to establish what the University would require as a condition for its support. Logan said they had to accept professorial units. UGC representatives had apparently told the University Court that some schools, including RFHSM, were antagonistic to clinical academic units.[xlii]

The School replied '*The institution of [professorial] units is…linked with development policy…the Board of Governors is now seeking to revise its existing plan for…Hampstead in favour of expansion of the Gray's Inn Road site…the*

Fig 13.1 'Huts on roof' (by Peter Jones)

Medical Committee had…reaffirmed that, provided [there were] a sufficient number of beds…on one site, such units were to be established as soon as possible.' Logan wrote to the Ministry advocating that School and Hospital should stay put. In 1957, following a meeting of interested parties, the Minister said he hoped soon to decide, with the University, his policy for London's teaching hospitals.[xliii]

The proposal that School and Hospital should not move may have been a ruse – prompted by the Ministry's sluggish approach to building at Hampstead. If so, it worked. On 2 August 1957 the Ministry proposed that RFH & SM should be rebuilt on the Lawn Road and Hampstead General Hospital sites, and that New End Hospital should join the teaching group. When the new complex was fully operational GIR, Liverpool Road, EGAH, New End and the Bayham Street Clinic were to close.[xliv]

On 27 November the Board of Governors agreed these proposals, but needed guidance about expenditure on GIR, given the time it might have to remain in use. It wanted to delay taking over New End Hospital. It questioned EGAH's place in the teaching group, either separately or as a wing of the new hospital, but recognized it met a particular demand and opposed its abolition. The University agreed to rebuild RFH & SM at Hampstead providing it did not have to fund the new School buildings. As the Ministry of Health could not do so it was hoped the UGC would play its part.[xlv]

Detailed planning commenced early in 1958 and building was supposed to start in 1960. Council appointed a Building Committee,[24] which was allowed to co-opt an outsider with practical experience of large building operations.[25] Its first meeting, on 10 February 1958, considered draft plans for the new School buildings in Hampstead. Alexander Gray,[26] the architect for the new RFH, was also to design the new School and needed to know the requisite square footage. Hospital and School were to be planned as one, with close integration at departmental level. The new Royal Free, intended to be the most modern hospital in Europe, was apparently the first to be designed with the aid of a computer.[xlvi]

RFH needed reassurance that the School would pay for its share of the new building but on 10 February Sir Keith Murray, the UGC chairman, wrote that the University could not assume there would be funds forthcoming to move RFHSM to Hampstead, or Charing Cross Hospital Medical School to Fulham. He thought rebuilding their preclinical departments might be avoided by 'rationalisation and coordination between the various preclinical departments in London, and by a fuller use...of any surplus capacity.' RFH&SM and the University were understandably disturbed. The University set up a committee to review its preclinical departments and in July the School's building subcommittee considered plans for a new school without such departments.[xlvii]

Council questioned whether it was worth continuing to plan, but it carried on as reaching the master plan stage would cost less than £1,000. Gray costed a complete new school at £1,060,000. As the preclinical component alone would cost far less Gray suggested RFHSM might raise the money itself if UGC funds were not forthcoming, and asked if Council wanted Hunter Street valued.[xlviii]

The University's preclinical committee concluded that London's other medical schools could not accommodate preclinical students from RFHSM or Charing Cross because dental students also needed places. The UGC's chairman responded that by maximizing use of laboratory space, and duplicating or triplicating classes RFHSM could absorb preclinicals from Charing Cross – whose departments could then be closed – and the Free's preclinical departments could then remain at Hunter Street and accept Royal Dental Hospital students.[xlix]

---

[24] Miss Diana Anderson, Sir Harold Claughton, Sir Arnold Overton, the Chairman & the Dean.

[25] The Gater committee on major building works had recommended vesting supervision and control of planning & building in a small committee whose members had business and financial experience.

[26] Lloyd-Williams visited Nigeria in November 1957 for the opening of University College Hospital at Ibadan. Gray designed it; he also designed Guy's surgical tower & St George's Hospital, Tooting.

RFHSM no longer wanted its own dental school but from 1954, at the UGC's request, it had admitted about twenty preclinical dental students a year, albeit on a temporary basis.[27] It benefited financially by taking them and in 1958 increased the dental intake.[l]

In December 1958 the UGC, somewhat surprisingly, withdrew its objection to rebuilding the two preclinical schools and in March 1959 announced Bart's would take dental students instead of RFHSM (thus depleting the latter's still meagre male population). However, it would not agree to fund a preclinical school at Hampstead, and was unlikely to allow such funding from the University's normal building allocation (already fully committed until 1964). Money for rebuilding would have to come from the sale of Hunter Street and/or by a public appeal. Unfortunately Hunter Street was deemed suitable only for institutional use, either by the LCC or the University, and if the University bought it the UGC might prevent the proceeds being spent on Hampstead.[li]

In February 1959 there was a House of Commons statement that building would begin at Hampstead in 1960/1.The MoH had to approve RFH's schedules of accommodation which in October still focused on issues like the number and allocation of beds and the size of ward units. The University sent details regarding clinical school matters to the UGC which, in November, requested details of the preclinical block as well. The Principal's suggestion that a professorial unit should be a 40-bed unit occupying two 28-bed wards was agreed – the extra 16 beds were to be allocated to a clinician linked to the unit by a common interest. If, subsequently, the unit needed more beds those extra beds could be reallocated.

Demolition of Lawn Road was initially to start after its 'evacuation' to another hospital. However, it was later decided to begin building on one half of the site and to house 'homeless' departments in temporary huts on the other half; the 'homeless' would then transfer to the completed first stage to allow the rest of the new hospital to be built. In October 1961 the Treasury allocated £160,000 to cover the expenses of decanting Lawn Road and Hampstead General Hospital. It seemed possible that the first bulldozer might be at work within a year – but it did not quite work out like that![lii]

Professorial Units

In 1957 the University supported the School and Hospital's plans for rebuilding only on the understanding they would accept professorial units. However, the Magazine for June 1957 contained an article on the subject by Lee Lander, the

---

[27] It accepted them only for admission to the second year; they had to have gained exemption from the first-year science course. As RFHSM did not admit medical students to read for the Conjoint diploma only, it would admit only dental students prepared to sit for the BDS. [CM 1954: 11 Oct]

Vice-Dean. He emphasized the important teaching role of part-time clinicians, arguing that 'full-time clinical professor' was a misnomer for those in university management, committee work and research. He suggested that in a hospital they were just clinicians, like other clinicians; even if they co-ordinated the systematic teaching of medicine a professorial unit would not teach students things they were never taught before – but 'with its staff and laboratories [it could] offer the more brilliant of its acolytes research posts and advice on what and how to undertake research.' [liii]

It may have been coincidental but the University's patience now seemed exhausted. In July, in a communication about grants, it insisted that a clinical professorial unit be established during the 1957/62 quinquennium. The Medical Committee had to choose between medicine, surgery or O & G. In May 1957 the surgeons had agreed to establish a unit in October 1958, but only if the necessary buildings existed.[liv]

The only firm commitment came from the physicians. In January 1958 they agreed to a clinical professorial unit in medicine, and in May recommended an appointment to the chair from October 1959. The School needed a professor quickly to help plan the unit in the new hospital and an application for the unit had to reach the University by October 1958. Arrangements were left to Frances Gardner, Lee Lander and Nigel Compston. They told the Dean initially that available accommodation was inadequate for a unit; however the physicians agreed to relinquish 30 beds at Lawn Road, and to vacate office and laboratory accommodation. If this proved insufficient they suggested using a temporary hut at Lawn Road until the new buildings were ready. On this basis Council applied for a chair of medicine.[lv]

To represent it on the University's Board of Advisers for the chair Council chose the Dean, the Chairman of Council, Lee Lander and Kenneth Hill, but the Education Committee wanted Ledingham substituted for Hill, as did the physicians who argued that Lee Lander was there as chairman of the Medical Committee not as their representative. As the physicians' support was deemed essential Hill withdrew and Ledingham replaced him.[lvi]

In March 1959 the advisers recommended unanimously that Sheila Sherlock, from Hammersmith Hospital and the Postgraduate Medical School, be appointed to the chair from 1 October 1959. Although only 41years old she had an international reputation for her work on diseases of the liver. Her appointment was to change the face of the Hospital and School and it was appropriate that RFHSM – formerly the London School of Medicine for Women – should be the first British medical school to appoint a woman to its chair of medicine.[lvii]

Sherlock was born in 1918 in Dublin. Brought up mainly in Folkestone she attended its County School for Girls. All her applications to medical schools were rejected but she got a late offer from Edinburgh in August 1936 and started there in October. Five years later she graduated top of her class, winning the Ettles Scholarship. As a woman a house job at the Royal Infirmary was denied her, but James Learmonth, the professor of surgery, made her his assistant and taught her about medical research. In 1942 she moved to Hammersmith Hospital and the Postgraduate Medical School, where McMichael (later Sir John, also an Ettles Scholar) taught her liver biopsy. Their 1943 paper (with Dible) on the pathology of acute hepatitis demolished the theory that 'catarrhal jaundice' was caused by obstruction of the bile duct. She subsequently studied all types of liver disease. After a year in Yale's department of physiological chemistry she returned to Hammersmith in 1948 as lecturer and honorary consultant physician. She was thirty! Research fellows from many countries joined her new liver unit. In 1951 she became the youngest woman to be elected FRCP. In 1955 she brought out the first edition of her classic textbook 'Diseases of the Liver and Biliary Tract'. By the time she applied for the chair at RFHSM she was famous.[lviii]

On 9 June 1959 it was announced that Sir Daniel Davies had relinquished 22 beds so that most of the clinical work of the new unit could be at GIR, rather than Lawn Road,[28] and Hill offered Sherlock temporary quarters until a hut was erected for her above the 'new' pathology block. The hut cost about £3,000, and £5,000 was spent on benches, plumbing and electrical work; a further £1,000 went to improve utilisation of space within the hut. In January 1960 Sherlock requested £580 worth of furniture for it. In July 1961 a smaller hut for metabolic studies, costing about £1750, was placed next to the main unit hut.[lix]

The UGC's report of its visit on 13 May 1960 noted the close relationship between School and Hospital and stated that the outstanding development was the establishment of the Medical Unit, its effect on teaching and research being already clear. At Council in June Lee Lander said this was a rapid and facile appraisal as the Unit had existed for only six months.[29] However, the UGC's satisfaction was hardly surprising. The Unit laboratories in the famous 'hut on the roof' (Fig 13.2) held the unit's staff plus about nine research fellows, all but one from overseas. There were fortnightly lectures (later weekly) by distinguished scientists, mostly from overseas, and in April 1960 the Unit hosted the first meeting of the International Association for the Study of the Liver of which Sherlock was President. She was also an excellent teacher.[lx]

[28] Sir Daniel Davies, the King's physician from 1949, was knighted in 1951. The Dean would have been just as excited by his election to the Gorsedd of Bards at the Welsh National Eisteddfod in 1957.

[29] A mean spirited reaction reminiscent of that towards McIlroy in 1925 (see Ch 9)

Fig 13.2 Medical Unit hut on roof

The UGC also wanted professorial units established in surgery and O & G before the move to Hampstead but was told there were insufficient beds for a surgical unit. The Dean had tried to reinstitute the chair of O & G when Dearnley retired in 1950. Gladys Hill was nominated as professor but, concerned about her private practice income, she lost interest in a full-time post. She was appointed 'part-time director' from 1 October 1951 at an annual salary of £1000. When, in 1957, the University demanded that a clinical chair be established, the Finance Committee suggested re-establishing the O & G unit when Hill retired in 1959, as the Annie McCall fund could pay for a research fellow.[30, lxi]

In 1959 the Dean said supplementary grants might allow the O & G chair to be re-instituted. The Medical Committee rejected the idea; instead Jocelyn Moore was appointed 'director' (not 'part-time director') to replace Hill. The Dean and the Board of Governors were disappointed, but at least agreement was reached that O & G should be an academic unit in anticipation of a professorial unit in Hampstead. The senior O & G staff got Hill's part-time post abolished, hoping RFH would then provide an additional registrar and a full-time secretary from Hill's salary, and asked the School to appoint a senior lecturer with consultant status; the post was taken by Philip Norris on 1 March 1960.[lxii]

[30] Annie McCall died 9 September 1949 leaving c £50,000 to RFHSM for a midwifery scholarship. The annual income of c. £1500 provided £1000 p.a. for the scholarship; the rest was used for equipment and/or technical & secretarial assistance. The first three scholars were Mary Egerton (1952-5), Valerie Thompson (1956-7) & Luba Epsztejn (1958-60).

Lecture theatres

The School and Hospital made frequent use of the lecture theatres in the Eastman Dental Hospital and the last's independence from RFH from 1948 created a problem as the small theatre in the proposed new pathology block was unsuitable for general use and there were no other lecture theatres at the Hospital. In 1950 it was suggested that a theatre seating 160 should be built over the new pathology block (where the Medical Unit hut was subsequently placed). The Dean pointed out that the roof over gynaecological outpatients (i.e. the west side of the Levy wing) would accommodate a larger lecture theatre, plus tutorial rooms and a medical library. Plans drawn up on this basis were revised when someone recalled that the Levy wing was designed to carry six more floors, a fact ignored in the new plans. In August 1951 'final' plans for a 300 seat lecture theatre costing about £24,000, plus a library and tutorial rooms for use by students, hospital staff and nurses, were forwarded to the Ministry of Health with a request for funds.[lxiii]

The need for a lecture theatre at RFH became increasingly urgent. Clinical lectures were held at Hunter Street but it could not accommodate the whole clinical timetable. In the autumn of 1951 Wilkinson, the Eastman's new director, said RFHSM could no longer use its theatres for five o'clock lectures, although they remained available for nine and twelve o'clock lectures. The afternoon lectures were switched to Hunter Street until someone pointed out that in 1949 the Eastman's previous director had assured the School it could rely on continued use of the Eastman theatres; Wilkinson then agreed to five o'clock lectures on four days a week.[lxiv]

The Board of Governors agreed to the new lecture theatre but even with MoH approval it would not be available for years. The Eastman had promised uninterrupted use of its theatres until March 1953. A prefabricated building was needed quickly. In July 1952 RFH provided £1250 from endowment funds and a temporary lecture theatre seating 150 was erected on the flat roof of the west wing of the Levy building. (See Fig 13.3) RFH wanted RFHSM to pay rent based on hours of use. Council resented this idea. There was no charge for the Eastman theatres, and the School did not charge for accommodating classes for nurses and radiographers, or for hospital use of the interdepartmental workshop. The idea of rent was quietly dropped.[lxv]

The Hospital Libraries

In February 1947 RFHSM's Library Committee rejected setting up a library for postgraduates at GIR, and suggested they should use the libraries of the BMA or

Fig 13.3 Lecture Hut at Gray's Inn Road

the Royal Society of Medicine. Clinical students were barred from staff libraries[31] and had no library of their own; theirs had been transferred to Hunter Street following the bombing of GIR in 1944. In February 1948 the committee discussed restarting the students' library at GIR; somewhat surprisingly the students there opposed the idea.[lxvi]

In January 1951 UGC inspectors commented on the poor library facilities for clinical students. There were unsupervised collections of student textbooks at GIR, Lawn Road and Liverpool Road, but many were stolen, or 'borrowed' for long periods, and thus unavailable when needed. In 1952 the Students' Union created a clinical reference library at GIR in a quiet room in the students' quarters; it raised the money by selling old white coats.[32, lxvii]

Early in 1958 it was decided the students' library at GIR would lose fewer books if they were signed for when borrowed. The books were transferred to a cupboard near the librarian's office and arrangements were made for access in her absence. Books still vanished. In March 1959 twenty-five were missing at GIR, only four or five were left at Lawn Road and a third of the Liverpool Road stock had gone. It was decreed that for six months no books should leave any of the 'students'

---

[31] During discussions about a library at Liverpool Road in 1954 Lloyd-Williams said students would not read there if it was used mainly by staff; students' books were moved to the tutorial room which was then called the Students' Reading Room.

[32] The Library Committee also made a contribution.

libraries'; if this solution failed one textbook for each major subject was to be chained for reference and the rest removed.[33] That June, a third of the stock was missing at GIR! In October Pat Fear from Middlesex Hospital Medical School replaced Mrs Brandreth as the RFHSM librarian.[lxviii]

Sherlock was shocked by the library. She, and the Students' Union, wrote to the Library Committee deploring the facilities for clinical students. A year later the Union supported a proposal to merge the Pathology and Medical Unit libraries with the hospital library if a suitable room could be found. In February 1961 the Library Committee heard students would be allowed to use the new library for reference purposes – but that did not happen for several years. That May it was agreed the existing registrars' room should house both the GIR library and a new telephone room; the registrars moved into the vacated previous library. With subsequent enlargement of the telephone room the rest of the old registrars' room provided inadequate space for the needs of the medical library, so an adjacent room was refurbished and used to house periodicals. By July 1962 the three libraries had amalgamated; the new arrangement proved satisfactory.[lxix]

Curricular Matters

When Lloyd-Williams became Dean London's 1st MB exam covered biology, chemistry and physics. The course lasted three terms. Pupils who had passed or gained exemption from 1st MB entered the second year directly. The 2nd MB course covered human anatomy and physiology (the latter including pharmacology) and lasted five terms. Those passing 2nd MB first time started clinical studies in April. Failures re-sat after the summer term; if successful they began clinical work in the autumn along with students who had spent four terms on an intercalated B.Sc. Until 1951-2 a B.Sc. could be taken only in physiology; the choice was then extended to include anatomy. The third & 'final' MBBS examinations, held twice a year, were in three parts: pathology, hygiene & forensic medicine; medicine & applied pharmacology and therapeutics; and surgery & obstetrics & gynaecology. The students sat pathology six months before medicine and surgery. The exams were held twice a year; in spring and autumn.

The MBBS clinical course also covered the four components of the final Conjoint examinations (medicine, surgery, O & G and pathology). These took place three monthly and could be taken individually. Only in exceptional circumstances were students admitted just to take diploma examinations, but many took them in case of failure in MBBS. When the UGC visitors queried this practice in January

---

[33] In November 1959 the Library Committee decided longer chains should be provided.

1956 the Dean said she discouraged it but could not prevent students taking Conjoint if they so wished.[lxx]

During and after the war only 100 students a year could enter LSMW – seventy to the first year (minimum age 17) and thirty directly to the second year (minimum age 18). In February 1946 the Association of Headmistresses requested more direct entries to the second year but this number had to be restricted to ensure that 'internal' students passing 1st MB could proceed. The Association asked if applicants with 1st MB, or exemption from it, could therefore enter the first year course – arguing that by admitting more to the first year LSMW penalised cleverer girls as only three applied for each first year place but ten for each second year one. Council took note and expunged from the prospectus the sentence 'students cannot be admitted to the First Medical Course if they have exemption from more than one subject of the First Medical Examination'. The following year students, for the first time, had to apply for admission either to the first *or* the second year, but those intending to gain exemption before entry could, if they wished, be considered for entry to the First Medical Course.[lxxi]

Owing to the large number of applications, selection from 1945 to 1947 was based on an entry examination, followed by an interview for some candidates.[34] Subsequently the examination was abandoned and admission was determined by interview only.[35]

For some extraordinary reason the University decided to introduce a revised preclinical curriculum which, after 1953, would preclude exemption from the first year course and so prevent direct admission to the second year. The new 1st MB exam was to cover elementary anatomy and physiology, while 'the application of biology and physics to medical science' was to be added to the 2nd MB exam. RFHSM prepared a new syllabus for entrants who had reached GCE advanced level in physics and chemistry, and had followed an elementary course in biology. To encourage those with an arts background it raised the age of entry for the new course from 17 to 18, so that such candidates could acquire a sound preliminary knowledge of science before admission.[36] Some London medical schools felt unable to run the revised curriculum. The University 'postponed' its introduction and subsequently abandoned it. The School's entry for October 1953 was adjusted by allowing those who had secured exemption from the First MB to transfer to the second year course.[lxxii]

---

[34] 417 took the examination in January 1945

[35] In June 1946 the Ministry of Labour wanted ex-servicemen given priority for university entry; the Dean was sympathetic but said vacancies depended on the entrance examination results. [CM 1946: 20 Jun]

[36] RFHSM continued encouraging applicants studying arts to Advanced Level, hoping to recruit students with a better educational background. [CM 1959: 15 Jun)].

In 1955 Council adopted the University's optional ruling that students might take only anatomy and physiology in the 2nd MB examination, deferring pharmacology until the end of the introductory clinical course – a move intended to relieve some of the pressure of the 18-month course and to provide a useful link between preclinical and clinical studies. This arrangement went on until about 1972.[lxxiii]

Throughout Lloyd-Williams's time as dean much of the clinical course involved three month attachments to different firms. For example in 1952-53 an introductory course was followed by eleven clerkships and dresserships – namely, general medicine, general surgery and pathology (whose firms also accommodated senior students); plus midwifery; gynaecology and V.D.;[37] orthopaedics & casualty; ENT-eyes-physical medicine & fevers; and children & skins. Psychological medicine was taught with senior medicine, and radiology on junior medicine, surgery and pathology posts.[38] Occasionally minor amendments were made to the programme, e.g. junior pathology was incorporated into a new introductory course in 1956, while in 1957 the fortnight's residence for instruction in fevers moved from the ENT post to senior pathology, and a fortnight's holiday went back to the ENT post.[39] There were also lectures for the main clinical specialties – and some subjects, e.g. applied pharmacology and therapeutics, forensic medicine and tropical medicine were covered only by lectures.[lxxiv]

Clinical teaching took place at GIR, Lawn Road, Liverpool Road (O & G and paediatrics), Hampstead General and EGAH; other hospitals were also used, particularly for specialities such as paediatrics and psychiatry. In 1961 EGAH was transferred from the RFH group to the NWMRHB and, although its staff wanted to retain the teaching link, it was omitted from the list of RFHSM teaching hospitals in the 1963-64 prospectus.[lxxv]

Midwifery was a long standing problem. When Shardeloes closed in February 1948 the City of London Maternity Hospital did not, as promised, vacate its thirty beds at Liverpool Road. Twenty students needed places each quarter but RFH could take only six and EGAH only two, unless they were non-resident. From January 1949 the post was shortened from three to two months owing to lack of beds:[40] as a temporary measure three students went to the City of London Maternity Unit at Brocket Hall, Welwyn Garden City.[lxxvi]

---

[37] From 1948 an FPA clinic taught students about contraception. [CM 1948: 6 Oct]

[38] In June 1952 the subcommittee organizing the clinical course was made permanent – to meet from time to time and report to the Education Committee. 'From time to time' probably explains why few meetings took place. [CM 1952: 11 Jun].

[39] Five years earlier residence on fevers was transferred from senior pathology to ENT.

[40] The six mths allowed for O & G exceeded the time suggested in the BMA publication *The Training of a Doctor*, but RFHSM told the RCOG Council it would deplore any reduction in allotted time.

The Mother's Hospital, Clapton closed to RFHSM on 1 April 1949. Beds became available at Liverpool Road in July and over the next three years all O & G beds at RFH were transferred there – to a new block with students' quarters and good facilities for teaching; the Duchess of Gloucester opened it officially on 30 June 1954.[lxxvii]

The impending retirement of the district midwife in July 1956 led RFHSM to consider discontinuing midwifery teaching on the district, i.e. attending patients in their homes either for the delivery or afterwards. The Dean said, if abandoned, it would be lost to the LCC but some O & G staff considered district experience of little value except as an aspect of social medicine. 'Midwifery Districts' was not mentioned in the prospectus for 1956-7.[lxxviii]

Apart from the war the biggest disruption of teaching came in July 1955 with the outbreak of an illness initially thought to be glandular fever but subsequently called 'Royal Free Disease'. Most sufferers were GIR nurses, including Matron, but medical students, doctors, ancillary and administrative staff and some nurses at EGAH were also stricken. Over 70 cases were recorded by 25 July; subsequently reports appeared daily in the national press. The epidemic lasted months and affected almost 300; many suffered relapses. GIR closed until 5 October. Affected nurses were admitted to Liverpool Road and 35 were still there on 1 November. Clinical teaching was arranged at other hospitals.[lxxix]

Controversy continues about the aetiology of Royal Free Disease. Melvin Ramsay, an infectious diseases consultant at RFH at the time considered it a specific communicable disease which he called 'myalgic encephalomyelitis' (ME); others attributed it to hysteria.[lxxx]

General practice was, educationally, a Cinderella subject throughout Lloyd-Williams's deanship. From 1952 a voluntary scheme allowed final year students to spend a fortnight with general practitioners; the students and the GPs liked it. From 1956-7 students wanting such experience could either choose a fortnight (full time) or attend one evening surgery a week for 12 weeks; second year clinicals could also participate in the latter scheme.[lxxxi]

Until 1953 formal training finished with success in finals. Newly qualified doctors could register and practise, either independently or in any hospital (or other institution) where they could find a job. Appointments as house physicians, house surgeons, resident anaesthetists, resident pathologists, obstetric house surgeons, registrars, and clinical assistants were open to qualified students at RFH and associated hospitals.

All this changed following the Medical Act of 1950. RFHSM's prospectus for 1953-4 announced that medical graduates were not eligible for full registration with the GMC until satisfactory completion of *'two posts in any approved hospital, six months in Medicine and six months in Surgery, or six months in Obstetrics and Gynaecology as an alternative to either medicine or surgery. During this period graduates will hold a provisional registration to enable them to carry out hospital duties and will be paid at the established rates for house officers under the National Health Service. Lists of the approved hospitals are available at the School Office and at the various hospitals of the teaching group.'* The transition from life as a student to a more permanent form of employment was profoundly changed by this innovation.

At a meeting of London's medical deans the Chief Medical Officer, George Godber, drew attention to the number of overseas doctors in British junior hospital posts. He suggested, erroneously as it turned out, that with change in their own countries fewer would arrive for postgraduate training, thus creating a problem in staffing British hospitals. On this basis the UGC, in December 1961, asked medical schools to increase their student intake. RFHSM agreed to admit 10% more to the second year from October 1962.[lxxxii]

Staff Changes

The biggest changes in the staffing of the clinical departments at RFH came with the arrival of Sherlock's professorial unit in October 1959. Anthony Dawson and Michael Turner were her lecturers, but Turner spent the first year in Rochester, New York;[41] Roger Williams was his locum. Barbara Billing, a senior lecturer biochemist, arrived early in 1960. They all came from Hammersmith with Sherlock, as did Stanley Shaldon, who was her first registrar at GIR. Her first house physician, Brenda Higgs, recollects a three-month 'locum' at Lawn Road before taking up the substantive post on 1 January 1960, when the beds became available at GIR.[42] Paul Turner was appointed SHO at Lawn Road, and covered a small number of unit beds, plus those of Richardson, the rheumatologist.[lxxxiii]

Of the nine research fellows who initially crowded into the famous hut on the roof there were just two British graduates, Patricia Wilkinson, an RFHSM alumna, and Soad Tabaqchali, a St Andrews graduate but Iraqi by birth. Wilkinson replaced

[41] Turner emigrated to the USA in 1963.

[42] Before graduating MBBS October 1959, Brenda Higgs (already MRCS,LRCP) asked to be Sherlock's first HP at RFH. Her University purple (lacrosse) would have impressed sports enthusiast Sherlock. In 1961 Higgs was SHO with Shaldon at Lawn Road. She moved to Hammersmith and got an MD having studied exercise after myocardial infarction. Due to return to RFH she married (Mrs Taylor) and became a consultant physician in Preston.

Shaldon as registrar. The rest were from the USA, Canada, Mexico, South Africa and Italy. Most were aspiring hepatologists, but some were gastroenterology trainees working with Dawson. In the Unit's third year there were sixteen research fellows, mostly foreign; only the biochemist, Anne Craigie, was not medically qualified.

Dawson was promoted to senior lecturer from 1 October 1961. Williams went to New York for a year on a research fellowship and Kaye Ibbertson, a young New Zealand endocrinologist, was appointed locum lecturer.

The NHS consultant staff also changed. With Jenner Hoskin's death in February 1954 Sir Daniel Davies became senior physician and Frances Gardner head of cardiology. The former, the King's physician from 1949, was the friend and doctor of Aneurin Bevan, the architect of the NHS; Sir Daniel retired in 1960, aged 60, and died six years later.

When Hazel Chodak-Gregory retired in 1947 Zina Moncrieff joined Ursula Shelley, now senior paediatrician. The physician/neurologist, Neill Hobhouse, retired in 1950. His replacement, Helen Dimsdale, was the first female neurology consultant in Britain having been on the staff at Maida Vale since 1947. That year Diana Kinloch Beck, an LSMW alumna, was made a consultant *neurosurgeon* at the Middlesex. Sadly Beck died in 1956, aged 53. After preclinical studies at Cambridge Dimsdale had enrolled at LSMW in 1929 but left after a year and completed her clinical studies at UCH. Her uncle, Sir Walter Langdon-Brown, was Regius Professor of Physic at Cambridge; the Keynes brothers (Maynard, the economist, and Sir Geoffrey, surgeon at Bart's) were her cousins.[lxxxiv]

In 1955 the dermatologist Charles Calnan joined Reginald Brain; both worked at St John's Hospital for Diseases of the Skin. In February 1960, after Brain retired, Imrich Sarkany was appointed dermatologist at RFH. That year Calnan took the newly created chair at the Institute of Dermatology; he remained at RFH but Sarkany carried the main clinical load.[lxxxv]

In January 1953 Alfred John Martin OBE,[43] physician in Physical Medicine at RFH from 1947, died suddenly, aged forty-three, while drinking tea with colleagues in Hampstead General outpatients. A. T. (Tony) Richardson replaced him. Fletcher, who was appointed in 1938, was designated as a 'rheumatologist' but before he retired in 1956 both he and Richardson were listed in the Annual Report as 'Physicians in Physical Medicine and Rheumatology' – a terminology still in use when Euan Campbell joined Richardson in 1962; the words 'Physical Medicine' were dropped in the Annual Report for 1970-1.[lxxxvi]

William Nicol, Medical Superintendent of Horton Hospital, Epsom from 1931 until 1951, was a psychiatrist at RFH from 1943. He resigned in 1957 to take up

[43] The OBE was for gallant and distinguished services with the RAMC in Burma during the war.

an appointment as Lord Chancellor's Visitor.[44] Sydney Hardwick, who joined RFH in 1948, became senior psychiatrist and Alick Elithorn replaced Nicol.[lxxxvii]

Several general surgeons retired during Lloyd-Williams's deanship. The ano-rectal surgeon, Lionel Norbury,[45] went in 1947. His replacement, Daintree Johnson, an upper gastrointestinal surgeon, had served with the 6th Airborne Division during the war and was in the first group of Allies to enter Belsen. Catherine Lewis, the second female FRCS (1919), retired in 1948. She gave up music for medicine, graduating from LSMW in 1917 aged thirty-five. She was the first woman to be appointed at St Peter's Hospital for Urinary Diseases and to be elected to the British Association of Urological Surgeons. Her replacement, Dorothy Barclay, also a genito-urinary specialist, retired early in 1957 to look after her four children; sadly she died of ovarian cancer in 1964, aged 50.

Barclay's replacement was the urologist John Hopewell, previously a senior registrar at KCH. He was keen to start a department capable of treating end-stage renal failure by haemodialysis and transplantation. For this he needed facilities for haemodialysis. A Baxter twin-coil artificial kidney was purchased in 1959 and installed in a cubicle within one of the Nightingale wards at Lawn Road. Roy Calne, then a surgical registrar at RFH, found that 6-mercaptopurine prolonged renal allograft survival in dogs. The drug was used as immune-suppression in three patients who, in late 1959 and 1960, received a transplanted kidney at RFH as treatment for chronic renal failure. The first two – with cadaveric grafts – survived for three and eleven days. The last received a kidney from his father, in the first organ transplantation done in Britain using a live, related non-sibling donor. Despite initial improvement the patient died after seven weeks. No further renal transplants were done at RFH until 1968. [lxxxviii]

In February 1960 the School had agreed to provide Sherlock with another lecturer, but preferably one with an interest in nephrology who might help Hopewell, with the artificial kidney. As there appeared to be no 'suitable' applicant Shaldon was appointed and moved to Lawn Road in November. Although not a nephrologist he made the most of the opportunity and, contemporaneously with groups in Boston and Seattle, pioneered the development of home dialysis for chronic renal failure.[lxxxix]

Clement Shattock, an outstanding surgical teacher, retired in 1952, as did his wife, Fede Mackenzie, a former student who taught anatomy at LSMW. Geraldine Barry left in 1960, after thirty years on the staff. Her replacement, Phyllis George, was for many years the surgeon most involved with Sherlock's hepato-biliary work.[xc]

---

[44] A Lord Chancellor's Visitor assists judges by investigating matters relating to a patient's capacity to manage and administer his or her property and affairs,

[45] Norbury's father was a former Director General of the Navy's Medical Services,

Rodney Maingot, Trinidadian by birth, joined RFH to fill the vacancy left by Joll's death in January 1945. An adept surgeon, many visited him to study his abdominal surgical techniques. He was a showman. He dressed immaculately and even his theatre suits were personally tailored. He retired in 1958 but retained his large private practice.[46]

After Lloyd-Williams became Dean Jean Dollar remained the only ophthalmologist at RFH until the arrival of Henry Hobbs in 1947-8. When Sir Douglas Maclaggan retired in 1958 John Ballantyne became senior ENT surgeon; John Groves joined him when Dorothy Collier left five months later.[xci]

Pathology had become a large department, and in October 1946 Council acted on Webb's suggestion that bacteriology, chemical pathology, clinical pathology, and morbid anatomy & histology should constitute four separate sub-departments with heads of appropriate status. Christine Pillman-Williams (chemical pathology) and Lucy Wills (clinical pathology)[47] were made senior lecturers in 1946. In May 1947, shortly before Wills retired, W.J.D. ('Peter') Fleming was promoted to senior lecturer and head of haematology (rather than clinical pathology), and Nuala Crowley to senior lecturer in charge of bacteriology, even though Webb himself was a microbiologist.[xcii]

Following Pillman-Williams's death in October 1953 Denis Baron, from the Middlesex, was appointed reader in chemical pathology. He spent a year as a Rockefeller Travelling Fellow in Chicago in 1961 and David Matthews acted as head of department.[48] On Baron's return Matthews went to the National Institutes of Health in Bethesda, Md. and subsequently to the Institute of Neurology.[xciii]

After Webb retired in September 1956 Crowley supervised pathology until Kenneth Hill arrived on 12 November. Hill, a morbid anatomist, served in West Africa during the war and in 1949 was the first professor of pathology at the new University College of the West Indies in Jamaica. Joan Ross ran morbid anatomy until 1947; she then joined the Ministry of Supply as consultant in pathology. Alfred Stansfeld, who replaced her, moved to Bart's in 1955 and G.B.D (Barry) Scott took the readership left vacant by Ross.[xciv]

Hill organized a new secondment scheme for lecturers. When a post became vacant in 1960 he used it to create the first joint pathology lectureship with an overseas university. The appointee, Elizabeth Hall, went to Ibadan in Nigeria; Ivan Janota replaced her there after two years.[xcv]

---

[46] A parrot in Maingot's consulting rooms was trained to say 'You've got gallstones – send for Rodney'.

[47] Wills attended Cheltenham Ladies' College. Considered naturally aristocratic, but anti-establishment, she cycled to RFH. After retiring in September 1947, aged 59, she lived in Chelsea & represented the Labour interest in that borough.(See Roe, D.A. 1978 J. Nutrition 108: 1379-83).

[48] Not the physiologist David L. Matthews who drowned in July 1970 (see Chapter 14)

Peter Scheuer started as lecturer in morbid anatomy on 1 October 1959, the day Sherlock arrived as Professor of Medicine. With encouragement from Sherlock and Hill he spent 1962-63 at Mount Sinai Hospital, New York, working with Hans Popper, the world's finest liver pathologist – an accolade often bestowed on Scheuer after Popper's death in 1988.

Ulysses Williams (Pillman-Williams's husband) retired as radiologist in 1947, having been head of the X-ray department since 1918 when he returned from wartime exploits with the Red Cross in France and in Serbia. He was an excellent golfer and an outstanding tennis player; as 'Laertides'[49] he played in the Wimbledon championships until middle age.[xcvi] In 1958 Bill Young joined the department. He was made its director, and was of great help to Sherlock in setting up the specialist radiological investigations needed by a top flight hepatology group.

Sir Bernard Spilsbury relinquished his lectureship in forensic medicine and toxicology in December 1947. His replacement William Bentley Purchase, who also taught at St Thomas' and UCH, was knighted in 1958. Purchase left the School the following year when he resigned as coroner of St Pancras to become coroner at Ipswich. Dr Francis Camps, reader in forensic medicine at London Hospital Medical College, replaced him at RFHSM.[xcvii]

When Lloyd-Williams became Dean Herbert Chalke taught 'Hygiene and Public Health'. His replacement Alan Stevenson, a reader at LSHTM, taught 'Public Health' as did John Brotherstone, who acted for a year when Stevenson left in 1948. Thomas Galloway and Alison Macdonald taught 'Preventive and Social Medicine' until 1955, but then Macdonald's successors taught 'Social and Preventive Medicine'. The first of them, Alexander Robertson, left in 1958. The second, Michael Warren, was made senior lecturer in 1959; from January 1960 he was '70% RFHSM', '30% LSHTM' but went full-time at the latter in 1964 and was not replaced at RFHSM where the title of the subject continued to change over the years.[xcviii]

The preclinical staff saw many changes during Lloyd-Williams's deanship. Lucas-Keene, a titular professor, retired in September 1951, aged 66, her appointment having been extended to facilitate the move into the new wing at Hunter Street. The University now agreed to establish a chair of anatomy but would not accept the nomination of Lilian Dickson.[50] The appointee, Ruth Bowden, was born in 1915 in India where her father was a missionary. Her aunt, Dame Edith

[49] Another name for 'Ulysses'

[50] Dickson, a Glasgow graduate, joined LSMW in 1929. During the war she worked at Aberdeen, Exeter, Guy's, Conjoint Hall & Hunter Street. After retiring she taught at the Christian Medical College in Ludhiana. She died 29 July 1981.

Brown, who qualified at LSMW, founded the women's medical school at Ludhiana in the Punjab in 1894. Bowden graduated at LSMW in 1940. From 1942 to 1945 she studied peripheral nerve injuries, first with Seddon in Oxford and then at LSMW, and from late 1945 ran a nerve injury clinic at RFH. Her promotion to reader in November 1949 came whilst a Rockefeller Travelling Fellow in the poliomyelitis laboratory at Johns Hopkins.[xcix]

In 1949 John Napier, a demonstrator in anatomy, moved to St Thomas' Hospital. He was appointed to a readership at RFHSM from October 1952, but spent the first year of it as a Fulbright Scholar in Iowa, and so Lucas-Keene, retired but still active in research, was made a part-time lecturer. In 1961, with the School's agreement, Napier also became curator of the primate palaeontological collection at the British Museum.[c]

In the summer term of 1952 Killick played host to Professor Cureton of Illinois University, an expert on the physiological conditioning of athletes. In the Hunter Street quadrangle he carried out strenuous fitness tests on notable athletes, including some of that year's British Olympic team. The visit of the boxer Freddie Mills seems to have caused the greatest stir, even though the medical student Roger Bannister was one of the Olympians tested – but he had not then run his famous 'four minute mile'. Soon afterwards Bannister started clinical work at St Mary's where Killick's husband was professor of physiology.[ci]

Hewer, a long serving member of the physiology department, retired as reader in histology in 1947, but stayed on as 'consultant histologist' until 1949, when the fifth edition of her classic 'Textbook of Histology for Medical Students' was published.[51] To recognise her services the School presented her with her microscope and lamp, and she carried on with her research.[cii]

From October 1949 Helen Duke was a physiology demonstrator and then a lecturer. Granted maternity leave in December 1952 she fell seriously ill and missed the whole of the Easter term in 1953. She moved to a senior lectureship at the Middlesex six years later.[ciii]

Charles Downman, reader in physiology from October 1954, resigned in May 1960 to move to Cornell University. However, Killick, aged only 58, died on 31 May following a cerebral haemorrhage.[52] Downman, due to sail in August, was considered an eminently suitable replacement. The paperwork was rushed to the University and he was appointed Sophia Jex-Blake Professor of Physiology from

[51] She brought out two more editions; subsequent editions were revised by Bradbury.

[52] In 1953 Mrs Pepys painted a portrait of Killick. She gave it to RFHSM in 1965 to mark the facilities Killick gave her husband, Jack Pepys, to help with his early immunological work.[CM 1965: 10 Nov]

1 August. Having sold his house and furniture he was given a £2000 interest-free loan to help him resettle.[civ]

John Coleridge from Leeds took Downman's readership in January 1962, and his wife accompanied him to RFHSM as a research fellow.

Scarborough retired in 1954. Until Colina Mackenzie (lecturer) and Phyllis Fraser (assistant lecturer) arrived in 1951 she had run pharmacology single-handedly. Her readership went to Eleanor Zaimis, renowned for work done with Paton on hexamethonium, the first anti-hypertensive drug, and on decamethonium, a neuromuscular blocking drug used by anaesthetists. In 1958 she received a personal chair and J. R. (Bob) Hodges, a lecturer since 1956, was promoted to senior lecturer.[cv]

Biochemistry was officially part of physiology until 1957. The School applied for a chair of biochemistry in 1952 but withdrew the application.[53] To cover the curriculum for a new preclinical examination, due to be introduced in 1953 (but scrapped, see earlier), biochemistry teaching was split for a while between physiology and chemistry.[cvi]

In 1956 Edward Walsh was 'reader in physiology', having arrived as a senior lecturer in 1947-8; the following year he was 'reader in biochemistry in the physiology department'; and in 1957 he and Brenda Ryman moved to the new 'Department of Biochemistry and Chemistry', headed by Lawson. Walsh went to Hong Kong as professor of biochemistry in 1960. From 1948 Ryman was demonstrator and lecturer, and in 1961 was made a senior lecturer in biochemistry – taking the slot left available by Anne Radcliffe who, after thirty years service, retired as a senior lecturer in chemistry.[cvii]

Mary Waller retired as head of physics in September 1947. Her successor Winifred Leyshon retired in 1952. Although the School wanted a chair of physics the University thought a readership more appropriate. Both School and Hospital decided the appointee should head a joint physics department, so Harold Simons (from Bart's) became 'Reader and Consultant Physicist to RFH' from October 1952; the principal hospital physicist, Harry Williams, was made honorary lecturer. Mrs Margarita Monk-Jones, who taught statistics, was promoted to senior lecturer in the department.[cviii]

Margaret Hughes, senior lecturer in biology since 1952, and lecturer for many years before that, replaced Catherine Lucas as head of department when she retired in September 1961. In 1962 R. J. (Sam) Berry was appointed lecturer in genetics.[cix]

[53] Withdrawn probably because the University considered the School's choice, Lawson, unsuitable. The title 'professor of organic chemistry' was conferred on him in 1961.

Myddleton House Sports Ground

In May 1950 the University's Inspectors noted that RFHSM lacked its own sports ground.[54] When co-education was introduced in 1947 it was agreed with Guy's students that RFHSM men could use the Guy's male sport clubs – and Guy's women the clubs and facilities at RFHSM. Membership cards were issued to prevent gate crashing by strangers. The arrangement lasted until 1953.[cx]

In 1951 the University suggested RFHSM should share a sports ground with the School of Pharmacy (SOP), soon to be its neighbour in Brunswick Square. They inspected the twenty-seven acre Myddleton estate in Enfield; its owner, Augustus Bowles, was a famous botanist.[55] The estate and its twenty-two roomed house, built in 1818, were named after Sir Hugh Myddleton whose 'New River', constructed in 1608 to carry London's water supply, ran through the grounds.

The estate, plus 10 acres to the west, was available for £10,000 provided Bowles could have life tenancy of a house and two cottages.[56] Although the money was available in May 1953 legal quibbles delayed the purchase until August 1954, three months after Bowles's death. The School of Pharmacy was the nominated purchaser.[cxi]

The Joint Athletic Ground Committee running the new acquisition was chaired by Clark, secretary of the University's Collegiate Council and of its Athletic Ground Committee at Motspur Park. He and McTaggart, the University's head groundsman, provided invaluable advice. Initially plans were made for one pitch each for rugby, soccer and lacrosse, three hockey pitches, two cricket squares and six hard tennis courts. The ground was drained and the cricket tables were laid.[cxii]

Temporary accommodation was created in Myddleton House itself for changing and refreshments. The Rugby Club found the washing facilities inadequate but other outdoor sports clubs used them during the 1954-5 season. A University grant of £13,000 allowed conversion of Myddleton House into a clubhouse with changing rooms and staff flats.[57, cxiii]

The head groundsman, Bates,[58] appointed in August 1954, moved into the gardener's cottage in January 1955, but without more accommodation it was difficult to find help for him. The three first-floor rooms of Myddleton House were, temporarily, made into a flat and an assistant groundsman moved in with his family. The University asked the two schools to contribute towards permanent flats for

---

54 There were tennis courts at Lawn Road and Liverpool Road and a netball court at Hunter Street.

55 Vice president of the Royal Horticultural Society, and an expert on crocuses, narcissi & snowdrops, Bowles was uncle to Andrew Parker-Bowles, first husband of Camilla Shand – now wife of Prince Charles.

56 He was 86 and in poor health.

57 It was also for renovation of the coach house block as a store for plant and equipment.

58 Bates left in 1960. Don Clarke from the Royal Aeronautical College at Cranfield replaced him and stayed for many years.

the two other groundsmen who were living in temporary quarters; RFHSM gave £1500. The Myddleton House conversion was finished by June 1956. The house and outbuildings were painted, and the handsome stable clock, in its wooden tower, was reconstructed to preserve the original character of the house. About thirty Pharmacy students, directed by the architect, decorated the interior.[cxiv]

Following Jenner Hoskin's death in February 1954 the School memorialized him – by a clock in the Council room, and by the Jenner Hoskin Memorial Pavilion, erected between the two cricket fields in 1956 at a cost of £505.[59] Subsequently Mrs Jenner Hoskin presented a gilt clock for the common room at Myddleton House.[cxv]

The house's old flower room became a kitchen, and the main dining room was refurbished. One outhouse provided cloakrooms for visitors to the ground and gardens. The Forty Hill Horticultural Society gave a teak garden seat in memory of Augustus Bowles, and paid for the repair of a lead ostrich that had fallen into the water – one of a pair balanced precariously on the edge of the New River.[cxvi]

In 1959 a gift of £350 from Mr Clee paid for a combined netball and tennis court at Enfield in memory of his wife, Dr Dora Mann, a German who qualified at LSMW in 1904. Clee had already contributed to the Warden's Fund and the Winifred Cullis memorial fund, and on two occasions presented many staff and students with tickets for the Zoo.[cxvii]

In May 1960 students made great use of the sports ground, tennis courts being booked for three weeks ahead. A year later this was no longer the case; the combined tennis and netball court presented by Clee, although used for tennis, was not once used for netball. It was suggested other schools might use the ground, or that a swimming pool might attract more students, but nothing came of these ideas.[cxviii]

Student Life

Nearly all the clubs and societies were under the aegis of the Students' Union, which distributed grants to them. In 1949, a particularly poor turnout at its AGM led to the suggestion that the quorum be reduced from one fifth of the student body (i.e. about 95) to just forty. As there were seventeen on the Union Committee the Magazine commented that such apathy might either allow an energetic minority to rule with a rod of iron or lead to collapse of the Union. With no Union to finance them clubs would depend on members' subscriptions; the Junior Common Room would be paperless and flowerless, there would be no 'elevenses', and no free afternoon tea. More seriously, students would have no representative on the 'Post Committee' and so no opportunity to discuss details of the clinical course with staff.[cxix]

[59] A reredos was placed in his memory in the chapel at RFH.

The Union survived but the Magazine went on complaining about low membership and lack of drive in the various clubs. A Natural History Society founded in January 1956 folded within a few years – so too did the Youth Hostel Group started in 1959.

In the autumn of 1956 the Students' Union donated £332 to the University of London Hungarian Student Relief Fund. Money collected at RFHSM and its hospitals was also sent to Hungary via the International Red Cross. However, the Union had a deficit of about £50 in 1958 and it appeared to rise to £90 a year later. The committee reduced grants to many clubs, bought fewer newspapers for the common rooms, and abolished the Tea Club (active for at least seventy years) for an indefinite period. However, when the accounts were finally audited a small surplus was found; the Union was solvent and afternoon tea was saved. In 1960 there was surplus of £300; but as there were several inquorate Union meetings that year, and little interest in extracurricular activities, the surplus was thought to reflect reduced expenditure by clubs and societies.[cxx]

Even without its own ground the School had been active in many sports. Traditionally it competed against other women's colleges or against co-educational institutions such as UCL and KCL, but as more women entered other London medical schools women's teams began participating in inter-hospital competitions.

After the war athletics had a low profile at RFHSM, but in 1954 the School joined Spartans Ladies Club for its good coaching and facilities for indoor training. This, and Roma Ashby's arrival in 1955, changed things. The following year Ashby broke the University's half-mile record (by 5.3 seconds), and won the quarter-mile and half-mile at the British University Championships. In 1958 she led a four-person RFHSM team to third place in the University Championships,[60] and won the English National Cross Country Championships. In 1960 she broke the national record for the mile, and RFHSM won the Imperial Cup for women's events at the UL Athletic Championships. The year she qualified, 1961, Ashby won the mile at the Women's AAA Championships and ran for British Universities in the World Student Games at Sophia.[cxxi]

The Hockey Club struggled until the late 1940s, but from 1949-50 it won the women's inter-hospitals challenge shield four years running. It then lost in the first round in 1953-4 and did not reach the final again until 1961-2, when it succumbed to St Mary's.[cxxii]

At the intercollegiate winter regatta in 1952 the junior IV gained RFHSM's first post-war success, and a few months later the rowing club put an VIII on the river

---

[60] Ashby won the 440 and 880 yards; Elizabeth Mandale got a second (discus) and third (javelin); Anita Follows was fourth at 100 and 220 yards, and Malcolm Lindsay second in the men's long jump. That year all four represented the University, and Ashby captained the women's section.

again. At the United Hospitals' regatta in 1953 the junior IV took the cup from Reading again after 20 years, and two club members won silver medals rowing in the University of London VIII representing England at the European Championships.[61] Helped by Ursula Shelley, Lilian Dickson's successor as President, the club bought a new racing IV which it named 'Orion'.[cxxiii]

In 1956 and 1957 four club members rowed for the University VIII, and for a United Universities VIII at championships in West Germany. There were seven members in the University VIII in 1960. That year RFHSM crews won events in the winter fours and the Lent and summer regattas, and at Durham the senior crew won the ladies' open. The club retained most of its intercollegiate trophies in 1961, and a novice IV won the Mackay challenge cup at Durham before being narrowly beaten by Edinburgh University in the open event the next day.[cxxiv]

The United Hospital's Sailing Club returned to Burnham-on-Crouch in 1947. At Burnham Week in September RFHSM's two Swordfish dinghies finished 2nd & 3rd in a handicap race. At Putney in 1952 'Otter' was cleaved in two by an Imperial College pair; it was salvaged and eventually returned to the water. In 1953 a new boat, 'Proteus',[62] proved fast against other Fireflies at the Welsh Harp.[cxxv]

The Tennis Club revived in 1952 and the first VI reached the final of the inter-hospital tournament. A men's section was formed in 1953. As there was no longer a court at Hunter Street courts were hired at Belsize Park for the 'home' matches held on Wednesday afternoons – plus extra courts so that those not in the team could also play. In 1956 enthusiasts practised at Lincoln's Inn Fields at 8 a.m., and many used the new courts at Myddleton House – but the Magazine ignored tennis for several years.[cxxvi]

A Squash Club formed in October 1945 found courts and a professional for coaching, but the Magazine's next mention of squash was in 1952 when Jean Watkins won the British junior women's open championship. In 1961 LSMW won the Inter-Hospital trophy and Margaret Evans won the Inter-University championship.[cxxvii]

Lacrosse, at which the Dean had excelled, was an enduring but minority sport at RFHSM; the club won the intercollegiate championship in 1950-1 & 1951-2.[cxxviii]

When a netball court existed in the Hunter Street quadrangle there were internal competitions at lunchtimes and the club fielded two VIIs.[63] After winning all its league matches in 1958-9 it was promoted to the University's first division. But

[61] Mary Thow (née Canvin – q.1957) still has her medal.

[62] Frances Gardner launched it with champagne provided by George Qvist.

[63] The court presumably went when – as a gift to the School from his daughters Diana and Hermione – a garden was created in the quadrangle in memory of Sir Alan Anderson. The quadrangle was relaid with York stone and had more flower beds and tubs. See CM 1957: 4 Feb

even though Beth Iddon, the University's captain, was a member the club struggled in 1960 and 1961; it was relegated and then disbanded owing to apathy. Re-formed in 1962 it entered the University's second division, but the Magazine carried no further reports about netball and the Prospectus for 1965-6 did not mention the club.[cxxix]

The fencing club revived in 1951 and employed Suzanne Ridley, the University women's coach. It won one of its three matches in 1952-3. Following victories against UCL and Bart's in 1955 fencing went unreported in the Magazine for some years.

Professor Killick, a keen alpine climber, was made president of the Mountaineering Club founded in 1956. Formed for rock climbers and fell walkers it organized day climbs at Harrison's Rocks in Sussex and weekend excursions to North Wales. It was affiliated to the University's club, which organized lectures and film shows about climbing along with walking and climbing meets.[cxxx]

In 1948 an RFHSM student, J. Dawes, captained the University Women's Cricket Club but the Magazine paid little attention to the School's team except to say that in 1952 it dominated its first two games, against KCL (won by 69 runs) and UCL (who were outplayed but drew). In 1953 one team member, Jill Prior, also played for Surrey.[cxxxi]

The sporting scene became more varied following the admission of men but several years elapsed before there were enough to field any sports teams; even then they competed only against the second, third or fourth teams of other medical schools.

The paucity of males at RFHSM in 1950-51 made recruiting fifteen players for a rugby team a tall order. Undaunted, Kevin Diamond and Dave Roberts persuaded fellow students (some never having played rugby), two physiology technicians, and a surgical registrar from Hampstead General, to play against St Thomas' 4th XV in January/February 1951. There was consternation among the opposition when it encountered an RFHSM XV containing seven women; after a commemorative photograph the women gave way to the other men.[64] RFHSM lost, and Diamond's nose was broken. The team played only three matches that season.

The following year (1951-2) RFHSM beat KCH 'Extra As', London Hospital 'Bs', a KCL team, the School of Pharmacy and St Mary's Hospital 'B', but lost to St George's and KCH 'As'.[cxxxii]

Of the sixteen fixtures in 1952-3 six were cancelled and nine lost, but the club beat the BBC's 1st XV. The following season RFHSM could not raise a team, nor

[64] One of those present claims the inclusion of women in the pre-match line-up was at a later match against Bart's.

could the School of Pharmacy; they amalgamated and played as 'Royal Free Hospital'. A full fixture list was arranged. The results against Betteshanger Colliery (near Eastbourne) illustrate the club's rapid improvement. It lost by 100-0 in 1952 and 50-20 in 1953; it drew in 1954, and won at home at Enfield in 1955. In 1956 the United Hospitals RFC agreed 'Royal Free Hospital' could enter its 'A' team competition.[65, cxxxiii]

In 1955-6 the club won 9 matches, drew 2 and lost 2. The following season it reached the semi-final of the United Hospitals 'A' team competition, losing 5-3 at home to St Thomas', a satisfactory achievement after only five years. In 1957-8 the club had 40 members and tried to field two teams, but raising a 2nd XV was difficult. In 1960-1 Richardson, the rheumatologist, followed Qvist as president.[cxxxiv]

A men's cricket team was started in 1951 but played few matches that summer – the one with St George's was tied. In 1952 it drew with KCL 3rd XI and Birkbeck College, but beat London Hospital's 2nd X1. Its early games were of necessity away games, but from 1955 there were excellent facilities at Myddleton House. For six years from September 1953 an annual entry of about twenty preclinical dental students boosted membership, but when that arrangement ended the Magazine stated pessimistically that '... the Cricket Club has apparently departed with the Dental Students'.[cxxxv]

The men slowly became involved in other sports. After a male IV finished last in a first heat at the United Hospitals' regatta in 1952 men's rowing was dormant for some years – and after making their debut in the University's Table Tennis league in 1953 the men finished bottom of the fourth division. They also started fencing, and in 1953 Tecwyn Jones defeated Henry Wyatt to win the School's challenge cup.[cxxxvi]

With the end of the war life the School's social life perked up. The Social Club had held occasional dances during the war, but held its first formal ball in the candle-lit common room on 9 February 1946; the £6 profit went to U.N.R.R.A. [66, cxxxvii]

Christmas at RFHSM ran its usual course with the 'Topicals' at RFH,[67] and the preclinical 'parties' at Hunter Street. The 'Topicals' were revues; they reflected the popular films, plays and television shows of the time, and caricatured hospital characters. The Magazine's 'critics' were sometimes harsh in their appraisals of the shows but two performers singled out for praise in 1955 were Arie Zuckerman, a future dean of RFHSM, and the surgeon George Qvist – the former for his role

65 Second teams from the main clubs played in the 'A' team competition.

66 United Nations Relief and Rehabilitation Administration

67 'The Topical' was dropped as the name for the Xmas show around 1964.(Mag 1965: Spring)

in 'La Ronde', a parody of the 1950 film about a romantic merry-go-round in Vienna, and Qvist as the 'victim' in 'This Is Your Life', the long-running TV show.[cxxxviii]

The highlight of Hunter Street Christmas parties was the 'Show' – a revue which, from 1956, was performed twice to avoid overcrowding. Traditionally all Hunter Street students took part, but by the mid-1950s the first and third year students left it to the 'second years' who faced no big exams. The star in 1956 was a UCH medical student, Jonathan Miller, whose wife Rachel was studying at RFHSM. He was soon famous (with Alan Bennett, Peter Cook and Dudley Moore) owing to the great success of their stage show 'Beyond the Fringe'.[cxxxix]

From 1946 to1951 the Dramatic Society thrived under the presidencies of Nancy Moller and John Napier. It then lapsed. The September 1956 Magazine noted the 'formation' of a Royal Free Drama Society,[68] triggered apparently by the discovery of the talented individuals who performed at that year's Midsummer Ball. Napier resumed as president, and at Toynbee Hall Theatre the 'newly formed' society produced Jacques Deval's 'Tovarich' in November 1956 and Arthur Miller's 'The Crucible' in March 1958. That Easter the company (twenty actors, and six in production) took 'The Crucible' to France – performing at Lille, Arras, Amiens and Douai.[69] With 'Harlequinade' the society won the Clee Cup at the ULU Drama Festival in November 1958, and the following year it performed T.S. Eliot's 'The Cocktail Party' at the School of Pharmacy.[cxl]

The Folk Dance Society re-formed in 1947 with Killick as President. The Jazz Club formed in 1955 practised at Lawn Road – and apparently rendered off-duty nurses sleepless in their rooms! For public performances it imported outsiders to fill instrumental gaps. The club survived for many years but received little or no mention in the Magazine after 1956.[cxli]

When it amended its constitution in 1945 the Contemporary Society, founded in Exeter 'to stimulate an interest in contemporary thought and activity', added 'with special reference to Literature and the Arts'. One wonders whether its membership included Elizabeth Kuanghu Tang, a fellow student who graduated MBBS with honours [70] in 1948. After the publication of 'A Many Spendoured Thing' in 1952 she became famous as the novelist Han Suyin. Her time at the Free is described in 'Birdless Summer', first published in 1968, the third volume of her five-volume autobiography which also covers the history of modern China.

---

[68] There had been a dramatic society at LSMW since 1896.

[69] The trip was under the auspices of the Central Bureau for Educational Visits and Exchanges. The French press was full of praise. The cast was lavishly entertained and appeared on French television.(AR 1957/8)

[70] Honours with distinctions in pathology and surgery.

In 1954 the society held informal play readings, listened to talks on a wide variety of topics, and organized theatre outings, visits to the Victoria and Albert Museum, the Tate Gallery, and Dulwich College picture gallery. A professor of architecture led an expedition covering the Albany, the Royal Academy's private rooms, and reconstruction work at St. James' Church, Piccadilly. The society seems to have foundered in 1961.[cxlii]

Other clubs and societies were even more transient. Many students expressed interest in a Film Society started in 1952-3, but the poor attendance at the inaugural showing led to its demise because of the financial risk involved. The Welsh Society founded in 1956-7 lasted only a year or two, despite its link with the Dean. The Natural History Society founded in January 1956 fared little better; its committee minutes petered out in January 1960.

The University Union's fortnightly post-war debates at the LSHTM were well attended. The motions generating the most interest in 1945-6 were 'That an open Palestine is the only solution for the Jewish Problem' – proposed by a Zionist and opposed by an Arab – and 'That this house views with dismay the prospect of five years under a Labour Government'. The result of the former motion was not recorded – the latter was lost by ten votes. There were abortive attempts to restart a Debating Society at RFHSM in 1956, and again in 1962.[cxliii]

The Medical Society founded in 1896 (see Chapter 6) was disrupted by the Second World War. Monthly meetings started up again in 1944. In 1948 the staffs's Clinical Society, which students sometimes attended, held at least three clinical meetings and heard talks on 'Sophia Jex-Blake' and 'The New Health Bill and its relation to general practice'.[cxliv]

After 1944 the Magazine ignored the Medical Society and it was not listed with other clubs and societies in the 1948-9 prospectus. Again the collective memory was short. In 1953 James Hope, a mature student, was concerned that RFH did not have a medical society and decided to 'start' one that would be open to all students and staff of RFHSM and of the RFH teaching group. There was a small annual subscription.[71] At its first meeting at Hunter Street on 27 October 1955 the president, Sir Daniel Davies, wished that none present would live to attend its final meeting! Sir Lionel Whitby, Regius Professor of Physic at Cambridge, then spoke on the origins of medical societies. In 1956 Sir Charles Dodds explained 'The Part of Chemistry in Therapeutics' and Sir Henry Cohen held forth on 'Brain, Machines and Mind'. The speaker, the secretary, and others dined with the president after meetings. That April two students gave presentations – Arie Zuckerman on skin grafting and the survival of homografts, and Nariman Bamji on the action of ephedrine.[cxlv]

---

[71] In 1960 students paid 2s.6d a year; staff paid 5s.

At its first AGM in November 1956, following heated debate about the Medical Society's constitution, members rejected incorporation within the Students' Union. They elected a new president, secretary and student vice-president.[72] The Hon. Treasurer, Philip Jackson, previously secretary of the Clinical Society, was the senior registrar who coordinated the large study on 'Royal Free Disease'.[cxlvi]

Although it held five to six meetings a year few were of interest to preclinicals. To mitigate this, and to adhere to its constitution, the society took corporate membership of the Faculty of the History of Medicine and Pharmacology at the Society of Apothecaries, thus providing access to many lectures. Student presentations continued until the society petered out in about 1974.[cxlvii]

RFHSM's original Medical Society, founded in 1896, was a forum where students presented interesting clinical cases, but the format changed with time. In 1959 some RFHSM students attended the Guy's Hospital's Pupils' Physical Society (founded in 1850) where patients were shown and discussed. In October four of them[73] founded a Royal Free Clinical Society. It met monthly on Saturday mornings; cases of interest were demonstrated and there were distinguished outside speakers. The Society seems to have folded in 1968-9.[74]

Having a rugby club certainly enhanced the School's social life. When Diamond heard students complain they could not afford RFH's annual ball he decided to hold a rugby club ball early in 1952. The BMA's Secretary offered the great hall of BMA House as a ballroom, and the library for refreshments – without charge. All teachers were invited. When Qvist bought his tickets he asked how the ball would be financed. Diamond said it would be self-financing; Qvist gave him a blank cheque to cover any 'shortfall'.

It was a great success. Tickets and bar receipts covered all expenses. The Rugby Club profited, but the Union Committee was unimpressed by its accounting procedures. The second ball, held at BMA House in February 1953, was equally successful and raised about £50. The Rugby Club Ball became a highlight in the School's social calendar.[cxlviii]

Formal balls were then relatively uncommon at RFHSM. The annual Royal Free Ball was put on hold during the war. The first one afterwards was at Grosvenor House, Park Lane, in November 1948 and the second at the Dorchester in January 1950. The third was held at Claridge's on 29 February 1952; before midnight, men

---

[72] Miss G Barry was president, Alain Brouet secretary, and Peter Hardwick student vice-president.

[73] Gerald Anderson, Rachel Miller, Gillian Freeman and Ann Jequier – helped by Sherlock and others from the Medical Unit. One early speaker was Sherlock's friend Jan Waldenstrom, who spoke on 'Macroglobulinaemia'. .

[74] Mag 1960: Sep; Clinical Society not in Prospectus for 1969-70

wore the hunted look befitting Leap Year's Day, while after midnight Welshmen brandishing leeks and daffodils celebrated St David's Day. John Napier, anatomy reader and member of the Magic Circle, provided the cabaret at the Park Lane Hotel in June 1955. 'Annual' balls continued for some years but by about 1960 were considered too expensive.[cxlix]

The first 'qualification ball' for final year students' was held in the Nurses' Home at GIR on 7 November 1958, with Peter Hardwick as honorary president. The 'Queens Head' (the local pub) ran the bar; Napier weaved his magic spell in the interval.[cl]

A more adventurous occasion was the Seven Bridges Ball in May 1959. The SS Abercorn left Westminster Pier at 11.30 p.m. and returned at 1.30 a.m. for consultants to disembark; those left on board admired Wapping, Millwall and Shoreditch at dawn before returning to the pier. Union funds benefited by £40.[cli]

Royal Free Dinners

The Old Students Association (OSA) lapsed during the war as did the annual RFH dinner. The OSA was revived in 1946, and dined at the Café Royal on 30 April 1947. It then lapsed again until 1949. Articles of Association were then drawn up,[75] although not actually approved until the June 1951 AGM. The November 1950 dinner was held at the Savoy as were those for the next three years. On the day of the dinners in 1952 and 1953 a clinical meeting was held for former students. However in December 1953 the OSA executive decided that the clinical meeting in 1954 should be followed by a cocktail party, not a dinner. RFH's Medical Committee and the Academic Staff Association (ASA) then agreed that a committee with both School (Ruth Bowden) and Hospital (George Qvist) representatives should organize future 'Royal Free' dinners.[clii]

The cocktail party in November 1954 was held at RFH, because RFHSM, as well as charging for food and wages, demanded an extra 33⅓% for use of its building; on learning of this Council remitted such charges for subsequent OSA functions at Hunter Street.[cli] The cocktail party proved popular and in June 1955 the OSA decided cocktail parties and dinners should alternate. In November 1955, 364 dined at the Royal College of Surgeons so a cocktail party was held in 1956. But there was no dinner in 1957 – ostensibly because of the large number of other hospital functions that year, but probably because no-one remembered to call a meeting of the ad hoc 'dinner committee'. A standing committee was created, with Gardner and Bowden as permanent OSA representatives, and a dinner for 325 was held at the College of Surgeons in November 1958.[cliv]

[75] Following prompting by Miss Moller in 1947.

RFH's consultants were probably more relaxed about the annual dinner v cocktail party debate than the School's staff ; for many years they had held their own annual dinner, usually in March, to which they invited retired consultants and heads of the School's non-clinical departments. In February 1957 the Medical Committee discussed the difficulty of continuing the OSA dinner as an 'RFH' function, and wondered if it might be combined with their annual staff dinner.[clv]

In 1959 Bowden proposed that the RFH dinner should be every third year. She and Gardner would arrange it but would not do it every other year owing to the work involved. The OSA agreed; as a result the next formal dinner was due in 1961 (at the Savoy). Some old students were unhappy about this and in November 1960 sixty-five held an 'unofficial' dinner at the Grosvenor Hotel.[clvi]

At the OSA's AGM in June 1962 its chairman (Miss Sandes) said that liaison with the hospital over RFH dinners remained a problem as Bowden and Gardner were no longer members of the OSA executive committee. A new standing committee was formed with members who also served on the executive committee. However, there was no mention of input from the Hospital.[clvii]

Switching from annual to biennial and then triennial dinners seems to have been a serious mistake. It did nothing to promote, and may have hindered, the development of a corporate spirit encompassing both School and Hospital. Subsequent triennial dinners were essentially School dinners attended by relatively few members of the RFH staff.

Remembering Former Students – lists, plaques and portraits

From 1883 the School's annual report included a list of all registered medical women – but from 1899 many more women qualified at other schools, so the list was restricted to those who trained at L(RFH)SMW. From 1914 an additional topographical list indicated where former students worked. From 1923 the Annual Report became known as the 'Yellow Book' owing to its new yellow cover; it was revised and reprinted every year. As it gave names and addresses for almost all registered old students it was a wonderful resource for the secretary of the OSA, for those wishing to contact old friends, and for the planning of class reunions.[76] In 1961 printing cost about £750. To save money it was decided that the 'complete' Yellow Book would appear every third year; the annual reports for the other two years contained additions and corrections.[clviii]

Plaques commemorating particularly distinguished former students were placed in the Memorial Porch on the north side of the Hunter Street quadrangle. (See Chapter 10) May Thorne's plaque was added in 1952. That October Council agreed

[76] And for historians!

to add one for Sir Alan Anderson; but he was not a former student and to avoid breaking with tradition and creating an undesirable precedent his memorial tablet was placed in the new Council room named after him.[clix]

In 1954 General Sir Andrew Thorne asked whether a plaque might be placed in the porch for his aunt, Isabel Thorne. Hers was the first name entered in the School's admissions book but the porch was meant to commemorate only qualified students. Quite properly an exception was made in her case as she had renounced her own chance of qualifying to serve as the School's Honorary Secretary from 1877 to 1907. It owed more to her than to any other former student except Jex-Blake.[77,clx]

Soon after Lloyd-Williams became dean someone realised that while there were portraits of its first three female deans (Garrett Anderson, Cock and Aldrich-Blake) the School had no portrait of Lady Barrett, who died in 1945, or of Bolton who had just retired.[78] Council revived the 'custom' of portraiture for deans in December 1946. Photographs of Barrett were available for copying and, although some wanted a female artist to paint her, Wolfgang Craig-Hainisch was chosen on Dorothy Hare's recommendation; he charged about 100 guineas. William Dring's portrait of Bolton was delivered in February 1948; the 250 guinea fee was covered by a subscription fund. Dame Louise McIlroy, who was not a dean, presented the School with her portrait by Miss Margaret Lindsey Williams in October 1947; it was hung in the students' common room.[clxi] (Fig 13.4)

In June 1948 Henderson suggested Lloyd-Williams's portrait should be commissioned before she retired. Early in 1951 Council members were dissatisfied with an unfinished version by the artist Percy Horton. He was paid 125 guineas (half the agreed fee) and kept the painting. A portrait by Anthony Devas, who painted Professor Hilda Lloyd for the Medical Women's Federation, was unveiled at a party in June 1952. (See Fig 13.5) He charged 250 guineas.[clxii]

Aldrich-Blake was commemorated not only by a portrait but by a monument in Tavistock Square Gardens. (See Chapter 9) In 1950 the St Pancras Town Planning and Amenities Committee agreed to retain it when the gardens became a public open space – providing RFHSM took responsibility for its care and maintenance. In March 1960 the Aldrich Blake Memorial Fund could not afford the cleaning so £15 was provided from the School's general funds. That December £165 was needed to re-cut the inscription, and to silicone-treat the stonework, but the annual income for upkeep was only £9. The Medical Women's Federation offered 15 guineas, but by May 1961 the cost of cleaning and covering the inscription with

[77] The memorial plaques are now in the Rowland Hill Street entrance of the new RFH building.

[78] Nor was there a formal portrait of either Anstie or Norton, the men who were the first two deans

Fig 13.4 Louise McIlroy (1878-1968)

Fig 13.5 Katherine Lloyd-Williams (1896-1973)

bronze plaques was £190; the capital of the memorial fund, approximately £160, was used for the restoration.[clxiii]

In 1951 Sir Frank Newnes suggested someone should write a history of the School. Two former students were approached as possible authors. One was Dorothea Fox, a distant cousin of the Garrett Andersons; she entered LSMW in 1919 & graduated MBBS in 1926. The other, Helen Ashton, entered in 1916, and qualified from the London Hospital in 1921. Ashton gave up medicine on marriage and became a successful novelist and screenwriter. Both declined the invitation, as did Woodham Smith, whose Florence Nightingale biography had just appeared. Constable & Co, chosen as publishers, approached E. Moberly Bell. Her book *Storming the Citadel:the Rise of the Woman Doctor* appeared in 1953. It is a good brief account of the opening of the medical profession to women, but hardly a comprehensive account, even of the early history of the School.[clxiv]

Before LSMW had a charter it was incorporated under the Companies Acts and so could not apply for a Grant of Arms at the Heralds' College.[79] The Students' Union contemplated applying for one in October 1917 but the cost, £76.10s, was deemed inappropriate in wartime. After receipt of the charter in 1938 Council wanted to apply but the Chairman and Hon. Treasurer, concerned about LSMW's financial situation, suggested raising the £81.10s. then needed by private subscription; the initiative was then stifled by the war.[clxv]

In February 1952 a coat of arms cost about £100, plus charges for a seal, a bookplate, a painting on vellum, and a design for headed notepaper. A legacy from Dr Josephine Brown covered the £100. Council's chairman formally presented the Earl Marshal with a memorial address reciting the School's constitution. Somerset Herald's design incorporated the Lion Rampant and the Rod of Aesculapius; the Rose and Open Book of the University of London appeared in the crest.[80] (Fig 13.6 Colour plate) Asked for a motto Council approved the Dean's suggestion of '*Virtute fideque*'. The arms were granted by Letter Patent dated 24 December 1954.[clxvi]

During the summer of 1958 the students wanted a mascot as well as a coat of arms. Van den Berghs Ltd, makers of Stork margarine, proffered a metal stork but some objected to the symbolic image of the stork as a bringer of babies. Instead, some clinical students made a handsome 224lb fibreglass lion. Several celebrities[81] declined invitations to 'inaugurate' the lion, eventually named 'Aloysius'. It went missing in 1960. Dental students accused of taking him denied the charge, but did kidnap him after he was found. When they tried to suspend him below a parapet at Hungerford Railway Bridge a rope snapped and Aloysius fell into one of the swiftest flowing parts of the Thames.[clxvii]

The Hospital's logo, introduced in 1961, originated in the badge – a Maltese Cross in red, white and blue – designed by its matron, Miss Rachel Cox Davies, for the League of RFH Nurses founded in 1910. The League's first President, HRH Princess Christian of Schleswig-Holstein, permitted the use of her crown as its centre. (Fig 13.7) In 1960, to celebrate its jubilee, the League offered the Board of Governors use of the badge. However, according to Elizabeth Hardman's brief note in the September 1962 Magazine/Journal (see below), it was found '*that the Official Seal of the hospital, the lion rampant, had been introduced when Queen Victoria ..., gave the Hospital its Royal Charter in 1837. It was, therefore, decided to incorporate the lion for the centerpiece of the badge, discontinuing the use of the crown*'. The Board of Governors accepted the badge in its new form in June 1961. (Fig 13.8) The League of Nurses also dropped Princess Christian's crown in favour of the lion. (Fig 13.9)

Unfortunately Hardman's story that the lion rampant was introduced as RFH's Official Seal in or soon after 1837 cannot be confirmed. There was a lion above the entrance to RFH's new building in Gray's Inn Road in 1843, but Queen Victoria did not give the Hospital a Royal Charter in 1837. She granted it a Royal Charter of Incorporation in 1892, and the Seal of RFH, which includes a lion, first appeared on the cover of its Annual Report that year. (Fig 13.10)

---

[79] This also meant it could not apply for a coat of arms.

[80] I am grateful to Bluemantle Pursuivant of the College of Heralds (Peter O'Donoghue) for the formal description accompanying the coat of arms in Fig 13.6

[81] Including Dirk Bogarde and David Attenborough

Fig 13.7 Princess Christian's crown

Fig 13.8 RFH Maltese Cross

Fig 13.9 League of Nurses Cross

The 'Magazine' or 'Journal'

The frequency of publication of the School's magazine was affected by the Second World War (but not the First). From 1895 to 1939 there were three issues a year, but only one in 1940 & 1941 and only two a year for the next seven years despite the end of the war in 1945. However, after a meeting of editors of UK medical school journals at BMA House in May 1949, RFHSM's two representatives argued for radical reform of the magazine, including publication at least quarterly. Despite concern that this would be impractical without more contributions it became a quarterly in 1950 and remained so until 1965.[clxviii]

Post-war the Magazine's format was like the original one, but for the January-March 1951 issue the name was changed, without editorial comment, from *Magazine of the Royal Free Hospital School of Medicine* to *The Royal Free Hospital Magazine*. Quarterly publication stretched the editorial staff. When Tecwyn Jones resigned after producing two issues, the December 1951 Magazine noted that there had been four editors in two years, and that producing a quarterly was particularly hard owing to a shortage of suitable articles. Editors resigned because they were wasting time cajoling them out of past contributors.

FOUNDED 1828, BY THE LATE DR. WILLIAM MARSDEN.

ROYAL FREE HOSPITAL,

GRAY'S INN ROAD, LONDON, W.C.

(Incorporated by Royal Charter 14th July, 1892).

THE

SIXTY-FIFTH ANNUAL REPORT

OF THE

COMMITTEE OF MANAGEMENT

TO THE

GOVERNORS OF THE HOSPITAL,

With Financial Statements, Medical Reports, etc.,

FOR THE

YEAR ENDING DECEMBER 31st, 1892.

Seal of the Royal Free Hospital.

PRINTED BY

WYMAN & SONS, LIMITED, GREAT QUEEN STREET, LONDON, W.C.;

AND REDHILL, SURREY.

1893.

Fig 13.10 RFH Annual Report 1892 (first with 'Lion' seal)

Early in 1958 the magazine faced a year-end deficit of £200. It switched to a cheaper printer and produced a larger magazine for half the cost. The first two issues that year carried the title *Royal Free Hospital Magazine* on the contents page, *and 'Royal Free Hospital School of Medicine'* on the grey and red cover. *Royal Free Hospital Journal* appeared on the white cover of the second two issues in 1958 – the Students' Union having changed the name to 'Journal', hoping to improve its image and to attract clinical/scientific articles from the staff. The September issue ran a competition to stimulate submission of articles from students; it also contained the first 'Medical Supplement' – with articles by Rodney Maingot and by R.T. Brain.[clxix]

In December 1960 the Editor pointed out that the Journal/Magazine was sent to students, former students & staff, and to many colleges and hospitals. Most readers wanted news of events at the Free, and of births, deaths, marriages and post-graduate examination results. Quarterly publication was a poor method for disseminating such information, particularly given the seven-week time lag before publication. Most letters to the Editor drew attention only to long term matters and any resulting correspondence was inevitably protracted. Delay was less important for letters giving news of former students and staff, but 'news' about current ones would inevitably be 'old' before appearing in print.

A development which probably influenced the future of the Magazine was the appearance in 1957-58 of *Free Comment,* a fortnightly news-sheet brought out by Roy Allen & Tom Lawson (son of the chemistry professor). The Magazine Committee welcomed it as it filled 'a long-existent gap in communications between the branches' and. 'will absorb all the time-labile news which we used to print'.[clxx]

One major problem with the Magazine/Journal over the years (at least for archivists and historians!)[82] is the cavalier way in which issue, volume and page numbers were handled. For example, the issue for March 1937 was Volume XXXII, No126; but because the format was changed the issue for July 1937 was Volume I, No 1. The December 1961 issue was Vol XXVII, No 73, while that for March 1962 was Vol XXIV, No 74. The September 1962 issue (Vol XXV, No 76) commented on this problem, recognizing its inconvenience for reference purposes. To bring things into line with pre-1960 editions, the June 1962 issue was changed to Vol XXV, No 75, not Vol XXIV as on the cover! For practical purposes the only sensible way of referencing an issue is to use the year(s) and month(s) or season(s) as there were some issues such as January-March 1945, or Winter/Spring as in 1966/7.

[82] Especially for historians.

The Dean Retires

In November 1960 Lloyd-Williams announced she would retire in September 1961. A subcommittee was set up to find her successor.[83] In February 1961 it reported she would serve another year, and recommended that Frances Gardner should then follow her as dean. Only Garrett Anderson's deanship lasted longer than Lloyd-Williams's term of seventeen years.[clxxi]

Lloyd-Williams was a remarkably successful and popular dean whose major contributions to the School and Hospital were the rebuilding of the School after the war, her support for the Myddleton House sports ground, the suggestion that the School and Hospital should move to the Hampstead site, and the introduction of clinical professorial units.

Her abilities were widely recognised outside the Free. She represented London University's general medical schools in the Senate from 1954 until 1962, and from 1956 to 1960 was the first woman dean of the faculty of medicine. In 1956 she was awarded a CBE and probably deserved better. For much of her deanship she spent one afternoon a week working at a children's clinic in Brixton – and considered it an afternoon's holiday.[clxxii]

To mark her retirement the Students' Union held a ball in June 1962 at Myddleton House; its house and lawns were bathed by floodlights, and smaller lights flickered throughout the gardens. In a giant marquee four hundred guests enjoyed a buffet supper, dancing and a cabaret. The festivities continued throughout the night, despite four degrees of frost at 2 a.m.! The Union President, Eleanor Durand, presented the Dean with a large wooden bench and other items for the garden at her family home – 'Brynele' in Bwlchllan, Nantcwnlle – where she spent much of her retirement. Council gave her £5,000 as a retirement present. [clxxiii]

After retiring she moved first to 37 Regents Park Road and, ten years or so later, to 8 Rosslyn Mansions, Goldhurst Terrace. Quickly returned to Council as a University Representative she served in that role until 1969. She was also a member of the General Medical Council, a Visitor for the King Edward VII Hospital Fund, and on the Board of the Royal Medical Benevolent Fund. She died on 10 January 1973 while on holiday in Portugal.[clxxi]

[83] Lascelles, Dr Aitken, Diana Anderson and Prescott.

CHAPTER 14

Dame Frances Gardner (1962–1975)

The Long Haul from Gray's Inn Road to Hampstead

Frances ('Fanny') Gardner (Fig 14.1 Colour plate) was the sixth former student of the School to become dean. She was born on 28 February 1913. Her father, Ernest, then sixty-seven, was the Conservative MP for the Wokingham district of Berkshire;[1] her mother was his second wife.[2] Ernest inherited 'Spencers', the Cookham estate of his uncle John Silvester when he was just eighteen. He proved an able farmer and prospered before entering local and then national politics. Knighted in 1925 he died two years later.[i]

Frances boarded at Headington School, Oxford, and then read mathematics and chemistry at Westfield College, Hampstead – the first London women's college to make residence a requirement. In 1935 she graduated B.Sc. and entered LSMW, qualifying MBBS with honours in 1940. She became a house surgeon at RFH, and was its RMO from August 1941. That year she won the Helen Prideaux Postgraduate scholarship but deferred taking it owing to the war. According to Edith Gilchrist, Gardner and her future husband, the young surgeon George Qvist, did much to maintain morale at RFH during the Blitz.[ii]

In 1943 Gardner proceeded MD and MRCP and became medical registrar at RFH. As the Prideaux Scholar she moved to Oxford, and later, as the Aldrich-Blake Travelling Scholar, to the Massachusetts General Hospital where she learned angiocardiography,[3] a technique she introduced to Britain.[iii] Appointed assistant physician at RFH in 1946,[4] and chief assistant at the National Heart Hospital in 1947, she also joined the staff of the Royal National Throat, Nose and Ear Hospital, the Hospital for Women in Soho, and the Mothers' Hospital, Clapton. She was elected FRCP in 1952.

---

1 He was Conservative MP for Wokingham 1901-18, and for Windsor from 1918 to 1922.

2 School holidays were spent in Nova Scotia with her mother's relatives. A fell walker and rock climber, Gardner loved outdoor pursuits and animals, particularly dogs and farm animals.

3 Gardner's studies on congenital heart disease using right heart catheterisation angiography were done in 1949 while RFHSM's Mabel Webb & A. M. Bird research scholar.

4 'Full' & 'Assistant' honorary staff would both have been equivalent to an NHS 'Consultant'. The word 'assistant' was rarely used subsequently. The old adjective 'Consulting' applied to senior clinicians on retirement from the active hospital staff.

In 1958 she married Qvist, after a long relationship that provoked much good-humoured gossip among RFH students and staff. George's jovial and gregarious nature contrasted with his wife's austere and abrupt public persona which often intimidated or antagonized. There was no doubt, however, of her devotion to School and Hospital; she and George were great supporters of student clubs and societies.

Sir Francis Lascelles was Chairman of Council when Gardner became Dean. He relinquished the post in December 1964. The Honorary Treasurer, Sir Donald Anderson, assumed both roles: Oliver Chesterton became vice-chairman.[5] When Lascelles left Council in 1966 his son Giles took his place.[iv] Anderson retired as Hon. Treasurer in 1968. When his successor, David Fleming, left Council soon afterwards Chesterton took over the post. David Webb replaced him as Hon. Treasurer in November 1973.[v]

Sir Donald died 20 March 1973, in the 99th year of his family's association with the School, having missed his last two Council meetings. Peter Samuel, Deputy Chairman of the Hill Samuel Group, was elected Chairman of Council in October, Chesterton having ruled himself out as a candidate. Samuel had been on Council from 1947-8, initially as a representative of RFH and later of the Members of the School. He chaired RFH's Board of Governors from 1957 until 1968. His successor, Dame Anne Bryans, had already replaced the Hon. Robin Borwick as RFH's second representative on Council. In 1966 Overton left Council after serving fourteen years, and Diana Anderson, Sir Donald's sister, resigned in 1974 after twenty-five years service; Robin Fox took her place.[vi]

With the NHS reorganisation of 1 April 1974 English Regional Hospital Boards were replaced by fourteen Regional Health Authorities (RHAs). They controlled 90 Area Health Authorities (AHAs), which in turn controlled 200 District Management Teams,[6] each with a District Medical Committee and a Health Care Planning Team, plus a Community Health Council to act as a public 'watchdog'. AHAs that included a teaching hospital were AHA(T)s, of which there were six in London. The reorganisation was subsequently deemed a disaster owing to the existence of the middle layer AHAs which were abolished in 1982.

With reorganisation undergraduate teaching hospitals lost their Boards of Governors and, consequently, some independence. Camden and Islington AHA(T)

---

[5] Chesterton joined Council in 1963. A relative of the author, G.K Chesterton, he ran the family estate agents. President of the RICS in 1968, he was knighted in 1969 and died 14 October 2007, age 94.

[6] Comprising an administrator, finance & nursing officers, community physician & two other doctors.

[7] The School charter stated Council should include "…not more than four representatives of the managing bodies of the hospitals associated with the medical school …'.

assumed RFH's relationship with RFHSM.[7] Its representatives on Council were Dame Anne Bryans, who had represented RFH, Mrs Lyndal Evans, Brian Salmon and William Wells. The last three replaced Patrick Salmon & Webb (both RFH) and Dr Haram from EGAH.[8] Wells, a protégé of Chesterton, was to play a major role at RFH and RFHSM.[vii] The Board of Governors had traditionally been responsible for the charitable donations and legacies which RFH had continued to accept after the founding the NHS in 1948. Following the NHS reorganisation in 1974 responsibility for charitable funds in an NHS hospital passed to a newly created body of 'Special Trustees'.

When Gardner became Dean Sir Harold Claughton and Professor Eric Warmington were the University's representatives on Council. Lloyd-Williams took Claughton's place in 1963. After she and Warmington left in 1969 Dr Brian Thwaites, Principal of Westfield College, became a University representative. He soon left to chair the management committee of the new Northwick Park Hospital, and was replaced by Dr Frank Hartley from the School of Pharmacy.[viii]

When nominations were called for University representatives in June 1974 Hartley was chosen again. The other nomination was deferred because Sherlock, who was away, favoured a medically qualified outsider. As RFHSM had access to 'medical' advice internally Hartley thought the University might consider expertise in other fields more useful. Despite this the physician George Smart[9] was nominated in June 1975, but did not join Council for several years.[ix]

Until 1960 the School had had only five paid Secretaries. This period of stability ended in 1965 when Stephanie Robinson resigned following her husband's appointment as Vice-Chancellor of the University of Hong Kong. In 1967 her replacement, K. V. Macquire,[10] was appointed Registrar to the University College of Rhodesia. His successor, Colin Moore, stayed six years.[11] In October 1973 Robinson, back from Hong Kong, returned to RFHSM. That month Pauline McCormick retired; she had been assistant secretary from February 1949 and, from 1954, the School's first Registrar.[12] Her replacement as Registrar was Mary Ellis, assistant registrar since 1970. She also showed staying power, retiring in 1996.[x]

---

[8] Haram was re-elected to Council by Members of the School. EGAH, part of RFH's Teaching Group from 1948, was transferred in 1962 to the NWMRHB but remained in the Teaching Group for another twelve years.

[9] George Smart, former Dean of Newcastle's Medical School and Director of the BPMF.

[10] Previously Permanent Secretary to Zambia's Ministry of Land & Works.

[11] Moore died in 1983 after a prolonged illness.

[12] Jukes was Registrar from 1918 to 1923, when she moved to UCL. The Registrar post then lapsed until 1954.

Gardner's vice deans – each holding the post for two years, with preclinical and clinical teachers alternating – were, in order, Ruth Bowden, Jocelyn Moore, Margaret Hughes, Nigel Compston, Eleanor Zaimis and finally Euan Campbell who held the post for just over three years.

When Gardner took office the School's annual showpieces were still the inaugural address – held, in the autumn since 1877, and the June prize-giving dating from 1878.

The second Lord Moynihan, chairman of the NWMRHB and son of the famous surgeon, gave the 1962 address. He was followed by Sir Colin Anderson (1963), Sir John Charles, the former Chief Medical Officer (1964), the Nobel Laureate Dorothy Hodgkin (1965), and Sir Theodore Fox, editor of *The Lancet* (1966). Illness prevented Sir John McMichael from giving the inaugural address in 1967; Lady McMichael read his address for him and also presented the prizes.

In 1968 the Education Committee questioned the cost (about £300) of the combined inaugural address & prize giving.[13] It was replaced by a freshman's reception at which the Dean welcomed new students in the junior common room; the only other invitees were academic staff and the Union Committee. Attendance of parents of new students and prize-winners was precluded by lack of space – so prizes were sent by post. Lloyd-Williams regretted the demise of the ceremony; she was told the decision would be reconsidered after a year.[14] A prize-giving ceremony was reintroduced in 1979 (see Chapter 15).[xi]

The New Royal Free Hospital and School

Negotiations about the Hampstead project occupied much of Gardner's time as Dean. Progress was painfully slow. The UGC did not approve plans for the School's component until June 1963 and it was October before it agreed to provide £1,155,000 towards the cost. Planning for the Hospital was more advanced, although in June 1964 news of plans for a six-lane highway passing through the Lawn Road site and over part of Hampstead Heath caused alarm; fortunately that scheme was abandoned. Detailed planning then began on the clinical departments, including the professorial units.[xii]

At the UGC's request RFHSM agreed, in return for extra staff and teaching space, to increase the student intake to the second year by 10% in 1962 (see Chapter 13) and by a further 15% in 1965. This necessitated revision of the Hampstead plans. When approved in March 1965 they included a CCTV studio and

---

[13] There had been a discussion at Council in December 1967 about the cost of providing gowns for the Union officers and the students acting as ushers. For formal occasions most students paid for the hire of gowns themselves.

[14] There is no evidence that the matter was reconsidered.

examination hall, plus an academic department of psychiatry, as the Government decided to include 60 psychiatric beds in the new RFH.[xiii]

The increased student numbers meant that 81 joined the 2nd MB course in October 1963 and 92 in 1965. Only about one in fifteen of applicants to RFHSM were accepted. The enormous numerical discrepancy between applications and acceptances occurred partly because candidates applied to many medical schools hoping for acceptance at one. This changed from 1964 when the UCCA (Universities Central Council on Admissions) scheme was introduced. It was a collaborative attempt to simplify application to universities by allowing applications to only six institutions (later five). In February 1965 London's medical schools were the only relevant institutions not involved with it; in May 1961 their deans had unanimously opposed participation. However, they eventually bowed to pressure from provincial medical schools, but were allowed to be considered as separate units. UCCA handled all applications from 1967.[xiv]

When UGC members visited in May 1965 they commented that students and staff seemed poorly informed about progress at Hampstead and queried why building was in two stages. The Dean said a cheaper, quicker one-stage operation had been rejected because no hospital could be found to provide temporary accommodation while Lawn Road was completely closed for demolition. She ignored the fact that RFH had accepted an offer of 200 beds at the Eastern Hospital, Homerton in 1960, before choosing to remain at Lawn Road during rebuilding.[xv]

It was anticipated that bed numbers might be inadequate for teaching even when the new RFH was operational so RFHSM welcomed NWMRHB's suggestion in October 1965 that New End and Coppetts Wood hospitals might join the Teaching Group. They did so formally in April 1968. The Royal Northern Hospital was to have the 'closest possible association' with the group.[15,xvi] When the NHS was reorganised in 1974 New End came under the Camden & Islington AHA (T), part of the North East Thames RHA, and was run by the North Camden Health District Management Team responsible for RFH.

New End's origins lay in the Hampstead Union workhouse – founded in 1800 and rebuilt in 1847. A four-storey infirmary block was erected in 1869, and a distinctive circular ward block was added in 1883; another four-storey infirmary block was built in 1896. With improved facilities, including X-ray equipment and an operating theatre, the institution served as a military hospital during the First World War. It was returned to the Hampstead Guardians in 1922; the building was then modernised and renamed 'New End Hospital'.

[15] According to the AR for 1969-70 the only obvious educational link with the Royal Northern was that students could attend its casualty department.

In 1930 it became an LCC general hospital with 260 beds – including 26 for children – plus a 19 bedded maternity department and out-patient and casualty departments. Its thyroid clinic, started in 1931, was renowned for its treatment of toxic goitre and myasthenia gravis. Sir Geoffrey Keynes performed the UK's first thymectomy there in 1942. When the NHS started up in 1948 New End had come under the aegis of the North East Metropolitan Regional Hospital Board (NEMRHB) and the Archway Group Hospital Management Committee. A comprehensive endocrine clinic was created there in 1955. Its head was Raymond Greene, a distinguished physician and a famous Everest mountaineer.[16]

New End (Fig 14.2) joined the RFHSM Teaching Group in the expectation that

Fig 14.2 New End Hospital in 1930s

its acute services would transfer to the new RFH and that New End itself would become a geriatric hospital. With this in mind Michael Green was appointed Physician in Geriatric Medicine at RFH in 1971. Some general physicians saw no need for the post, considering themselves quite capable of caring for the elderly – even though one avoided his aged inpatients by placing them at the far end of his Lawn Road wards; during rounds he saw younger patients on one side of the ward, then crossed over to see the younger ones on the other side.[xvii]

[16] Two of his brothers were Graham Greene, the author, and Hugh Carlton Greene, a Director-General of the BBC. The third was a Japanese spy!

Beds were made available to Green at St Pancras Hospital and St John & St Elizabeth's Hospital prior to the opening of the new geriatric unit in New End in 1972. He had some beds at the new RFH when it became fully operational, and many more subsequently at New End. Green was a young, enthusiastic and pro-active geriatrician; his activities, both in the wards and in the community, and the effort he put into teaching students, were welcomed by many if not all of his colleagues.

In May 1966 a Government White Paper – 'Hospital Capital Building Programme' – announced that building at Hampstead would start with a residential block and be uninterrupted until completion. The UGC approved revised plans for the School's component in October and set an expenditure limit of £1,230,000.[xviii]

Soon after becoming dean Gardner appropriated as her office the Garden Room occupied by the Students' Union, which moved to the basement cloakroom. The students also lost their Henderson wing common room after the Wellcome Trust agreed in 1965 to fund an extension to the pharmacology department.[17] The ground floor junior common room was used for 2nd MB examinations. As it was now their only common room the Students' Union asked in October 1965 if the March 1966 exam could be held elsewhere; the School of Pharmacy obliged.[xix]

Building of new student accommodation on the north side of the quadrangle, between the junior common room and the Dean's new office, was delayed by the 1965 moratorium on construction work at universities. It was finished by February 1967, the existing colonnade being moved out into the quadrangle to preserve architectural continuity. (Fig 14.3) This extension housed the School's first permanent bar.[18] Within the quadrangle itself, despite objections from the senior common room, a hut was erected as a planning office for the Hampstead project.[xx]

In 1969 the students requested a cigarette machine in their Hunter Street common room – with profits to be split between the Students' Union and the tobacconist. As the Ministry of Health discouraged smoking by medical students the Dean, herself a heavy smoker, was wary. Even so Council approved the idea, and suggested the Ministry's anti-smoking poster be placed near the machine! '*Free Comment*' claimed most students opposed the installation, but an opinion poll suggested the opposite. The Medical Committee was not amused that 'in spite of the knowledge that medical opinion was opposed the cigarette machines had been installed'.[xxi]

Hospital students also lost space. In 1961 the X-ray department expropriated the whole of the students' quarters in the old Helena building, except for the

17 This extension opened in April 1967.

18 The Mecredy fund paid for a cashbox, cash registers and dartboard for the bar (CM 1967: 8 Feb)

Fig 14.3 Students' Bar from 1967

cloakrooms. To provide a new common room a hut was erected on top of the Marlborough Wing; (Fig 14.4) it was accessible through the first-floor corridor of the wing, or by an outside entrance opposite the Nurses Home. A second hut was placed next to it as a small lecture theatre, and the existing tutorial room became a quiet room. It is unclear how much these huts were used; they were certainly unpopular.[xxii]

In a witty article in the December 1962 Magazine a student, Mary McCarthy, wrote as if she was a journalist investigating medical student facilities. Commending the directions given her she admitted responsibility for her inordinate delay in reaching the quaint hut, atop a four-storey building and subjected to gale force winds and the proximity of aeroplanes. Those swotting there for 'Finals' used oxygen and grumbled at having to descend to sea level before climbing again to the main lecture theatre.

The Magazine for March 1963 commented more seriously on the 'notorious' common room hut, and on the 'cloakroom' four floors below where students jostled for lockers outside the female toilet while waiting to enter the canteen. The last, while a popular place for coffee, was overcrowded when students, ancillary staff, porters, ambulance men, clerical staff and visitors all arrived for lunch.

The Union Committee suggested improvements to the students' quarters in May 1964; these also were delayed by the building moratorium in force. Eventually a prefabricated common room was placed over the roadway passing from the entrance to the casualty department to the hospital's rear entrance in Cubitt Street.[xxiii]

Library facilities for students and staff at the hospitals comprising the RFH teaching group were poor and offered little encouragement for students to seek information about their patients' problems. GIR and Lawn Road had small collections of student textbooks but many went missing and some were still chained to prevent removal.[19, xxiv]

[19] This problem did not go away. During the three months before the Library Committee met in November 1971 fourteen books disappeared from the GIR clinical students' library.

Fig 14.4 Students' Common Room on Marlborough Wing roof

When in 1966 the architects vacated the upper floor of the planning hut in GIR's front square the decision was made to use it as a medical library, thus freeing rooms in the medical staff corridor for conversion into resident staff accommodation. That corridor, giving access to the outpatient block from the southeast corner of the front quadrangle, was created in the ruins of the Levy Wing segment struck by the V1 in 1944.[xxv]

In November the Library Committee asked if students could also use the library when it was accommodated in the planning hut. That request was rejected. Instead the students' library moved to the Marlborough roof hut which had served as the students' quarters. Staffed from 9:30 a.m. to 5 p.m. during weekdays it remained open for lending and reference in the evening. Students proved reluctant to cover for the staff during the lunch hour.[xxvi]

Fig 14.5 RFH Library at Gray's Inn Road

The Hospital library moved to the planning hut in the summer of 1967 (Fig 14.5), and in October the Medical Library subcommittee decided, belatedly, that students could use it for reference if space was available. The students' own library appears to have been well used despite its inconvenient location.[xxvii]

In December 1969 the School and Hospital library committees agreed that from 1972 RFHSM would assume overall responsibility for a joint library at Hampstead; it was to open soon after Stage I was completed. Initially there were two library committees – one representing preclinical interests, the other clinical interests; costs were to be shared.[xxviii]

Things were moving in Hampstead. In March 1968 Peter Samuel conducted the 'topping off' ceremony for the new residential block, which included a renal unit on the ground floor. It was occupied by September. Messrs Taylor Woodrow, who won the contract for the first two stages of the main building, started work on Stage I after Dame Anne Bryans performed the 'turf-cutting' ceremony on 28 May.[xxix]

The Todd Report

These developments were welcomed. However, frustration followed with the publication in April 1968 of the report of the Royal Commission on Medical Education chaired by Lord Todd. 'Todd' recommended, *inter alia*, the reorganizing of London's medical schools into six groups constituting the medical faculties of large multi-faculty schools, each with a preclinical intake of 200. RFHSM was to link with UCHMS and merge eventually with UCL. If the medical school, hospital and multi-faculty institution could not co-exist on one site 'Todd' wanted preclinical departments near science departments, not teaching hospitals, a viewpoint diametrically opposed to that of the Goodenough Report in 1944.[xxx]

RFHSM now had to reconsider its plans for a preclinical school at Hampstead. Most preclinical teachers wanted to move there but the biochemists, the only major group without a medically qualified member, were keen to join a new, larger school near UCL.

The Dean, convinced of the advantages of having the preclinical departments at Hampstead, suggested linking with her alma mater, Westfield College, a multi-faculty institution in Hampstead. If the new Royal Free complex could be adapted to take 200 students a year such an arrangement would comply with the letter of 'Todd', if not its spirit. The Dean, with others, met Westfield staff in July 1968 – but while its Principal supported the association his colleagues foresaw little benefit for Westfield.[xxxi]

RFHSM committees wrestled with 'Todd' that summer. The UGC wanted to delay further planning for Hampstead, pending discussions with the University about 'Todd'; but the School pointed out that Stage I was scheduled for completion in August 1972 and that planning needed to resume if building of the preclinical departments was to run concurrently with Stage II.

In September the University's Todd Report Steering Committee suggested that the preclinical school should be built at Hampstead – even if its staff would eventually move to Gower Street – provided it took only 100 students a year and was convertible into para-clinical departments. On 25 November the UGC's chairman, Wolfenden, told the Principal the preclinical departments would not be built, but he did tell RFHSM to prepare plans for para-clinical departments – as advocated by 'Todd' (para 430) – to provide basic science facilities for clinical departments. At Council on 11 December Dr Haram asked the prophetic question: if the para-clinical departments were similar in size to the planned preclinical school could they be converted into preclinical departments if the Gower Street building did not materialise? [xxxii]

In May 1969 the UGC's new chairman, Kenneth Berrill, stood firm about preclinical departments.[20] The School submitted the requested plans for para-clinical departments which, like those for a preclinical school, included animal house facilities and staff-student amenities, along with schedules for new departments of paediatrics, community medicine and haemostasis.[xxxiii]

[20] Wolfenden had left to become Director of the British Musuem.

RFHSM, forced to accept the UGC's decision as final, agreed to amalgamate with UCL and UCHMS – provided there would be a new preclinical building in Gower Street and a para-clinical building at Hampstead. Without the latter curricular changes would have to be deferred, and demarcation between pre-clinical and clinical training, strongly criticised by 'Goodenough', would become absolute.[xxxiv]

UCL welcomed the idea of a large preclinical school in Gower Street; but there was no obvious site for it or any assurance of planning permission and Government finance. If the project foundered RFHSM's preclinical departments faced academic isolation. Three joint sub-committees were set up with UCL and UCHMS in December 1968 – to cover academic aspects of integration; to plan the new building in Gower Street; and to ensure that RFH and UCH could arrange a comprehensive clinical education for the large number of students. RFHSM also sent representatives to a joint curriculum committee.[xxxv]

In July 1969 the UGC agreed to provide a Clinical Sciences Building (CSB) of 70,000 sq ft. at Hampstead.[21] By this time part of the old Lawn Road hospital had been demolished, 150,000 tons of earth had been removed and 24,000 tons of concrete poured. Work had reached the ceiling of floor C and the new building (situated on a steep slope) was to emerge above ground in September. However, Stage 1, due for completion in August 1972, was running about six weeks late.[xxxvi]

In August the UGC and the University announced, jointly, that linking RFHSM with UCL and UCHMS *'now agreed on, will be put in hand as a matter of priority and every effort made to secure the necessary site close to University College'*. The RFHSM/UCHMS/UCL Joint Committee told the Vice-Chancellor that 'agreed on' might be an overstatement as several issues needed resolution, including the proportion of women students to be admitted. Furthermore there was concern about planning permission, given the opposition of societies wishing to preserve Georgian Bloomsbury.[xxxvii]

No such difficulties affected plans for the School building at Hampstead. In November 1969 it was announced, somewhat surprisingly, that the work would be under the control of the Department of Health, not the UGC, and that RFH, not the School, would run the project and employ the architects.[xxxviii]

By July 1970 the new hospital's foundations were complete; the central cruciform shape had reached its sixth floor and the surrounding site had been levelled and excavated to allow work on the two lower sections of Stage I. (Fig 14.6) All beds were expected to be operational by mid-1973, by which time it was hoped the clinical academic departments in Stage I,[22] most of the new library, and part of the joint interdepartmental workshop would be fully commissioned.[xxxix]

---

[21] The original submission was for 88,000 sq. ft.

[22] Medicine, Surgery, O & G, and Psychiatry, and parts of Medical Physics and Pathology.

Fig 14.6 The new RFH in mid-1970

In 1966 the School wished to purchase houses around Hampstead for student residences but the University said funds would be unavailable for several years. Planning permission was granted for 424 residential places in the new RFH complex, including a students' hostel, but in 1972 the Department of Health recommended that hospitals should provide married quarters for some junior medical staff. RFH therefore needed more space and plans for the hostel were dropped. Lodgings were still required nearby – not only for students but for visiting postgraduates and lecturers on short stays.[xl]

Residential accommodation was also needed near GIR and Hunter Street. The School contemplated acquiring 2 Myddleton Square from the New River Company in October 1967. The high cost of repairs, alterations and maintenance appeared to exclude letting at acceptable rents, but it was deemed feasible if students redecorated it and cleaned their own rooms. The School took a 21 year lease and the University paid for repairs and alterations. The house provided eleven single rooms and four double rooms with a large well-equipped kitchen-dining room for general use.[xli]

It was originally intended for clinical students, who would be resident throughout the year, but they showed little interest. Pre-clinicals were happy there during term-time, but their absence during vacations created financial problems. Initially reserved for men, it accepted women from July 1972.[xlii]

There was little progress with the proposed new preclinical block in Gower Street. In May 1972 the UGC suggested building within the UCL rectangle in order to avoid demolishing a Georgian terrace. As a quid pro quo it offered to rebuild old and inconvenient parts of UCL. The college agreed and the RFHSM/UCHMS/UCL building sub-committee (established in 1968/9 but hitherto not convened) met to plan a building of about 26,000 square metres to stand behind the existing biological sciences block overlooking Gower Street. However the new block could not be ready before the 1977-82 quinquennium. [xliii]

In December 1972 Annan claimed that building within its rectangle entailed much sacrifice by UCL and suggested that RFHSM, as a beneficiary, should donate the proceeds of the sale of Hunter Street as a 'dowry'. Sir Donald Anderson pointed out that private subscriptions intended to further medical education had paid for much of Hunter Street, and that money thus raised had to be devoted to that aim – i.e. to benefit RFHSM's staff and students, whether at UCL or in Hampstead – not to pay for a building which should be financed from public funds.[xliv]

When Dame Anne Bryans 'topped-out' the new RFH in June 1971 the contract was running a year late, so completion of Stage II and the CSB was unlikely before 1975-76. The School's planners toiled that summer preparing a detailed costing of the CSB. The resulting figure was £1million more than the UGC's notional limit! A bargain was struck. The UGC increased its limit, acknowledging site problems and special requirements, and the School reduced its estimates by £500,000.[xlv]

Stage 1, due for completion in August 1972, was to be taken over in phases so that key service departments were working before patients arrived. As the necessary equipment was not bought until July 1973 commissioning was further delayed and patients did not arrive until October 1974, a year later than intended. Some departments moved in earlier and the partial transfer of medical physics freed space at Hunter Street for interdepartmental use during preparation of the new curriculum (see later). Work on the rest of the Hampstead complex was to start after demolition of the remaining parts of the old Lawn Road hospital.[xlvi]

During 1974-5 the new hospital (now known as 'Pond Street') became fully operational and all clinical departments moved in. Those in sole possession of their permanent homes enjoyed spacious new quarters, but some occupied shared or makeshift accommodation until building was completed. The Academic Department of Surgery, nominally on the 9th floor but actually the twelfth of fifteen floors, provided temporary offices for the Dean, the Assistant Registrar and secretaries; and two teaching rooms served as students' common rooms.[xlvii]

To mark the transfer of the Hospital's work to Hampstead an Act of Thanksgiving – 'Farewell to Gray's Inn Road' – was held in the front square of the old hospital on the afternoon of Sunday 22 June 1975. Anglican, Roman Catholic, Free Church and Jewish chaplains took part. The music was provided by the Regent Hall Band of the Salvation Army, which for many years had played in the Hospital's front square on Christmas Eve.

Early in 1974 it was feared that Stages II & III of the new building at Hampstead would be delayed by the financial crisis and the resulting moratorium on new building. This would have caused problems because to implement the new curriculum as planned certain facilities were needed in the CSB, and students were due to begin the relevant part of the course in October 1976. Fortunately the DHSS and UGC agreed in December that building could go ahead. Even so RFHSM did not anticipate occupying the CSB until October 1978.[xlviii]

The moratorium did affect the new Gower Street pre-clinical school as its earliest completion date was now 1985. The prospect of teaching an integrated curriculum from an isolated pre-clinical school in Hunter Street for another ten years, and the expected completion of the CSB within three years, led RFHSM's Education Committee to appoint a Working Party in 1975 – *'To review…future use of the teaching rooms, laboratories and other facilities in the Clinical Sciences Building and Stages I and II of the hospital for teaching the integrated New Curriculum, and…report [on the] feasibility of transferring the Pre-clinical School to Hampstead.'*[23, xlix]

It became clear that it could not be transferred simply by reallocating space in the CSB; some re-designing was essential, particularly if anatomy was to have a dissecting room. Furthermore, extra space was needed for preclinical students; they had not been catered for in plans for the CSB as they were supposed to go to the new preclinical building at UCL. Council diplomatically stressed that the idea of moving the preclinical departments to Hampstead was not a rejection of 'Todd', but a way of ameliorating RFHSM's problems until the Gower Street buildings were completed. This remained the situation until the end of Gardner's deanship.[l]

Financial Woes

Britain struggled economically throughout Gardner's time as Dean. A balance of payments problem undermined confidence in the pound, and it remained under pressure despite devaluation by Wilson's Labour government in November 1967. Allowed to float by Heath's Conservatives in 1972 its value fell by about 30 per cent over three years, a period encompassing an oil crisis and a stock market crash. The inflation rate, below 5% p.a. until the late 1960s, peaked around 24% in 1975.

---

[23] The working party was also to assess the future use of and need for the Hunter Street building, and to compare the facilities at Gower Street UCRF & Hampstead

RFHSM's annual grant for the 1962-1967 quinquennium was clearly inadequate.[24] Supplementary grants covered rising costs and allowed some new developments during its first three years – but not in the last two. In 1968 all departments took a 4% cut in overall expenditure to save the £50,000 needed to establish the planned professorial units. Over the next three years supplementary grants again covered general price increases, and a surplus of £18,000 in 1970-1 allowed new staff to be employed in psychiatry, pathology and pharmacology. The following year a £59,000 supplement allowed restoration of a histopathology lectureship, paid for building at Hunter Street, and provided for some three-year research fellowships and for the attendance of preclinical staff at conferences. However the grants did not cover nationally negotiated salary increases, for which no money was earmarked. The future seemed bleak. As well as providing basic necessities,[25] RFHSM needed to rectify academic deficiencies, support developments at Hampstead, and pay its staff, some of whom were due for promotion.[li]

There were serious financial problems in 1973-4, with retrenchment in all departments and no new developments except those involving both School and Hospital at Hampstead. Only essential posts could be filled following resignations and retirements. Supplementary grants, normally triggered by rises in the 'Tress-Brown' index,[26] were cut for 1974-5 but the stringent measures taken, and an unexpectedly large recurrent grant for 1975-76, allowed reinstatement of 'frozen' academic posts; but there were unavoidable pay rises, cost inflation, and increased maintenance costs at Hunter Street so frugal housekeeping had to continue.[lii]

In 1968 the UGC introduced a new system for awarding scientific equipment grants. It encouraged saving until cash was needed to equip new buildings. RFHSM therefore placed 10% of its £237,500 equipment grant for 1967-72 into a general reserve fund, and the rest into departmental reserves. This proved fortunate as the UGC had not envisaged such grants for Hampstead – and after the Public Accounts Committee complained that universities had hoarded too much of the equipment allocation the policy was changed. The School's accumulated reserves were still inadequate, but the University provided £150,000 towards equipping academic clinical departments in Stage 1 of the new building.[liii]

The pay of the teaching and technical staff of medical schools was determined by the Departments of Health and Education, in collaboration with the UGC. NHS clinicians were treated differently. To deal with doctors' widespread dissatisfaction

[24] The 1967-72 block grant ranged from £439,000 a year (1967-8) to ££468,000 (1971-2)

[25] General expenditure consumed about £714,000 in 1970-1.

with their remuneration a Royal Commission on Doctors' and Dentists' Pay was set up in 1958. Its 1960 report concluded doctors were paid too little; it recommended a 22% increase above the 1955/6 pay level and, in addition, a permanent impartial Review Body, chaired initially by Lord Kindersley, to advise on doctors' pay. The award did not resolve all the problems of general practice. In 1965 thousands of GPs threatened to leave the NHS and so the 1966 Review Body, which used a new 'Charter for the Family Doctor Service' to cost GP services,[27] suggested increasing doctors' salaries by up to 30%, with GPs as the main beneficiaries. The Government agreed the award, but angered doctors as it was phased in over two years and coincided with the onset of a six month pay freeze.[liv]

Not surprisingly these (and later) pay increases for clinicians hindered the recruitment of medically qualified individuals as pre-clinical teachers. The BMA, with direct access to the UGC, could influence the salaries of clinical academics, but not those of medically qualified preclinical teachers. The latter benefited from the second report of the National Board for Prices and Incomes on salaries of university teachers (1970) – but the report rejected reduction of the salary differential between medically qualified pre-clinical teachers and their clinical academic counterparts.[lv]

In 1966 all but two of the 23 members of the anatomy department at RFHSM were medically qualified. So too were the four most senior physiologists and the head of the pharmacology department; only biochemistry lacked medically qualified staff. Twenty years later two full time anatomy teachers were medically qualified, one of eight physiologists, and no preclinical pharmacologist. The situation was similar at other schools, and clinical teachers thought it had a deleterious effect on students' knowledge and understanding of preclinical subjects.

Clinical academics themselves suffered financially by comparison with their NHS counterparts. From 1960 the BMA and the UGC met to discuss clinical teachers' pay in relation to that of NHS hospital doctors; but in 1966 the Government decided, in view of the White Paper 'Prices and Incomes Standstill: Period of Severe Restraint', that clinical academics would not get the increase awarded to their NHS colleagues from 1 January 1967. Furthermore future increases would have to be justified under the then current incomes policy criteria and be dependent on the decision of the Prices and Incomes Board. Consequently clinical academics throughout Britain, concerned that the BMA would not serve

[26] The Tress-Brown index was used then to monitor the 'cost of living' at universities.

[27] From 1948 the GPs' capitation fees had to cover running costs. Doctors with better staff, and thus higher costs, became disgruntled. The Family Doctor Charter allowed GPs to claim 70% of staff costs & 100% for premises; this encouraged improvement of premises, employment of secretaries & delegation of work to practice nurses.

their best interests, voted in November 1966 to form an Association of University Clinical Academic staff (AUCAS). Ian Bouchier, then a senior lecturer in medicine at RFH, was its first secretary.

The 1968 Prices and Incomes Board report, like 'Todd', considered senior clinical academics should not be worse off than their peers in the NHS. However, the non-professorial academics with honorary consultant contracts were upset, because the UGC proposed a most inequitable system for assimilating them on to the NHS scales for consultants – and the Government was reluctant to reconsider it.[lvi]

Like other London medical schools RFHSM had to embrace GMC recommendations about the curriculum and conform to University regulations. For decades the preclinical course lasted five-terms. Those passing 2nd MB in April started clinical studies; the failures resat in June and, if successful, started clinical studies in October with those students, initially a year above them, who had taken a four-term intercalated B.Sc. (and occasionally with Oxbridge students).

From early 1965 the School, for three reasons, paid more attention to its curriculum. Firstly, the GMC was preparing *Recommendations as to Basic Medical Education, 1967* and invited schools to suggest curricular changes; secondly, the Faculty of Medicine wanted comments on its 'Outline Suggestions for Revised Regulations for the MBBS Degrees'; and, thirdly, RFHSM had to give evidence to the Todd Commission.[28] Not surprisingly the 1965-6 annual report mentioned a growing appreciation of the need for flexibility; co-operation between disciplines; joint appointments between pre-clinical departments; and visits of preclinical students to hospital wards to help them appreciate the relevance of their studies.[lvii]

In replying to the GMC RFHSM suggested replacing the pre-medical and preclinical courses by a three-year course for a B.Med.Sci., followed by two clinical years leading to the MBBS. Students who completed the preclinical course, but not clinical training, would then have a degree to show for their efforts. The GMC's 1967 *Recommendations*...did not endorse this idea but 'Todd' did in 1968. [29, lviii]

The GMC divided medical education into four periods – 'Pre-medical'; 'Basic'; 'Vocational Training' (for a particular career path); and 'Continuing Education'. 'Basic' medical education was to cover the medical sciences, promote students' understanding of scientific method and of man in sickness and in health, and

[28] Todd was considering the position of women in medicine so the BMA asked about the fate of RFHSM's former students. One helped the Dean respond to the request. 'The careers of women graduates from the Royal Free Hospital School of Medicine, London' by C.A. Flynn, & F. Gardner was published in Brit J Med Education, 4: 28-42: 1969.

[29] See 'Todd Report', paras 207, 223 & 224.

acquaint them with man's physical and social environment; it also included the 'pre-registration' period intended to prepare new graduates for vocational training. The GMC wanted exams to reflect the principles of basic medical education but, not wanting students burdened with too many tests, it suggested special attention be paid to their overall record through continuous or progressive assessment.

The GMC asked universities not only to inspect and supervise pre-registration jobs but also to care for those occupying them. To help the Dean with these tasks RFHSM created the post of Clinical Sub-Dean, first held by the gynaecologist Jocelyn Moore. The rheumatologist Euan Campbell replaced her in 1970, and remained in this post after becoming Vice-Dean in 1974.[lix]

While RFHSM did not respond promptly to the GMC's recommendations, it certainly did to 'Todd'. Within weeks a 'Curriculum Committee'[30] was set up to review the whole course and to consider in-course assessment (ICA) and conduct of examinations. To assist it five Academic Advisory Sub-Committees (AASCs) were introduced – pre-medical/preclinical; pathology; medicine; surgery; and O & G: all teachers were involved in at least one.[lx]

At the students' request a Staff/Student Committee on Medical Education (SSCME) was created in December 1967; it flourished when the Curriculum Committee began work and many of its recommendations were acted upon.[31]

There was a joint UCL, UCHMS and RFHSM Curriculum Committee but the schools held different views on medical education, and it soon became clear that there would be limited collaboration until the new preclinical building was available. It was agreed each school should plan its own new curriculum and review the situation when there was a timetable for implementing the merger.[lxi]

RFHSM's Curriculum Committee presented two plans in January 1969. One was an integrated five year course. The other, the preferred option, also chosen by UCL & UCHMS, began with a three-year B.Med.Sci. course (including some pathology and an 'Introduction to Clinical Method') followed by clinical practice involving two 'years' each of 46 weeks. The early part of the clinical years was taken up with general medicine and surgery; later four of the twelve weeks of 'elective' had to be taken in one of six 'optional subjects';[32] an 'integrated' course occupied the last 18 weeks.[lxii]

---

[30] Bouchier, Douglas, Downman, Hopewell, Kember, Lucy and Trindade – but no pathologist! Curriculum sub-committees set up in 1952 and 1958 had been short-lived.

[31] The Curriculum Committee had two student members from November 1968, plus representatives from UCL & UCHMS. In 1970 a UCHMS student joined SSCME, and an RFHSM student joined the UCHMS Undergraduate Teaching Committee. (AR 1968-9, 1969-70)

[32] Anaesthetics, dentistry, geriatrics, plastic surgery, radiology or radiotherapy.

Clinicians, however, wanted a preclinical two years, a 'para-clinical' year, and two years of clinical work. The students opposed any reduction in clinical teaching time and favoured a five-year integrated course.[lxiii]

The preclinical teachers' plans for a B.Med.Sci. course were dashed in June 1971 when the University asked the GMC about including such a degree within a five-year MBBS course. The GMC ruled that although universities could award a first degree after three years of a medical curriculum a five-year course had to include at least 30 months of clinical instruction. This meant that clinical or 'para-clinical' work had to occupy at least six months of a three-year B.Med.Sci. course so the idea was dropped. The curriculum committee continued working on an integrated course that would meet the GMC's requirements. The final version was ready for submission to the University in December 1972.[lxiv]

In anticipation of the new regulations coming into effect in October 1973 the University asked schools if they wished to organize their own curricula and examinations within the regulations. RFHSM chose a school-sponsored course with school-based examinations, but as the facilities needed for the new clinical course would be unavailable in Hampstead until 1976 the University allowed introduction of the revised regulations to be postponed until 1974.[lxv]

The 1st MB (pre-medical) course was a casualty of the revised regulations. The new entry requirements for MBBS were three GCE *Advanced* Level subjects including chemistry and/or physical science; candidates without mathematics or other science subjects at *Advanced* Level could enter if they had passed them at *Ordinary* Level. A 1st MB course (chemistry, physics and biology) was therefore unnecessary,[33] but as RFHSM still offered one (in the UCCA handbook and in the Compendium of University Entrance Requirements) students without a chemistry or physical science A Level[34] were accepted until 1973-4. Subsequently there was no 1st MB course; those studying arts at school had to satisfy the new entry requirements elsewhere.[lxvi]

The GMC wanted all medical students to work for their own university's degree. Provincial schools discouraged students from sitting for diplomas before their degree courses were completed, but many London students took Conjoint as insurance against failing MBBS, a practice that tended to interfere with preparation for the latter.[35] In May 1968 the Education Committee suggested students should complete 36 months of the clinical course before sitting any part of Conjoint, unless they had failed MBBS pathology (taken six months before the other subjects); in that case they could take Conjoint pathology after 33 months.[lxvii]

---

[33] Many 1st MB students were exempt from one or two subjects; for them the course was hardly taxing.

[34] Hitherto about half the School's first-year students were in this category.

[35] Only exceptionally were students admitted to RFHSM to read for a diploma but not a degree.

The Dean said students would resent the proposed ruling. Council compromised and decided that from January 1969 students could take only one part of Conjoint finals before completing 33 months of the clinical course; they were to prepare for it only on relevant attachments and were not to miss formal post work to prepare for any diploma examination.[lxviii]

Electives

In 1967 the GMC advocated the introduction of elective periods, study of some subjects in greater depth, and involvement of students in research. In Lloyd-Williams's time there were no statutory 'electives', but students did participate in international exchanges in 1960-1. Pauline Moore received one of the new British Medical Students Association (BMSA) scholarships for study in the USA, as did Glennis Haworth the following year.[36] A Nuffield Foundation grant enabled Heather Suckling to take her three month senior pathology post at the University of the West Indies, a link set up by Professor Hill; five more RFHSM students subsequently received Nuffield grants. In September 1961 Hill, a strong advocate of international exchange, arranged clinical attachments for three RFHSM students in Malta, where he was an examiner; others followed them.[lxix]

A so-called 'elective period' was introduced at RFHSM in 1963 but choice was somewhat restricted – students had to spend their month clerking patients with either neurological disorders or psychological problems.[lxx]

In 1965-6 all final year students had a statutory one month's elective. Most spent it in mainland Britain. However, one went to Orkney, others to Morocco, Toronto and Trinidad. More went overseas the following year; some received help with travel expenses from the Mary Schofield bequest. [37, lxxi]

Initially few travelled far for electives. A month's elective precluded two long sea journeys and flying was expensive. Only three RFHSM students went overseas in 1970-1; two went to Israel and one to the West Indies. The elective period was two months in 1971 (although timetabling problems meant some could have only six consecutive weeks). In 1971-2 students went to Ghana, Hong Kong, Los Angeles, Melbourne, Newfoundland, Vancouver and Zambia as well as European and Mediterranean countries. It seemed that time, not money, determined the location of an elective and that nowhere was too remote for students having two

---

[36] Moore & Howarth studied at St. Luke's Hospital, Massachusetts (Mag 1962 Dec). Grants helped one student to attend a Polish study tour, two a German study tour and four a Summer School in Denmark.

[37] In 1965-66 Dr. Mary Schofield, an old student left £5,000 – for a scholarship to help graduates from other fields to enter the pre-clinical course. For such individuals LEA awards were available only for the clinical course, and to fund overseas elective periods.

months at their disposal. Finance remained a problem for some, but two Drapers' Company scholarships of £100 a year helped one woman and one man to cover their expenses.[lxxii]

In the next two years the more adventurous students went as far afield as Hawaii, South Vietnam and Nepal. Africa was popular in 1974-5, students travelling to Botswana, Ghana, Kenya, Malawi, Nigeria, South Africa, the Sudan and Tanzania.[lxxiii]

Overseas students visited RFH's teaching group before RFHSM students went abroad for electives. Two Maltese and two Americans arrived in 1962-3. The following year students came from Heidelberg, Gottingen, Louvain, Duke University, Albert Einstein College of Medicine and the State University of New York, Syracuse, and in 1964-5 there were students from Lille, Erlangen and eight American universities. There were about thirty-five overseas students in 1969-70 and 1970-1 and they continued to outnumber the outflow from RFHSM. Fewer visited while building was in progress at Hampstead.[lxxiv]

In 1968 the dean of the medical faculty at Charles University, Prague, tried to arrange an exchange of students with RFHSM. Politics intervened. Dubček's reforms during the 'Prague Spring' of 1968, which included loosening of restrictions on the media, speech and travel, led the Soviet Union and its allies to invade Czechoslovakia in August. Many fled the country. RFHSM admitted three Czech students, already in London, who could not return to complete their course in Prague, and waived the basic tuition fee.[lxxv] One of them, Eva Demant(ova), qualified MBBS in 1974; now Mrs Korach she lives in Switzerland; another, Ivan Pokorny (MBBS 1971), is a plastic surgeon in Pennsylvania.

Throughout Gardner's time as Dean general practice teaching was primitive by later standards. The 1970-72 prospectus stated '... to give students some insight into this branch of medical work a scheme...arranged...with...old students and others in general practice whereby students may, if they wish, attend...for a fortnight full-time, or for one session a week...over three months.' This voluntary 'fulltime fortnight' was introduced around 1954; the 'weekly over three months' was added around 1961 to allow more students to gain such experience.[lxxvi]

At the School's AGM in 1963 a local general practitioner[38] suggested the new RFH should have a general practice unit that taught students, like the professorial unit in Edinburgh. Gardner said fellow London deans thought such units useful for postgraduates, but doubted their value for undergraduates, and cautioned against curricular overload. Voluntary attendance at general practices would continue. She

[38] Dr Philip Hopkins, who lived opposite the new RFH on Haverstock Hill.

said facilities would exist for GPs in the new RFH, but that an academic unit was unlikely.[lxxvii]

In 1967 the GMC recommended a period of attachment to a GP – rather than the '*opportunity to learn something of the work of the general practitioner*' advocated ten years earlier. In 1969 the School's Education Committee suggested all students should have experience of general practice during the course; but it opposed SSCME's suggestion of a compulsory two weeks during the elective, and when interim changes were made to the curriculum in 1971 the social medicine/GP attachment was not made compulsory (see above).[lxxviii]

For many years senior (final year) and junior (first clinical year) students at RFHSM were taught together on general medical and surgical firms. Some thought this helped the juniors, but many teachers thought the educational needs of the two cohorts were, and certainly should have been, different. The AASC in Medicine, supported by SSCME, persuaded the Education Committee to separate seniors and juniors on general medicine posts from July 1970. Lee Lander's firm was, without explanation, excused compliance.[lxxix]

To promote interaction between students and staff a general tutorial scheme[39] was introduced from January 1969. The purpose was not academic. Tutors were to take a friendly interest in their group's progress and, if necessary, advise on personal problems – although students remained free to consult any member of the School staff. In June 1970 the Union President said students enjoyed the social contact with staff but that few would discuss personal problems with the tutors allocated; instead she suggested an appropriate panel of preclinical, clinical and administrative staff. Council thought her judgment premature but, a year later, following a Students' Union report, the Education Committee supported her alternative scheme which was already operating informally.[lxxx]

Students wanting psychiatric advice were meant to contact the consultant psychiatrist Nancy Swift, who was the student health officer from 1963. She either treated them herself or referred them to a colleague. The number needing help increased and in 1969 Swift recommended employing, for one session a week, a consultant psychotherapist interested in students' problems; Dr Edgar Wooster took on the task.[lxxxi]

The new preclinical course, introduced in October 1974, began with two new inter-disciplinary courses – 'Cell Studies' and 'Man and his Environment' – that were intended to promote integration between the 'traditional' preclinical subjects,[40]

[39] As suggested in para 506 of the Todd Report (p 208).
[40] Primarily anatomy, physiology, biochemistry and pharmacology.

between those and the behavioural sciences, and between preclinical and clinical subjects. Clinicians were to participate in preclinical teaching, and clinical students were to maintain contact with the basic medical sciences, particularly during a six-week science elective in the second clinical year. Preclinical and clinical teachers were to co-operate in integrated teaching in the final year. In-course assessment (ICA) was to play an important role throughout the five year course.[lxxxii]

Both the GMC and 'Todd' had suggested special weight should be given to the student's record throughout the course by introducing progressive or continuous assessment. However, neither clarified exactly what they meant by 'in-course' (ICA), 'continuous' or 'progressive' assessment. Various RFHSM committees discussed the issue for several years post-'Todd', but in April 1972 draft regulations for the new curriculum remained vague about ICA – even though it was agreed ICA marks should constitute up to 50% of the final marks in both preclinical and clinical subjects.[lxxxiii]

During the early 1970s two important factors influenced thinking about clinical ICA at RFHSM – the introduction of the Problem Orientated Medical Record (POMR) and a move to clarify the School's educational goals and objectives.

In 1968, while a research fellow at the Massachusetts General Hospital, McIntyre read Lawrence Weed's paper 'Medical Records that Guide and Teach' in the *New England Journal of Medicine.*[lxxxiv] While an instructor at Yale, Weed, a physician and biochemist, contrasted the rigour with which scientists documented their work and the chaotic nature of doctors' workbooks, i.e. their clinical records. Good scientists record their hypotheses, methods used to test them, and the results and conclusions; others can then judge the quality of their work. However patient records are poorly structured, of variable content and quality, and rarely record the logic pathways of clinical decision making. They are thus of little value for assessing quality of care.

In 1956, wishing to remedy this situation, Weed moved to a hospital in Bangor, Maine, where, he and his first intern, Harold Cross, top of his class at Yale, designed and tested POMR as a template for clinical action and as a record that facilitated audit of medical care.

McIntyre returned to RFH as a senior lecturer in 1968 and ran a firm of students at Lawn Road. Impressed with its educational potential he used POMR to write his clinical notes, and encouraged junior staff and students to do the same. Junior students took to it well and it became clear that it offered the opportunity not only to audit the quality of care actually received by patients, but also medical students' simulation of patient care – arguably the most important aspect of medical education. From January 1973 two lectures on POMR were given to all clinical students during their introductory course.[lxxxv]

In 1972 a paper on POMR from RFH appeared in the British Journal of Hospital Medicine,[41] [lxxxvi] and many visited RFH to see POMR in use. The gastroenterologist Sir Francis Avery Jones mentioned POMR when addressing the Association of Medical Records Officers in 1972. Told it was used at Lawn Road he visited to inspect some 'problem-orientated records'; he then persuaded the King's Fund to pay to bring Weed to Britain.

At a meeting on POMR at the Senate House on 9 January 1973 the highlight was Weed's talk on 'The Implications of POMR'. While in London he also spoke on 'Medical Records and Medical Care, the Role of the Computer', and on 'Auditing of Clinical Care'. He visited Southampton, Newcastle and Glasgow before returning home. Audit of the notes of HPs and students was introduced on the Medical Unit firm at Lawn Road soon afterwards and was considered potentially useful for ICA.

In late 1973 the King's Fund provided RFH and Guy's with a total of £90,000 over three years for work on the application of POMR in Britain. At Guy's the whole hospital agreed to switch to POMR on 1 May 1974,[42] but it was not properly applied on many services and never really caught on. At RFH effort was concentrated on the educational use of POMR, particularly through one-to-one audit of the notes students made on their patients, in the hope that it might play a major role in the ICA of clinical students.[lxxxvii]

In September McIntyre attended an AMEE[43] workshop on "Objectives of Undergraduate Medical Education' held in Edinburgh. There was general agreement that specification of objectives was desirable when planning curricular change and in choosing methods for student assessment – and that a faculty should be collectively responsible for objectives. But there was little enthusiasm for detailed low level 'Magerian' objectives.[44] Delegates wanted high-level objectives within which achievement of low level objectives could be assumed. (See below)

A report of the Edinburgh meeting went to the Education Committee with the suggestion that RFHSM should discuss 'objectives' at a future date. The matter was referred to a working party on ICA set up primarily to agree a marking scheme for the new curriculum to be submitted to the University.[lxxxviii]

Sponsored by the King's Fund McIntyre visited the USA in November 1974 to study the use of POMR at several centres. He visited a rural general practice at Hampden Highlands, Maine, whose partners, all POMR enthusiasts, were renowned for the quality of care they provided. The senior partner, Harold Cross,

---

41 A leader about POMR (by Dr AE Bennett from Oxford) appeared in *The Lancet* earlier that year.

42 An initiative led by the surgeons Ian McColl (now Lord McColl) and Max Rendall .

43 Association for Medical Education in Europe.

44 Described in Robert Mager's short text 'Preparing Instructional Objectives' (1962).

was reading Robert Mager's 'Goal Analysis' which so impressed McIntyre that he bought it and five of the author's other books.[45] He realised that Mager had been badly misrepresented in Edinburgh.

Mager stressed the need for both 'Goals' – i.e. broad statements of intent – and matching 'Objectives', preferably of a 'high level', describing what a student had to do to indicate achievement of each goal. A draft set of RFHSM goals was accepted in principle, and the ICA working party asked all clinical groups, including pathology, to prepare objectives which matched the goals and were relevant to their own differing specialties. In subsequent years 'Goals and Objectives' played a key role in curricular development at RFHSM. (See Ch 15).[lxxxix]

Staff Changes

Gardner's thirteen years as dean saw inevitable staff changes. Robert J. (Sam) Berry, genetics lecturer since 1962, replaced Margaret Hughes as head of biology when she retired in 1968; he received a personal chair in 1974. Mrs Monk-Jones (physics) retired in 1970; she taught statistics for twenty-three years, and provided statistical advice for colleagues at RFHSM. That year Brian Mawhinney returned as a physics lecturer after two years at the University of Iowa.[46] At the general election in October 1974 he stood as Conservative candidate for Stockton-on-Tees; unsuccessful on that occasion he subsequently had a glittering political career (see Chapter 15).[xc]

After thirty-one years at the School, Lawson retired as professor of organic chemistry in 1973. He was the first adviser to male students in 1956, and from October 1966 the official fire officer. In 1972 the School's President, Lucas-Keene, anticipating an appeal associated with the School's centenary, proffered her resignation so that a distinguished person, well known to the public, could replace her as President. In November 1973 Council chose Lawson – which was probably not what she had in mind! [xci]

W. F. (Bill) Whelan from the Lister Institute was appointed as RFHSM's first professor of biochemistry in December 1963. His research team needed space so in March 1964 the School took a seven-year lease on the nearby Presbyterian Church and converted it into four laboratories. Whelan left for Miami in 1967. His successor, Jack Lucy, from the Strangeways Laboratories in Cambridge, applied successfully to the MRC for funding for a research group on membrane

[45] Including – *Preparing Instructional Objectives,* (1962*); Developing Attitudes Toward Learning,* (1968); *Goal Analysis,* (1972); *Measuring Instructional Intent,* (1973).

[46] Where he was an assistant professor in radiation research.

biochemistry. Host institutions had to support such groups after five years and the School agreed to find the £40,000 needed.[xcii]

Brenda Ryman, reader in biochemistry from May 1968, moved to the chair of biochemistry at Charing Cross Hospital Medical School in 1972 and retained it four years later after her election as the first married Mistress of Girton, her old Cambridge college.[47] Anthony Diplock inherited her readership; Terry Hallinan became senior lecturer and Richard Bruckdorfer lecturer.[xciii] .

Bowden (Fig 14.7) headed anatomy throughout Gardner's time as dean. In 1967 two of her readers departed. John Napier became Curator of Primates and Director of the International Primate Biology Program at the Smithsonian Institution in Washington, and Peter Davies was appointed professor of human biology at the new University of Surrey. John Harris, from the London Hospital Medical School, took Napier's readership and received a personal chair six years later. Don Grieve, from the MRC's Human Biomechanics Laboratory, was appointed senior lecturer and subsequently reader. In March 1964 Pamela MacKinnon left RFHSM after eight years to become university lecturer in human anatomy at Oxford, and a fellow at St Hilda's College. She trained at KCL and KCH; sadly her husband, an anatomist at KCL, died in May 1962.[xciv]

Fig 14.7 RuthBowden (1915-2001)

In October 1961 John Coleridge from Leeds took the readership in physiology vacated when Downman assumed the chair (see Chapter 13); his wife Hazel joined him as a research fellow. Pearl Scott, curator of the animal house from 1947 to 1958 (and from 1966 to 1971), was made reader in 1962 and got a personal chair (as Professor of Nutritional Physiology) in 1974-5. In 1967 the Coleridges left following John's appointment as professor of physiology at New York Medical College,[48] and Roland Moore, a senior lecturer, took the chair of physiology at Trinity College, Dublin.[xcv]

Coleridge's readership went to W.H.H. ('Digger') Andrews, senior lecturer at London Hospital Medical College. Andrews had returned to Britain for family

---

[47] In October 1948 Ryman joined RFHSM which had admitted men in 1947. In 1977 she presided over Girton's change from a women's college to a mixed college.

[48] The Coleridges, highly productive researchers, moved on to the Cardiovascular Research Centre in San Francisco.

reasons having been professor of physiology in the University of the West Indies from 1963. In 1961 he was a founder member of the Liver Club (later the British Association for the Study of the Liver). Lawson's successor as adviser to male students, he received a personal chair in 1974. He died, aged 60, in 1978.[xcvi]

Zaimis headed pharmacology throughout Gardner's deanship; her deputy, Bob Hodges, was made reader in March 1963 and received a personal chair in 1970.[xcvii]

Tragedy struck two departments in 1970. In July David L. Matthews, physiology lecturer since October 1966, drowned in an unsuccessful attempt to rescue his younger daughter while sailing on the Ouse. Weeks earlier Derek Woods, an honorary lecturer in pharmacology, had died in a gliding accident.[xcviii]

Professorial Units

The biggest changes in clinical staffing during Gardner's deanship were related to new professorial units. The School had put aside £14,000 towards creating another unit towards the end of the 1962-7 quinquennium – for either O & G or psychiatry. In 1963 the Education Committee opted for O & G, mainly because it already had some academic appointments. Beds and operating theatre sessions were provided, plus £11,600 for staff and running expenses. The unit was to be based initially at RFH Liverpool Road.[xcix]

Charles Primrose Douglas, senior lecturer at the University of the West Indies, assumed the chair in October 1965. Jean Ginsburg joined the new unit as endocrinologist in 1966, Jocelyn Moore, the Teaching Unit's director, reverted to RFH's consultant staff and Valerie Thompson, Moore's first assistant after Norris's resignation in 1963, became senior lecturer in the new department. In 1968 Thompson joined Kathleen Robinson as an NHS consultant and Luba Epsztejn took the senior lectureship. In 1969 Moore, at age 65, moved to Ahmadu Bello University in Nigeria where, as Professor of O & G, she established a new department. Philip Chalk replaced her at RFH.[c]

When in the early 1960s the Government decided the new RFH should have 60 psychiatric beds provisional plans were made for a Professorial Unit in Psychiatry. University approval came in March 1970. As RFH then had no psychiatric beds NWMRHB offered beds at Friern/Halliwick hospitals. Gerald Russell, senior lecturer and Dean of the Institute of Psychiatry, took the chair on 1 January 1971.[49] His first senior lecturer was Anthony Wakeling; David Pitcher and Patrick Campbell were lecturers; Fay Fransella was senior lecturer in clinical psychology. Felix Brown, RFH's senior psychiatrist, died soon after Russell arrived. The

---

[49] In 1971 Russell became a Foundation Fellow of the new Royal College of Psychiatrists & Wakeling was made a Member.

remaining four NHS consultant psychiatrists were Alick Elithorn, Nancy Swift, Sylvio Benaim and Donovan Hailstone. Joan Cornwell was appointed NHS consultant in child psychiatry in 1973-4.[ci]

For many years the School and Hospital dragged their heels over a chair of surgery; it was always to be established when conditions were suitable! There was a 'surgical unit' hut at Lawn Road in 1963 and Council offered to support a surgical senior lecturer and research assistant from October 1965. The Medical Committee declined the offer.[50] In 1966 the School applied to the University for a chair of surgery but by then other schools were also applying and no funds were available until late 1967.[cii]

In February 1968 Richardson[51] told Council that, lacking a surgical unit, RFH was handicapped as a teaching hospital. However, he cautioned that as clinical senior lecturers and above had honorary consultant contracts care was needed in distributing them among the specialties, lest a lack of balance emerged in the hospital staff.[ciii]

If, as the University had been promised, the School was to have a surgical unit in the next quinquennium an application had to be made for it in 1969. Although an Academic Department of Surgery was mentioned in the Annual Report for 1971-2, with Phyllis George as tutor and Oswald Fernando as lecturer, there were still problems about accommodating a professorial unit, particularly as the last part of Lawn Road Hospital was to be demolished in September 1972.[civ]

Owing to the delay in completing stage I of the new RFH the NWMRHB was asked if, temporarily, it could accommodate the new professor of surgery in another hospital, as it had done for psychiatry (see above). It was unable to help so the RFH surgeons said they would do so by relinquishing some beds.[cv].

K.E.F. (Ken) Hobbs, a senior lecturer at Bristol with an interest in liver surgery, was appointed in May 1972, but did not assume the chair until October 1973. In the unit's brief pre-Hampstead days Os Fernando, then working with Hopewell on renal transplantation (which had resumed at RFH in 1968), remained a lecturer, and Patrick Davis, an honorary lecturer, worked at Barnet General Hospital. Within a year Santi Parbhoo was appointed senior lecturer, and Arthur Li lecturer. Parbhoo had spent several years in Sherlock's Medical Unit before moving to the department in Bristol where Hobbs was then working.[cvi]

Hobbs performed the first surgical operation at the new RFH on Wednesday 16 October 1974. Coincidentally and very appropriately the patient – a London taxi

---

[50] In December 1965, when there was no academic surgical presence, 1124 ft.^{2} of the future professorial surgical unit was allocated to anaesthetics, to provide a self-contained unit that would be a charge on the Ministry of Health. [CM 1965: 8 Dec] Sherlock objected to this decision.

[51] One of the two Medical Committee representatives on Council (see later)

driver named Gerard Brennan – was born in Lawn Road, went to a local school, and worked from the cab rank on Haverstock Hill, about 100 yards from the Hospital. He was admitted on 14 October. Curiously his wife was admitted to HGH on 15 October. Fortunately both were soon discharged.

There were few changes among the general surgeons in the Royal Free Group before Hobbs arrived. R.M. (Jerry) Kirk was appointed at HGH in 1964 when Cameron MacLeod retired. Lionel Gracey joined RFH in 1966 (and HGH later) as a replacement for Daintree Johnson. The latter retired, after 19 years at RFH, owing to gradual but severe visual deterioration; he was only 55. [52, cvii]

HGH, part of the RFH Teaching Group since 1948, was demolished in 1975. Kirk and Gracey transferred to the staff of the new RFH. Several of its other surgeons, including Emlyn Williams and Harland Rees (also senior urologist at KCH), retired around this time; so too did two of RFH's general surgical staff – Radley Smith and George Qvist.

Several years before Qvist retired, aged 65, he developed multiple myelomatosis. He continued doing locums, finished two books – '*Surgical Diagnosis*' (written with Cedric Gilson, head of RFH's medical illustration department) and '*John Hunter 1728-1793'*, and taught anatomy at the School, attending up to ten days before his death on 28 July 1981.

Colin Madgwick was appointed orthopaedic surgeon at RFH in 1966-7. His senior colleague, Charles Gray, retired in 1974. Derek Wilson took over orthopaedics at HGH when Hindenach retired in 1973, and in 1974-5 R.W. (Dick) Rushman joined Madgwick and Wilson at the new RFH.

Lorimer Fison was an ophthalmologist at RFH and Moorfields from 1962, He left RFH within a year or two, and in 1965 David Abrams joined Henry Hobbs and Jean Dollar. Dollar retired in 1966; ten years later J. S. ('Joe') Conway replaced Hobbs.

Surgeons needed anaesthetists. In 1962 there were seven such consultants at RFH – Willis, Tamsin Winter, Odell, Green, Deacock, Gilchrist and Carter Steel; the last two also worked at HGH with Massey Dawkins and Kaufman. By 1965 Willis, Winter and Carter Steel had left and Howells, Grogono, Hardwick and Browne had been added to the list. When New End joined RFH's teaching group in 1968 the School's annual report mentioned a 'Group Department of Anaesthesia' although that term was soon dropped. The Board of Governors appointed Hilary Howells as Director of Anaesthesia.[53] He had changed his contract to full-time and six of his eleven 'notional half days' were intended for academic development,

[52] Daintree Johnson was a remarkable man. He studied engineering before medicine, built and drove his own racing cars at Brooklands, and conceived the ideas of clover-leaf road crossings and safety binding for skis, both of which came into general use.

[53] Bill Young & Jocelyn Moore were also 'Directors' – of radiology and O&G respectively..

teaching and research. The Board of Governors and the RFH Trustees funded a laboratory technician and a research registrar, and 'Anaesthetics' was allocated a laboratory and several offices within the proposed academic surgical unit on the ninth floor (see earlier). As that would not be available for several years it was provided with space that had accommodated nurses at Lawn Road.

With great help from the hospital engineer, Archie Dean, a three-bedded Intensive Therapy Unit (ITU) was opened, close to the two operating theatres at Lawn Road, in space that had provided residential accommodation for nurses. A senior registrar, Doreen Brown, went to work at the Massachusetts General Hospital which was pioneering the new discipline of 'Intensive Therapy' (IT). On return she ran RFH's ITU and when Lawn Road was being demolished she provided a temporary peripatetic IT service for the other RFH units. Hospital transport was provided for the necessary equipment, which included large ventilators and various types of monitor. Howells lobbied hard for a dedicated ITU in the new hospital and, thanks to the support of the microbiologist Nuala Crowley it was established in space that had been allocated for a reverse isolation unit.[cviii]

The Medical Unit thrived in its main base at GIR. In October 1965 it acquired more general medical beds at Lawn Road and established a separate teaching firm there. The number of research fellows, from Britain and overseas, peaked at fifteen in 1964-5 and 1969-70. Some Unit staff and research fellows went to laboratories in the USA for a year or two to obtain what was humorously referred to as the 'BTA' ('Been To America') qualification.

The Unit served as the centre for much of the postgraduate medical education at the Free. On Wednesday afternoons Sherlock held a 'grand round' – in the less than grand surroundings of a large gynaecological outpatient room. It was followed by Scheuer's liver biopsy session, held in a small roof-top hut contiguous with the main lecture hut where the afternoon's formalities ended with a talk by a distinguished visitor, often one of Sherlock's wide range of contacts. Her contacts were also used to promote the career prospects of junior doctors at RFH – and not just those from her own department. Introductions were sometimes made when the speaker joined members of the audience for a glass of wine.

In 1963 Victor Rosenoer was appointed as lecturer in Therapeutics, a post held jointly between the departments of medicine and pharmacology. He was soon promoted to senior lecturer but moved to the Children's Cancer Research Foundation in Boston in 1967. At GIR his research was conducted in a two storey hut, erected in the 'inner square' of RFH in 1964 and paid for by Mr Mulder Canter, one of Sherlock's patients. His co-workers included Tony Tavill, Tony Jones and the Australian Dick Smallwood.[54] Ian James was appointed as a lecturer to replace Rosenoer, and was subsequently promoted to senior lecturer (1969) and reader (1984).[cix]

Dawson left in 1965[55] and created a first class gastrointestinal unit at Bart's.[56] His replacement, Ian Bouchier, another gastroenterologist, moved to the chair of medicine in Dundee in 1973, and subsequently to the Regius Chair in Edinburgh in 1986. Bouchier's readership went to McIntyre who from 1968 shared a two story research hut at Lawn Road first with Tavill, who had returned from two years in New York, and then with Tony Jones, who had worked at the National Institutes of Health, Bethesda, Md., for a year.[57] Derek Jewell was appointed senior lecturer to replace Bouchier as gastroenterologist when the latter departed for Dundee.

In 1965 the renal unit set up Lawn Road in 1960 was still run by the surgeon Hopewell and by Shaldon, whose appointment as lecturer in the Medical Unit, was due to expire in October. The Medical Committee wanted the renal unit staffed by Hopewell and a senior lecturer in medicine with consultant status. The post was advertised but for complex reasons the School decided not to proceed with the appointment. The Board of Governors appointed Shaldon as full-time first assistant to the renal unit. The following year John Moorhead, a young renal physician joined the Medical Unit as a locum lecturer and in May 1967 was made NHS physician in renal diseases, Shaldon having left RFH to set up his National Kidney Centre.[cx]

The NHS physician Una Ledingham retired in late 1964. She died a year later. She was not replaced immediately. When New End became part of the teaching group in 1968 its two physicians, Cecil Symons and Gordon Beckett, joined the RFH staff. The latter, previously Ledingham's senior registrar, ran her diabetic clinic. The oncologist Thompson Hancock retired in 1969; he died in January 2004, 23 days short of his 100th birthday. Lee Lander went in 1972 and Harold Davies followed in 1973 – something of a clear out before the move to the new Royal Free.

The endocrinologist Raymond (Bill) Hoffenberg left South Africa in 1968 having been banned by the Vorster government. Supported by Sherlock he joined

---

[54] Smallwood moved to Boston and then back to Melbourne. He became chief of medicine at the Austin Hospital – and later President of the Australasian College of Physicians, Chief Medical Officer of Australia, and President of the Australian Medical Council

[55] The lecturer Roger Williams took an NHS consultant post in Southampton in 1965 and later set up a liver unit at King's College Hospital .

[56] Dawson, physician to the Queen from 1982, was knighted in 1993. He died, aged 69, in 1997,

[57] In 1971 Tavill moved to the MRC hospital at Northwick Park and subsequently to Cleveland,Ohio. Jones went to Liverpool in 1972. Two years later he returned to NIH where he headed the Liver Diseases Section from 1977-92.

the thyroid unit at New End Hospital, but moved to Northwick Park Hospital in 1970 and to the chair of medicine in Birmingham in 1972. [58]

Peter Kynaston ('PK')[59] Thomas was appointed neurologist at RFH in 1962 and at the National Queen Square the following year. Helen Dimsdale, his senior colleague at RFH, retired prematurely in 1967. Three years later PK was joined by John Newsom-Davis who, like PK, was a gifted research worker and a consultant at Queen Square. Until they moved to Hampstead they were accommodated, along with staff from psychiatry and medical illustration, in a row of buildings on Gray's Inn Road, directly opposite RFH.

Several North American departments tried to recruit PK, but if suitable research facilities could be made available he wanted to stay in Britain and have a chair of neurobiology. He found a way of getting a salary and accommodation through RFH – and became an NHS 'full-timer'. Despite strong support at the Free it was October 1973 before Council recommended him for a chair of 'Neurosciences' – although the title conferred in 1974 was 'Professor of Neurology'.[cxi]

In 1965-6 David Skeggs replaced Wade as radiotherapist. The former was to lead the team that pioneered computer-controlled precision radiotherapy, which allowed lethal irradiation of tumours but spared surrounding normal tissues.[cxii]

Ursula Shelley and Zina Moncrieff were RFH's paediatricians when Gardner became dean. Their beds were at Liverpool Road. Shelley had a particular interest in cerebral palsy. She retired in 1971 and was replaced by David Flynn.[cxiii]

Kenneth Hill was an outstanding head of pathology. Popular with colleagues, and beloved by students, he chaired RFH's Medical Committee from June 1970. Having a major interest in medical education he advised and examined at many universities, particularly in underdeveloped countries. Through his International Museum Exchange he provided teaching material to countries where autopsies were infrequent, and medical schools worldwide used tapes from his Overseas Audiovisual Aid scheme. He was a pioneer in the use of television for teaching pathology.

In June 1972 he mediated in a pay dispute between the Lagos State government and its medical officers. He was then, with the School's approval, to spend two years as the Vice-Chancellor of the University of Benin before returning as director of the RFH museum. He took up office in Nigeria in September, but illness forced his repatriation after four months. He died 19 February 1973; in June his widow endowed a Kenneth Hill Memorial Prize for Pathology.[cxiv]

[58] In 1983 he narrowly defeated Sherlock in the presidential election at the Royal College of Physicians.

[59] Always referred to as 'PK'.

In September 1972 Gardner met Baron, Brumfitt, Fleming & Scott to confirm that at Hampstead the Pathology Department would be a Division of Pathology – with autonomous departments of chemical pathology, medical microbiology, haematology and histopathology (formerly morbid anatomy), each with an appointed teacher as head.[cxv]

Initially Hill's senior colleagues in morbid anatomy were Barry Scott and Isobel Beswick. Scott, a titular professor since 1969, headed 'histopathology' after the reorganization;[60] Beswick remained a senior lecturer,[61] Scheuer had been promoted to senior lecturer in 1964 and to reader in 1970, two years after the appearance of his classic textbook *Liver Biopsy Interpretation*.[62] He received a personal chair in 1975.[cxvi]

Through Hill's connections, many of the pathology lecturers worked overseas, mainly in Jamaica or Nigeria (Ibadan) and from 1967 the Ministry of Overseas Development supported an extra lectureship at RFHSM. The holders were to spend two years or more at an overseas university – initially that of the West Indies – which paid their salary; when they returned to RFH the Ministry paid the salary. W. F. (Bill) Whimster, later head of histopathology at KCH, was the first appointed under this scheme.[cxvii]

Hill pioneered diagnostic cytology and the training centres he promoted throughout the country facilitated the general introduction of cervical smear screening in the mid-1960s.[63] At RFH cytology was done initially by two research assistants – John Crabbe and Chandra Grubb. Crabbe and a newcomer, Mary Egerton, were appointed consultant cytologists in 1963 as was Grubb in 1967. Following Crabbe's retirement in 1971 and the death of Egerton in 1973 Grubb was a lone cytologist at RFH.[cxviii]

Denis Baron was made Professor of Chemical Pathology in 1963. His lecturer, J.R. (Jack) Hobbs, left for the Hammersmith in 1964. Later, at Westminster Hospital, Hobbs was instrumental in setting up the Anthony Nolan bone marrow donor registry, now housed at RFH. (See Chapters 15&16) Michael Wills joined Baron as senior lecturer in 1965; he was made reader in 1970 and Professor of Metabolic Chemical Pathology in 1974.[cxix]

Nuala Crowley, head of bacteriology,[64] was promoted to reader in 1964-5 and Jean Bradley to senior lecturer two years later. Crowley succumbed to chronic

---

[60] Scott, a medical officer in the 1st British Airborne Division, took part in the Arnhem landings in 1944.

[61] Beswick was one of the first to realize the significance of vascular damage in renal homograft rejection.

[62] The seventh edition appeared in August 2005.

[63] He was chairman and later president of the British Society of Clinical Cytology.

[64] The department's name changed to Medical Microbiology in 1971, after Crowley's death.

chest disease in May 1970, four months after receiving a personal chair. In December 1971 William (Bill) Brumfitt, Foundation Professor of Pathology at Southampton, was appointed to the newly established chair of microbiology at RFHSM. Bradley remained senior lecturer, and Kosmidis and Jeremy Hamilton-Miller joined as lecturers. Kosmidis soon left but Hamilton-Miller remained at RFH for many years. Paul Noone was appointed NHS Consultant in Microbiology in 1972-3.

Fleming retired as head of haematology in 1972. Still a senior lecturer he had been supported by three other senior lecturers and a series of lecturers. The first senior lecturer, Chris Pitcher, arrived in 1962; he soon left and was replaced by Katherine Dormandy, a former student who was then a senior registrar at Great Ormond Street. The haemophilia centre she created, initially in a caravan at Lawn Road and later at the new RFH, became one of the finest in the country; she was made reader in 1969. The third senior lecturer, Michael O'Shea, arrived in 1968; he moved to Shrewsbury as an NHS consultant in 1974.

After Victor Hoffbrand assumed the newly established chair of haematology in April 1974 he appointed John Pettit, a New Zealander then working in Canada, to replace O'Shea. The department, initially small, was to grow rapidly during MacGillivray's deanship.

When Gardner became dean the consultant radiologists at RFH were Stanley Davis, Young, Kreel, Madden and Hector-Jones – the last two being more closely associated with HGH. Colin Mackintosh and Bob Dick joined the others at RFH. It was a disparate group. For most of the Second World War Bill Young (brother of Terence Young, the director of the early Bond films) was a prisoner of the Japanese in Singapore's Changi jail, as was Bob Dick's father. Louis Kreel, a South African, was one of the three radiologists who, in the late 1960s, worked with Geoffrey Hounsfield in the development of CAT scanning, supplying him with human organ samples for testing in prototype machines. Kreel left RFH for Northwick Park where in 1975 he was the first to use a whole body scanner in clinical practice.

Michael Warren, a part-time senior lecturer in Social and Preventive Medicine, took a full-time post at LSHTM in 1964. He was not replaced at RFHSM where, in 1972, Dr. Jocelyn Chamberlain was made Senior Lecturer in Community Medicine in a joint appointment with UCHMS.[cxx]

In 1966 the University agreed that RFHSM could appoint 'Visiting Professors' to lecture, teach and share in research. They were to be 'leading persons in…medicine and sciences allied to medicine…from…another academic or research institution… a Government department, industry or commerce'. The first two were the Nobel laureate Sir Hans Krebs, recently retired from Oxford, and Dr. Otto Edholm, head of the Division of Human Physiology at Hampstead's MRC laboratories.[cxxi]

F. W. Rogers Brambell (Anatomy), L. G. Goodwin (Pharmacology), & W. V. Mayneord (Medical Physics) were added to the list.[65] When Brambell died unexpectedly in 1970 Miriam Rothschild of St. Hugh's College, Oxford, took his place. Others appointed included Lucille Bitensky and Sir Cyril Clarke.[cxxii]

In 1965 London's medical schools were being encouraged to link with those in developing countries. In April 1966 Dr Hussein Gezairy, a young Saudi surgeon backed by his government, asked Gardner for help in establishing a medical school in Riyadh.[66] Clinical academics at the Free thought the choice of Gardner surprising – not just because of the Saudi attitude to women but because they doubted whether she was the best person to give such advice. The British Council had already arranged for Sir Brian Windeyer, Dean of the Middlesex Hospital Medical School, to visit Riyadh in November; Gardner went in August.

In her report 'Measures necessary for the establishment of a medical school in the Kingdom of Saudi Arabia' the first two recommendations were that students should dissect the human body, and attend and perform post mortems – an odd suggestion given the Islamic attitude towards desecration of a body.[cxxiii]

Gardner thought RFHSM should help Riyadh and said the University, the British Council and the Ministry of Overseas Development would support RFHSM's participation, preferably in association with other London schools. In November, Council and HODs agreed in principle to second staff to Riyadh, and to train Saudis at RFHSM so that they could become teachers in the new school. To coordinate matters three subcommittees were set up; they included members of pre-clinical/premedical departments, and of sub-departments in the pathology unit; no RFH clinicians were involved.[cxxiv]

In February 1967 Sir Brian Windeyer wrote that even the resources of two London medical schools would be insufficient to help establish the school in Riyadh. He suggested involving the University, but the Principal said the medical schools had to accept the responsibility. Although eleven of London's twelve schools agreed to collaborate there is little evidence they did so.[cxxv]

It is not clear how much input either Gardner or the School had into the early development of the Riyadh medical school. RFHSM's annual reports indicate that Sam Berry (Biology) examined there three times (1971-2 to 1973-4); Simons

[65] Rogers Brambell, was Emeritus Professor of Zoology in the University of Wales; L. G. Goodwin, Director of the Nuffield Institute of Comparative Medicine; W. V. Mayneord, Emeritus Professor of Physics as applied to Medicine at the Institute of Cancer Research.

[66] Gezairy became its first dean.

(Medical Physics, 1972-3) and Bowden (Anatomy, 1974-5) did so once. The latter also taught there with Pearl Scott (Physiology) in 1975-6. The following year Bowden and Gardner attended the first medical graduation ceremony. Gardner's visits to Riyadh were not recorded in the annual reports. Gezairy said she visited only twice.[cxxvi]

The only mention of Saudi students coming to RFHSM was the statement in the 1975-6 annual report that 'Pre-clinical women students from the newly established Medical School in Riyadh made use of the library and facilities in the Anatomy Department for private study during the summer vacation' (i.e. after Gardner left office).

Student Life

RFHSM's clubs and societies offered students many extra-curricular activities. One of the more cerebral of them, the Contemporary Society, founded in Exeter, had seemed doomed. Resuscitated in 1961 it maintained a permanent exhibition of student art in the new wing common room, and in the junior common room it displayed pictures on loan from the Tate Gallery's Contemporary Art Society. In 1963 it ran what was intended to be the first of a series of annual art competitions but although well supported by staff and students it proved a one-off. The Society folded later and was not included in the prospectus from 1969.[cxxvii]

In the spring of 1963, after a period of inactivity, the Dramatic Society staged an evening with the Music and Choral Society. It performed two one-act plays, and the choristers sang madrigals and excerpts from Gilbert and Sullivan. In 1965 'Cyrano de Bergerac' ran for four nights in the Hunter Street quadrangle (with Stuart Ungar playing the title role). In subsequent years Dramatic Society productions included Christopher Fry's 'Curtmantle'; Brendan Behan's 'The Hostage'; 'Tom Jones' (which entertained capacity audiences for five nights); 'A Day in the Death of Joe Egg'; 'Arsenic and Old Lace'; 'Antigone' and 'The Fire Raisers'.[cxxviii]

The Music and Choral Society performed the 'Messiah' at Christ Church, Highbury, in July 1965. The soprano, Susan Mitchley, and the contralto, Ann Bridgewater, were 4th year students; the tenor, R. Donovan, was an outsider. George Champion, the bass, who died a year later, was chief technician in the Anatomy Department and an expert on church music. Christopher Hood, an assistant anatomy lecturer at RFHSM, conducted the choir. Afterwards Mitchley and Bridgewater wrote a scathing letter to the Magazine complaining that the number of School and Hospital Staff attending could be counted on the fingers of one hand.[cxxix]

In August 1967 the Society participated in a TV programme from the RFH chapel. In 1970 and 1971 it chose 'Trial by Jury', and 'H.M.S. Pinafore' as its main productions and Gay's 'The Beggar's Opera' in 1973.[cxxx]

From the School's earliest days students sang Christmas carols in the wards of RFH and the New Hospital for Women. Under the aegis of the Music and Choral Society the carol service became a much grander affair and in December 1974 it included orchestral pieces, and prose and verse readings.[cxxxi]

Musical and dramatic talents combined for the preclinical and clinical Christmas shows. The former, held at Hunter Street, were straightforward revues. The clinical shows ran for several nights in the outpatient hall at GIR. Although the shows' titles usually suggested a pantomime they were essentially a series of unrelated sketches with a medical flavour. The 1964 clinical show, 'Cind-a-lot' was memorable because the finale was a film – considered by the Magazine's reviewer to be a little masterpiece. It was shot early one Sunday at Hampstead General Hospital and apparently needed no cutting. Nearly all subsequent clinical Christmas shows finished with a film.[cxxxii]

A two-week Royal Free Arts Festival in June 1973 was intended as a dry run for the more ambitious project planned for the School's centenary the following year. The 'actors' performed 'Romeo and Juliet' and Rostand's 'The Fantasticks'; the musical entertainment included Purcell's `Dido and Aeneas', African dancing, Blues and Folk Music. There was also a concert by the 'Cantores Medicini', a choir founded in 1967 by a group of RFH doctors and medical students. It sang sixteenth century music at Sunday services in the RFH chapel, but had a repertoire ranging from madrigals to American barber shop harmony.[cxxxiii]

The School's branch of the BMSA was active. In 1962 it organized lunch-hour film shows and lectures by outside speakers – and filled its quota for regional BMSA visits to renowned departments like Stoke Mandeville's paraplegic unit and East Grinstead's plastic surgery centre. RFHSM's Naomi Barclay was the BMSA's Assistant International Secretary for 1962-3, and Geoffrey Lloyd its President for 1968-9.[cxxxiv]

The new sports ground proved a great success. In 1963 the Metropolitan Water Board offered to relinquish the Myddleton House stretch of the New River. During Bowles's time it had agreed to keep the river filled,[67] but it now offered to fill, topsoil and seed the bed of the river in the Myddleton grounds,[68] to convey the land to the two schools, and to pay half of the legal costs and the surveyor's fee. The offer was accepted.[cxxxv]

---

[67] Bowles took water from it for £2 a year.

[68] This improved the drainage of the playing fields.

In November 1966 the Lee Valley Regional Park Authority (LVRPA),[69] anticipating its formal constitution in January 1967, wanted Myddleton House as its headquarters. The two schools wanted a new pavilion/clubhouse costing £34,000 so they sold Myddleton House to LVRPA for £20,000. The two schools and the University met the shortfall of £14,000. The pavilion was ready by the spring of 1969 and had two formal openings – at the School of Pharmacy's annual open day on 18 May, and at RFHSM's athletics day on 7 June.[cxxxvi] (Fig 14.8)

Fig 14.8 Pavilion at Myddleton House Sports Ground

Although the Rugby Club had many players for the 1963-4 season it often struggled to field a team and lost most matches. The following season it regularly fielded two XVs. The 1st XV began with several wins but after three games against the Metropolitan Police it had ten injured players, two being out for the rest of the season. As performances improved the 1st XV fixture list was revised to provide stronger opposition – and fewer games against the Metropolitan Police! The 2nd XV took over many of the former 1st XV fixtures.[cxxxvii]

By Christmas of the 1965-6 season the 1st team had won 10, lost 3 and drawn 1, scoring 215 points against 87. The 2nd XV now had a full fixture list (playing twice a week), and despite losing key players when 1st XV members were injured no match was cancelled.[cxxxviii]

---

69 The LVRPA controls a long narrow park linking East India Dock Basin to Ware in Hertfordshire. The largest site near London dedicated to recreational use, it was the venue for the 2012 Olympic Games.

In 1967-8 the club won the Chelsea College Sevens and reached the final of the University's Gutteridge Cup. In January 1970, after four years of trying, it had its first success in the main Hospitals Cup competition, beating King's by 20-8 in a first-round replay. That season three XVs were fielded.[cxxxix]

From 1962 to 1975 the Magazine reported on only two cricket seasons and then only about a men's team. In 1964 many matches were cancelled owing to bad weather or impending examinations. However Bart's were beaten by nine wickets and were outplayed again in 1965 when the Free scored 143 for 9; Bart's scraped a draw at 58 for 9. That year the team performed well but, with half the side unable to play, the Free had to withdraw from the semi-final of the United Hospitals Cup.[cxl]

In the early 1960s the women's Boat Club flourished under Professor Hill's presidency. It had good boats and coaching, and excellent facilities at Chiswick. Each year one or two crews competed against college crews from all over Britain at the Durham Regatta, where Hill was a well known figure. In May 1964 the Dean launched 'Borborygmi' – a new clinker IV, which was the envy of other clubs.[cxli]

In 1965 four RFHSM women rowed for the University and for England but their frequent absence meant that the School's crews achieved limited success at regattas, although at Durham a Royal Free IV reached the final of the Novices' event. Margaret Gladden, captain and stroke of the University VIII, qualified in 1965; soon afterwards she represented Great Britain in the single sculls at the European Championships.[cxlii]

The Squash Club used the nearby Tonbridge Club in Cromer Street until 1964 when a court became available twice a week at Canterbury Hall. However most matches still had to be played away, and the club performed poorly in competitions.[cxliii]

In 1964-5 RFHSM, jointly with the School of Pharmacy, formed a Judo Club and a Rifle Club. Initially all the RFHSM members were beginners at judo, but in 1968 Herma Carpenter was awarded a University purple.[cxliv]

In December 1963 the Fencing Club, although virtually defunct, requested a Union grant so that its two members could receive coaching at Regent Street Polytechnic. Individuals performed well. In 1966-7 Kenneth Pearman was Junior Fencing Champion of Great Britain, and in 1974 Nick Bell won gold with the England men's foil team at the Commonwealth Championships in Ottawa as well as a bronze individual medal; he also represented Britain at the World Championships in Grenoble.[cxlv]

A men's rowing club was started in January 1964, and a men's tennis club about a year later. But the club with the most dramatic initial impact was the Men's Athletic Club – formed in March 1964 with Qvist as president, McLaughlin captain, and Gaynor secretary. Two months later some of the team failed to turn up at the University championships so McLaughlin competed in seven events, Terry Meanley in five, and Gaynor in three – and the track events involved heats! Six others competed in one or two events. McLaughlin reached five finals and Gaynor two. With a favourable handicap of 45 points the team accrued enough points to win the Thierry Trophy, the first sporting prize to be awarded to RFHSM men. That year McLaughlin and Meanley represented the University; the former also ran for United Hospitals and Yorkshire, and represented England against Ireland.[cxlvi]

A stronger RFHSM team participated the following year. Its handicap was cut to 18 but with this, and a tally of 25 points, the team retained the Thierry Trophy, edging out Westminster and St Mary's.[cxlvii]

At Myddleton House on 12 June 1965 intermittent rain failed to dampen enthusiasm at the Royal Free's first sports day for many years. Students, nurses, physiotherapists and radiographers competed in tugs-of-war and five-legged races as well as track and field events. Ian Ross excelled over short-distances, Allan Gayner over middle distances, and Jennifer Clay and Sherwood Burge in the long distance events. The 2nd year students were overall winners, and the Victor Ludorum Cup went to Deborah Meanley (Terry's sister).[cxlviii]

A Darts Club was founded in May 1963. In its first match it beat St. George's (considered the strongest hospital side) and subsequently bested the Household Cavalry, the Gentlemen of Marylebone, the Beaumont Union, the City Slickers and the Royal Naval Reserve. However it lost to the Scots Guards and, after its annual dinner at 'The Sun in Splendour' in May 1965 it lost, perhaps not surprisingly, to the landlord's team. Two months later it toured Dorset, Devon and Cornwall. Understandably it was not affiliated with the Students' Union.[cxlix]

In the 1960s and early 70s the two big events in the School's social calendar were the Winter Ball, held at a leading hotel, and a Summer Ball, usually staged at Hunter Street, the quadrangle being transformed with exotic scenery and lighting effects. In 1966 a Summer Ball was deemed too expensive, as it was in 1969 when a Myddleton House barbecue was held instead. The annual Rugby Club ball remained popular.[cl]

The Old Students Association (OSA) continued to run its annual clinical meeting for former students. Held on a Thursday/Friday in November it was organised by the consultant responsible for postgraduate education at RFH.[70] In 1971 the cardiologist Cecil Symons persuaded RFH's Board of Governors to institute an annual Marsden Lecture, and it was decided to link it with the OSA's clinical meeting. Dr Henry Miller of Newcastle gave the first one in the outpatient hall at

[70] Ian Bouchier and then Derek Jewell.

GIR on Thursday 25 November 1971. The following year Ian Ramsey, Bishop of Durham was due to speak; sadly he died on 6 October and so no lecture took place. The speaker in 1973 was Sir Keith Joseph, the Secretary of State for Social Services – a department which then included Health and Social Security.

The OSA's formal dinner, held at the Savoy, although originally an annual affair, had been triennial following the decision made in 1959. (See Chapter 13) There were 263 at the 1964 dinner, 175 in 1967, 263 in 1970, and approximately 250 in 1973. At the 1967 dinner, which cost four guineas, the Bishop of Southampton proposed a toast to 'The Hospital and Medical School', to which Melvin Ramsay responded; Jocelyn Moore responded to a toast to 'The Old Students Association' proposed by Mrs Margaret Thatcher, MP, the future Prime Minister, whose husband Denis was to join RFHSM's Council in 1978.

From 1895 the School's Magazine (but called the *Royal Free Hospital Journal* from 1958)[71] was a wonderful source of information about the social, sporting and professional life of School and Hospital.[72] It reported examination results, the fate of old students, and births, marriages and deaths. Sadly it deteriorated during Gardner's deanship.

It remained more or less quarterly for three years – with March, June, September and/or December issues. Sadly issue and volume numbers again became chaotic (see Chapter 13). The September 1964 issue was Vol XXVII No. 84; Winter 1964/5 was Vol XXVII No. 85. But Vols XXVIII and XXIX were single issues – both numbered 85. Three more Vol XXIXs followed – Nos. 86, 87 & 88! There was seasonal nomenclature until 'Autumn 1967' (Vol XXXI No. 89) but then three issues (Vol XXXI No. 92 & Vol XXXII Nos. 93 & 94) gave no indication of the year, season or month of issue either inside or outside the journal. Seasonal labelling resumed with Vol XXXII No. 95 (Winter) and continued for Vol XXXIII Nos. 1, 2 3, 4 (the last erroneously labeled Vol XXXIV: the covers of these five issues displayed anatomical drawings from Cortonense & Romano's '*Tabulae Anatomicae'* (1741) and were the finest covers in the Magazine's history.

Most of the eleven editors between 1962 and 1974 had to plead for articles. Although the Autumn 1965 editorial noted a heartening response to an appeal for contributions a letter in the same issue asked what function the Magazine was supposed to serve – as 'To maintain this magazine in its present moribund state can surely only do the Royal Free a disservice.'

Perhaps in response to that letter the Winter/Spring 1965/6 issue announced changes in the journal's constitution, and formation of a management committee

[71] It was published by the Students' Union until the end.

[72] It was initially entitled the '*Magazine of LSMW and RFH*'.

of senior staff to provide stability and continuity. However the fuller details promised in the next edition did not materialize; the only obvious change was that the anaesthetist Hilary Howells became Hospital Sub-editor.

September 1958 was the last issue to contain a substantial section (four pages) entitled 'Reports of Union societies and clubs' Such submissions gradually dwindled away, as did announcements of 'Births, Marriages and/or Deaths' and of examination results. The items were no longer properly indexed and can be found now only if one has a proper reference (a problem in itself), serendipitously, or by wading through many volumes and pages.

The editors' lives were not happy ones. In the Summer 1967 issue the editor complained his task was unrewarding and difficult, entertainment appearing to be the Journal's only function. It contained too few original papers and he considered 'Free Comment' a better student newsletter. The Magazine cost about £1200 a year to produce; old students' subscriptions raised only £120. Some money came from advertisers and the Board of Governors took 300 copies, considering it a House Journal for RFH. In the first issue of 1970 the new editor describes the previous editor as fading *'quietly from the scene of so much abuse with hardly a word of thanks being offered to him*'.

Financial problems – apparently some subscriptions were not forthcoming – caused a nine month delay in the appearance of the lone 1972 issue, (No 98 Vol XXXV), which had a new look, size and format. Dr. Doreen Brown had joined the Editorial Committee in the hope that news of OSA meetings would promote a liaison between students and old students. Maria Scouros, the first female editor for some years, was clearly exasperated and questioned whether staff and students wanted a journal or not. Her successor, Anabelle Baugham, started off 'with wild unrealistic enthusiasm…determined to bring out three thick interesting Journals this year'. There were two thin ones. In the second of them (Winter 1973) she noted that thirty people were asked directly to write articles; all refused. Of the twenty people she wrote to only one replied – and said no! No one would help on the business side of the Journal and the sub-editor, who would have been expected to replace her, declined to do so.

The situation was clearly desperate. Roger Crabtree agreed to become editor for the Centenary issue of the Journal in 1974. It turned out to be the final issue, even though his editorial announced '*Our plans…are to publish two editions every year…As for content, the new offer of £3 for every contribution printed has been well received and it is hoped that this…will once again spark off the letters column and an interchange of ideas and opinions in these pages*'. It didn't.

At AGM of OSA Nov 1976 Dr Jean Infield expressed concern about the demise of the Magazine/Journal; even though it had appeared less frequently it was a way in which old students could stay in touch with the School. It was a sad feature of Gardner's last years as Dean and one wonders why it was simply allowed to happen.

The Centenary Celebrations

The centenary celebrations in 1974 were far less grand than those for the Jubilee in 1924. (Chapter 11) The thanksgiving service was held on 10 June in the University Church of Christ the King. It was attended by Queen Elizabeth the Queen Mother, the University's Chancellor. Sir Colin Anderson gave the address and the Bishop of Edmonton the blessing.[cli]

Gerald Nevitt, a final year student, composed the fanfare played as the Queen Mother entered the Church; fellow students provided the choir. After the service over 600 attended a Senate House reception where there was an exhibition covering the School's history.[73] For some weeks afterwards the exhibition was open to the public in the Hunter Street physiology laboratory.

The Centenary Festival lasted two weeks, and was blessed by good weather. The Dramatic Society gave five performances of Shakespeare's 'The Comedy of Errors'. On three evenings a musical soirée started with a festival overture, 'The Rights of Women', composed and conducted by Nevitt.[74] It concluded with a masque-oratorio, 'The Wisdom of Solomon', commissioned especially for the centenary and conducted by its composer, Francis Shaw. On two evenings there was a display of African dancing – followed on the first evening by an African play, and on the second by whole audience participation in African style dancing. The 'Cantores Medicini' gave a concert.

For many the highlight of the festival was a *son et lumière* covering the School's history. It was performed in the quadrangle and brought each evening to an end – except for that ending with communal African dancing.

In June 1972 Council had begun considering an appeal for funds to mark the Centenary of LSMW/RFHSM. After large grants became available from public funds gifts were no longer essential for the School's survival but were still invaluable for other purposes. Council thought that potential donors needed to be made aware of the specific objectives of the appeal if it was to succeed, – e.g. programmes of research and/or endowment of Chairs to be associated with the new Hampstead complex, and in particular the Clinical Sciences building, which was to preserve the identity of the School as opposed to the Hospital. Other developments considered worthy of support were a recreational centre for Royal

[73] Arranged by Ruth Bowden and Edith Gilchrist.

[74] For several years Nevitt also wrote the overture for the Christmas Show..

Free staff and students, and funding of mid-career training/retraining for RFHSM graduates.[clii]

Council and the Board of Governors initially determined on a single appeal to mark both the School's Centenary and the opening of the new RFH in 1974 which coincided with it. The Appeal Committee set up to identify the specific objectives included staff, students and lay persons; Peter Samuel was its chairman.[cliii]

In 1924 the School had initiated an appeal to endow three chairs bearing the names of Blackwell, Jex-Blake and Garrett Anderson, but RFH had already appealed directly for funds to past students in connection with the RFH jubilee due in 1928. Council therefore thought it inappropriate to approach them again about the endowment fund. (See Chapter 9)

A similar situation had now arisen. In February 1973 Council considered the need to avoid a conflict between its Centenary Appeal, an appeal seeking support for the Royal Free Research Trust (initiated by Mr Jarvis Astaire), and a possible appeal for funds for amenities for the new hospital. During the discussion it was noted that RFHSM had to obtain the University's permission before making a public appeal or accepting any benefaction.[75] It was eventually agreed in principle that a Centenary Appeal Committee be set up to examine the objectives, methods and timing of the appeal, to coordinate with RFH, and to consult with staff and students. Council was represented by its Chairman, the Dean and Dr Haram: the Education Committee, the MAC, the ASA, and the Students Union each nominated a representative.[cliv]

In the event plans for the School's appeal fizzled out. The annual report for 1973-4 noted *'It had been hoped that the Centenary celebrations would be linked with the completion of the new hospital at Hampstead to provide a suitable background to the launching of a joint Royal Free Hospital and School Appeal for funds. Delays in completion of the building programme and the inauspicious economic climate made it necessary to defer the Appeal. However the Appeal Committee continued working to establish a Charitable Trust and to prepare Appeal literature.'* [76,clv]

In 1965, following a request from the Education Committee (made two years earlier), the Academic Staff Association (ASA) agreed to admit as members full-time academic staff in pathology and medicine.[77] As a quid pro quo its representation on the Education Committee was increased from six to eight. In

[75] In accordance with University of London statute 38.

[76] It was suggested that some RFHSM representatives were unhappy about a joint appeal, as they considered the boxing promoter and business tycoon Jarvis Astaire 'persona non grata'.

[77] The academic departments of pathology and medicine were created in 1920 and 1959 respectively..

1967, because of the anticipated increase in clinical academic staff, the ASA suggested amending article 9 of the charter, which allowed only two preclinical and two clinical teachers to serve on Council. Clinical academics were particularly disadvantaged as the two clinical places were traditionally held by the senior physician and senior surgeon, and occupied since 1960 by Lee Lander & George Qvist.[78, clvi]

A subcommittee was set up to consider revision of the charter, Richardson said the Medical Committee, of which he was secretary, now wanted its chairman and secretary to represent it on Council.[79] He also said that while it rejected 'sectional' representation, wanting as it did to blur the distinction between full and part-time teachers, it acknowledged the clinical academics' problem. The Dean suggested the subcommittee should make no decision about representation, given the Principal's advice 'that the [University] Committee on Organisation and Administration of Schools (COAS) were…considering…representation of teaching staff on councils of medical schools' – the inference being that the Principal advised against taking action.[clvii]

Over three years later ASA asked what progress COAS had made. Told that a reply was awaited it requested further discussions about the charter. Lucy said colleagues now wanted more than four teachers (plus the Dean and Vice-dean) on a Council of twenty, which alone appointed the Dean. However, Simons clouded the issue by interjecting that the main problem was the excessive size of the Education Committee.[clviii]

Council's chairman said staff could be consulted about appointing the Dean, and that the Education Committee could be improved without revising the charter. He suggested ASA should nominate one of the six 'other persons' elected to Council by Members of the School. Two such vacancies had existed for some years and by this route Sherlock joined Council at the Members' next AGM.[80] Sir Donald also offered ASA two 'observers' at Council (Bouchier and Hodges were elected) and assured it of wide consultation over future appointments of deans. However, ASA remained unhappy and continued to press for charter revision.[clix]

In November Anderson told Council it must identify problems soluble only by revising the charter. ASA wanted discussions about the role of deans and the method of electing them. The Charter simply stated 'The Dean shall be appointed by Council'. Acland's statement in 1926 that it was customary for the School Committee (later the Education Committee) to nominate the dean was either long forgotten or simply ignored. Anderson said that before Gardner's election a Council

[78] Neither of whom would have been considered as appropriate representatives by clinical academics.

[79] i.e. Lee Lander and Richardson, rather than Lee Lander and Qvist.

[80] Sherlock had then been at the School twelve years.

subcommittee had consulted the Medical Committee's chairman, the senior professor and the then dean, and had been 'open to receive suggestions…from medical and academic staff' about suitable candidates. There was no record of how suggestions were sought, but there was wide consultation over a long time.[81] Anderson believed Council's wish to consult in future about the terms of appointment and the appointee had to be governed by the situation at the time.[clx]

At Council in June 1972 Anderson announced Gardner's wish to resign in September 1973. However, he said the negotiations needed with the UGC, the University and UCL would tax a new dean. He had consulted some teachers, Council members and observers; while their views were not unanimous most wanted her to stay on for a limited period.[clxi]

After Gardner left the room someone suggested Council should either accept her resignation or start discussions with the Education Committee and ASA. ASA's 'clinical' observer[82] said that for a year teachers had wanted the whole issue of appointing a Dean examined, and that her retirement should not be postponed without further discussions. The 'preclinical' observer[83] said his colleagues wanted Gardner to stay on, but agreed consultations should begin about the method of appointing a Dean.

Anderson thought it improper for bodies other than Council to discuss the situation. At its next meeting Gardner accepted its invitation to continue until September 1976.[clxii]

The decision to extend Gardner's appointment, without the wide consultation promised less than a year earlier, was received angrily at the Hospital. Thirty consultants (academic and NHS)[84] signed a letter, dated 6 July 1972, asking that a committee examine all matters relating to the School's future.

On 12 July Council discussed the letter, which mentioned poor communication between clinicians and the School and its governing body, dissatisfaction about School matters, and the lack of a clear policy for deploying the CSB at Hampstead. It suggested RFHSM's representatives operated on an ad hoc basis in negotiations with UCL/UCHMS, without a well prepared brief; matters were thus determined largely by UCL representatives to the detriment of RFHSM's future. The

[81] Not strictly true. When Lloyd-Williams said she would retire in September 1961 the subcommittee to choose her successor was to consult the chairman of RFH's Medical Committee, the senior professor and the Dean, and receive suggestions from clinical and academic staff. Lloyd-Williams had agreed to continue until September 1962 at Council on 1 February 1961; on that day the subcommittee recommended Gardner should succeed her.

[82] Ian Bouchier (Medicine).

[83] Bob Hodges (Pharmacology)

[84] There were initially 31, but one withdrew his name.

signatories considered Council's non-representational character (and the poor access to it) inimical to the School's best interests. Council needed to be a forum representing wide interests, one receiving information and recommendations from the general body of opinion on School affairs. RFHSM was the only London teaching school without an adequate balloting procedure for the election of its academic officers.

Council thought action was needed before its October meeting, and Anderson expressed willingness to investigate the criticisms in order to correct deficiencies found to exist.

Council representatives met MacGillivray and five other signatories on 20 September to discuss the 6 July letter. Anderson first quoted the unconfirmed minutes of an ASA meeting on 26 June stating that he 'had assured the ASA Chairman that in future appropriate consultations would be taken regarding the appointment of the Dean', and that 'many members felt that the action of Council (i.e. asking Gardner to continue in office until 1976) was not in accord with the spirit of his letters of 2 August and 17 November 1971 or the letter of 20 June 1972.' Anderson argued that postponing the retirement of a Dean was quite different from appointing a new Dean; not everyone was convinced.

The signatories present subsequently reviewed a draft report of the 20 September meeting. In a letter to Moore, the School Secretary, Havard [85] corrected some of the statements in the draft report; he also mentioned that the meeting had not been harmonious and wrote that '…the Chairman's aggressive attitude towards the deputation on September 20th has aggravated the discontent we had hoped to heal'.

At Council on 11 October Anderson implied that its real problem was its relationship with the Education Committee. Council's representatives at the 20 September meeting had suggested that that relationship should be considered by a working party whose composition and remit needed to be determined. Sherlock said the remit should extend beyond the Education Committee and that changes in the Charter should also be considered. Patrick Salmon, a lay member of Council, supported her and it was agreed 'That a working party be set up to examine and make recommendations on: i) the composition, method of election, terms of reference and title of the Education Committee and of its subcommittees; and ii) the representation of teachers in the committee structure of the school.' Its terms of reference were to be interpreted fairly widely.

The working party (four preclinical teachers, three senior clinical academics,

[85] MacGillivray was in South Africa for family reasons.

and four RFH consultants)[86] elected the psychiatrist Gerald Russell as chairman. The Students' Union president (Chris Zachary) asked if students could attend discussions on the committee structure.[clxiii]

The working party first met in November. It held twenty-seven meetings and admitted student representatives after confidential discussions were completed. Its interim report was received at Council on 14 February; that meeting was chaired by Peter Samuel as Sir Donald was ill and died five weeks later. The final report (of twenty-seven pages),[87] went to Council on 11 July, and was then distributed to all teachers and to the Students' Union committee.[clxiv]

To ensure fuller representation of teachers the working party recommended enlarging the Education Committee and the setting up of a Committee of Teachers, composed of all academic staff, which should meet at least yearly.[88] Advisory Boards of Studies (ABSs) were to replace AASCs and do much of the work needed before recommendations went to the Education Committee, the policy-forming body on all academic issues.

The report was favourably received by the Education Committee, the ASA and RFH's Medical Advisory Committee. After discussing their comments Council agreed on 13 March 1974 that the report's constitutional proposals, with amendments, would be implemented from 1 October 1974. The new committee structure was to be re-examined after three to five years.

The enlarged Education Committee, with a quorum set at a third of its membership, could no longer meet in the Council Room. Its subcommittees determined their own quorum. ASA's chairman joined the Education Committee ex officio.[clxv]

The working party proposed that the Education Committee should nominate the Dean. Council wanted a committee '*to consider the office and function of the Dean and the procedure...for consultation over the appointment of a Dean*', but the Education Committee wanted assurance that a Dean would be elected. Samuel suggested 'the procedure...for consultation over the Dean's nomination by election', but Sherlock said this did not indicate who would do the electing. Eventually Council accepted Scheuer's suggestion of 'a committee to look into the working party's recommendation on the nomination and appointment of the Dean'.[clxvi]

---

86 Professor CBB Downman, Dr JWS Harris, Dr MJ Maclagan, Professor HAB Simons, Professor CP Douglas, Dr N McIntyre, Professor GSM Russell, Miss PA George, Dr CWH Havard, Dr EDR Campbell & Dr BB MacGillivray,

87 I could find no copy of the complete report in the Royal Free archives.

88 Council agreed that a meeting of the Committee of Teachers should be convened if called by ten or more teachers..

Samuel suggested all its members should be from Council; Sherlock wanted full time and part-time teachers included, plus a student and the chairman of the Education Committee, which she suggested should organise the working party. Council's approval of Samuel's proposed committee[89] disturbed the Education Committee and ASA. In June Samuel said Council's motives had been misunderstood and suggested that a questionnaire about the appointment of a Dean should go to the Education Committee, ASA and the MAC; if there was no consensus the matter was to go to the Committee of Teachers.[clxvii]

Campbell's appointment as clinical sub-dean expired on 30 September 1974, when his second year as Vice-dean started. When the Dean asked Council to renew his appointment for another year Sherlock said the matter should be discussed at the Education Committee. Samuel agreed, but said reappointing him would provide the Dean with assistance until such discussions took place; Campbell was reappointed.[clxviii]

The proposed new Council was similar to its predecessor, but included two student representatives. There was initially no observer from ASA. It had requested one in December 1974, arguing that its two observers had been its only formal source of information about Council's meetings. An ASA observer was added to the 1975-77 Council.[clxix]

The first meeting of the new Council in March 1975 received Gardner's resignation with effect from 30 September 1975, a year earlier than expected. The consensus reached via the questionnaire regarding the appointment of a Dean was that the Education Committee should receive a nomination from the Committee of Teachers, which should also decide whether the appointment should be advertised. External and internal candidates were acceptable, as was a part-time or full-time appointment. A five year term was favoured, with the possibility of re-election (again via the Committee of Teachers). Appointment of sub-deans was to be at the Dean's discretion. Council asked the Education Committee's chairman to convene a meeting of the Committee of Teachers to arrange for the nomination of a Dean to take office from 1 October.[clxx]

Following a postal vote in which no one received an overall majority the Committee of Teachers nominated the two leading candidates (Douglas & MacGillivray) to the Education Committee. It made the final decision by counting the votes of those present at its next meeting plus those of individuals who voted by proxy. On 23 July Council appointed MacGillivray as Dean from 1 October.[clxxi]

---

[89] Samuel himself; the chairmen of the Finance Committee, the MAC and the Education Committee; the University representative on Council, and one preclinical (Bowden) and one clinical (Sherlock) appointed teacher.

In June 1975 Gardner was appointed DBE in the Birthday Honours List. As it was International Women's Year six such awards were made instead of the usual one. Her co-recipients were Vera Lynn, Wendy Hiller, Betty Ridley, Bridget D'Oyly Carte and Margaret Kidd.

Gardner stepped down as Dean in September 1975 and retired from the staff of RFH in 1978. That year Lawson died and she was elected, unopposed, to replace him as RFHSM's President. In retirement Dame Frances indulged her passion for gardening. The Highgate Horticultural Society commemorates her annually at its autumn meeting by awarding the Dame Frances Gardner Cup for the best single vegetable exhibit. Although she usually drove a Rolls-Royce she used an electric milk float to reach her allotment. Dame Frances died at home, Fitzroy Lodge, Fitzroy Park, on 10 July 1989. The funeral service was at St Anne's, Highgate.

CHAPTER 15

Bruce MacGillivray (1975–1989)

School and Hospital – Together at last ......

Barron Bruce MacGillivray (Fig 15.1) was born in Durban, South Africa, on 21 August 1927. His Scottish father, John, ran a dairy farm 25 miles north of Johannesburg and also a company importing builders' hardware. His mother, Doreen (née Eastwood), was a nurse – born in Durban, but half-Swedish. Bruce boarded at Johannesburg's King Edward VII School from the age of six. His father died in 1939. The following year the school allowed Bruce use of its facilities to start a night school that taught reading, writing and general knowledge to local black people.

In 1946 he entered the University of Witwatersrand medical school. During an intercalated B.Sc. he studied neuroanatomy – particularly that of the tortoise brain. He was a member of the National Union of Students and sat on the medical school's council. In 1951, distressed by apartheid, he used a small legacy to move to Britain. He entered Manchester's medical school and qualified LRCP MRCS in 1955. That year he married Ruth Valentine, a fellow student. After house jobs at Manchester Royal Infirmary he spent two years as RMO at Stockport's Stepping Hill Hospital and acquired the MCRP in 1959. External students could then sit for London University's medical degree. After first passing its 2nd MB he went on to graduate MBBS in 1962. By then he had spent three years at the National Hospital for Nervous Diseases as registrar and senior registrar. In 1964 RFH appointed him consultant in clinical neurophysiology & neurology, but before starting the post he spent a year as a research fellow at the University of California Los Angeles. The National Hospital made him a consultant in 1971.

MacGillivray, with two sons and a daughter, was only the second of the School's deans to have offspring. Of the five other deans who had married four were childless: namely Anstie (who died before LSMW opened), Norton (who was single while dean), Barrett and Gardner. The fifth was Garrett Anderson and the School Council which MacGillivray joined as Dean was the first for about sixty years not to have one of her descendants as a member.[1]

---

[1] Donald died 1973. Sister Diana left Council in 1974 & died 6 May 2003, age 92. Brother Colin died 1980.

Fig 15.1 Bruce MacGillivray (1927-2010)

Another family had a longstanding representation on Council. Peter Samuel, its chairman in 1975, had been a member since 1947. He was a major benefactor of School and Hospital, and played an important role at both institutions. In October 1981 he announced his wish to resign as chairman. His brother-in-law, the Hon L.H.L. ('Tim') Cohen,[2] was chosen to succeed him. Cohen joined Council in March 1982 and assumed the chair in November. Following his brother's death in 1986 Samuel was ennobled as the 4th Viscount Bearsted. His son, the Hon Nicholas Samuel, replaced him on Council in 1988. (See also Chapter 16) [i]

The other key lay member of MacGillivray's Council was David Webb – Honorary Treasurer and chairman ex officio of the Finance and General Purposes Committee (FGPC). When he resigned in 1984 Robin Fox became treasurer. Webb left Council in December 1985.[ii]

Mrs Robinson retired as School Secretary in July 1976. Her replacement was Geoffrey Fenn, assistant secretary at the School of Oriental and African Studies. A member of the London Society of Rugby Football Union Referees, Fenn was a friend of its treasurer, Denis Thatcher, husband of the soon-to-be Prime Minister, who replaced Chesterton on Council in February 1978; Thatcher attended regularly before resigning in November 1982.[3] Ill-health forced Fenn's resignation in October 1984; he died the following March. His successor, Bryan Blatch,[4] was, like Fenn, a sports enthusiast; both were popular with the students.[iii]

The University was entitled to two representatives on Council. Dr Frank Hartley, Dean of the School of Pharmacy, served alone from 1970 until 1978 when he was joined by Professor Sir George Smart who served four years. Smart's replacement, on Council and as director of the British Postgraduate Medical Federation, was the

---

[2] 'Tim' Cohen, son of Lord Cohen, a Law Lord, was educated at Eton and Oxford. Severely wounded during the Second World War he later became a barrister, a director of Hill Samuel & Co, and a Master of the Skinners' Company.

[3] When Chesterton left Council in February 1978 Giles Lascelles became Vice-chairman.

[4] Blatch, an LSE graduate, had worked in the Overseas Colonial Service, at the Senate House and as a sugar planter in the Sudan; he joined RFHSM from the Royal National Throat Nose & Ear Hospital.

surgeon David Innes Williams.[5] Hartley, London's Vice-Chancellor from 1976-8, was knighted in January 1977 and remained on Council until 1988. He was replaced in November 1989 by Tony Diplock, the new dean of the Faculty of Medicine, who had left RFHSM in 1977 for the chair of biochemistry at Guy's.[iv]

Dame Anne Bryans, Wells, Evans and Salmon were Camden and Islington AHA's four representatives on Council in 1975. In 1978 the last two gave way to J. N. Harvey and Arthur Soutter, who were replaced in turn by Gwyneth Williams and Hazel Allen. The 1982 NHS reorganisation abolished AHAs, so when Jennifer Walden and John Carrier joined Council, replacing Dame Anne and Allen, they, like Wells and Williams, represented Hampstead Health Authority (HHA).[6] Rosemary Bondy replaced Walden in October 1983, and Diana Ratzer took Williams's place in October 1986. There were no further changes in HHA's representation during MacGillivray's deanship.[v]

In 1975 Professor Downman was the Education Committee chairman and *eo ipso* Vice-Dean – posts held contemporaneously for two calendar years. Professors Baron and Harris followed him. The physician Bill Havard was appointed for 1981 & 1982 but continued until December 1983 as the term of office was increased to three years. He was succeeded by Lucy, and then by Scheuer who was still in post when MacGillivray retired in 1989.[vi]

In 1968 Gardner created the post of 'Clinical Sub Dean'. The incumbent was to help in the supervision of pre-registration house jobs. MacGillivray appointed Ken Hobbs to the post from January 1976, but changed the title to 'Postgraduate Sub-Dean'. Hobbs served five years.[7] The surgeon Adam Lewis took over in 1981; he was followed by the physicians Ron Dubois (1985-7) and Paul Sweny (1987-90).[vii]

The title 'Clinical Sub-Dean' was retained but the role now involved supervision of the education of undergraduates not postgraduates. McIntyre assumed the post in October 1976 to oversee the introduction of the new clinical curriculum. He was succeeded by Wakeling (1981-5) and Pounder (1986-90).[viii]

The post of 'Clinical Tutor' was re-introduced in May 1976. Derek Jewell held it before leaving for Oxford in 1980. His replacement, Dubois, switched to the Postgraduate Sub-Deanship in June 1985, but moved to the Brompton Hospital in 1988. Sweny succeeded him both as Clinical Tutor and Postgraduate Sub-Dean – Owen Epstein replacing Sweny as Clinical Tutor.

In December 1977 Council agreed the appointment of a sub-dean to chair an

---

[5] Sir David from June 1985.

[6] Wells was chairman of HHA – and then of RFH NHS Hospital Trust until Carrier took over in 1994.

[7] Sub-deans were intended to serve for three yrs., but from 1978 they could be re-nominated for up to a maximum of five yrs.

Admissions Advisory Committee which also included the Dean, three preclinical and three clinical teachers, a member of the General Practice Unit, and the School's Secretary and Registrar. Peter Scheuer was the first Admissions Sub-Dean.[ix]

MacGillivray, at his first Council meeting as Dean, reported that St George's Hospital Medical School, Tooting, was now top of the UGC's list of priorities. The UCRF project had dropped to fourth place. UGC members visiting in November were sympathetic about the School having to operate on two sites but said that if modification of the CSB was contemplated, so as to accommodate the whole School at Hampstead, the University would need detailed plans – and as merger remained official policy it was unlikely the UGC would provide funds for it.[x]

In May 1976 the architects reported that if all the preclinical students were to be accommodated at Hampstead the CSB would need enlarging by 20,000 sq.ft. – either on top of Stage II or in the car park area to the south. More design work was needed urgently if work on the CSB was to start when Stage I was completed – as there were potential problems with positioning of the post-mortem room.[xi]

A proposal 'to enhance the CSB' was drafted for submission to the University and for discussion with other 'interested parties'. Intolerable overcrowding was foreseen if the preclinicals moved to Hampstead without the CSB being enlarged – but few problems if space was added to house anatomy, biochemistry, administrative offices, a lecture theatre and general users' teaching laboratories. The £1million extension proposed would take eighteen months to build – with little modification of the existing structure – and, being adaptable to other use, would not hinder the UCRF merger.[xii]

Following problems with commissioning of the CSB the Dean suggested telling the UGC it would be used as originally planned – to house departments supporting the planned integrated curriculum and to facilitate clinical research. Some preclinical departments could then, wholly or partly, occupy parts of the CSB; the other parts would remain empty until firm decisions were made about their use.[xiii]

Before the new hospital became fully operational an event occurred which became a part of 'Pond Street' folklore. One night a white MG Sprite[8] was seen driving up and down the main corridor leading from the Pond Street entrance of the Hospital; it left 15 ft skid marks on the floor and scratches on the door through which it entered and left. Press reports suggest the incident happened at 3 a.m. Sunday 4 July 1976 (but one of the drivers claims it was some days earlier). Initially male medical students got the blame but the culprits were three doctors – Anita Harding, the owner of the car, who had been an HP at RFH the previous

[8] Not a Triumph Spitfire or a 2CV, as some sources suggested.

year; Murdoch Laing, who had just finished the same HP post; and a locum registrar who had been working with him. The three confessed, were reprimanded and fined £30 each. Their names were not released to the press. The Sprite was not the first vehicle driven down those corridors. The former Dean, Dame Frances Gardner, had traversed them in her milk float for a scene to be shown in the film ending the students' Xmas Show.[xiv]

Financial Matters

RFHSM's financial situation was dire. The annual inflation rate, about 24% in 1975, stayed in double figures until 1981.[9] MacGillivray was unaware of the size of the School's 1976-7 block grant until May 1976,[10] so budgeting was largely guesswork although the strict national pay policy then in force made it easier to allow for salary increases.[xv]

Uncertainty was exacerbated in 1976 with the report of the Resource Allocation Working Party (RAWP) set up to try to ensure that regional resources were allocated on the basis of health care need.[xvi] RAWP deemed funding for central London and its teaching hospitals over-generous, and suggested its reduction by national and regional redistribution. Had the RAWP proposals been implemented promptly and fully London's teaching hospitals would have been particularly hard hit but there was a short delay before action was taken. This, and the provision of a **S**ervice **I**ncrement **F**or **T**eaching (SIFT) that reflected the extra costs incurred by teaching hospitals, ameliorated but did not nullify the damage.[xvii]

Sharing a modern building with RFH meant shared maintenance costs. In October 1977 RFHSM, having already contributed £600,000, still owed £350,000 towards such costs for the main building and it was shocked to learn that maintenance costs for the CSB would be an extra £500,000 a year. The AHA, following the District Finance Officer's recommendation, would not allow the CSB to open without guarantee of payment. As new hospital/school complexes faced similar maintenance costs nationally the University said the DHSS and UGC had to resolve the problem, but in December it provided another £400,000 towards such costs.[xviii]

The CSB was handed over in January 1978 and £550,000 was provided for equipment and furniture. Commissioning problems were exacerbated by industrial action, which prolonged installation of telephones and hampered some essential works; by inadequacy of staffing for domestic services and maintenance; and by failure of suppliers to deliver furniture and equipment on time.[xix]

---

[9] Except in 1978 when it was 8.3%.

[10] 1976-7 was the last year of that quinquennium and of the quinquennial system itself. However universities still had to prepare estimates for what might have been the next quinquennium.

Fig 15.2 Clinical Sciences Building 1978

The building was welcomed. (Fig 15.2) For the first time in the School's history it had purpose-built clinical lecture theatres and teaching facilities. An assembly hall seated 500 for academic functions, stage presentations and conferences.[11] (Fig 15.3) Two large lecture theatres accommodated 250 and 100, while a smaller one had excellent audio-visual aids for pathology demonstrations. Students had a junior common room, a bar, television and table tennis rooms, a writing room, Union offices, and two squash courts, and there were common rooms for senior staff and for technicians. The CSB also housed the Katharine Dormandy Haemophilia Centre and Haemostasis Unit, and a Neurological Sciences department.[12]

Medical physics, pharmacology, physiology, cell studies and part of anatomy and biomechanics soon moved to Hampstead. Biochemistry, some anatomy, the photographic unit,[13] the interdepartmental workshop, and most of the administration remained at Hunter Street. Staff and students were stretched by the commuting between Hampstead and Hunter Street, especially for anatomy teaching. The Queen formally opened the new complex on 15 November 1978, the year of RFH's 150th anniversary. After a ceremony in the new Assembly Hall she toured the building, visited the Medical Library and the main multi-user laboratory,

[11] It had facilities for simultaneous translation.

[12] Funded largely by a grant from the Muscular Dystrophy Group.

[13] Subsequently there was a shared photographic unit in the main Hospital building at Hampstead.

Fig 15.3 Assembly Hall

unveiled a commemorative plaque, and met students and staff. (15.4 Colour plate)[14,xx]

By early February 1978 the UCRF merger was in trouble. The University's resources were depleted and its non-medical institutions and the UGC thought medicine received too big a share of them.[15] The DHSS, like 'Todd', thought reducing the number of London's medical schools might ease matters. The planned merger had been agreed on the condition that a new joint preclinical school would be built in the Gower Street area, but MacGillivray suspected it might not be built at all if the schools amalgamated too quickly.[xxi]

In March he told the Vice-Chancellor that RFHSM staff's opposed the merger; it had cost them their new medical school and made it difficult to replace staff. The School would honour its commitment to the merger if the new preclinical building became a reality but its cancellation would be considered an abrogation of the merger proposals. Initially UCL was unhappy about preclinical staff transferring to the CSB but, after a 'satisfactory' UCRF joint policy committee

---

14 A poor picture of HM! Others L to R MacGillivray, Scheuer, Dr Wendy Kelsey, McIntyre, Hobbs

15 Medicine's share rose from 30.6% in 1969-70 to 33.5% in 1978-9.

meeting in July, Council agreed the Dean should write to UCL and propose moving the whole school to Pond Street until the merger took place.[xxii]

On 23 November the UGC's chairman wrote to Annan, Hartley's replacement as Vice Chancellor,[16] that there was little prospect of funding all promised building at UCL, but that the new preclinical school might go ahead if RFHSM contributed all proceeds from the sale of Hunter Street.[17] MacGillivray deemed this unacceptable, said 'Todd' should now be abandoned, and set out for Annan the financial implications of moving RFHSM's preclinical school to Hampstead.[xxiii]

However another factor entered the equation. Annan feared that there was insufficient money to maintain all London's medical schools and postgraduate institutes so in February 1979 he set up a Working Party on Medical and Dental Teaching Resources. Chaired by Lord Flowers, Rector of Imperial College, it was to consider reorganisation of medical education in London, and the closure of some institutions.[18] 'Flowers' had serious repercussions.[19,xxiv]

On 7 February the UCRF joint committee was sympathetic about transferring the rest of Hunter Street's departments to Hampstead, presumably because it seemed unlikely that the new preclinical school would be available in the near future. UCL, UCHMS and RFHSM set up a small working party to explore other ways of collaborating – arguing that, although 'Todd' might be dead, 'Flowers' might encourage initiatives such as joint departments.[20, xxv]

When the 'Flowers' working party visited the CSB in July to discuss RFHSM's submission to it, and to hear more about the new clinical curriculum (see later), they hinted that it might be possible to move the whole School to Hampstead – if the move was funded by selling Hunter Street, if the annual student intake rose to 130, and if Barnet General, Edgware General and North Middlesex hospitals were involved in teaching.[xxvi]

The architects now suggested three ways of expanding the CSB to accommodate the whole School – building on its roof; building on stilts over the car park; or a combination of the two. The cost, £1.75 to £2.65million, was far more than the 1976 estimate of £1million, but it reflected both the high inflation rate and the extra space needed for preclinical students who would be based in Hampstead rather than Gower Street. Given the shortage of UGC funds the School hoped outside bodies might contribute to the new building.[xxvii]

---

[16] Annan resigned as Provost in 1978 to become London University's first full-time Vice- Chancellor.

[17] The UGC was entitled to the proceeds of selling the parts of Hunter Street acquired with public funds. The School kept the rest (and most) of the money.

[18] The medical members were Profs Sir John Butterfield, A. H. Crisp, J. H. Kellgren & N.F.Morris.

[19] The word 'Flowers' was often used alone to refer either to the working party or its report.

[20] MacGillivray approached UCL a year earlier about joint departments of genetics & paediatrics, as he was concerned that the Free had no academic paediatricians. (CM 1978: 8 Feb)

Government support for universities was through a 'dual-funding' system. One component was the UGC's annual 'block' grant that was part of a quinquennial allocation requested in advance; 'supplementary' grants were sometimes added to it to minimise the effects of inflation. In theory a university could distribute its share of the block grant as it wished, but the UGC often indicated areas it wanted developed. The other component was the money allocated to research councils (e.g. the Medical Research Council) for distribution to groups or departments that had applied to them for funds and were deemed worthy of support. Universities and colleges also sought money from charitable bodies, pharmaceutical companies, or directly from the public.

Thatcher's election victory in May 1979 exacerbated the financial problems of universities, which soon faced several years of 'level funding', i.e. survival on the equivalent in real terms of their 1979-80 grant.[21] The Government stopped subsidising overseas students who were therefore to pay full cost fees, but as grants were correspondingly reduced the block grant was effectively cut in real terms.[22] From 1980 less money was allocated to research councils, which were then hard pressed to fund even 'first rank' research applications.

Lord Flowers's working party was clearly influenced by the new Government's policies, as was the reaction to its report 'London Medical Education – a New Framework' which appeared in February 1980.[23] 'Flowers' suggested over £3million a year[24] would be saved if London's thirty-four separate medical and dental schools combined within six schools. Five were to be the 'Lister and St Thomas' Joint School';[25] the 'Harvey School'; 'St George's School'; 'Charing Cross School of Medicine'; and 'St Mary's and the Royal Postgraduate Joint School of Medicine and Dentistry'. Westminster Medical School was to close and there was to be no preclinical teaching at King's, the London and the Royal Free.

The sixth school suggested was University College School of Medicine and Dentistry which was to swallow up RFHSM and Middlesex Hospital Medical School (MHMS). 'Flowers' clearly considered it unjustifiable to spend £1.75million to move RFHSM's preclinical teaching to Hampstead. If that teaching could be done at UCL and MHMS it would be possible to sell Hunter Street. The planned reduction in acute beds in the associated Health Districts[26] meant their

[21] 'Level funding' was a key element of Thatcher's approach to reducing university expenditure.

[22] From October 1980 overseas clinical students paid £5,000 per annum; preclinicals paid £3000. Eight yrs. later the equivalent fees were £9860 & £5,330 respectively.

[23] The publication of the Flowers report coincided with a London Health Service Consortium report suggesting the number of acute beds in London teaching hospitals would fall by about a quarter.

[24] At 1978-9 prices.

[25] The medical schools of KCH and Guy's were to merge as the Lister School.

[26] As a consequence of RAWP.

hospitals would be unable to support the number of students then receiving clinical teaching. It was therefore suggested that the Middlesex, UCHMS and RFH should share clinical teaching with an upgraded Whittington Hospital.

'Flowers' triggered a furore. Many letters and articles, nearly all hostile, appeared in the national, local and medical press. The schools most threatened by Flowers ran vigorous campaigns to generate public support. Royal Free students produced colourful posters and windscreen stickers. (Figs 15.5 a & b Colour plate) Over 300 students from RFHSM, King's, Westminster and the Middlesex marched to the Senate House on 11 March singing and waving banners.[27] They tramped on *flowers* emptied from a coffin, burnt a copy of the report, and climbed onto the Senate house portico to chalk 'Save our Schools' slogans on the walls. RFHSM women, beautifully attired as suffragettes, chained themselves to the gates at the main entrance to the Senate House. (Fig 15.6) The demonstration received wide coverage on television and in the national press. The students cleared all the resultant debris, and received many compliments on their excellent behaviour. Five RFHSM students[28] wrote and produced a programme for BBC TV's Open Door series criticising the Flowers Report and its likely effect on RFHSM.[xxviii]

The School 'rejected' 'Flowers', but the crucial response was that of the University. When the JPC(U) reported to Senate in October it did not approve all the 'Flowers' proposals – but did recommend four mergers: Bart's & the London; Guy's, King's & St Thomas'; Westminster & Charing Cross; and UCL & the Middlesex. St George's and St Mary's were to remain independent, as was RFHSM which was to move in its entirety to Hampstead.[xxix]

The Senate rejected 'Flowers' by two votes, calling instead for 'level funding' for the medical schools. However it did agree to reconsider reduction of their preclinical capacity. The JPC(U) set up a working party, chaired by Professor Leslie Le Quesne, the Deputy Vice-Chancellor, to cost preclinical education. When it asked if it could recommend closure of a whole school it was told there was a prima facie case for closing the Royal Free, St Mary's, St Thomas' and/or Westminster. MacGillivray joined the working party later when it was asked to survey clinical as well as preclinical costs.[xxx]

After receiving the Le Quesne working party's report in March 1981 JMAC recommended *inter alia* that RFHSM should remain an independent school teaching preclinical and clinical medicine at Hampstead. The JPC(U) agreed in 'Medical Education in London, March 1981' and the Senate concurred on 25

---

27 The protest was to coincide with a meeting of the University's Joint Medical Advisory Committee.

28 Marcus Flather, Velia Wortman, Johnathan Joffe, David Veale & Elizabeth Wright.

The 1980 suffragettes

DON'T LET
FLOWERS
DESTROY
THE
ROYAL
FREE

Free protest: One of the student banners

WOMEN medical students dressed as suffragettes chained themselves to railings outside London University's Senate House yesterday.

They were protesting at the threatened closure of medical schools all over London. The 15 women, mostly from the Royal Free and Westminster Hospitals, staged a two-hour vigil.

The Royal Free School of Medicine at Hampstead, N.—along with other medical schools—faces closure if the recommendations of the Flowers Report are implemented.

Fig 15.6 'RFH suffragettes storm the Senate House' (Daily Mail 12 March 1980)

March. RFHSM was saved, at least for the time being; however the Dean pointed out that as a small medical school it might face problems in the future.[xxxi]

Plans to transfer the whole school to Hampstead were well advanced but the hope that the administration would move in September, and that there would soon be a school entrance off Rowland Hill Street, proved optimistic. Additional space for biochemistry and the rest of anatomy was to be provided by covering in a courtyard at lower ground floor level, building up to the roof on one side of the courtyard, and/or by building on the roof. The £530,000 needed was to come from money set aside for the purpose, and from the eventual sale of Hunter Street.[xxxii]

Building began in February 1982, but was frequently interrupted because the noise it created affected teaching and research (and Sunday chapel services!). As the project was phased some areas had to be completed before others could be evacuated. All delays had a knock-on effect and this, plus late delivery of materials, equipment and furniture, meant the project fell well behind schedule.[xxxiii]

Biochemistry eventually moved around Christmas 1982 and anatomy in the summer of 1983. Then, for the first time, preclinical and clinical departments were united on one site – in new buildings with splendid facilities and equipment. Life at RFHSM, academic and social, was enhanced for students and staff. Despite the grim financial situation the future seemed rosy.[xxxiv]

Sale of Hunter Street

The Hunter Street site – the School's only major asset – was now for sale. The Principal said RFHSM could appoint its own agents and sell the whole site – and that its share of the proceeds could go towards the cost of conversion at Hampstead.[xxxv]

Unfortunately Camden Council would only allow Hunter Street to be sold for educational use; this reduced its commercial value and put off potential purchasers. There was no rush to buy. A former student, Paul MacLoughlin,[29] tried to raise money to convert it into a private medical school.[30] His efforts, widely reported in the national and medical press, went unrewarded. Curiously there is no mention of his plans in RFHSM's Council minutes.[xxxvi]

There were no offers for Hunter Street in 1983. RFHSM contemplated linking up with a local housing association to provide low rent housing in the old part of the building and office premises in the 1951 wing, but Camden Council was unyielding. The Kings Cross Centre Campaign, which Camden supported, wanted Hunter Street for a health and leisure centre – but it had no money.[xxxvii]

Fortunately in January 1985 three potential buyers emerged; owing to their educational status no permission was needed for change of use.[xxxviii]

About £1million was expected for the old part of the School, built without public funds, and the University and UGC agreed that £300,000 from the sale of the publicly funded Henderson wing could be used to fund a proposed courtyard development at Hampstead (see later). There was some delay because the two purchasers – the Institute of Neurology and the National Hospital for Nervous Diseases – needed separate transactions; the former was concluded by October 1985, the latter by February 1986, more than four years after Hunter Street went on sale. The Members of the School established a trust fund with the proceeds.[xxxix]

From 1980 to 1985 RFHSM adjusted to a reduction in UGC funding of about 14% in real terms, and the block grant was expected to continue falling by 2% a year. The seriousness of the situation was emphasized when the Secretary of State for Education hinted to the CVCP that with the 2% reductions some university departments/institutions might do no research and become 'teaching only' units – although it was unclear whether this threat applied to medical schools.[xl]

As income went mainly on salaries, wages and pensions, RFHSM had little room for manoeuvre; all possible economies had been in force for years. An annual

[29] In 1964 MacLoughlin captained the men's athletic team that won the Thierry Trophy at the University of London Sports Day. It was the first trophy won by RFHSM men. (see Chapter 11)

[30] To be known as the 'Hunter School of Medicine'.

deficit of about £500,000 was predicted by 1989-90 unless 10 senior academic and 10 senior technical posts were lost.[xli]

In 1984 the UGC pressured universities to improve their management. The CVCP set up a 'Steering Committee for Efficiency Studies in Universities' with Sir Alex Jarratt as chairman.[31] The Jarratt Report (1985) revolutionised the management of academic institutions, including RFHSM. Vice-chancellors were to become chief executives, with deans and heads of departments reporting to them as line managers; governing bodies were to see themselves as boards of directors. Universities (and their colleges) each had to have a corporate plan formulated by a small group drawn from their lay councils and senior academic management. 'Jarratt' was explicitly hostile to the power of departments. It urged the use of performance indicators, but failed to mention the functions of teachers, researchers or students.[xlii]

Jarratt recommended systematic gathering of sound management data. Universities were collectively to create a system of quantitative performance indicators covering management and the delivery of services, using such indicators as the quality and value of research, publications, the number and quality of their graduates – and whether they got jobs! Jarratt also suggested formal annual appraisal of academic staff – and an investigation of the role, structure and staffing of the UGC.[32]

In mid-1985 the UGC announced that 70% of the value of recurrent grants would be allocated on a unit cost basis linked to the numbers of students and courses in each university. The other 30%, reflecting 'institutional performance', was to be heavily weighted by external funding for research; the 'strong' would get more money, the 'weak' less – although the amount was not intended to fluctuate by more than 1.5% in any one year.[xliii]

RFHSM was seriously disadvantaged by this new 'formula funding' based on a nationwide unit cost as it ignored the vast expense of running a modern hospital/medical school complex. The School's share of maintenance costs took almost a third of its total grant of £4.5million. The fact that the Hospital controlled these costs explains why the School showed a surplus, not the anticipated deficit, when UGC funding fell in 1985-6 and 1986-7. Because RFH itself faced a large deficit it made big savings on maintenance – so therefore did the School.[33,xliv]

A Research Assessment Exercise (RAE) was introduced nationally as a further

---

31 Jarratt was a prominent businessman and Chancellor of Birmingham University.

32 This investigation was carried out by the Croham Committee. Its 1987 report was largely ignored by the Government which made more radical changes; the UGC was downgraded and its name was changed to Universities Funding Council (UFC).

33 The District Health Authority faced an estimated deficit of £2million in 1986-7.

measure of institutional performance. Submissions from 'specialist groupings' were used to determine whether their work was of a national or international level of excellence; the resultant grades determined how much quality weighted research funding (QR) an institution would receive from its funding council, i.e. the UGC in the case of universities.

In June 1986 RFHSM was the only London medical school, and one of only three nationally, with a below average grading for clinical medicine as a whole. As there were no published criteria for such judgments the School told the University it rejected the grading and considered the RAE a subjective rather than an objective exercise. Of the three relevant specialist groupings RFHSM was considered average in medicine, average to below average in surgery and O & G; and below average in pathology. These results prompted the School to create a Research Advisory Committee, chaired by Professor Dennis Chapman, FRS, to look in detail at the School's research.[xlv]

Given the likely effect of the RAE on the School's grant it was fortunate that research income from other sources doubled between 1980 and 1985, reaching £2,285,000 in 1984-5. Expressed as a percentage of total income the previous year's research income (28%) was second to Bart's (32%) among London medical schools and eighth nationally. Using 'research income: UGC grant' ratio as the yardstick RFHSM was in the middle bracket of undergraduate medical schools and it received four of the clinical 'new-blood lectureships', funded by the Government but managed by the MRC – a number not exceeded by any other medical school.[xlvi]

When the UGC visited in January 1987 it was concerned about the School's financial situation; it noted the good relationship with RFH but said the joint maintenance costs were the highest nationally, and that other schools were better supported by the NHS. It recognized the outstanding research done in many departments but made it clear that RFHSM's clinical research grading would not be revised, and that funding would remain at a fixed level for some years.[xlvii]

In December 1986 the UGC had requested an academic plan for dealing with reduced funding. It had to include reduction of staff, be congruent with the DHA's plans and acceptable to the MEC. To obtain funds for a restructuring involving early retirements and redundancies a draft version was needed by April. A working party was set up to prepare it. The final version was presented in January 1988; by then many of its recommendations had been acted upon.[xlviii]

Based on 'worst case' assumptions and continuation of existing government policies – and using funding projections supplied by the University Court – the working party calculated a cumulative deficit of about £1.8m by 1991. It therefore advocated a continued freeze on academic posts, early retirement of eight academic staff, loss of ten technical staff (by natural wastage), and closure of the Medical Physics department. Birkbeck College was to teach medical physics pending curriculum revision.[xlix]

In line with the Jarratt recommendations an R &D Committee was set up to implement and monitor the Academic Plan and a staff evaluation programme was introduced. Departments were grouped into three academic divisions (Clinical, Clinico-pathological and Basic Sciences) answerable to an Executive Management Committee (Dean, Division Heads and School Secretary). Plans were made for academic departments of Geriatric Medicine, Community Child Health, Oncology and Protein and Molecular Biology. Cross-disciplinary groups were introduced – to facilitate the integration of both research and teaching by bridging departmental boundaries, and to provide a basis for longer-term reorganization of School activities.

A number of cross-disciplinary groups had already been set up at the Free. Most involved the Haematology department which had expanded greatly under Hoffbrand's direction. In 1975 he had two senior colleagues, Katherine Dormandy (reader) and John Pettit (senior lecturer), a lecturer and an honorary lecturer. Mark Pepys joined as senior lecturer in Immunology in 1976 but moved a year later to the Postgraduate Medical School.[34] When Pettit returned to New Zealand in 1978 Grant Prentice was appointed senior lecturer to set up bone marrow transplantation at RFH. Director of the transplant programme from 1984, he was awarded a personal chair in 1988.

The choice of George Janossy (MD Budapest) to replace Pepys proved inspired. On arrival in June 1978 he inherited Pepys's accommodation – a small 5th floor office, a tiny windowless laboratory next to the rubbish chute on the 2nd floor, and the autoimmune serology service laboratory on the lower ground floor. Within a year he had larger accommodation on the first floor. He was soon promoted to reader and was made a titular professor in 1982, after Immunology had became a separate department.

Working with Melvyn Greaves at the Imperial Cancer Research Fund (IRCF) Janossy had used monoclonal antibodies (MAbs) to immunophenotype (IPT) leukaemic cells, a diagnostic tool for determining treatment options for leukaemia. MAbs are produced by hybrid cells created by fusing myeloma cells with antibody-producing cells from mice deliberately exposed to a specific antigen of interest. The hybrids, effectively 'immortal', divide rapidly and repeatedly and can be used produce large amounts of the required MAb. At RFH Janossy needed help with the cell fusion – a field in which Jack Lucy, head of biochemistry, was an expert, as was

[34] He returned to RFH in 1999 as chairman of the department of medicine.

Alison Goodall, who had just completed a PhD on the topic in Lucy's department. With his agreement she was temporarily seconded to immunology, and soon after she and Janossy obtained funding from the MRC and the National Research and Development Corporation (NRDC) to set up a MAb-producing laboratory.

Janossy continued working on leukaemia. For fifteen years from 1980 his laboratory provided a routine leukaemia diagnostic service for 127 hospitals, and its results underpinned two national MRC leukaemia trials. In the early 1980s he showed, with Prentice and other colleagues, that severe graft versus host disease could be prevented by using MAbs to remove T cells from the donor marrow. Subsequently, with support from Sandoz, Janossy's group created MAbs that prevented the rejection of transplanted organs (see Chapter 16).[l]

Janossy recognized the great diagnostic and therapeutic potential of MAbs for many clinical disorders other than leukaemia and made his expertise available to colleagues in other departments. He supplied MAbs to Newsom-Davis and his colleagues for the histological study of the normal thymus, and the thymus in myasthenia gravis, while Poulter, then lecturer in immunology, used MAbs to study immunological aspects of rheumatoid arthritis.

Not only was the research done with MAbs excellent but much of it helped to improve the School's financial status. The first commercially successful project involved Goodall and the Medical Unit's Howard Thomas. They created MAbs against the hepatitis B virus surface antigen (HBsAg) and used them to measure its level in serum. NRDC provided initial funding for the project and also arranged patents for the MAbs and transfer of the technology to various companies.

The potential rewards to the School, and to the scientists themselves, from the commercial exploitation of research led RFHSM to seek advice on the handling of new developments. In June 1983 the system for the sharing of royalties was revised so that the inventors got the highest proportion when the total amount was relatively small, but as the royalties increased the department and the School benefited more.[li]

The second major income-generating project started with the raising of MAbs to clotting factor VIII. Most factor VIII used to treat haemophiliacs came from pooled plasma from blood donors, but in the mid-1970s a chronic 'post-transfusion' hepatitis was identified that was neither hepatitis A nor B; it was later found that much pooled plasma, especially that from the USA, was infected with the virus of hepatitis C and/or HIV. Efforts began to manufacture uncontaminated coagulation factors.

This issue was of particular relevance at RFH as Dormandy, head of RFH's haemophilia unit, had pioneered home treatment of haemophiliacs with frequent injections of factor VIII-rich cryoprecipitate which enhanced the quality of life, particularly for young patients, by minimizing deformities caused by bleeding into joints. Sadly cancer forced Dormandy's retirement in March 1977. She died the following year, aged 52. To honour her, the new haemophilia unit, funded partly from the trust she set up in 1971 to raise money for research on coagulation disorders, was named the Katharine Dormandy Haemophilia Centre and Haemostasis Unit.[35, lii]

To replace Dormandy the School and Hospital appointed two experts on coagulation disorders as co-directors of the unit. One, Peter Kernoff (NHS), created a large bank of plasma and serum samples that proved invaluable for studying the epidemiology and clinical course of hepatitis C and HIV in haemophiliacs. From 1981 to 1996 it was used for a classical study done at RFH on the natural history of (untreated) HIV infection leading to AIDS; Janossy's group provided the necessary T-cell subset MAbs CD4 and CD8.

The other co-director, Ted Tuddenham, a senior lecturer, was determined to purify factor VIII and characterize it biochemically. He, Rotblatt, Goodall and Janossy made MAbs to Factor VIII (and factors IX & X). This enabled them – with help from Speywood, a British firm based in Wrexham – to produce a relatively large amount of highly purified Factor VIII. After it was sequenced Genentech, an American firm, cloned its gene and expressed it in a hamster kidney cell line that then secreted Factor VIII into the surrounding medium. This was an immense collaborative achievement. Tuddenham and his team subsequently made other major contributions to the biology and patho-biology of haemophilia A using the new genetic tools resulting from their work.

In exchange for an assured supply of factor VIII, Speywood ceded the worldwide production rights to Genentech, which passed them on to Cutter, a subsidiary of Bayer, along with marketing rights for North America and the Far East. Speywood retained the marketing rights for the UK and other European Countries but transferred them to Cutter in 1985.[liii]

New Building Projects

In October 1984 it was decided to erect in the southeast courtyard a two-storey building to be used for general teaching purposes and to accommodate Clinical Epidemiology and General Practice, thus releasing space elsewhere. The four-storey structure envisaged fell foul of fire regulations. The eventual scheme, for two storeys, was to cost no more than £300,000, i.e. the UGC's share of the Hunter Street proceeds (see earlier), so when Council learned that the money would be

[35] She planned the unit which was funded by her trust and a generous endowment from Mr. Laurence Knight. In 1977 Dormandy was awarded the first McFarlane Gold Medal of the Haemophilia Society.

unavailable after 1988 completion became a matter of urgency. The new building, which provided only lecture and seminar facilities, was finished in early November 1988. The 1988-89 annual report hailed it as 'a superb teaching complex of great value'.[liv]

Clinical Epidemiology & General Practice was left out of it because in January 1987 Council agreed, at a cost of about £250,000, to provide that department with 6000 sq.ft. of temporary accommodation on the second floor of podium A on the north-west corner of RFH. It was situated alongside a new geriatric day care facility. Two new departments – Protein and Molecular Biology under Dennis Chapman, and Virology headed by Paul Griffiths – moved into the space on the ground floor previously occupied by Clinical Epidemiology and Medical Physics.[lv]

Council noted in June 1987 that lack of accommodation constrained development in Hampstead. After completion of the Podium A and courtyard schemes it appeared future building would have to be on the School's roof. Before Council's next meeting plans were being prepared to provide accommodation for research on the roof adjacent to the renal transplant centre, should funding become available from an external source.[lvi]

However, Council had ignored a potential site outside the main building. In 1974 Mrs Shirley Nolan had begun compiling a register of potential bone marrow donors, because her son Anthony suffered from Wiskott-Aldrich syndrome, a rare serious inherited disease potentially treatable by bone marrow transplantation.[36] The matching of donors with 'unrelated' recipients involved 'tissue typing', a complex and expensive process. In 1978 an Anthony Nolan Laboratory opened at St Mary Abbott's Hospital, Kensington. That hospital was later incorporated within the new Chelsea and Westminster Hospital. The land was sold for re-development so Mrs Nolan's laboratory needed a new home.

In 1987 RFH gave it temporary accommodation at the bottom of the south car park. It also provided a site there for a new and more permanent building costing £350,000. The Anthony Nolan was to share the building with RFHSM's new Molecular Cell Pathology group, headed by Gillie Francis, and to contribute £150,000 towards its cost. Francis anticipated a grant of £460,000 grant from the Wellcome Trust, plus £150,000 for accommodation. To expedite matters Council agreed to underwrite the £200,000 cost of accommodating Molecular Cell Pathology, which meant finding £50,000 after receipt of the Wellcome contribution. The new laboratories were fully operational by the end of 1990.[lvii] (See Chapter 16)

The extra space available in Hampstead allowed the appointment of more staff

[36] Anthony died, aged 8, in 1879. His great suffering led his mother to contemplate euthanasia. Later, having developed Parkinson's disease, she committed suicide in 2002. (*The Telegraph,* 17 July 2002)

– particularly in the professorial surgical and psychiatric units whose size had been deliberately restricted prior to the opening of the new RFH. Working beneath one roof helped to promote closer relationships between academic staff (clinical & preclinical) and NHS staff, and this, and the change of Dean, led to a more academic ethos.

Preclinical Staff Changes

In 1975 full-time teachers were the backbone of the anatomy department. When Bowden retired in September 1980 (with an OBE), John Harris took the established chair. Both were medically qualified, as was the lecturer Piasecki, but Pheasant (a lecturer) and Grieve (reader in biomechanics) were not. The increasing gulf between clinical and preclinical salaries (see Chapter 14) was clearly a disincentive to medically qualified individuals who might otherwise have considered a career in a basic medical science. Another factor also began to affect the School's ability to recruit suitable staff. In 1988 Council heard that candidates from outside London were hesitant about coming to the metropolis owing to the high cost of housing and the high cost of living – a situation which seemed likely to get worse.[lviii]

There were some part-time lecturers and honorary lecturers with medical qualifications – mostly clinicians past or approaching retirement age. The two stalwarts in the early 1970s were Marny Mitchell and Oliver Harris; Desmond Sharland joined them in 1976. Harris left in 1978 – aged 78. Sharland and Mitchell moved to Hampstead in 1983. The latter was a former student. She had contracted 'Royal Free Disease' (see Chapter 13) in 1958, while a gynaecological HS at EGAH; persistence of symptoms led her to abandon a clinical career. Fortunately family circumstances meant she had no need to earn a living. She became an assistant lecturer in anatomy at RFHSM, and later a part-time lecturer. Her research on progesterone earned her a Ph.D. in 1963. She then married and started a family, but returned to RFHSM in 1970 as a part-time lecturer. She was exceptionally popular with the students.

Anatomy shared a lectureship with Surgery from 1976 and in 1978 the incumbent, Feathers, was seconded to Nigeria's Amadu Bello University for two years. Another lectureship was created to assist someone studying for the FRCS. Both lectureships were short-lived. However from 1983 some aspiring young surgeons were provided with joint appointments – as demonstrators in Anatomy and SHOs in A & E.[lix]

In 1986 Grieve was promoted to Professor of Biomechanics. For his work on locomotion and muscle power he needed a laboratory with a very high ceiling and structural alterations were made to the CSB to accommodate it.[lx]

Downman died in January 1982. When he retired on health grounds in

September 1979 Michael Spyer, a neurophysiologist from Birmingham University, was appointed as the Sophia Jex-Blake Professor of Physiology. Christopher Richards, a senior lecturer since 1978, was promoted to reader in 1980-1.[lxi]

Downman's two senior colleagues in physiology, Andrews and Pearl Scott, received personal chairs in 1975. Andrews died in January 1978, while Scott, after 41 years at the School, retired as Professor of Nutritional Physiology in 1980-1, having directed 'Cell Studies', the large interdisciplinary course introduced as part of the new preclinical curriculum in 1974; she was assisted in this by John Monjardino, a lecturer from 1972-3 and senior lecturer from 1975-6.

When the new curriculum started the Hunter Street departments, understaffed owing to economy measures then in force, were severely stretched by the travelling required between Hampstead and Hunter Street. The thankless and arduous, but much appreciated, task of devising the new timetable, including allocation of space, was carried out by the physiologist Marjorie Duckworth until October 1977 – and then by the pharmacologist Jenny MacLagan. Duckworth took early retirement in 1983.[lxii]

In September 1980 Nora Zaimis retired as head of pharmacology. She was a colourful character. Born in Greece in 1915 she became a member of its national pistol shooting team. In 1938 she qualified in medicine in Athens, where she spent the war. She moved to London when her second husband, John Zaimis (who, like her first, did not last long) was appointed naval attaché at the Greek embassy. Their home had a tennis court. Asked to join a doubles match Bill Bowman, one of her research fellows, found Rod Laver was one of the four players. Zaimis loved driving fast sports cars – often 'by all accounts with a young admirer by her side'.[37, lxiii]

Bob Hodges followed Zaimis as head of pharmacology.[38] He retired in September 1986. Replacing him was considered a high priority but initial attempts to do so were unsuccessful. As the department needed an investment of about £100,000 Council agreed in June 1989 to delay re-advertising until the results of the recent research selectivity exercise were available. An appointment was eventually made in June 1990 (see Chapter 16). [39, lxiv]

During these deliberations two of RFHSM's pharmacologists were appointed to chairs elsewhere – Julia Buckingham at Charing Cross & Westminster Medical School (1987), and Denis Wray at Leeds (1989). Maclagan remained at RFHSM and was promoted to reader.[lxv]

---

37 This story is in a 'Reunion Update' produced for the 50yr reunion of the 1958 graduates.

38 The Education Committee reminded Council in October 1980 that Hodges, a titular professor, should have assumed the *established* chair of pharmacology. He did so in May 1981.

39 RFHSM's rating improved. It achieved grade 3 for both preclinical & clinical units of assessment.

Lucy, head of biochemistry, served as 'acting head' of pharmacology following the departure of Hodges. Brian Cooke, who replaced Diplock as reader when the latter left for Guy's in 1977, was given the title Professor of Endocrine Biochemistry in June 1982.[lxvi]

The biophysicist Dennis Chapman joined biochemistry as a senior lecturer in October 1977 after a distinguished career at Unilever, Cambridge, Sheffield & Chelsea College; he was soon made Professor of Biophysical Chemistry. His special interest was in finding materials capable of interfacing with body tissues without provoking an adverse biological response. He identified phosphorylcholine (PC), a constituent of human cell membranes, as a suitable material for coating contact lenses and tubes inserted into various parts of the body. In 1984, to exploit the commercial opportunities stemming from his research, he set up Biocompatibles – a highly successful company – but for some reason the School did not profit from it. He also co-founded an Interdisciplinary Research Centre (IRC) in biomedical materials at Queen Mary College. Chapman was elected FRS in 1986. He died in 1999. Each year a Chapman Medal is presented for work in this field at London's Institute of Materials.[lxvii]

Simons, head of medical physics, retired in 1983. Following his death in 1986 his family provided £2500 for a bursary for students studying for a degree in physics as applied to medicine; they subsequently agreed it should instead endow an annual prize for the best B.Sc. thesis.[lxviii]

During MacGillivray's deanship one staff change was one purely political. Mawhinney, a senior lecturer in medical physics, was elected Conservative MP for Peterborough in 1979; his RFHSM appointment was converted to half-time. Re-elected to Parliament in June 1983 he left the School three months later. A glittering political career followed. He is now Lord Mawhinney.[lxix]

Clinical Staff Developments

In the new hospital Sherlock's Medical Unit occupied most of the 10th floor. Its two wings contained offices, teaching rooms, laboratories, store rooms, and a state of the art X-ray facility. The other two wings on the same floor of the tower block were taken up by the 28-bedded Hassall and Crawshay wards, the latter being shared with dermatology. The Surgical Unit was similarly arranged on the 9th floor.

Initially 'Medical Unit' was synonymous with the official terms 'Professorial Unit in Medicine' and 'Academic Department of Medicine'. Its members' main interests were in liver disease, gastroenterology and clinical pharmacology, but its senior staff shared the general medical take with NHS physicians; the last were autonomous except in relation to curricular matters. Those with appointments in some other 'medical' specialties (e.g. cardiology, chest diseases, endocrinology, rheumatology & nephrology' were not considered 'Medical Unit'.

Some clinicians with academic appointments were allocated to the 'Academic Department of Medicine' for administrative purposes. This did not apply to the neurologists P.K. Thomas and John Newsom-Davis, both outstanding scientists. Neurology was formally recognised as an RFHSM department in 1977. In 1988 PK, a titular Professor of Neurology, assumed an established chair of Neurological Science held jointly at RFHSM and the Institute of Neurology.[lxx] Owing to his work on the immunology of myasthenia gravis Newsom-Davis was, in 1980, appointed to RFHSM and the Institute of Neurology as the first 'MRC Clinical Research Professor'. The accompanying grant, £269,244 over five years, was then the largest single grant received by the School. Newsom-Davis moved to Oxford's chair of Clinical Neurology in 1987. Elected FRS in 1991, he died in a car crash in Rumania in 1997.[40, lxxi]

The first 'addition' to the 'Academic Department of Medicine' was the young chest physician Roderick Bateman – appointed joint lecturer in medicine and physiology in 1975-6.[41] Philip Sutton, Roderick Taylor and Monica Spiteri followed him. All worked with the chest physician Stewart Clarke, a part-time senior lecturer in thoracic medicine from 1980-1. Dubois joined Clarke as an NHS consultant in 1981-2 and was a part-time senior lecturer from 1986.[lxxii]

The second addition was Jean Ginsburg – a senior lecturer in endocrinology in the O & G Department. She 'transferred' to the Academic Department of Medicine in 1979 on the understanding that when she retired the post would return to O & G.[lxxiii]

The virtual 'Academic Department' expanded to include Paul Sweny- a senior lecturer in Nephrology and Renal Transplantation who, from 1979-80, worked with the NHS consultant John Moorhead – and also Joan Slack, part-time senior lecturer in clinical genetics from 1881.

When Zina Moncrieff retired as paediatrician in 1979 the AHA offered to contribute the funding for her seven NHS sessions so that an academic paediatric post could be created. The School paid for four more sessions and in 1982 Graham Watson, a 'bone marrow transplanter', was appointed as a full time senior lecturer. Around that time David Flynn, an NHS consultant paediatrician since 1970-1, became a part-time senior lecturer. Watson soon moved to Newcastle.[42] Trompeter, a paediatric nephrologist, replaced him in 1984. Paediatrics became a separate department at RFHSM four years later, when Brent Taylor arrived from St Mary's as Professor of Community Child Health.[lxxiv]

---

[40] JND hit the national press in 1983 (e.g. Daily Express 24 August) by suggesting that Samson suffered from myasthenia gravis and that Delilah was not to blame for his inconvenient episode of weakness. He still held this view in 2005.

[41] Surgery & anatomy had a similar arrangement. Clinical lecturers equated to NHS senior registrars.

[42] Sadly Watson and his wife died following an accident while climbing in Glencoe in 1989.

Dame Sheila Sherlock[43] retired in 1983 and was succeeded as head of department by McIntyre, a titular professor since 1978. Before taking over on 1 October he spent four months on sabbatical at the MRC Molecular Biology Unit in Cambridge. Sherlock did not leave RFH. Hobbs provided her with rooms in the surgical department, and she attended Medical Unit meetings, saw private patients (helped by research fellows) and went on inspiring members of the unit.

A few weeks before her official retirement celebrations in her honour were attended by the staff of the unit and by individuals worldwide who had worked with her in the past. There was a day of scientific presentations, an evening buffet reception at the Science Museum, and a dinner at the old Whitbread Brewery in the City. Her portrait, painted by Ruskin Spear, (Fig 15.7 Colour plate) was presented to her at the dinner, along with a diamond and ruby brooch which, at her request, incorporated the coat of arms of RFHSM. She chose the artist for her portrait but was not enamoured by it when it hung at her home in Regent's Park. It is now in the Sheila Sherlock Postgraduate Centre at RFH.

The biochemist Professor Barbara Billing retired in 1985, having been a great help to new members of the unit from its inception. The clinical pharmacologist, Ian James,[44] was promoted to reader in 1984. He hit the national press in 1977 after he established that beta-blockers improved the performance of some musicians.[lxxv] Derek Jewell, a 'hollow-organ' gastroenterologist surrounded by hepatologists, moved to Oxford in 1980. His replacement, Roy Pounder, was made reader in 1985.

The medical unit had three lecturers when MacGillivray became dean. Two left soon afterwards: Elwyn Elias spent two years in Chicago before setting up a liver unit in Birmingham, while Jenny Heathcote, an RFHSM graduate who had studied the epidemiology of hepatitis B infection, worked in San Francisco before settling in Toronto. Howard Thomas remained at RFH until 1987 when he left for the chair of medicine at St Mary's; John Summerfield moved with him. To fill the gap left by Thomas another hepatitis expert, Geoffrey Dusheiko from Johannesburg, was appointed senior lecturer in 1988; he was soon promoted to reader and received a personal chair in 1996.

Some lecturers from the 1980s – Marsha Morgan, James Dooley & Andy Burroughs – stayed within the liver unit as senior lecturers, and Owen Epstein was appointed NHS consultant gastroenterologist at RFH.

Dame Frances Gardner retired from RFH in 1978. Tom Evans replaced her as cardiologist. Lawson died in December 1978, having been the School's President

[43] Sherlock was appointed DBE in 1978.

[44] A joint appointment with the pharmacology department.

for five years.[45] At their AGM in January 1979 Members of the School elected Dame Frances to replace him. [lxxvi]

Nigel Compston was an RFH physician from 1954, and led the medical team planning the move of the School and Hospital to Hampstead. He retired, in poor health, in 1983 and died three years later aged 68. He served as treasurer of the Royal College of Physicians from 1970 to 1985. The Duke of Kent named an RFH ward after Compston in 1998.[lxxvii]

The cardiologist Cecil Symons died nine days after retiring in 1987. Fifteen years earlier, concerned that RFH might neglect its history after the move to Hampstead, he commissioned from the artist Peter Jones a series of small paintings (the 'Symons Bequest') depicting all the hospitals of the Royal Free group. (Fig 15.8) In 1974 he set up a Works of Art committee, which he chaired, and in the

Fig 15.8 Cardiology & X-ray departments at Lawn Road (Symons bequest)

corridor near the Pond Street entrance of the hospital he launched an art gallery (later called the Symons Gallery) where local artists could exhibit their work. The committee commissioned the large oil-on-board mural (261 x 484 cm) which is on display in the narrow hall of the Rowland Hill Street entrance to RFH. (Fig 15.9

45 Lawson was the only man to hold the position.

a & b Colour plate) Painted in 1986 by William Utermohlen (1933-2007), an American working in London, it depicts the story of the School and Hospital.[46]

It was Symons who persuaded the Board of Governors to institute the annual Marsden lecture. The first was given by the ebullient Newcastle neurologist Henry Miller in 1972. (See Chapter 14). Many eminent individuals followed him as lecturer. As a singular honour, Symons was the first member of the hospital staff to be invited to give the lecture. Sadly he died before he could deliver it. The BBC newsreader Robert Dougall read it in 1987 with the assistance of Cecil's widow, Jean.[lxxviii]

RFH's biggest work of art is the 16 foot high two-ton modern sculpture 'Pisces' created by Jesse Watkins. On 19 December 1974, despite a few technical hitches, it was successfully lowered into an internal open space near the Pond Street entrance to RFH. To install it an enormous crane was needed. Just over twenty years later it was again moved by crane as the space it occupied was chosen for the erection of the multi-purpose Sir William Wells Atrium. Wells himself opened the atrium in November 1996 to mark the bicentenary of William Marsden's birth. Pisces is now on the forecourt of the main Pond Street entrance to the Hospital. (Fig 15.10)

Gordon Beckett was a general physician with a special interest in diabetes mellitus. The eye complications of that condition triggered in him a wider interest in medical ophthalmology. He became a physician at Moorfields and, with the neurologist Simon Behrman and Sherlock's husband Gerry James, he founded the Eye Physic Club. He retired in 1985 and died four years later from a mysterious illness that blighted his last years.

Fig 15.10
Pisces outside RFH

The Surgical Unit remained small, rarely having more than two lecturers. David Osborne took Fernando's lectureship when the latter was made consultant in renal transplantation in 1976. Osborne's co-lecturer Arthur Li moved to the Massachusetts General Hospital for a year in 1977; Andrew Higgins acted as locum lecturer. George Hamilton replaced Li in 1982, and two years later Hugh Rogers replaced Osborne.[lxxix]

In October 1986 Hobbs began a two-year spell as Vice Dean of the Faculty of Medicine, and was soon a member of the UGC's medical committee and the University's Senate. Just before MacGillivray retired as Dean the surgical

[46] Symons's collection of medical instruments, mainly Georgian period, is on display in the Royal College of Physicians On the other side of the same 'Royal Free' wall is Victor Hoffbrand's collection of Delft apothecary jars.

department made a successful application for one of the 'New Blood Lectureships' then available; it brought Nagy Habib into the department. Hobbs started a liver transplant programme in September 1982 but relatively few such operations were done at RFH until Keith Rolles left Calne's unit at Cambridge in 1988 to become director of RFH's liver transplant unit, run in conjunction with Andy Burroughs, a senior lecturer in the Medical Unit.[lxxx]

The merger with HGH and New End meant that in 1975 Raymond 'Jerry' Kirk (HGH) and Meyer Lange (New End)[47] joined Hopewell, Phyllis George & Gracey on the general surgical staff of the new RFH. The growing tendency was for surgeons (and physicians) to be appointed as 'specialists' although Adam Lewis (a colo-rectal surgeon) and George Hamilton (a vascular surgeon) were simply called 'surgeon' when appointed in 1976 and 1987 respectively. However Robert Morgan was designated 'urologist' on appointment in 1981 and when Hopewell retired in 1986 Amir Kaisary joined Morgan as a 'urologist'. Phyllis George left the staff in 1988.[lxxxi]

In 1976 the Whittington Hospital's neurosurgical service, created by the surgeon Ian McCaul in 1952, was transferred to the new RFH. Robert Maurice-Williams joined it in 1980 and took charge when McCaul retired in 1981; that year Ken Lindsay was appointed as a second neurosurgical consultant.

The two big growth areas following the opening of the new RFH, both linked to the developments in surgery, were anaesthetics and radiology. In 1975 there were eight consultant anaesthetists. By 1989 there were twelve; three had retired but seven new ones had been recruited. During the same period radiology had started off with four consultants; it ended up with nine, three newcomers being neuro-radiologists.

Charles Douglas left in 1976 to take the foundation chair of obstetrics and gynaecology at Cambridge. While head of O & G at the Free he was supported by a senior lecturer (Luba Epsztejn) and two lecturers. There were also three NHS consultants. Life was relatively peaceful.[lxxxii]

Douglas was replaced by Ian Craft, a senior lecturer at Queen Charlotte's Hospital and the Institute of Obstetrics and Gynaecology. Craft's relationships with his new colleagues were less harmonious than Douglas's. Poor relationships between clinical academics and 'non-academic' colleagues were of course not unknown in British medical schools, and characterised the O & G department at RFH throughout the 1920s and 30s. (See Chapters 10 & 11)

In 1977 Craft appointed Yehudi Gordon as a senior lecturer. Craft was a 'high tech' obstetrician. Gordon favoured natural childbirth, whose advocates believed

---

[47] Lange was a thyroid surgeon at New End Hospital. He retired in 1977.

squatting or standing, without technological intervention, the healthiest form of childbirth. This led to conflict. Departmental morale deteriorated and relationships soured between the NHS consultants and both academics. Colleagues from other specialties were puzzled, believing that offering expectant mothers a choice about their delivery could only enhance the department's status. Unfortunately the dispute between Craft and Gordon, two talented clinicians, became an issue in the national press.

A perceived threat of the banning of natural childbirth at RFH led the National Childbirth Trust to hold a rally on Hampstead Heath in April 1982, at which Anna Ford, the TV presenter, and Dr Michel Odent, a French advocate of non-interventionist methods, addressed a crowd of about five thousand, some bearing banners with the apposite messages 'Squatters' Rights' and 'Stand and Deliver'.[lxxxiii]

Subsequently Craft received hate mail and had graffiti scrawled on his car. In June he announced he would leave RFH in November. In April he had delivered Britain's first 'test-tube' twins and was being hailed for his pioneering work on in vitro fertilisation (IVF). So while natural childbirth supporters celebrated his resignation, barren women hoping for his help considered it a disaster, as his IVF service was then the only one within the NHS.[lxxxiv]

Gordon followed by announcing he would resign in October. A search for Craft's replacement had begun but the unit would have been without full-time consultant cover from November. Fortunately Braithwaite Rickford (recently retired from St Thomas' Hospital) agreed to take charge for three months.[lxxxv]

The appointment of Craft's successor caused further problems. Eight of the University's board of advisers voted for a particular candidate, but one (an RFH obstetrician) objected, claiming correctly that Council had not discussed the appointment. Without unanimity among the School's representatives no appointment could be made. Abrams, the MEC chairman, presented to Council the views of those obstetricians opposing the appointment. Hartley, a former Vice-Chancellor, stressed that O & G needed a professorial head, and forecast problems if the recommendation of a properly constituted appointing committee was rejected. Council concurred and Robert Shaw assumed the chair on 1 May 1983.[lxxxvi]

In October 1975 the professorial psychiatric unit had three honorary consultants – Russell and his senior lecturers Wakeling and Pitcher. There were also five NHS consultant psychiatrists.[48] By 1978 there were four senior lecturers, but when Russell left to take the chair of Psychiatry at the Maudsley Hospital in 1979 one, Campbell, went with him. Wakeling, then a reader, took Russell's chair at the Free.

[48] Elithorn, Swift, Benaim, Hailstone & Shepherd.

Anthony Mann, senior lecturer from 1980 and reader from 1984, received a personal chair in 1986-7; he moved to the chair of Epidemiological Psychiatry at the Institute of Psychiatry in 1989.

Pathology

In 1977 Barry Scott, a titular professor, was appointed to the established chair of histopathology. When Scott retired in September 1983 Scheuer replaced him. Isobel Beswick, who joined the pathology department in 1946, retired in 1985 as did John Cruse, who had been a senior lecturer for just two years; their replacements were Julie Crow and Amar (Paul) Dhillon. That year Beswick was elected President of the Old Students Association (having been vice-president from 1982), and was awarded the School Medal.[lxxxvii]

Denis Baron retired in 1988 after thirty-four years as head of chemical pathology. A titular professor from 1963 he had assumed the newly established chair of Chemical Pathology and Human Metabolism in 1976. His replacement, A. F. (Tony) Winder from the University of Leicester, was a keen saxophonist who performed regularly with musical groups set up at the Free, including the orchestra for the students' Xmas show. In 1977-8 Sidney Rosalki was appointed consultant chemical pathologist, and Michael Wills, then Professor of Metabolic Chemical Pathology, left for the University of West Virginia. Paresh (Bini) Dandona was appointed senior lecturer in Wills's place.[lxxxviii]

Paul Griffiths joined the Medical Microbiology department as senior lecturer in 1981-2. A specialist virologist, he was promoted to reader in 1985-6 and was awarded a personal chair in 1989. Hamilton-Miller was a departmental senior lecturer from 1976, reader in 1981, and a titular professor in 1988, the year Jean Bradley retired as senior lecturer.[lxxxix]

In February 1989 the NHS consultant bacteriologist, Paul Noone, a provocative but highly competent and popular colleague, died from an aggressive lymphoma. In 1976 he was a co-founder of the NHS Consultants Association,[49] and chairman until his death. There is a Paul Noone Memorial Lecture at its annual conference, and an eponymous memorial lecture is held each year at RFH.

In 1973 RFHSM had agreed that Dr A.G. (Gerry) Shaper's MRC team from LSHTM should form the nucleus of a department of clinical epidemiology at RFHSM. On arrival in 1975 it was housed temporarily at 21 Pond Street. Shaper soon had a personal chair, and in 1987 was appointed to an established Chair of Clinical Epidemiology. When J. Austen Heady, reader in medical statistics, retired

[49] An organisation still strongly committed to the founding principles of the NHS.

in 1881-2 the senior lecturer, Stuart Pocock, was promoted to reader. A titular professor from 1987 Pocock moved to LSHTM as Professor of Medical Statistics in 1989.[xc]

In 1979 NETRHA gave Shaper a grant of £16,458 to develop general practice teaching at RFHSM.[50] Eight sessions a week were allocated to GP tutors.[51] In March 1980 the department was renamed 'Clinical Epidemiology and General Practice', and six GPs became part-time senior lecturers. In 1981 the President of the Royal College of General Practitioners (RCGP) was John Horder, a local GP. He was made a visiting professor at RFHSM and served for ten years as chairman of the General Practice Teaching Group. Margaret Lloyd, a full time lecturer in general practice from 1986, was soon promoted to senior lecturer. By 1988 the School had 130 GP tutors.[xci]

In October 1986 Anne Cockroft was appointed director of the Occupational Health Department at RFH, and became an honorary senior lecturer in Medicine and in Clinical Epidemiology and General Practice. From November 1989 she was a part-time senior lecturer in Occupational Health and, still employed by HHA, was seconded for four sessions a week to teach at LHSTM.[xcii]

There were major changes in RFH's geriatric services towards the end of MacGillivray's time as dean. While acute problems were dealt with mainly at Pond Street, rehabilitation and the care of long term patients were concentrated initially at New End Hospital, which had 143 beds in 1978 and 127 in 1985.

Despite much opposition, New End was sold in 1986 and was eventually converted into luxury apartments. Before his burial in Highgate Cemetery Karl Marx was laid out in New End's mortuary, which was across the road from the hospital and linked to it by a tunnel. In 1974 the mortuary became the home of the New End Theatre; when that closed in 2011 the building became a synagogue for the Village Shul, an independent Orthodox Jewish congregation of around 50 families.

The proceeds from the New End sale were used to redevelop Queen Mary's House, at the top of East Heath Road. Founded by Queen Mary after the Great War as a maternity home for servicemen's wives it was evacuated to Oxfordshire during the Second World War. At Queen Mary's request The London Hospital administered it from 1946. RFH took it over in 1972 and closed it as a maternity hospital in 1975. Until 1986 it was used for staff accommodation and community health offices. It was then refurbished. New wings were added on each side of the

[50] RFHSM's GP teachers had lobbied for a unit undertaking research & teaching undergraduates in 1977.

[51] Drs M. Campkin, MA Carmi, D. Cohen, J. Cohen, C F Donovan, RC Hume & G. F. Norris.

old mansion and on the east side they formed the arms of an entrance courtyard. The pleasant garden on the building's west side was used one year as a key location during the shooting of the film for the students' Christmas show.

When New End was sold elderly inpatients had to be accommodated somewhere else until the beds were available at Queen Mary's House. At that time inner London's NHS hospitals were struggling financially as funding was being transferred to other regions as a consequence of the 1976 RAWP report. Some hospitals closed and many others shut wards to save money. The closing of four acute wards at RFH caused some departments problems with their teaching and research. Even so it was decided in October 1986 that, when New End closed, those wards would house geriatric patients until the Queen Mary's unit opened in October 1991. The official opening, by Prince Charles, was in May 1992.[xciii]

Michael Green was the lone consultant geriatrician from 1971. He had a large clinical load, with twelve beds at Pond Street and many more at New End; he ran a firm of students and had responsibilities in the community; but he received relatively little support. He moved to a post in Guernsey in 1985 but could hardly have forgotten RFH. His twin sons were born there in 1978; one was named William Marsden Green. Nori Graham was appointed as a consultant psychiatrist before Green left; her lasting interest in the mental problems of the elderly developed as a result of seeing his patients.

Jackie Morris and Archie Young were appointed consultants in geriatric medicine in place of Green. Young soon became a part-time senior lecturer, as did Shah Ebrahim, the third geriatric consultant from 1987.[xciv]

In March 1988 Young was appointed to the chair of Geriatric Medicine at RFHSM. The following year Ebrahim took the equivalent chair at the London Hospital Medical College, but returned to RFH three years later as Professor of Clinical Epidemiology.[xcv]

PROMIS

One matter that exercised the clinical, pathological, radiological and administrative staff of the School and Hospital during the early years of MacGillivray's deanship was their campaign to persuade the DHSS to support the installation at RFH of a remarkable new computer system for handling medical records.

In May 1973 Geoffrey Rivett, a medical officer in the DHSS's computer section, told McIntyre that the Chief Medical Officer, Sir George Godber, might support a pilot study of a computerised version of the Problem Orientated Medical Record (POMR – see Chapter 14), and suggested a visit to Burlington, Vermont, to examine Weed's 'Problem Oriented Medical Information System' (PROMIS). Rivett went in April 1974. He thought PROMIS visionary and worth pursuing –

'for it may provide a method of measuring the quality of care and the process by which it is administered'.

Six months later McIntyre visited Weed. Impressed by PROMIS he returned with a slide show for presentation to colleagues at RFH whose Computer Policy committee, chaired by MacGillivray, had made an unsuccessful application for a major computer system five years earlier. In 1978, after prolonged discussions and with MEC support, it decided to look closely at PROMIS.[xcvi]

In March 1979 an RFH group spent five days in Burlington along with Professor Bob Cohen and 'Bud' Abbott, members of a DHSS team examining US computing projects.[52] The RFH group was enthusiastic about PROMIS, as was Cohen. It began work on an application for funding for a PROMIS pilot system. Surprisingly the DHSS advised RFH to apply for a whole hospital system.

PROMIS was a remarkable system intended to minimize reliance on imperfect human memory. Unfortunately it could not, and still cannot, be described *both* adequately and briefly.[53] Entry and retrieval of information was primarily via touch screen terminals (many years before their widespread use). A huge menu of branching displays facilitated data retrieval and the selection of words and phrases for inclusion in patients' records.[54] Response times were rapid – 90% in less than half a second; delays exceeding a second were rare.

The patient's history could be recorded quickly and in considerable detail and patients could enter some of it themselves – using an on-screen questionnaire presented in either Spanish or English, with all answers displayed in English. Such a facility, applicable to virtually all languages, would of course be particularly useful in countries, like Britain, with a large and diverse immigrant population.

PROMIS did not simply store and display patient information. It guided its collection; e.g. a doctor recording a physical examination of the heart could simply enter 'Heart normal' but would be 'invited' to note findings on 'inspection', 'palpation', 'percussion' and 'auscultation' – even more advanced options being available under each sub-heading. When clinicians perused the results of investigations PROMIS suggested methods of supporting or refuting possible causes of abnormal results. Similarly when drugs were prescribed it drew attention to contraindications, possible complications and/or potential interactions with other medications.

---

[52] The RFH team were MacGillivray, McIntyre, Ms C. Lewis (District Nursing Officer), Rogers (District Finance Officer), Humphries (Principal Scientific Officer, Pathology); Wadbrook (Computer Manager). Cohen chaired the NHS Computer R & D Committee; Abbott chaired the NHS Computing Technical Committee and was Computer Services Manager of NETRHA.

[53] A copy of the detailed application and economic appraisal can be inspected at the RFH Library.

[54] If unavailable they were entered via a keyboard. All such entries were analyzed so that the relevant words & phrases could be included in new or revised displays.

The educational value of PROMIS was immense and its potential even greater. Instant access was provided to a vast amount of information that was relatively easy to update. When evaluating clinical features for diagnostic purposes the user could compare them to images, sounds etc. stored in on-line libraries. PROMIS facilitated clinical research as it allowed selected data to be abstracted from a group of patients so that one could check, for example, the incidence of a particular complication in those given a new drug. It also estimated the probable cost of a patient's hospital admission – and in patients with multiple problems could establish how much individual diseases contributed to the total cost.

Preparing the application involved frequent correspondence with the DHSS computer section. From the start it seemed uncomfortable about supporting another 'experimental' computerised medical record system, having been castigated by the Public Accounts Committee over money deemed wasted on such a system at King's College Hospital in the early 1970s. A draft application was submitted to the DHSS's Computer R&D committee in October 1979. The Regional and Area Health Authorities associated with RFH refused to contribute to the project.

The final application was submitted at the beginning of 1980. The health economist, Tony Culyer, was asked for advice on the accompanying economic appraisal. He wrote in January that 'having read all the documentation I am even more impressed by PROMIS...married to a doctor I'm probably more aware of problems of medical records than others in my field. I have often speculated on the feasibility of fully computerising medical records but PROMIS seems to surpass even these speculations. It would seem...essential that the NHS gains experience with this system in order to keep track of state of the art in this area.' [xcvii]

A DHSS Computer R&D working group visited RFH on 27 February 1980 to sound out staff and senior management, and to establish the extent of manual use of POMR by junior staff at RFH.

When asked by the DHSS Computer Section to clarify the terms on which PROMIS might be available to the NHS the DHHS in Washington[55] foresaw no restrictions on use of the software as it was in the public domain – and while the PROMIS laboratory was contracted to the National Center for Health Services Research its staff could help RFH.

The DHSS's Computer R&D Committee and its Computer Policy Committee supported the Royal Free application. However, on 27 August 1980 Maddison wrote (for the DHSS) that with Ministerial agreement, PROMIS would not be supported. *'...even for a research and development project, the risks involved were*

---

[55] The Department of Health and Human Services was created when Education was removed from the remit of Washington's Department of Health Education and Welfare in 1979.

too great and the benefits too speculative for an investment on this scale in present conditions of financial stringency'...'If you should decide to apply again I suggest you leave it until there have been major developments in America.'

A brief accompanying statement noted that installing PROMIS throughout RFH would take about eight years and cost about £3.8million (including £2.7million from central R&D funds); and that although operational in two wards (in Burlington and in the Cancer Research Institute in Baltimore) and in a primary health care centre linked to Burlington,[56] PROMIS had not yet serviced a whole hospital. It stated that all were 'most impressed' by its potential – '*Indeed the advisory NHS computer R&D committee took the view that PROMIS was the only worthwhile solution to emerge to deal with the problem of storing and accessing medical records'*. However, the DHSS was not convinced that it improved patient care or was acceptable to clinicians using it. The cost of adapting it for a whole hospital, in an NHS environment, would be considerable and speculative. Furthermore it considered the project would strain the District's management and resources at a time when other more important matters (e.g. NHS re-organisation) had a higher priority.

The application's authors were disgusted with the skimpy response to their detailed application and wondered whether, financial considerations seeming paramount, the decision makers had bothered to read the economic appraisal accompanying the application. Technically PROMIS was fully developed. After a lengthy trial in a gynaecological ward it had supported a general medical ward for almost three years. The DHSS's statement that it provided only a limited range of facilities to one ward was erroneous; all relevant information for that ward was channelled through PROMIS even though it was not linked directly with all departmental computers.

The final decision was made by a small group of very senior DHSS officials; none was a practising clinician. The vote, apparently not unanimous, was represented as such. RFH's District Administrator wrote to express disappointment with the outright rejection and of his concern that neither those involved with the project at RFH, nor members of the R&D Committee or the Computer Policy committee, were allowed to explain PROMIS to those making the decision. RFH suspected, given the complexity of PROMIS, that those who rejected it were unaware of its potential.

On Monday 29 September 1980 *The Daily Telegraph* announced that Cohen, the chairman of the DHSS's Computer R&D Committee, had resigned, with three other

[56] Grand Isle Medical Clinic, 17 miles from Burlington.

members,[57] partly because its advice to install PROMIS at RFH for only £2½million spread over 8 years had been rejected. Apart from storing medical records it would have provided a wealth of analytical information – about the amount spent on drugs, on treating individual diseases, and on different specialties – thus facilitating more cost-effective planning. DHSS officials rejected PROMIS because of the cost but Cohen said '… the money is available. The committee was given a £3million a year budget, but gets nowhere near spending even half that.'

MacGillivray had written to the Minister (Dr Gerard Vaughan) on 17 September criticising the decision. He pointed out that if PROMIS went commercial the subsequent cost would be horrific, as the computer industry's future profits would come primarily from software. The NHS was being offered, gratis, two hundred man years of software development for a system still adaptable to British needs. It seemed madness to reject it.

On 1 December 1980 Vaughan met briefly with an RFH group that reiterated its concern that commercial exploitation of PROMIS would render it unaffordable. Maddison subsequently quoted the DHHS as stating that PROMIS would remain in the 'public domain', and that the program tapes and documentation would be available. However, the idea that RFH, or any other group, could simply set up PROMIS without help from Weed's group was absurd.

Vaughan viewed a slide show of PROMIS on 14 January 1981. He was forewarned that given the complexity of PROMIS it would be of limited value unless followed by a discussion. He arrived late and left immediately after the last slide was shown. He later acknowledged the need for effective medical information systems, and claimed to understand RFH's enthusiasm for PROMIS, but would still not support it.

The DHSS's rejection may have influenced the eventual fate of PROMIS. Following the election of the Republican Reagan as President in late 1980 the funding of many US government departments was cut, including that for the DHHS. Weed's group suffered in consequence. It had hoped PROMIS would be introduced as a whole hospital system at RFH. With that hope dashed, and withdrawal of federal funding, many in the group felt further development of PROMIS and widespread dissemination could come about only with support from private industry.

In May 1981 they formed a company, PROMIS Information Systems Inc, to produce management information systems; these were not necessarily medical as

[57] They were Ian Wooton, Professor of Chemical Pathology at RPMS; JP Payne Professor of Anaesthesia at RCSEng; and Dr Gordon Cumming, medical director at Midhurst Medical Research Institute. Subsequently James Altey, Professor of Computing at Liverpool University, and Dr DJ Deeley, Director, South Wales Radiotherapy and Oncology service also resigned.

the basic PROMIS software was applicable in other fields. The company financed itself initially on the proceeds of a sale of an Atlas system (essentially PROMIS minus the medical data base) to Merrill Lynch, which also invested in the company's equity.

At the time there was particular interest in PROMIS at the Contra Costa County Health Service in Martinez, California, and at the Baycrest Geriatric Centre in Toronto. A feasibility study at Contra Costa in 1982 supported the funding of a pilot PROMIS installation, but following the narrow victory of the Republican candidate in California's gubernatorial election the project was scrapped. At Baycrest a pilot system was introduced in the mid-1980s. However PROMIS Information Systems Inc. now had to make money to survive and for commercial reasons switched to cheaper hardware suppliers; this had a deleterious effect on response times and the system did not work as well as it did in Burlington.

Sadly a system created with about $13 million dollars of federal funding was effectively abandoned by the end of the 1980s. One factor that may have influenced acceptance of PROMIS in the late 1970s was that the software was in the public domain. The American computer industry would not have wanted such software effectively free of charge and may have exerted pressure to prevent its adoption. Knowing what we know now about the interrelationship between the NHS and the private health sector in Britain one wonders whether companies hoping to profit from the enormous potential market for NHS computing might have influenced the DHSS's decision about PROMIS.

Many still consider PROMIS as the best medical record system to have been created. Developed as intended it would also have been one of the cheapest. In Britain the Government has spent tens of billions of pounds on NHS computing. None of the medical records systems introduced has shown any promise of wide acceptance. The rejection of RFH's application to transfer PROMIS from Burlington in the 1980s is arguably the most expensive error in the history of the NHS.

Curriculum Change

When MacGillivray became Dean the School had been running its new curriculum for a year. He set up a new curriculum committee, with preclinical and clinical subcommittees and appointed McIntyre as Clinical Sub-Dean. The clinical subcommittee reviewed plans for the clinical curriculum, due to come into effect in October 1976, considered them unsatisfactory and decided to start afresh.

There were several problems. For decades students passing 2nd MB in the spring had entered RFH in April (except for those starting a four term intercalated B.Sc. course). The failures at 2nd MB who passed on re-sit in the summer started clinical studies in October, along with recent B.Sc. graduates[58] and some Oxbridge students. Both cohorts were attached initially to either a general medical or surgical firm, the option favoured by virtually all clinical teachers. However, under the new University regulations the 2nd MB course lasted six preclinical terms, not five. This meant that a single cohort would enter RFH in October and graduate MBBS in June three years later – and that not all of its students could start on a 'general' firm. Furthermore clinical training was reduced from 36 months to 33 and was to include more elective time, including a six-week 'science elective'. Not surprisingly clinical teachers fought to retain the time allocated to their own specialities.

Before reorganising the curriculum the clinical subcommittee defined the school goals,[59] and wrote objectives for some of them using Mager's approach to the setting of educational targets (see Chapter 14). It also made recommendations on in-course assessment (ICA) that influenced the choice of the educational methods to be employed.

The newly revised clinical timetable came into force in October 1976. Following an introductory course the students spent one year 'rotating' through four three-month 'posts', including General Medicine, General Surgery and Psychiatry/Neurology. Because some departments refused to participate in a first year rotation, wanting only students who had already done general medicine and/or surgery, the fourth post was a compromise cobbled out of Geriatrics, Nephrology, Anaesthetics and 'A & E'.

The second clinical 'year' began with four weeks of clinical pathology.[60] A full year of attachments followed – to Histopathology, General Practice, Clinical Epidemiology and other clinical specialties. The first cohort to experience it spent six weeks of the second year on a science elective which was subsequently abolished – its six-week slot being allocated to clinical pathology whose original allocation of four weeks proved unacceptable to teachers and students.

The final 'year' was a 24-week period made up of an eight-week clinical elective, and eight two-week attachments – to medical, surgical, paediatric and psychiatric firms, and to general practice and A & E. There were then four weeks for revision before the final examinations.[xcviii]

Much of the teaching was traditional, i.e. ward rounds, outpatients, tutorials and a relatively small number of lectures, during which students were largely passive

---

[58] Those who graduated with an intercalated degree in June had passed 2nd MB four terms earlier.

[59] The 'goals' changed little before the merger in 1998. In 1995 the 'aims' of the Glasgow medical school were a copy, almost verbatim, of the RFHSM goals. (Letter McIntyre to Pattinson – 2 Oct 1995).

[60] i.e. Chemical pathology, haematology, microbiology & immunology.

participants. It did not match the School's goals which emphasized learning (i.e. an activity of students). Nor did it deal with the School's greatest priority – that students should learn by simulating whole patient care. To do that great emphasis was placed on the 'clerking' of inpatients allocated to the student's 'care'. Notes were to be written using a POMR template; this promoted a disciplined approach to clinical problems, by guiding students through all stages of clinical activity, and ensured that their notes preserved the logic behind their 'simulated care'. Teachers went over a student's notes on current inpatients during frequent one-to-one 'audit' sessions, and provided feedback by pointing out deficiencies and praising good performance. This approach was evaluated by impartial outsiders before being used in the new clinical curriculum in October 1976.[xcix]

Audit was a key component of ICA which was used primarily for early identification of poor performance. Most clinical posts ended with a written test assessing achievement of specific objectives; the results contributed to an overall grade that also reflected physical examination skills and professional behaviour. While assessment of the last was inevitably subjective, attempts were made to improve validity by asking teachers to comment specifically on 'motivation & determination', 'relationships with patients, teachers and colleagues' and 'attitudes to learning' – in the hope of detecting and correcting unacceptable behaviour.

There were four grades: A (outstanding), B (good pass), C (pass) and D (weak, and so unacceptable). D grades had to be accompanied by a recommendation for remedial action. A Collegiate Committee of Examiners reviewed grades and recommendations three-monthly.

Students could not sit finals without passing ICA, which assessed qualities tested poorly in conventional final examinations. Therefore its marks were not combined with marks obtained in finals and could play no part in failing students; but if good enough, they could be used to prevent some borderline students from failing.

To evaluate the effectiveness of the new clinical curriculum specialist outside help was used – to avoid bias, and because students and staff would be more likely to criticize it if they were speaking to an outsider rather than one of the Curriculum Committee. The lead person was Janet Grant,[61] an educational psychologist; her assistant, Liz Wyn Pugh, was a gynaecologist and an RFHSM alumna. They sought the opinion of teachers and students about goals and objectives, POMR, audit, other educational methods, and ICA.[c]

The new curriculum had an important but limited impact on clinical education. Many teachers revised their teaching to match it; others did not. Criticism was, in

[61] Grant was then with the British Life Assurance Trust Centre for Health & Medical Education and was later Professor of Medical Education at the Open University.

general, directed not at its basic principles but at its implementation. Organizational problems were inevitable, given the haste with which the new curriculum was introduced. Communicating with students was not a problem, because the Clinical Sub-Dean met regularly with student representatives from each post. What was surprising was the difficulty of communicating with busy clinical staff; many failed to attend meetings and/or ignored the documentation sent to them. It helped if curriculum planners spoke to them individually, but to do so was time-consuming and strained the limited resources available for curricular implementation.

To aid understanding of the new clinical curriculum a small booklet was produced (for staff and students) entitled *Everything You Have Always Wanted to Know About The New Clinical Curriculum But Were Afraid To Ask!* Most found it helpful but some considered its light-hearted approach inappropriate for such a serious matter as education!

Electives

More and more Royal Free students now took electives overseas – 23 did so in 1976-7 and for the next seven years the annual figure was 19, 44, 58, 56, 68, 58 and 70. The annual reports give no figures for 1984 to 1987; 72 went abroad in 1987-8. The USA (7) and Canada (6) were popular venues in 1976-7, as were Africa and the West Indies; India and Nepal proved more attractive from 1978-9.[ci]

In 1985 and 1986 there were scholarships and bursaries available for clinical electives. The Hampstead Wells and Camden Trust provided £2,000; ICI Pharmaceuticals (UK) gave four annual bursaries of £100; and the Medical Sickness Travel Scholarship rose in value from £200 to £350. Riker Laboratories/3M Health Care provided an interest free loan of £6,000 and annual prizes of £200, £150 and £100, while Roussel Laboratories gave an annual prize of £300.

The awarding of prizes was based on work done during the elective and the quality of the subsequent written report. The best were presented orally at the Old Students Association's annual clinical meeting. Karim Meeran won 3M/Riker's national prize of £1,000 in 1988 for a project on leprosy and HIV infection that he carried out at the Chikankata Salvation Army Hospital in Zambia; the hospital received medical equipment worth £1,000.[cii]

Overseas students taking their electives at RFH came mainly from the USA or Germany. Virtually all were clinical students. The annual reports rarely recorded the numbers, but there were 75 in 1983-4. Most stayed a month or two but in 1982-3 three German students spent the whole academic year at RFH, and two spent eight months the following year.[ciii].

Finals

The first final examinations under the new regulations were held in June 1979. The major innovation was that pathology was taken with the clinical subjects – not six months earlier. This sent the message that it was not something to get out of the way before taking medicine, surgery and O & G. Furthermore, it addressed the long standing problem of a relatively high failure rate in pathology that resulted, at least partly, because its examiners knew 'failures' could retake in six months; consequently the only students sitting all four subjects six months later were the weakest ones. Although this change was initially unpopular with students and some pathologists its benefits soon became apparent.

The pathology and O & G exams involved one paper, a practical or clinical, and a viva. The combined medicine and surgery exam also included clinical pharmacology and therapeutics, psychiatry, clinical epidemiology, general practice and paediatrics. There were two papers, several oral exams, some short cases and a long case. For the last the student had to take a history and conduct a physical examination – on an adult or a child with medical/surgical problems, or on a psychiatric patient – and then list the patient's problems and write a plan for each problem requiring action.

The medicine/surgery papers reflected the School's 'goals and objectives' and were radically different from those for the University's examinations. Short non-cued questions tested the formulation of diagnostic hypotheses by requesting the likely cause of symptoms, physical signs and/or abnormal test results, e.g. 'A 20-year-old woman has a three-month history of weight loss and increased appetite. Give two causes'. Longer interdisciplinary questions required brief but relatively specific answers. e.g. 'What clinical features would suggest that a 50-year-old man has suffered a myocardial infarction? What tests would confirm the diagnosis? If the infarct appears uncomplicated how would you manage the patient?...etc, etc.' The questions reflected situations faced in clinical practice, and some of the longer ones encompassed therapeutics, epidemiology and psychiatry.

During the first four years of MacGillivray's deanship the students sat the University's examinations, which took place in the spring and autumn. As in the past those awarded distinctions in one or more subjects were recognized by the University as graduating with 'honours'. In April 1977 Andrew Gellert was awarded distinctions in four of the five subjects and won the University Gold Medal.[civ]

The first cohort exposed to the new clinical curriculum sat the new style examinations in June 1979. They took 'school-based' examinations but to earn a distinction they, like students at other London schools, had to undergo extra sets of viva voces conducted by 'university examiners'.

Over the first six cohorts of new curriculum students (1979-84) twenty-seven were awarded honours (i.e. about four to five a year) and between them achieved a total of forty distinctions. Of the next four cohorts thirty-two students (i.e. on average eight a year) shared forty-seven distinctions. This apparent improvement may have resulted because the examiners at RFHSM, internal and external, realised they were not putting up as many examinees for honours as other schools. The best results were in 1987, when ten Royal Free students gained seventeen distinctions. Mark Hamilton got distinctions in all five subjects and won the University Gold Medal. The previous year RFHSM held the top six places in medicine, had the highest percentage of honours (13.7%), and had only three failures out of 102 candidates. In MacGillivray's last year as dean 7.5% of candidates failed, apparently a lower figure than was usual at other medical schools, and seven students graduated with honours.[cv]

'Going down' Ceremony

In December 1978 the Dean proposed that soon after the final examinations there should be a formal 'going down' ceremony in the new Assembly Hall attended by the graduands' relatives and/or close friends. It was to supplement, not replace, the University's degree presentation held each autumn at the Albert Hall. The first such ceremony, on Friday 29 June 1979, included the prize distribution and proved a great success. At the same event two years later the Assembly Hall was officially named the 'Peter Samuel Hall'.[cvi]

At the 1983 ceremony the Students' Union President, Ian Mack, presented Jean Stanton with the first John Glanister Memorial Prize and Medal. After Glanister died in December 1981, during his final year at RFHSM, his fellow students launched an appeal so that a prize in his name could be awarded annually to the final year student who contributed most to the School. The Dean and student representatives selected the winner from a list submitted by the final year students.

In 1984 HODs suggested the annual ceremony should include a guest speaker. Dame Sheila Sherlock, recently retired, spoke that July and the practice continued. The hall's acoustics were poor, and each year the platform party struggled to hear the proceedings. Initially this mattered little but it became a major problem when there was a formal address. Attempts to improve the acoustics had a limited effect.[cvii]

Clubs and Societies

Student life at RFHSM was certainly not all work. The 1987-9 prospectus listed seventeen clubs and societies affiliated to the Union. Some, including the Medical and Debating Societies, had withered and disappeared; new ones, like the Photographic Society and the Wine Circle, had sprung up.

The Dramatic Society and the Music and Choral Society were particular beneficiaries of the move to Hampstead; Instead of performing on makeshift stages at Gray's Inn Road and Hunter Street they now had a proper stage in the Assembly Hall. There the Thespians performed both unorthodox Shakespeare (*The Marowitz Hamlet,* 1977) [62] and the orthodox (*Twelfth Night,* 1978 & *A Midsummer Night's Dream,* 1981), as well as classics (*The Importance of Being Earnest*, 1979) and modern plays ('*The Crucible*', 1976, '*A Man for all Seasons*', 1982, '*The Rocky Horror Show',* 1983; and '*Grease*', 1985).

Each year the Music and Choral Society carolled at Christmas and held one or two major concerts. In the one at Christ Church, Hampstead in 1977 the programme included Schubert's Fourth Symphony and Haydn's *Harmoniemesse*. The following year Ting Hoi To, a final year student at the School, was the soloist for Beethoven's First Piano Concerto.[cviii]

The Dramatic Society and the Music and Choral Society sometimes combined for shows such as *The Pirates of Penzance* (1977-8, 1986-7), *The Sorcerer* (1980), '*Orpheus in the Underworld'* 1983) and *Guys and Dolls* (1988). 'Dramsoc' worked with 'the orchestra' [63] in *The Mikado* (1976) & *How to succeed in business without really trying* (1984).

The Fourth-Year Xmas shows were still highly entertaining and irreverent revues. Their highlight (at least since 1964) was the 'home-made' movie with guest appearances by staff. The 1986 film *'Don't Mess with Werewolves!'* won the National Surrey Film Festival and a Gold Seal Award at the London International Film Festival; that year the Xmas show raised £10,000 for charity.[64]

Sporting Activities

Sport remained important at RFHSM but the demise of the Magazine in 1974 made it more difficult subsequently to follow the fortunes of the various sporting clubs. Sixteen were listed in the prospectus for 1970-72 but only thirteen in that for 1987-89; however, by then the students had access to the RFH Recreation Centre which had a small swimming pool and facilities for badminton, netball, weight-training and five-a-side football. In the later list the athletics, badminton, judo & karate, rifle, swimming and table tennis clubs had gone; basketball, skiing and water polo clubs had been added. The Canoe and Sub-Aqua Clubs formed in 1985-6 seem to have been short-lived.

The first three LSMW sports clubs – tennis (1888), swimming (1895) and hockey (1897) – remained active. In 1979-80 Elizabeth Allan captained the ULU

[62] In *The Marowitz Hamlet* all the lines are by Shakespeare, but their order is changed!

[63] Presumably 'the orchestra' was made up of Music Society members

[64] The following two shows raised about £4,000

Ladies' Tennis Team, and the following year RFHSM women won the Hospitals' Cup.[65]

In 1975-6 two RFHSM students captained the University's swimming team and water polo teams (Denise Lee & Iain Hutchison); both became vice-presidents of ULU's Sports Council and Hutchison also served as its chairman. The School's water polo team, started in 1976-7, came second in the ULU championships in 1982-3.

Women's and men's hockey flourished. In the mid 1970s Joanna Walker captained the University Ladies and Jack Edmonds was captain of United Hospitals and secretary of the University team. In 1985-6 the men's and women's 1st XIs were promoted to their University first divisions, and the women won the Hospitals Cup. Mixed hockey was popular in the mid-to-late '80s. The club toured Norfolk in 1984-5 and the Isle of Wight in 1987-8. It played host to a Dutch hockey team and toured Holland several times, travelling by double-decker bus in 1988-9.[cix]

The Free had two squash courts at Hampstead. Not surprisingly the Squash Club membership increased and the men were promoted to ULU's league four at Christmas 1978. The 1879-80 season began with victories over St Thomas', London Business School, UCL, Imperial and the Middlesex – thanks to some staff stalwarts, including the chest physician Stewart Clarke. The women had mixed success in ULU's league two.[cx]

Royal Free rugby continued to improve, and in the late 1970s the Free often had representatives in the United Hospitals and/or University teams. Otto Chan played for English Students against England Under-23s in 1978-9 and captained the University the following season, during which RFHSM lost in the final of the University's Gutteridge Cup.

In 1984 RFHSM reached the final of the Hospitals Cup, having never before reached the semi-finals. Many supporters turned up at Richmond to watch RFH draw with a slightly weakened St Mary's side, both teams missing an easy penalty in the closing minutes. Council postponed its meeting on 14 March so that members could attend the replay. Sadly, St Mary's was at full strength and won by 22-3.[cxi]

The Free was a semi-finalist four times in the next five years, and by beating Charing Cross-Westminster[66] it reached the final again in 1988. St Mary's, again its opponents, won 32-0 and took the cup home for the ninth time in twelve years. The following season there were Royal Free players in the United Hospitals and London University teams and at the Students World Cup held in Britain in 1989.[cxii]

---

[65] ARs 1978-9, 1979-80, 1980-1.

[66] The medical schools of Charing Cross Hospital & Westminster Hospital merged in 1984.

RFHSM's soccer team, like the rugby team, included players from the School of Pharmacy. In 1980-1 their joint first XI won only three of twenty matches and was relegated to a lower division. The soccer link with Pharmacy was severed and a purely RFHSM team joined division two of the University league. In 1984-5 both the 1st & 2nd XIs reached their respective Hospital Cup finals, but lost. The 2nd XI won the ULU Cup in 1986 and 1987, and the 1st XI topped its division in 1987.[cxiii]

Cricket went on as usual and one match in 1981 – a ULU cup game against the Royal Veterinary College – will have stuck in the memory of all playing in it. RFHSM scored 194 for 5 in 40 overs – the Vets scored only 11 runs; Khan took 7 wickets for 7 runs and Cox 3 for 1.[cxiv]

Rowing prospered at the Free. In the 1981 Tideway Head of the River Race 420 crews participated, and to its credit the men's first VIII completed the course; it later won the novice VIIIs at the Chiswick regatta. By braving a 75-mile sponsored row (including an overnight stop in Henley) male and female members raised £1,500 towards the purchase of a new 'VIII' called 'George Qvist'. To help with coaching a motor launch was acquired in 1983-4, and the following season the club won several tournaments plus two 'blades' in the UH bumps. In 1985-6 the women became head of the river at the UH Bumps, won the Junior VIII and the Senior Coxed IV at the UH Regatta, and rowed at Henley. The following year two men's IVs from RFHSM finished first and second in the UH Regatta.[cxv]

By 1885, despite the acquisition of 'George Qvist', the club claimed dire need of another boat. The Union couldn't help, so in 1988 the club raised £5,000 (including £3,700 from the Worshipful Company of Fishmongers) towards a new one. Council provided an interest free loan of £3,000 to speed up the purchase.[cxvi]

Although sailing started again towards the end of the war the Sailing Club lapsed on several occasions. Although listed in the 1976-8 prospectus it was said to have been 'restarted' in 1979-80 when it had two Firefly dinghies moored at the Welsh Harp Reservoir.[cxvii]

In 1979-80 the golf club was another 'resurrection' even though one with links to Highgate Golf Club had started in 1970 with the surgeon Lionel Gracey, a Cambridge blue, as its president. Golf became a more serious matter at RFHSM in the early 1980s when three students – Alastair Wells, his sister Alison and David Monkman – were key members of the University team, Alistair being its captain.[cxviii]

Sporting pride of place during MacGillivray's deanship went to the students Clare Halsted and Nick Bell. Both fenced for Great Britain in the 1976 Montreal Olympics. Halsted was already an Olympian, having competed in Munich in 1972; Bell fenced again at Los Angeles in 1984.

Students' Union

In May 1981 the Students' Union agreed a new constitution. The terms of office of committee members were altered to run from October to September as at other medical schools.[67] This meant there were two Presidents in 1981; Peter Stubbs served for nine months; Anthony Kostick then took over. Student nurses and radiographers were accepted as associate members of the Union.[cxix]

The Union's representatives on School committees behaved responsibly. They were particularly interested in curricular matters and about the difficulty students had in finding accommodation around Hampstead. In 1983-4 students from RFHSM and other schools lobbied MPs as part of the 'clinical grants campaign' – which resulted in £2.80 a week being added to the allowance students received for the extra weeks spent during the three years of clinical training.[cxx]

The Students' Union's first Rag Week was held in May 1982. It included a Rag Queen competition, a celebrity auction and 'DramSoc' performances of 'Androcles and the Lion' at two local public houses. The most spectacular event was a sponsored walk across Hadrian's Wall in Roman uniforms. The £1,400 raised went to local charities supporting mentally handicapped children and towards a CT body scanner for RFH. The week ended with a May Ball at Myddleton House; it was a social success but a financial disaster![cxxi]

Rag Week 1983 included a sponsored hitch-hike to Paris, a 'Lunatic' entertainment afternoon in Covent Garden, and 'Lunchtime with Capital Radio' on Hampstead Heath; it raised £1,200. The May Ball, run prudently, was a financial success but even so it became a sporadic rather than an annual event.[cxxii]

Rag Week profits rose strikingly – from £3,900 in 1984 to £12,000 in 1989. The beneficiaries were not just big charities like NSPCC, Oxfam, Mencap and the British Heart Foundation. Equipment was bought for RFH departments, and to say 'Thank You' for teaching Royal Free students over the years some money went to Great Ormond Street's Appeal. Rag Week also supported two small charities founded by RFH students – 'STOP', a campaign against heroin abuse, and 'Spectrum', which helped students with part-time care of disabled children.[68,cxxiii]

Money was raised in other ways. In 1987-8 more than ninety students took part in a sponsored 300 mile relay, from the top of Snowdon to Hampstead, which raised £11,000 towards the CT body scanner (see above). The profit of £4,600 from the 1988 4th Year Show went to Shelter, Help a London Child and RFH's department of Vascular Research.

---

[67] In 1915 the election of officers was moved from October to January so that 1st yr. students could get to know each other before choosing their representative.

[68] Spectrum's activities were described in the BMJ (Vol. 290. 13 April 1985, p.1144)

Student Residences

Lack of suitable residential accommodation for students was a persistent problem. Few could afford Hampstead rents, and only a small number could be housed in Dame Frances Gardner's three Roderick Road houses, which were close to the new RFH, or at 2 Myddleton Square, near Hunter Street. But before MacGillivray left office the School acquired its own hall of residence. The United States Embassy no longer needed Carlton Mansions, a block of 17 flats in West End Lane, West Hampstead that had housed some of its staff. It offered it to the University, which offered it to RFHSM.

The price was £1.6million. For its size and location it was a bargain, being convertible into about 85 study bedrooms, with shared pantries and bathrooms. An initial outlay of £150,000 was needed. The rest of the purchase price could then be covered by commercial loans repayable from rental income over 35 years; the School would then be left with the freehold.

MacGillivray jumped at the chance and, at his last meeting as Dean, Council agreed to provide the £150,000. It was hoped an appeal would cover the full cost of purchase and alterations; rental income could then serve other purposes. Contracts for the acquisition of Carlton Mansions were exchanged on 20 July; it cost £1,642,550.[cxxiv]

The R & D Committee set up a working party to identify projects that would attract funds and to determine the scale of the resulting appeal. In a policy statement on fund raising it recognized the local population as a potentially important source. To avoid conflicting aims or competition there were to be discussions with the District and the Special Trustees.[cxxv]

On 10 November 1988 Council heard that the Ronald Raven Trust[69] had pledged £750,000 to fund a Ronald Raven Chair of Oncology, and subsequently promised another £270,000 so that oncology could be housed over the radiotherapy department being built by RFH. RFH knew that NETRHA was unhappy about expanding radiotherapy at RFH, but thought it might agree if oncology and radiotherapy were shared with North Middlesex Hospital.[cxxvi]

RFH already had links with the North Middlesex. From October students were attached to its medical and surgical firms, and one of its surgeons, Rodney Croft, joined RFHSM's examiners in surgery. Earlier that year the School supported a proposal that Haringey and Hampstead health authorities should merge, believing that the larger population base created by having North Middlesex as a second teaching hospital would strengthen its position as an independent school. However,

[69] Supported mainly by the Millicom Corp. and Racal PLC)

the Haringey-Hampstead merger foundered, probably as a casualty of the major reorganisation of the NHS which resulted following the publication in January 1989 of 'Working for Patients' – the outcome of the deliberations of a Cabinet team chaired by Thatcher and charged with reducing NHS expenditure. (See Chapter 16) [cxxvii]

In November 1988 MacGillivray indicated his wish to resign as Dean the following September. According to the Statute the Dean was to be appointed by Council – which asked the Education Committee to forward one nomination from those submitted to it by the Committee of Teachers. The last set up a working party (Havard, Scheuer, Spyer & McIntyre) to consider possible successors, and to recommend whether there should be a part-time or full-time appointment, and an internal or an external candidate.

The position was advertised in *The Lancet* and the *BMJ*. The working party interviewed several candidates and suggested Professor Arie Zuckerman's name to the Committee of Teachers. Zuckerman was the Director of Medical Microbiology at LSHTM and a distinguished old student of RFHSM. There were no other nominations, and both the Committee of Teachers and the Education Committee voted *nem.con.* for his nomination as Dean – although abstentions were recorded owing to disquiet over the way in which the working party had proceeded.[cxxviii]

On 22 June 1989 MacGillivray attended his last Council meeting having served the School with distinction for fourteen difficult years. He oversaw the move of the medical School to Hampstead, fought the School's corner in the struggle over 'Flowers', and battled with the effects of the low-grade given to the school in the UGC's assessment of universities. The curriculum was radically revised under his supervision. Research grants rose from £140,000 p.a. to over £4million. All this was achieved by one who was nominally a part-time Dean. He also played a major and significant role in the University and was the first Pro-Vice-Chancellor for medicine at the University of London.

His portrait, (Fig 15.11 Colour plate) painted by William Bowyer RA, was added to those of other former deans hanging in Committee Room 1 of the medical school building at Hampstead. Until then he was then the only male honoured in this way as no formal portraits existed of either Anstie or Norton. He died, after a long illness, on 17 December 2010.

CHAPTER 16

Arie Zuckerman (1989–1998)

…… But not for Long. The Merger

Arie Zuckerman (Fig 16.1) was born on 30 March 1932 in Jerusalem, in what was then the British mandated territory of Palestine. His father was a senior judge working for the British Government. Arie was educated at St George's School, just outside the walls of the Old City; established in 1899 it remains a highly regarded institution run by the Anglican Episcopal Diocese of Jerusalem. The Rev W.V. Fawdry, author of *Thomas the Tank Engine*, taught there from 1933 to 1936.

Fig 16.1 Arie Zuckerman

Arie joined his brother in England in 1947 for educational reasons. Their parents remained in Jerusalem and became residents of the State of Israel created in May 1948. Arie attended Hasmonean Grammar School, an observant Jewish School founded in north London in 1944. Initially based in Golders Green it moved to Hendon in 1947.

He transferred to Sir John Cass College in Aldgate to prepare for the Higher School Certificate and went on to study anatomy and physiology at Birmingham University. The professor of anatomy was Solly Zuckerman[1] (no relation). After graduating B.Sc. with first class honours in 1953, Arie moved to RFHSM for clinical studies. On graduating MBBS in April 1957 he won the University of London Gold Medal.

His first pre-registration job was as obstetric HS to Gladys Hill and Kathleen Robinson at RFH. The second was 'Bob' Pearson's HP job at the Whittington Hospital where he also worked as a Casualty Surgeon & Admissions Officer before being called up for National Service in September 1959.

[1] Later Lord Zuckerman

Serendipitously he opted for a three year short service commission in the Royal Air Force. After basic training, he moved to an advanced flying school. There he taught aviation medicine and was also an MO looking after the very fit pilots – clinical work so undemanding that he requested a transfer. Seconded to the Public Health Laboratory Service (PHLS) he studied the epidemiology of viral hepatitis in RAF personnel. The work not only led to the award of an MD in 1963 but determined his subsequent career – one dominated by his interest in hepatitis viruses.

Before leaving the PHLS he spent time in the pathology department at Guy's. He moved to the London School of Hygiene and Tropical Medicine (LSHTM) in 1965 as a senior lecturer; by the time he left he was Professor of Medical Microbiology and Director of the Department. His two children are medical graduates; Mark qualified from UCHMS in 1985, and Jane at the Free in 1987; both have worked on viral hepatitis.

Zuckerman, like MacGillivray, was helped as Dean by academic colleagues serving as Vice-dean or Sub-deans, or as chairmen of various School divisions and committees. His first vice dean, Scheuer, had only three months left of his three year term as vice dean. He was replaced by Denis Chapman on 1 January 1990; McIntyre took over in 1993 and Spyer in 1996. During Zuckerman's nine-year deanship Sue Tuck, Adam Lewis, and George Hamilton acted as Clinical Sub-deans and supervised the clinical curriculum (Rodney Croft serving in this capacity at the North Middlesex Hospital from 1989). At the end of 1990 Sweny, Postgraduate Dean from 1987, made way for James Dooley who was, in 1997, appointed Director of Postgraduate Medical Education – a new post, run jointly with the NHS Trust, which incorporated the duties of the Postgraduate Sub-dean. Bob Dick, Roy Pounder and Marsha Morgan served successively as Admissions Sub-dean.[i]

At his first Council meeting as Dean on 9 November 1989 Zuckerman noted the generous legacies to the School in the will of Dame Frances Gardner; £650,000 was received in 1990 (and her trustees transferred another £200,000 to the School's reserves in 1993). Gardner, who had died in July, was the School's seventh President. The eighth and last was Dame Sheila Sherlock, formally elected by Members of the School (MOS) in March 1990. The role was largely ceremonial; the President's main functions were to chair meetings of MOS and attend Council.[ii]

As always the key working members of Council, other than the Dean and the School Secretary, were the Chairman and the Honorary Treasurer, the latter also chairing the Finance and General Purposes Committee (FGPC).

In December 1991 'Tim' Cohen announced his wish to resign as chairman. Giles Lascelles and Nicholas Samuel, both sons of former chairmen,[2] were nominated to succeed him. Lascelles, a member since 1967, was Council's Vice-chairman, but Samuel, Cohen's nephew, a member since 1988, was elected and assumed the chair in June.[iii]

In March 1992 David Dutton took over as Treasurer from Robin Fox whose resignation after eight years meant he also lost his seat on Council; however the MOS quickly elected him to replace the architect Sir Anthony Cox (who died soon afterwards).[3]

Hampstead HA's four representatives on Council at the end of MacGillivray's deanship (Bondy, Carrier, Ratzer and Wells) carried on when Zuckerman took over and were joined by John Cooper, Hampstead HA's new chief executive. Professor Tony Diplock from Guy's joined Sir David Innes Williams as a University representative.

Council met about eight times a year when Gardner was Dean and six or five times during MacGillivray's time. During Zuckerman's first two years there were four meetings a year but subsequently only three, and some thought this number insufficient for dealing properly with Council business.

Initially Zuckerman's main concern as Dean, like that of Gardner and MacGillivray, was the School's serious financial situation. He worried that the deficit for 1989-90 might exceed £440,000,[4] and that the building reserve might not cover the £135,000 still needed to upgrade Protein and Molecular Biology and/or the £375,000 cost of the Anthony Nolan/Molecular Cell Pathology building in the car park.

The worries about capital expenditure proved groundless. In December the Wolfson Foundation provided the £150,000 MacGillivray requested in June and in October 1992 Lord Wolfson 'opened' the Protein and Molecular Biology Laboratory named after him. Similarly in March 1990 the Wellcome Trust, as promised, contributed £100,000 towards the Anthony Nolan/ Molecular Cell Pathology building. Anthony Nolan provided £150,000 and to make up the shortfall the Hunter Street Fund provided a long-term loan, to be refunded if external monies became available. The Wellcome Trust also lent RFHSM a substantial sum on preferential terms (on the understanding that Dr Gillie Francis's Molecular Cell Pathology laboratory would be secure).[iv]

---

[2] Sir Francis Lascelles and Peter Samuel, later Viscount Bearsted.

[3] Before Cox left the six Councillors elected by Members of the School were Cohen, Lascelles, Gilchrist, Durham, Cox & Samuel..

[4] Although some months earlier the estimated deficit had been £900,000.

Concern about the cumulative deficit was justified. In December 1989 the estimated cumulative deficit for 1988-9 rose from £780,000 to £881,300 owing to a technicians' restructuring exercise. However, the annual deficit fell from £195,000 to £105,000 thanks to a surplus the previous year.[v]

The accumulated deficit was manageable in the short term but clearly annual expenditure could not exceed annual income indefinitely and needed to be brought under control. The main problem was that salaries consumed 85% of the School's grant and although they outstripped inflation the grant lagged behind.

The Dean, determined to get things under control, urged all academic staff to include running costs of around 20% (and later 40%) in research grant applications – hoping thus to increase income by some £200,000 – and he encouraged recruitment of more overseas PhD students, each worth about £10,000 a year.

Zuckerman was unhappy that some academics kept private practice income, professional fees, and research funds in RFH Special Trustees accounts, thus depriving the School of the interest generated on those funds. He got the Special Trustees to transfer research grants handled by them. However difficulties arose over issues such as the private patient fees exceeding the '10% of salary' that senior clinical academics were allowed to take as income if they chose to do so, as the extra funds helped them in running their own groups or departments.

Consideration of the matter was deferred to permit further discussion between School and Hospital. The Dean continued negotiating with clinical academic staff but they saw advantages in using Special Trustees accounts which incurred no charges, paid interest and were easy to access for legitimate purposes. Furthermore, in a period of financial uncertainty some were concerned about losing control over money they had raised themselves. The issue was never properly resolved.[vi]

The most effective way of saving money, also employed by Gardner and MacGillivray, was through voluntary early retirement schemes and the freezing of vacant posts. To ensure cash savings were made Zuckerman introduced a minimum delaying factor of three months on all recruitment. He hoped thus to save £400,000 in 1989-90. However an apparent deficit of £260,000 rose to £421,000 – owing largely to unpaid tuition fees (c. £24,000), expenditure of £40,000 on Frances Gardner Hall, and HHA's retrospective recalculations of the shared maintenance costs for the RFH financial years 1988-9 and 1889-90.[vii]

In March 1991 the estimated deficit for 1990-1 was £511,000; this would have taken the cumulative deficit to over £1million by the end of July,[5] but after rising to £711,000 the estimated deficit fell to £245,000. In 1991 the School was on a list

---

[5] Council had noted on 25 June 1987 that, left uncorrected, the projected cumulative deficit would be almost £2million by 1990/91.

of six in the University causing particular concern to the UFC. Zuckerman hoped that measures put in place would get it removed from that list. Subsequently there was little mention of cumulative deficit in Council minutes.[viii]

In 1993 student grants fell by 10% and payment of students' fees by local authorities by 45%. The Government imposed an efficiency gain (i.e. a cut) of 4% for three years so deficits continued to appear on the income/expenditure account. However from 1995 matters improved strikingly owing to a larger grant from HEFCE and an increasing return on the School's intellectual property. (See later) [ix]

The annual report for 1991-2 had noted that with commercial exploitation of its intellectual property the School's income was increasing – largely owing to the work of groups collaborating with Janossy's department, which produced monoclonal antibodies for their research. (See Chapter 15). In 1994 the immunology department's expertise widened when, after prolonged negotiations, David Webster, head of the MRC immunodeficiency research group at Northwick Park's Clinical Research Centre, moved with his group and joined Janossy at RFH.[x]

Commercial development and technology transfer were costing RFHSM about £75,000 a year, so in 1993 Cengiz Tarhan, the Finance Officer, suggested setting up a wholly-owned limited company, Freemedic plc, which he hoped would save VAT on patent and professional fees and play an entrepreneurial role in exploiting the School's inventions.[xi]

Freemedic proved a great success. By 1998 it transferred about £5million to School funds.[xii] An early 'winner' was Gillie Francis's Molecular Cell Pathology (MCP) group which had collaborated with pharmaceutical companies for some years. In the early 1990s its main goal was to devise methods of 'pegylating' therapeutic agents (i.e. attaching polyethylene glycol [PEG] to them) without increasing their toxicity or impairing biological activity. They developed a novel 'pegylation' technique that prolonged the half-life of various cytokines in the circulation, enhanced their bioavailability and rendered them 'invisible' to the immune system. When liposomes capable of carrying anti-tumour agents were pegylated their hepatosplenic uptake was reduced and tumour uptake increased.

To 'market' the group's work PolyMASC Pharmaceuticals was incorporated in 1995 and in December a private placing of its shares raised £5million. PolyMASC was the first company originating in an academic unit to be launched successfully onto the Alternative Investment Market (AIM), a forum for share trading in smaller companies. Francis, who became PolyMASC's chief executive, was voted AIM Entrepreneur of 1996.

The School assigned the relevant patents portfolio to PolyMASC.[6] In return,

---

[6] PolyMASC remained on the Royal Free site.

through Freemedic, it received £750,000, an annual income of £100,000 for five years, and 26% of the company's shares (worth over £5million). Nine scientists from the MCP unit retained a 32 per cent stake worth almost £7million. David Dutton (the Hon. Treasurer) joined the PolyMASC board as a director, and Zuckerman and Tarhan became directors of Freemedic. The PolyMASC deal transformed the School's financial situation and there was a large surplus in 1995-6.[xiii]

PolyMASC was not the only success story. At the end of 1996 the School accepted Speywood-Porton's offer of a lump sum of £4.25million for its rights in recombinant factor VIII technology. Paid to Freemedic it was gifted it back to the School as a capital endowment. After the three inventors and their departments (Haematology, Haemophilia Centre and Immunology) were rewarded the School was better off by £3million. The inventors, departments and School could have made much more from Factor VIII.[7] However, as no patents were taken out in the early stages of the work the School was in a weak negotiating position when Speywood transferred the intellectual property to Genentech. (See Chapter 15) [xiv]

A subcommittee of FreeMedic set up to advise on the best use of these funds considered a scholarship fund to assist needy students with tuition costs; enrichment of the M. J. Michael Fund; and additional residential accommodation for clinical students. Subsequently the FGPC agreed to use uncommitted Freemedic funds for five high priority capital projects – and suggested £285,000 for clinical oncology; £360,000 for a JCR/SCR extension scheme; £250,000 for an outpatients development; and £270,000 for a Courtyard rooftop development. The largest amount, £2million, was to be spent on the shell and partial fitting out of a floor on the roof of the Medical School – a project that would cost about £3million. The Hon. Treasurer suggested meeting the shortfall either by a further appeal, by selling more PolyMASC shares (then worth about £4.5million), or simply by prudent management of the School's cash flow.[xv] The rest of the PolyMASC shares were finally sold in 2000 following the merger with UCL; the £7million raised was applied to fund a state of the art transgenic facility and also to provide the shortfall on the school's rooftop scheme, which by then had become a two-floor 3000 sq.m. building.

Apart from Factor VIII the biggest money spinner created at RFHSM – by Janossy, Arne Akbar and Peter Amlot – was basiliximab (trade name Simulect) a CD25 chimerized MAb that hinders rejection of transplanted organs by blocking the IL-2 receptor on activated T lymphocytes; it has been used in well over 250,000 transplant recipients. The rewards – royalties of more than £20million – came

---

[7] One estimate suggests over £500million based on a 5% royalty on sales in Europe & Australasia.

mainly after the merger with UCL (see later); however, as a 40% operational cost had been added to the Sandoz grants that funded the original research (done from 1985 to 1995) RFHSM received an extra and invaluable £400,000.

When Zuckerman took over from MacGillivray the School's departments were already grouped in three academic divisions (Clinical, Clinico-pathological, and Basic Medical Sciences) answerable to an Executive Management Committee (Dean, Division Heads and the School Secretary). It was subsequently agreed that divisional chairmen should sit on the curriculum committee ex officio – and that the work of the preclinical and clinical curriculum committees should be undertaken by the divisions.[xvi]

In November 1990 an 'Academic Division of Communicable Diseases' was conceived – combining virology and medical microbiology, the Dean's WHO hepatitis centre, and academic aspects of the AIDS unit and Coppetts Wood Hospital (which housed RFH's infectious diseases beds). The virologist Paul Griffiths was its first chairman.[xvii]

A fifth division – Population and Health Care Sciences – was set up in March 1991; it included as separate departments Clinical Epidemiology, General Practice, Occupational Medicine and Environmental Health (each having a Chair), along with Medical Statistics, Health Services Research & Monitoring, and the Health Psychology unit. The divisional chairmanship was to rotate around the departments. Council also agreed in principle that the Dean should pursue further reorganisations within the divisional structure and be able to redeploy all grades of staff – not only to allow rationalisation in line with the School's strategic plan for 1991-95 but also to ensure cost-effective use of resources.[xviii]

Further reorganisations took place. In December 1993 the departments of Psychiatry and Community Child Health were incorporated within the Division of Population Health Care Sciences, while from October 1994 the divisions of Clinical Pathological Sciences and Communicable Diseases merged as a new Academic Division of Pathology chaired by Griffiths.[xix]

This flurry of administrative changes was associated with a striking increase in the number of professors in the School.[8] Some were outsiders assuming new established chairs; some replacements for professors who were retiring; and some promotions to a personal chair. The Dean himself was an appointee; when Brumfitt retired in 1992 Council agreed Zuckerman should take the chair of medical microbiology for a limited period; a formal university appointments board ratified the appointment.[xx]

[8] In 1974 RFHSM had 18 statutory professors; in 1997 there were 37.

In the Medical Unit the title Professor of Medicine was conferred on Pounder in 1992 and on Dusheiko in 1996, the year Poulter was made a Professor of Immunology.[xxi]

The NHS physician Bill Havard retired in 1990. To replace him an academic appointment was made – that of Pierre Bouloux as senior lecturer in endocrinology. Four years later Bouloux was promoted to reader and following the merger with UCL he received a personal chair.[xxii]

Before Zuckerman's first Council meeting the HHA had approved the creation of a professorial department of oncology, and was planning a radiotherapy/oncology building at RFH.[9] There was to be no charge to the School. The £350,000 cost of the upper floor shell (to accommodate oncology), and the cost of an endowed chair, had been underwritten in 1988 by the Ronald Raven Trust (of which Sir Ernest Harrison of Racal plc and the Millicom Corp were the main supporters). Having raised £1million it set a new target of £2.5million. Richard Begent was appointed Ronald Raven Professor of Oncology from 1 December 1990. In 1998 the oncology department expanded into the space vacated on podium A when Public Health and Primary Care moved into the new rooftop development over the medical school buildings.[xxiii]

In 1990 the child psychiatrist Israel Kolvin assumed the newly established 'John Bowlby chair of Child and Family Mental Health', a joint appointment with the Tavistock Clinic. Bowlby, a distinguished child psychiatrist at the Tavistock, had died that year. His eponymous association with the chair was short-lived. In the early 1990s the Leopold Muller estate provided £900,000 to establish a chair in the specialty and in 1994, when Kolvin retired, Alan Stein was appointed to the 'Leopold Muller Chair in Child and Family Mental Health'. Stein and Kolvin were South Africans; both trained at the Johannesburg medical school.[xxiv]

When Gerry Shaper retired in 1992 his department of Clinical Epidemiology and General Practice was renamed Public Health and Primary Care. Its head from October was Shah Ebrahim; he was returning from the London Hospital where he had been Professor of Geriatric Medicine since 1989. (See Chapter 15) Now Professor of Clinical Epidemiology he intended to participate in the British Regional Heart Study set up at RFHSM by Shaper in 1975, and to set up a health services evaluation unit. He moved to Bristol as Professor of the Clinical Epidemiology of Ageing in 1998, the year Archie Young left the Free to become Professor of Geriatric Medicine at Edinburgh.[xxv]

General practice became a separate department. Through the generosity of the

9 Initially it was to be linked with the North Middlesex Hospital but the latter declined the offer.

John S. Cohen Foundation a David Cohen Chair in Primary Health Care was established. Paul Wallace, a senior lecturer at St Mary's, was the Foundation Professor from May 1993. David Cohen, a local GP, was a great supporter of the School. In 1979, when Shaper received a grant from the RHA for GP teaching, Cohen was one of the first seven part-time senior GP tutors. In 1994 he was one of two people awarded the newly inaugurated School Fellowship; the other was Michael Garston, chairman of the Leopold Muller Estate trustees.[xxvi]

In June 1993 the title Professor of Renal Medicine was conferred on John Moorhead. When Moorhead retired in 1997 Stephen Powis, a senior lecturer from UMDS (Guy's campus), was appointed to the newly established chair in Renal Medicine; it was funded by charitable organisations, the RFH NHS Trust and the School. To honour Moorhead, who raised a lot of money for the renal unit, the new chair was named the Moorhead Professorship of Renal Medicine.[xxvii]

In 1994 Carol Black was made Professor of Rheumatology. She was later medical director at RFH, and was the second woman President of the Royal College of Physicians from 2002 until 2005, the year she was appointed DBE.[xxviii]

In 1989 the RFH NHS Trust appointed Margaret Johnson, a chest physician, as the first consultant in HIV medicine in the UK. The RFH HIV Centre that was created provided a walk-in out-patient service with in-patient care in Elizabeth Garrett Anderson ward. It has played a key role in improving the management of HIV and AIDS patients. A new out-patients' centre, named after the actor Ian Charleson, was inaugurated by Sir Ian McKellen in 1992, and later Sir Elton John opened a garden in which patients could relax. In 1996 Mike Youle was made director of HIV clinical research, and Clive Loveday was appointed Professor of Retrovirology – the first such appointment in Britain. Loveday developed the first viral load tests long before they became part of routine HIV management. His newly refurbished laboratories at RFHSM were next to the Department of Virology and the Wolfson Unit for Molecular Biology.[xxix]

P.K. Thomas retired in 1991, having been appointed CBE in the New Year's honours list, and A.H.V. (Tony) Schapira took the chair of 'Neurological Sciences' established three years earlier. That was the title 'PK' wanted when appointed 'Professor of Neurology' in the early 1970s, but in 1993 Schapira had the department renamed 'Clinical Neurosciences'. Around that time Geoffrey Burnstock and his research team were planning to transfer from UCL to Hampstead to set up an 'Institute of Autonomic Neurosciences', with Burnstock and Spyer as joint directors, but that move did not take place until 1997.[xxx]

Robert Shaw vacated the chair of O & G in April 1992 and moved to the University of Wales College of Medicine in Cardiff. His successor, Allan Maclean, a New Zealander who trained at Dunedin, left Glasgow for the Free in October; his major research interests were gynaecological oncology and papilloma viruses.[xxxi]

In December 1994 Wakeling relinquished the headship of the University Department of psychiatry after 15 years. Michael King took the position on 1 January 1995 and the title Professor was conferred upon him early in 1996. Wakeling remained at the Free until he took early retirement in September 1996.[xxxii]

Peter Scheuer, the head of histopathology, retired in September 1992. In 1951 he was the first male student at RFHSM to win a class prize. After retiring he remained a loyal servant of both School and Hospital, where he had spent almost his entire professional career. He was replaced by Peter Revell, a reader in histopathology at the London Hospital.[xxxiii]

In 1996, twenty-two years after becoming RFHSM's first professor of haematology, Victor Hoffbrand retired having built up a large and highly productive department. His successor in the established chair was Grant Prentice, head of the bone marrow transplant programme and a titular professor since 1993.[xxxiv] Chairs also went to others with a haematological bent. Lorna Secker-Walker became Professor of Cancer Cytogenetics from June 1993. In 1997 Anthony Madrigal, of the Anthony Nolan Research Institute, was made Professor of Haematology, and Christine Lee Professor of Haemophilia. The title 'Professor in Transfusion Medicine' was conferred on Marcela Contreras in 1998. Chilean born, she was Director of Diagnostics, Development and Research at the National Blood Authority, which funded the appointment. She was appointed DBE in 2007. [xxxv]

Tragedy struck the Haemophilia Unit in 1991. Kernoff suffered a cardiac arrest near RFH. Although resuscitated by two of the School's students he was rendered tetraplegic and unable to work. He survived another 15 years but needed both a tracheostomy and a gastrojejunostomy as he could not swallow and suffered repeated episodes of aspiration pneumonia. Despite his profound physical disability and loss of speech, he developed his own method of communication, was nursed devotedly at home from 1993 and spent little time in hospital.[xxxvi]

Ken Hobbs retired a little earlier than expected in 1998, having been active in the University as Vice-dean and Dean of the Faculty of Medicine (1986-90 & 1994-8 respectively), and as a member of Senate and Council. He served on the General Medical Council from 1996 to 2001. Marc Winslet, a Royal Free graduate (1982) and a titular professor since 1996, succeeded Hobbs as head of the University Department of Surgery at RFHSM. Brian Davidson, a young surgical senior lecturer, was awarded a personal chair in February 1997.[xxxvii]

The smallest clinical department in the School was Clinical Genetics, headed by Joan Slack, who had transferred from Great Ormond Street as a senior lecturer in 1981. Lady Slack (wife of Sir William Slack, Dean of UCMSM and Serjeant

Surgeon to the Queen) retired in 1990.[xxxviii] Her senior lectureship was taken by Kay MacDermot who was still in post at the time of the merger with UCL.

Students Accommodation

At Zuckerman's first Council meeting Carlton Gardens, the new Hall of Residence, was renamed 'Frances Gardner Hall'. When it was formally opened by HRH the Princess Royal, Chancellor of the University, in July 1991 it had already been occupied for eighteen months. Hoping to let rooms quickly RFHSM had, by November 1989, spent over £144,000 on the building and installed a housekeeper. Most students had found lodgings for 1989-90 but some still wanted to move in. Occupancy was relatively high in early January 1990, mostly in shared accommodation at a rent of £40 a week. In 1991 the rent rose from £48 to £55 for single rooms, and from £42 to £48 for shared rooms.[10,xxxix]

In 1989 some students still lived in the three Roderick Road houses and at No. 2 Myddleton Square. The School wished to retain the latter until July 1995 but when Islington Council increased the rent to £25,000 p.a., with no reduction for a long term lease, the School was forced to take a one year tenancy and to subsidize those living there until June 1990.[xl]

The *raison d'être* of Frances Gardner Hall was to counter the high housing costs in Hampstead so the newly formed Residents Committee, while appreciating the need for economic viability, wanted rents that were affordable to students and competitive with comparable accommodation elsewhere in the University. Its suggestion of a subsidy of about £26,000 during the first year seems to have been ignored, but a discretionary fund helped students struggling to afford accommodation.[xli]

To help cover the annual running costs of Frances Gardner Hall holiday lets were considered essential but the School did not employ specialists to market them. In two years they raised only £3882 (i.e. total lettings of about 540 days) and there was little subsequent increase in such income.[xlii]

The RFHSM staff supervising Frances Gardner Hall included an Administrative Assistant (George Taylor as Bursar), an Accommodations Officer, someone from Accounts, and the housekeeper, Mrs Cochrane. They also managed the Roderick Road houses (owned by the Qvist Trust), one of which was unfit for letting in 1989-90. Dame Frances had left £100,000 for 'provision and maintenance of low cost bare necessity living accommodation for medical students'; £35,000 of it was allocated for upgrading at Roderick Road.[xliii]

[10] In 2003 UCL sold Frances Gardner Hall(at a profit of £4,054,000) and replaced it with Frances Gardner House, a new hall of residence, situated behind the old RFH site in Gray's Inn Road, which opened in 2004. The Qvist Trust also sold the Roderick Road houses in 2003, and the trustees (Robin Fox & Cengiz Tarhan) agreed to donate the residue of the funds to provide accommodation for clinical students.

In October 1989 Peter Scheuer reported on the Students Residence Appeal. Aimed initially at the Old Students Association, and then at School & Hospital staff, Council members and Members of the School, it had raised only £63,880. Owing to the small size of individual contributions it was decided to pursue the appeal largely through personal contacts. Asked to support the Appeal during Rag Week the students were reluctant to collect money from the public for their own student residence.[xliv]

The sluggish response to the appeal may explain why in November the Hunter Street Fund allocated a £600,000 bridging loan to reduce borrowing against Frances Gardner Hall in the hope that the appeal would eventually replenish the fund.[11, xlv]

In the early 1980s RFHSM students raised money for a John Glanister Memorial Prize to commemorate a fellow student who died in 1981. (See Chapter 15) When his mother died in 1995 she left RFHSM about £125,000. Plans were made to purchase a five to six bedroom house costing about £250,000 as accommodation for clinical students; the balance was to be funded from rents paid, from surplus income from Frances Gardner Hall, and by an appeal. Sadly, although another £41,000 was raised for it, plans for 'Glanister House' fell through.[xlvi]

Examination Results

During Zuckerman's deanship the students followed the clinical curriculum introduced in 1976. As a group, they appeared to achieve better results in finals than their predecessors – at least in terms of honours. In 1987, the best year of MacGillivray's time, ten students qualified with honours and shared 17 distinctions; one took the University Gold Medal. During the 1990s there were at least five occasions when more than ten students got honours, and usually more than one was awarded multiple distinctions. In 1995, the best year, twenty-one graduands shared 46 distinctions; Lisa Hamilton and Rodney De Palma got distinctions in all five subjects, and the former was awarded the University Gold Medal. The following year fourteen collected 27 distinctions and for the second year running a Royal Free student – Barry Newall – won the Gold Medal with four distinctions.

However, the results of the MBBS examinations seem to have shown considerable 'grade inflation' over the years. Looking just at RFHSM only four RFHSM students graduated with 'honours' in the academic year 1948-9, each gaining one distinction. In 1957-8 two students gained 'honours' with a single distinction as did the only student to be awarded 'honours' ten years later.

---

[11] The amount actually transferred was £550,000.

General Practice and Electives

During the 1990s the students had several opportunities to gain experience of general practice. In their first month at medical school they spent a day with a GP during which they interviewed patients in their homes, and in their third year they practised clinical skills during a two day attachment in general practice.

Fourth year students spent a month with a North London GP and carried out 'consultations' alone, defined the patient's problems and their management, and discussed the case with their GP tutors. In the fifth year they visited a general practice outside London. The School's 130 north London tutors took first, third and fourth year students; the practices of the ninety 5th year tutors were scattered from the Western Isles of Scotland to the tip of Cornwall.[xlvii]

RFHSM students' elective experiences became more unusual and exotic. In 1991 Alistair King, son of a former student, visited the remote Kimberley district of north-west Australia; Simon Clare, after a brief sojourn at a military hospital in Hong Kong, joined a jungle warfare team training soldiers in Brunei; Anna Casburn-Jones went to Goroka in Papua New Guinea. The following year Maia Tracz spent her elective at the Gahini Hospital in rural Rwanda.[xlviii]

1993-4 was 'expedition year': three students joined a British team exploring south-east Zanskar, a relatively unknown part of the Indian Himalayas, and four accompanied an expedition to the remote Lido district of Belize looking for the source of the infectious disease 'Leishmania Braziliensis'.

In 1996 Mark Davies, a medical cadet officer, was chosen to visit the Uniformed Services University in Washington DC. Advanced courses there were followed by a week-long exercise in San Antonio, Texas, where classroom lessons were put into practice – the hazards including scorpions, poisonous spiders, heat stroke and dehydration, and freezing temperatures at night.

There were still many overseas students taking electives at the Free, and in 1992 HoDs recommended charging them a registration fee of £150. Council supported the international exchange of students, but accepted that taking large numbers from one or two countries might adversely affect the education of the School's own undergraduates. It recommended a registration charge of £150 and a quota based upon WHO regions, but gave the Dean discretion to exempt students from payment should circumstances warrant.[xlix]

The Peter Samuel Hall

In June 1992 the students were concerned about restrictions on their use of the Peter Samuel Hall because some activities, particularly those involving large audiences, were deemed to contravene fire regulations. The School Secretary hoped it could be brought up to an acceptable standard, but warned the cost of doing so might exceed £100,000.[l]

To accommodate the Fourth Year Show in December 1992 the students had to pay the recreation centre £1100, and had to build a stage in its gymnasium, and the Dramatic Society had had to hire the hall at William Ellis School to produce 'Grease'. There was little progress over the next six months, and although the Peter Samuel Hall had excellent facilities for stage productions doubt arose whether it could again serve as more than an assembly hall. Instructions were given for the installation of emergency lighting (costing £7,000) to allow safe egress; the School underwrote the cost, but expected a contribution from RFH's Special Trustees. Student representatives said they would make every effort to expedite the installation of the emergency lighting, which was also required before the next Marsden Lecture.[li]

When Council met in December 1993 the students were happy that that year's Fourth Year show was, once again, to take place in the Peter Samuel Hall, the necessary fire precaution measures having been undertaken. The first night followed the Council meeting.[lii]

Sport

Sport still played a big part in student life and memorable achievements were reported in the School's annual reports. By beating the London Hospital Medical College the men's tennis team won the Hospital's Cup for the third year running in 1992; it won it again the next year by overcoming the same opposition 9 – 0.[liii]

1992 was also a good year for men's hockey. The team won the Hospital's Cup for the first time by scoring the only goal in the final against UCH/Middlesex. That year it was the underdog, but it won the Cup again in 1996 by beating Charing Cross /Westminster 2-1, having previously disposed of UCH and St Mary's.

To buy a new boat the Rowing Club had raised £5,000 and borrowed £3000 from the School. In 1991 it was about to pay off the £1500 still owed when its best boat was sunk following a collision with a UCL crew. Prosecution of one or both crews was contemplated but charges were dropped. Another boat was needed urgently if the club was to keep racing. Mr Kaisary and other consultants contributed £2500, a sponsored row raised £1000, and £1000 came from Dr Joan Haram who rowed for LSMW in the 1920s. With this down payment, and an interest-free deferred payment scheme, the club bought a new VIII for £10,500. It was called the 'Joan Haram' and Dr Haram attended the launch.[liv]

The Boat Club enjoyed success in 1994. The men's second VIII and the ladies' third VIII won important events, and the club, for the first time in years, was competitive at the summer regattas.

The men's soccer club flourished in 1994-5. The first XI was the only medical school team in the UL Premier league – and with a solitary goal five minutes before the end of extra time the second XI overcame St George's Hospital to win the United Hospital's Cup.

In 1996-7 the women's football club, then in its fourth season, chalked up victories in its own league's second division and in a tournament organised by the Association of Medical Schools; these successes encouraged members to start a second team.

In 1996 the Cricket Club reached the final of the University of London Cup for the first time, but lost to Royal Holloway by 78 runs.

The Rugby Club was the dominant male sports club at RFHSM from its formation in 1953. In the 1990s it still included players from the School of Pharmacy and, over the years, had become a force to be reckoned with at university and hospital level. In 1996-7 it won the Gutteridge Cup (the ULU knockout competition) and yet again reached the semi-final of the United Hospitals cup.

The best individual sporting performances by a Royal Free student during Zuckerman's deanship were clearly those of the long jumper 'Yinka' (Oluyinka Lola) Odowu who graduated MBBS in 1997. European junior champion in 1991 she took a break between her first and second years at RFHSM to train for the 1992 Barcelona Olympics where, narrowly missing the final round, she came 23rd. She won silver at the Commonwealth Games in 1994. Yinka was the School's third Olympian – Clare Halsted and Nick Bell had both fenced for Britain – Halsted in Munich and Montreal, and Bell in Montreal and Los Angeles. (See Chapter 15)

In 1997 a ceremony was held for the award of RFHSM 'Colours', most of which were given for efforts on behalf of the various sports clubs. Those organising it thought it was the first time 'Colours' had been awarded at the School and a large number were presented to deal with the backlog. But over the years the Magazine reported the award of 'Colours' by several sports clubs – e.g. swimming (1917), boating (1921), hockey (1930), cricket (1935) and rowing (1939). The School's Annual Reports made mention only of those 'honours' awarded to students by the University's sports clubs.[lv]

In June 1993 UCL students quoted the Provost as saying that Myddelton House Sports Ground was to be sold, and that the Free would share UCL's ground at Shenley. RFHSM students asked Council not to relinquish the Enfield site, whose excellent facilities had contributed to the School's success in several sports. The rumour persisted and in December the student body asked to be consulted and to participate in negotiations if this or any other matter of such direct significance to students was to be seriously considered.[lvi]

The Myddelton House Sports Ground was owned jointly by the School of Pharmacy and RFHSM. (See Chapter 13) Eventually the former suggested selling it and UCL, after consulting its Students' Union, deemed it surplus to requirements. It sold for £630,000 in 2003.[12] Public funds paid for it in 1954 so the proceeds were not 'free money'; however it was Government policy to allow them to be used to fund new projects if they were deemed appropriate. UCL wanted to refurbish the Gower Street Sports Centre; students wanted the Junior Common Room at the RFH campus refurbished. RFHSM's ContinuingTrustees proposed allocating enough money for the latter purpose and making the balance available for the Sports Centre.

Rag Weeks

Rag Weeks continued during Zuckerman's deanship. The longest one, lasting ten days, was in 1991. It raised £10,000 for the NSPCC, the Terence Higgins trust, Shelter, the Royal Free Special Care Baby Unit and Marie Curie Cancer Care (Eden Hall). Council wanted Rag Week to contribute to the School's own charitable appeal. The students were reluctant to ask for money for their own student residence, but they bowed to pressure and so 'Investment in Health' was one of the charities benefiting from Rag Week 1992 which raised over £11,000.[13, lvii]

After the 1994 Rag Week, which raised £10,500, Council again commented on the lack of support for 'Investment in Health'. Subsequently the Students' Union discussed the matter and decided, as a matter of policy, that it was undesirable for it to be seen raising money for its 'own' charity.[lviii]

In June 1996 the Dean opined that Rag Week, which lasted eight days, was too long, occurred at the wrong time of year, was just before examinations and gave students an excuse to absent themselves from school. But Rag Week continued; over £7000 was raised in 1997, and the 1998 Week, the last held by RFHSM as a free-standing school, supported the National Kidney Foundation, the British Heart Foundation, the Marie Curie Cancer Centre, the RFH Paediatric Gastroenterology Unit and Friends of the Royal Free.[lix]

The MMR Scandal

RFHSM's last year as an independent school saw the beginning of a scandal with enormous, widespread and longstanding repercussions. In November 1988 a relatively young surgeon, Andrew Wakefield,[14] joined RFHSM. He had eschewed clinical practice for research and spent three years at Toronto General Hospital on

[12] It is now the site of Tottenham Hotspur football club's new training ground.

[13] The students wanted to support RFH's new Ian Charleson AIDS day centre, but Council suggested they reconsider as AIDS charities were well supported from other sources.

[14] After graduating at St Mary's in 1981 Wakefield began surgical training, qualifying FRCS in 1985.

a Wellcome Medical Graduate Fellowship; his project was entitled 'Development of an intestinal transplant model to study graft survival and immunological mechanisms of transplant rejection'. The fellowship was transferred to RFHSM, where he was supervised by the gastro-enterologist Roy Pounder.

With Pounder and colleagues from other departments, he studied the arteries in diseased intestinal segments surgically removed from fifteen patients with Crohn's disease. Affected areas showed focal arterial inflammation and occlusion.[lx] This finding was potentially important and Wakefield and Pounder sought a Wellcome Trust grant to support further studies. It was supposed that the application would be more likely to succeed if Wakefield held a substantive position at RFHSM. Although some thought a salaried post in a department of medicine inappropriate for an ex-surgeon, who did not teach or practise and was relatively inexperienced in research, he was appointed senior lecturer in 1990. The grant application was unsuccessful.

Ab initio Wakefield seemed convinced the lesions seen in Crohn's tissue were virally induced. He, with others, wrote papers implicating persistent measles infection in the genesis of inflammatory bowel disease and in a paper in *The Lancet* of 29 April 1995 he suggested measles vaccination as a possible risk factor. Weeks earlier he had filed for a patent claiming that detection of measles virus in the gut and body fluids might prove a useful diagnostic test for Crohn's disease and ulcerative colitis.[lxi]

Wakefield and Pounder sought money for a Centre for the Study of Inflammatory Bowel Disease at the Free, and in February 1995 entered into an agreement with professional fundraisers (Sawyer, Edwards & Butler of Bath) using the Medical School's name without formal consent. On 15 March 1995 Blatch, the School Secretary, wrote to Wakefield pointing out that the School had not endorsed the venture, nor had RFH's chief executive been consulted about its implications for the Trust.[lxii]

Blatch's greatest concern was the agreement itself. Already in force it named Wakefield and Pounder as 'clients' and Clause 4 stated 'the consultancies shall require all donors and prospective donors to draw cheques, other negotiable instruments and promissory notes in favour of the Client'. Blatch thought it '…a preposterous proposal. No charity has been set up for the venture and there was no charity number. It would seem that you intend the cheques to be made out in your name or that of Roy Pounder rather than the School or any other recognised charity. The opportunities for abuse are manifest.' He instructed them to terminate the agreement forthwith.

In September 1995 Professor John Walker-Smith and his academic department of paediatric gastroenterology moved from St Bartholomew's Hospital Medical

College and Queen Elizabeth Hospital for Children, Hackney Road, to Hampstead where, as a separate academic department within RFHSM, it occupied hospital accommodation in a rooftop development.[lxiii]

In late 1995 or early 1996 Wakefield told Walker-Smith he had been contacted by the parents of autistic children who also had symptoms suggesting a bowel disorder. They thought their children's problems followed immunization with the MMR vaccine. Walker-Smith, intrigued, thought it important to identify the nature of the bowel problem. He saw the children and decided the necessary investigations should include ileo-colonoscopy (an invasive technique used routinely in the diagnosis of inflammatory bowel disease). In view of the severity of the regressive autism seen in some of the cases thorough neurological investigation was also arranged, including lumbar puncture.[lxiv]

Walker-Smith was unaware, as he believes were his paediatric colleagues, that in January 1996 Wakefield was approached by the solicitor Richard Barr whose firm, Dawbarns, had been awarded a contract to coordinate claims relating to the MMR vaccine introduced in 1988. For this purpose the Legal Aid Board made funds available to Barr who planned a class action against MMR manufacturers on behalf of persons allegedly harmed by the vaccine.

Presumably encouraged by Wakefield's paper suggesting that measles vaccination might trigger inflammatory bowel disease Barr asked him for advice on medical aspects of the proposed litigation, and about research that might establish whether MMR caused problems. For his services Wakefield was to be paid £150 per hour plus expenses.[15] In the newsletter of the anti-vaccine group JABS, founded in 1994, Barr suggested parents of children developing autism and bowel disturbance after MMR might through him contact Wakefield.[lxv]

The paediatricians were also unaware that Wakefield had given Barr a protocol for investigating a new syndrome – *'Disintegrative disorder and enteritis following measles and measles/rubella vaccination?'* – and had costed a study involving special tests and a four night stay at RFH. In June 1996 Barr submitted these documents to the Legal Aid Board which agreed in August to provide up to £55,000 to fund the studies.[lxvi]

In September 1996 RFH's 'Ethics Committee' was asked to approve a project involving 25 children with 'disintegrative disorder' and features of intestinal disease previously given measles or measles/rubella vaccine. Similar to the protocol submitted to Barr it named Wakefield, Walker-Smith and Murch (a senior lecturer and honorary consultant in Walker-Smith's department) as the responsible

[15] In 2006 it was revealed that Wakefield received fees of £435,643 plus £3910 expenses from the Legal Aid Fund – out of £3.4million distributed to doctors & scientists involved in what proved an unsuccessful lawsuit against the vaccine manufacturers.

consultants, but it was signed by Pounder. The study was to be funded as 'Clinical research at RFH (E.C.R.)'. [16, lxvii]

Questioned by the Ethics Committee Chairman in October 1996 Walker-Smith said the invasive investigations involved were for diagnostic purposes and would be done even outwith a formal study; five children had already been investigated on the basis of clinical need.

Approval was given but the project as such was abandoned. Even so, in two instalments, Dawbarns transferred to RFHSM the £50,000 of Legal Aid Board money that was to fund it. Zuckerman was uncomfortable about the School's receiving this money, even though the BMA's legal department and ethics committee told him the money could be accepted if there was proper research oversight and transparency over funding and patient sources. The money ended up in an account that the Special Trustees of RFH had already set up for Wakefield, and which held money that they had provided to pay someone working with him.

In September 1996 Wakefield and Pounder met RFHSM managers to discuss market projections for a new business based on a method of diagnosing Crohn's disease through the presence of measles virus, and nine months later Wakefield applied for a patent on a 'safer' single measles vaccine, and for treatments for autism and inflammatory bowel disease.[lxviii]

Children with autism and bowel symptoms continued to be referred to RFH's paediatric gastroenterology unit. It was decided to publish the findings in the first twelve patients investigated. The resulting article '*Ileal-lymphoid-nodular hyperplasia, non-specific colitis, and pervasive development disorder in children'* appeared in *The Lancet* of 28 February 1998. The thirteen authors presented clinical details and claimed to have identified a chronic enterocolitis, possibly related to neuropsychiatric dysfunction, and 'generally associated in time with possible environmental triggers'.

It was stated that the study was supported by Special Trustees of the RFHNHS Trust and the Children's Medical Charity.[17] The Legal Aid Fund was not mentioned.

There was immediate criticism of the paper but its most serious defect was not then appreciated. Most of table 2 (entitled 'Neuropsychiatric diagnosis') dealt with 'Exposure identified by parents or doctor', 'Interval from exposure to first behavioural symptoms' and 'Features associated with exposure'. The only exposure mentioned, apart from 'recurrent otitis media', was MMR. However, the authors stated 'We did not prove an association between MMR and the syndrome

[16] E.C.R. = 'Extra-Contractual Referral' indicating RFH would receive extra money for the referrals.

[17] The nature of this charity is unclear.

described. Virological studies are underway that may help to resolve this issue'. What was not made clear in the paper is that the parents of some patients were involved in Barr's class action against MMR, and that Wakefield benefited financially from his association with Barr.

On 16 January Pounder had written to Calman, the Chief Medical Officer, enclosing an advance copy of *The Lancet* paper stating 'It seems likely that at least some members of our team will recommend a switch from MMR to monovalent vaccination,…We believe that there is only a limited amount of monovalent measles vaccine available at the present time and your department may wish to investigate this potential problem.'

The paper itself would probably have had little impact had Wakefield and Pounder not organised a press conference at RFH a few days before publication (although planning for it had started about six months earlier).[lxix] Walker-Smith refused to attend the press briefing. In a video news release distributed beforehand Wakefield questioned the safety of MMR, and suggested single vaccines might be safer. He also did so at the press conference where the Dean, the virologist Zuckerman, who was on the panel, strongly defended MMR. Wakefield's senior paediatric colleagues, dismayed, subsequently issued a statement confirming their belief in the safety of MMR. But the damage was done. The MMR inoculation rate fell from 92% in 1998 to 80% in 2003/4. In 1998 there were 56 cases of measles in the UK; in 2008 there were 1348 cases with two confirmed deaths.

Within days of the press conference Wakefield and his business partners (including a venture capitalist and Child 10's father) met representatives of RFHSM to discuss forming 'Immunospecifics Biotechnologies', a company to market methods for detecting Crohn's disease and for treating autism, and 'a replacement for attenuated viral vaccines'. Its business plan was to raise £2.1million from investors. Trading was to be fronted by Carmel Healthcare Ltd – named after Wakefield's wife – which was registered in the Irish Republic. Wakefield was to hold 37% of the equity, Child 10's father 22.2%, Pounder 11.7% and O'Leary 11.1%. All of this went on in secret on the grounds of 'commercial confidentiality'.[lxx]

On 1 August 1998 RFHSM merged with UCL to create RF & UCSM (UCL Medical School from 2008) and events since then are technically outwith the purview of this book. However, the affair caused consternation in paediatric and public health circles. Over the next few years many papers appeared challenging the findings of Wakefield et al, particularly regarding MMR as a cause of a new syndrome linking autism and bowel disease, or as a cause of autism (although the accumulated evidence did suggest a link between autism and bowel disease).

There was a dramatic turn of events in 2004 after Brian Deer, an investigative journalist with *The Sunday Times,* revealed Wakefield's links with Barr, and the planned mass action suit against vaccine manufacturers that gave both a vested interest in incriminating MMR. Deer was to attack Wakefield for more than eight years.

One consequence of Deer's discovery was that two MPs – John Reid, then Secretary of State for Health, and Dr Evan Harris – called for a General Medical Council inquiry into the affair. After a long and somewhat inexplicable delay charges were brought against Wakefield, Walker-Smith and Murch. They were heard in the longest and most expensive 'fitness to practise' hearing in the GMC's history. It began on 7 July 2007, took 217 working days and lasted until May 2010. Walker-Smith and Wakefield were struck off the Medical Register, subject to appeal; Murch was cleared of serious professional misconduct.

Walker-Smith appealed the verdict and on 7 March 2012 Mr Justice Mitting quashed the GMC's finding of professional misconduct. He said that the 'fitness to practise' panel's decision that Walker-Smith was guilty of serious professional misconduct was flawed in that its reasoning was inadequate and superficial, and that in several instances it had drawn the wrong conclusion. He called for changes in the way such hearings were conducted in the future.

The MMR saga clearly needed to be investigated but at the hearing the GMC placed too much emphasis on the idea that the children mentioned in the paper were ill-treated – an idea that stemmed from the erroneous belief that invasive investigations were done purely for the purpose of research. This diverted public attention from the issue of the financial rewards that might have accrued to Wakefield and others if MMR could be discredited. As it appeared that no child had suffered any serious side effects or complications of the investigations done on them, and that the parents made no complaints about the way they were treated, there was some sympathy for the authors of the infamous paper, many of whom were, primarily, simply trying to help the children; this sympathy was exploited by the anti-MMR movement.

Working for Patients & Merger with UCL

From November 1987 a Cabinet team chaired by Thatcher herself considered methods of reducing NHS expenditure. It published its conclusions, '*Working for Patients*', in January 1989. The NHS was to remain centrally funded but without extra funding; instead productivity was to improve via an internal 'market' that separated purchasing of services from their provision. 'Fund-holders' (GPs and health authorities) would buy services from self-governing 'Acute Hospital Trusts' which would be able to run private patient units competing with private hospitals. The latter, as a quid pro quo, could treat NHS patients referred by fund-holders.

Trusts would have boards of directors from which key interest groups – such as the community, local authorities and clinicians – were excluded.[lxxi]

When the first 56 trusts came into being on 1 April 1991,[18] Hampstead Health Authority (HHA) relinquished management of RFH to the Royal Free Hampstead NHS Trust.

Waldegrave, then Secretary of State for Health, was concerned about London and announced in October that Newcastle's Sir Bernard Tomlinson, a retired neuro-pathologist and Chairman of the Northern RHA, would advise on organisation of the NHS in London – *and on medical education and research*!

The inclusion of medical schools in his remit, while the University was considering 'academic clusters', raised the spectres of 'Todd' and 'Flowers' at RFHSM – so when visited by UCL's Provost, the Pro-Vice-Chancellor and the Dean of the Faculty of Clinical Sciences RFHSM agreed to discuss collaboration and curriculum development, but not amalgamation or merger.[lxxii]

Tomlinson's report, published in October 1992, envisaged that the 'internal market' would reduce non-local inpatient numbers and, *pari passu,* the income of central London hospitals – leaving many financially vulnerable. Tomlinson, a UCHMS alumnus, thought UCH and the Middlesex the most vulnerable – but noted that they underpinned 'one of the highest graded clinical research institutions in London'. As UCH had better road access for an A & E department he suggested closing the Middlesex. Although not considered vulnerable RFH was to be grouped with UCH and other local hospitals.

Regarding medical education, Tomlinson thought the curricular changes to be promoted in the GMC's 'Tomorrow's Doctors' (1993) would require more integration of clinical and basic science teaching, and more options for students outwith their core studies.[19] He anticipated financial diseconomies if small schools tried to deliver such solutions (although common sense suggests integration of clinical and basic science teaching might be easier in a small school).

Changes in UFC funding also called for more efficient teaching, and although no small schools seemed at serious financial risk Tomlinson thought they should rationalise resources and avoid duplication of posts. As unit costs for clinical medicine at UCL and King's were apparently below the London average he foresaw further isolation of free-standing medical schools, especially as the UFC was to introduce direct funding of large multi-faculty colleges from 1992-3.

Tomlinson believed London's experience in the 1980s showed academic

[18] Another 99 trusts were created in April 1992.

[19] When the GMC's Education Committee visited RFHSM on 26 February 1992 for informal discussions on undergraduate education it found the School had already implemented many of the recommendations that were to appear in 'Tomorrow's Doctors' (1993).

integration and rationalisation were best achieved in unified medical faculties within multi-faculty colleges so, although St George's was to remain independent, he suggested merging the other eight undergraduate schools within four colleges – UCL, King's, Imperial and Queen Mary & Westfield. Mergers between King's & UMDS and of Imperial College & Charing Cross/Westminster were already well advanced; Tomlinson recommended expediting those between RFHSM & UCMSM, and between Bart's, Royal London & Queen Mary/Westfield.[20]

Merged schools would have larger intakes than existing schools. Not surprisingly some London deans considered an annual intake of over 250 students at a single school logistically undesirable. Tomlinson also foresaw problems in handling London's existing student intake, owing to reduced patient flows into inner London and problems in involving GPs in teaching. He therefore suggested reducing the total annual intake of London's medical schools by 150, through redistribution of the national quotas for medicine.

NETRHA had assessed the likely impact of the internal market before Tomlinson reported and on 1 September 1992 representatives of RFHSM & UCMSM/UCL joined it for discussions on a 'Future Strategy for Education and Research in North Central London'. On 14 September Zuckerman, the Provost, and the Dean of UCMSM issued a statement, which went to the Court of the University, anticipating 'significant opportunities for academic collaboration to improve the quality and cost-effectiveness of both undergraduate and postgraduate training…[but]…recognised the autonomy of these two medical schools within the University of London'.

In November, before Council discussed 'Tomlinson', Zuckerman announced that discussions had begun 'which may…lead to an affiliation with UCL tailored to the specific objectives of both partners and with appropriate preservation of identity'. Council was not contemplating merger – believing, naively, that with the University's support both institutions would remain autonomous.[lxxiii]

In '*Making London Better*', published in February 1993, the Government accepted Tomlinson's proposals. Although Virginia Bottomley, the new Secretary of State for Health, suggested that existing institutions/authorities would make the final decisions, she set up a London Implementation Group (LIG) to support, cajole and pressurize them.

This changed matters. In March Council considered a draft Heads of Agreement which Zuckerman had drawn up with UCL. RFHSM was to 'become an associated School of UCL…, whilst preserving its identity within the federal structure of the

[20] Tomlinson thought the Queen Mary/Westfield link little more than a paper exercise at a clinical level.

University of London'. The sting in the tail came in the last paragraph – 'The period of association is not intended to last [over] 4 years,...an operational plan [would be developed] for future affiliation and to position the institutions to meet the necessary requirements of Government and the Funding Councils and to take full advantage of the funding opportunities available'.[lxxiv]

Not surprisingly many at the Free, believing independence a viable option, were unhappy about this and particularly concerned about 'future affiliation'. However some anticipated there would be financial benefits from collaboration – and/or help for the RFH Trust when negotiating on health care provision in North London. The Heads of Agreement was approved.

Zuckerman's involvement in drafting the Heads of Agreement sat uneasily with his letter to the *BMJ* of 6 March 1993 in which he argued that staff-students relationships would deteriorate, along with a concomitant reduction in the quality of teaching, if a school's annual intake increased to more than 100-150, and that amalgamating institutions had no advantages beyond administrative convenience and economies in services like catering and purchasing.[lxxv]

On 22 March the Provost sent the Heads of Agreement to HEFCE's Chief Executive, along with a progress report indicating that as UCL promoted research excellence matching international standards it welcomed 'Tomlinson' and 'Making London Better'. He added 'Being the best medical School in London is of no great significance' – UCL wanted to be a world leader. In his covering letter he welcomed 'any comments on how...the process could be accelerated if you consider that desirable'.

The juggernaut gathered momentum. In June HEFCE asked RFHSM and UCL to submit, by 30 September, a plan outlining how they would come together, and 'reminded' RFHSM that Tomlinson specifically recommended merger with UCL.[lxxvi]

Council discussed whether to accept merger or fight again for independence, which the Members of the School (MOS) thought should be relinquished only if inevitable. Everyone wanted to secure RFHSM's continuing separate identity. Given the forthcoming summer vacation the September deadline was considered unrealistic; instead Council planned an interim response. A draft version was to be considered in July but the Dean then recommended sending a full joint strategic plan. This volte-face followed a warning letter from the Vice-Chancellor pointing out that HEFCE could make grants to institutions 'subject in each case to such terms and conditions as ...[HEFCE]...may think fit'. In other words it could make things very difficult for RFHSM.[lxxvii]

In December Council discussed 'Proposed Merger of University Institutions: UCL and RFHSM' – a document sent to HEFCE in late September without

Council's approval. The President complained about paucity of information relating to the merger, noting that published statements by the Provost suggested fundamental decisions had already been taken. She had wanted the new document to go to all MOS; but the Dean said it would have been inappropriate for them to see the strategic and operational plans before Council. He was assured of Council's support, but urged to keep MOS, staff and students fully informed of developments.[lxxviii]

The document sent to HEFCE set out four options:-

1 – Virtually the status quo, except for RFHSM's affiliation with UCL.

2 – All preclinical teaching and most basic research to be at Gower St.

3 – A new preclinical school at Hampstead to house the combined intake.

4 – An evolutionary plan envisaging a unified curriculum, with pre-clinical & clinical teaching at Hampstead and Bloomsbury.

Both schools favoured the fourth option.

Under 'Progress to Date' the document announced *inter alia* the setting up from October 1993 of a central medical education unit (directed by McIntyre)[21], and the designation of joint heads for a number of departments.

The first joint departments, established in April 1995, were medicine (head, Leon Fine UCMSM), physiology (Michael Spyer RFHSM), and primary care and population sciences (Paul Wallace RFHSM). Two years later clinical oncology, pharmacology and surgery became joint departments – with Richard Begent (RFHSM) as head of oncology and D. A. Brown (UCL) of pharmacology. Surgery was organised on a divisional basis with a head at each site.[lxxix]

Following the retirement of Bob Hodges in 1986 the biochemist Jack Lucy acted as head of pharmacology until Annette Dolphin was appointed to the chair in October 1990. A productive researcher she received a Wellcome grant of over £1million in 1996. The following year some pharmacologists moved to UCL but although there was now a joint department Dolphin remained responsible for those remaining at Hampstead.[lxxx]

Jack Lucy retired in 1994. A candidate selected to fill a new joint chair in biochemistry withdrew after months of prevarication, and so Brian Cook, already a titular professor, acted as head of department before his appointment was made substantive.[lxxxi]

John Harris retired as Professor of Anatomy in September 1991. His

[21] McIntyre resigned about two years later. He was unhappy about some developments & particularly about extending the course to six years to accommodate an obligatory B.Sc.

replacement, Geoffrey Goldspink, director of the veterinary molecular and cellular biology unit at the Royal Veterinary College, was previously professor of anatomy and cellular biology at Tufts University School of Medicine in Boston. Unlike his predecessors at RFHSM Goldspink was not a topographical anatomist but an expert on gene expression during muscle growth and development.[lxxxii]

In July 1994 HEFCE requested a more detailed plan about merger. Sent in November, before December's Council meeting, it claimed the joint school would have 5500 beds available for teaching.[22] Core subjects would be taught at Gower Street although only a half of each annual intake could be taught as one class. There were to be basic science 'modules' on all three main sites. After seeing the plan 300 students from both schools expressed anxiety about an annual intake of 330 and the possibility of excessively large clinical teaching firms.[23, lxxxiii]

UCL and RFHSM requested £57million for capital developments linked to the merger – but only £20million was available. In June 1995 HEFCE allocated £14.5million to adapt the Cruciform Building for preclinical teaching. It also provided £310,000 to pay for additional seating in lecture theatres, integration of RFHSM's financial management system with that of UCL, and accommodation at RFH for the UCMSM Professor who was to head the joint Department of Medicine – but it would not pay to adapt the Peter Samuel Hall to hold 350 students. In September it released another £3million for work including a rooftop development at Hampstead.[lxxxiv]

Council thought it almost impossible to give proper consideration to a draft Bill by November 1995, and some still thought RFHSM should affiliate not merge. However as political pressure was anticipated if submission of the Bill was deferred by a year the Dean was instructed to continue negotiating – on the understanding that Hampstead developments would be adequately funded and that RFHSM would have parity with other parties in the negotiations. He was also to stress the importance of preserving the School's identity; eighteen months earlier the Provost had apparently given the Dean a written assurance that RFHSM would retain its name and identity.[lxxxv]

There was an Extraordinary Meeting (EGM) of Council on 9 October. Beforehand Zuckerman, the Provost and the Dean of UCL Medical School had

---

[22] At RFH, UCLH, the Whittington, & the associated hospitals, i.e. North Middlesex & Wellhouse Trust, Watford General/Mount Vernon, & Chase Farm Hospitals Trust.

[23] The UL Medical Group wrote to Dr Peter Simpson of LIG recalling the concerns of students he met in October 1993 (i.e. reforms were NHS led, undergraduate teaching had lowest priority; pace of change was educationally detrimental; new schools were too large; special historical character of London medical schools would be lost). See CM 1994: 3 Mar

agreed: i) The new medical school would be 'Royal Free University College London Medical School'; ii) Trustees safeguarding the facilities, resources and assets of RFHSM would serve for at least ten years after merger; iii) UCL Council would have four Royal Free representatives (the Dean, Vice-Dean, Chairman of Council, and one other lay member); iv) The new school would have a Medical Advisory Board answerable to UCL's Council. The student entry was expected to increase by 10% in 2000-01, with the possibility of a graduate entry of 50-60 graduates to the Royal Free campus for a one year course in basic medical sciences, and of a clinical entry of 30-40 'Oxbridge' students.[lxxxvi]

The UCL and RFHSM draft bills had been pre-circulated. So too had the minutes of a meeting on 12 September at which five 'lay' members of Council expressed concerns about the merger to the Chairman, Dean and School Secretary; those attending[24] learned *inter alia* that Zuckerman would, for one year, be the joint school's first Dean,[25] and that Sharpe Pritchard, solicitors and Parliamentary agents, was helping RFHSM to draft the Parliamentary Bill.

At the EGM the President complained that as the documents had arrived only four days earlier there was inadequate time for careful perusal. A working party was therefore chosen to study the draft Bills in detail.[26]

Some thought the UCL draft described a takeover rather than a merger, and that the School should request another year to allow detailed consideration. The Dean warned that HEFCE could simply close the whole School or its preclinical departments, and while some questioned its authority to do so it was deemed a high risk strategy to stand against the express policy of the Government, HEFCE and the University of London.

RFH consultants supported the merger and so did the Trust which wanted 'Royal Free' to feature prominently in the name of the new school. The Students' Union had long accepted there would be a merger and had already drafted a joint constitution with UCL students.

Some were concerned about RFHSM's vulnerability as a small free standing medical school. Reminded of his letter to the *BMJ* in March 1993 extolling the virtues of such schools the Dean said times had changed, and that RFHSM could no longer survive as an independent school. Merger now seemed inevitable and several argued for a speedy conclusion so as to minimize the damaging effects of planning blight.

The resolution 'This council…advise[s] the MOS that the best interests of RFHSM will be served by a formal merger with UCL' was approved by 13 votes

---

24 Alderman, Carrier, Croft, Dutton & Lascelles. 'Lay' meant not employed by RFH or RFHSM.

25 Zuckerman was then due to retire in September 1999.

26 The Dean, School Secretary, Martin Else, Edith Gilchrist, Carrier, McIntyre & Sian Stanley.

to 3. A further resolution asked the Dean 'to continue negotiating with UCL…with a view to an enabling bill being agreed by all parties for presentation to Parliament during the coming parliamentary session';[27] it was passed *nem. con.*

The working group charged with examining the two draft bills met on 19 October to decide whether they formed a basis for a final version reflecting the School's reservations about merger. A revised version of UCL's draft Bill had arrived only that morning, leaving no time for prior perusal, so Blatch pointed out how it differed from the earlier draft.

The group was unhappy about the revised UCL Bill which still contained inaccuracies. It wanted the note on RFHSM's history checked and corrected, and something added on the history of RFH. The draft stated that from time to time UCL might alter the name of 'The Royal Free University College Medical School of UCL'. The group suggested a moratorium of at least ten years before the name could be changed.

The Sharpe Pritchard Bill was considered a better safeguard of RFHSM's interests than that prepared for UCL, but it soon became irrelevant. At a second EGM on 30 October the Dean said the Provost had argued strongly for the adoption of UCL's short Enabling Bill, covering merger of up to six institutions, rather than Sharpe Pritchard's more detailed one. Essential prerequisites for merger were to be listed in a legally binding Memorandum of Intent, and safeguards sought by RFHSM were to be implemented before the passing of an Act of Parliament. Helen Kemp of Sharpe Pritchard assured Council that, if the conditions of the Memorandum were not met, support for the Bill could be withdrawn almost up to the time of Royal Assent – and that if either school refused to agree an appointed date the Act would not be implemented. Barring major obstacles the Bill could take 12 to 18 months to pass.[28]

Continuing Trustees of RFHSM, to be appointed immediately, were not to be mentioned in the Bill;[29] however, when enacted, the Bill would recognise all existing Trusts, giving the Continuing Trustees an ongoing role relating to RFHSM's assets.

The word 'and' was inserted into the proposed name for the new school so that after merger the full name would be 'Royal Free AND University College Medical School (RF&UCMS), University College London'.[30] It was to be embodied in the

---

[27] For consideration during the next Parliamentary Session the Bill had to be submitted by 27 November.

[28] It went through very quickly. The UCL Act received the Royal Assent in July 1996

[29] There was a discrepancy here; Council minutes stated the Continuing Trustees would be secured under the Act, but the minutes of the 20 October meeting stated 'There should be no reference to Trustees in the Bill'.

[30] Someone pointed out on 9 October that Royal FUC might otherwise be used as an anagram.

Bill with an undertaking that it could not be changed for 10 years from the appointed date. No argument seems to have been made for keeping Middlesex in the title.

Given the emphasis placed throughout on securing the name and identity of the 'Royal Free' it seems surprising in retrospect that Council did not insist that 'Royal Free' should remain in the school's name in perpetuity. As it was a merger, not a takeover, it was not much to ask and it is difficult to see how UCL could have justified rejecting such a proposal.

Few now wanted to delay submission of the Bill until November 1996 as most thought continuing uncertainty would lower morale among staff and students. The Students Union President thought good students were already hesitating to come to RFHSM, but believed this would change once potential applicants were reassured about the continuity of their studies.[lxxxvii]

The working party studying the draft Bills met again before the 30 October EGM and agreed to accept the UCL Bill (dated 20 October). At Council the proposal to recommend it for acceptance to the MOS was passed by thirteen to two with one abstention.

The EGM of the Members of the School on 20 November was effectively the last hurdle to be cleared as RFHSM's Charter vested in the MOS the 'power to make and when made to revoke, alter or suspend Statutes of the School' and 'the authority to call for such Reports as they shall think fit from the Council and from any officers of the School'. The EGM approved *nem. con.* the University College Bill as tabled, its deposition with Parliament, and the signing and sealing of the Petition for leave to introduce the Bill – which was deposited in Parliament on 27 November.[lxxxviii]

Council's major concern now was the Memorandum of Intent. The matter was not urgent (the final version was not signed until December 1997) but discussion of a draft version constituted the main business of its December 1995 meeting.[31]

There was no controversy about the first four requirements – completion of essential capital schemes; availability of necessary public funding; a joint curriculum; and a joint admissions procedure. Council supported the fifth – the creation of a Medical Advisory Board or similar body to advise UCL Council on medical matters concerning the new school – but realised there was little support for it at UCL.

The sixth concerned the choice of Royal Free representatives on UCL's Council. Three had been agreed (Council's chairman, the Dean and Spyer, the Vice-dean elect). Council wanted the MOS to choose the fourth but UCL, adamant it would

[31] The Memorandum was revised after the meeting of MOS – and underwent further revisions

not have anyone imposed on it, invited Robin Fox.[32] Council considered UCL insensitive in refusing an RFHSM nomination for someone purporting to represent it. Subsequently Martin Else, the chief executive of RFH NHS Trust, was made an observer on UCL's Council.[lxxxix]

UCL nominated Professor John Pattison as its representative on RFHSM's Council but in June 1996 Geoffrey Alderman questioned whether the Statutes permitted his joining Council without filling a vacancy; Pattison was therefore made an observer and later appointed a University representative.[33, xc]

The rest of the Memorandum of Intent – regarding the administrative structure of the new medical school; heads of joint departments/divisions; continuance of full professorially led clinical academic departments at RFH; and matters affecting students (particularly halls of residence, and Union and sports facilities) – caused little concern. RFHSM was keen that 'The College should remain within the University of London for so long as it retains its present federal structure' – but given UCL's views on the matter it was considered unrealistic to press the point. Finally Council agreed on 'Adequate steps to be taken to safeguard the archives of the RFHSM'.

At the same meeting Council appointed eight Continuing Trustees, as the Dean wished them in place with immediate effect, to safeguard RFHSM's assets and ensure appropriate use of its resources – including benefactions, trusts, prizes, etc.. They were Council's Chairman; the Dean; the President and another from MOS; the chairman of the FGPC (Dutton), the chief executive of the NHS Trust (Else), the MAC chairman (Geoffrey Lloyd), and McIntyre (the current Vice-dean). After a preliminary meeting to consider their remit the Trustees were concerned that their functions contradicted certain provisions in the UCL Bill. Before the June Council meeting legal advice was taken. It determined that the Continuing Trustees could act effectively to safeguard RFHSM's assets, despite clause 8 of the Bill, as UCL had voluntarily ceded powers to them. Both schools subsequently agreed the Trustees 'Terms of Reference'.[xci]

Full merger was to await completion of the Cruciform Building as access to the new preclinical school was likely to be restricted until building finished on the other floors. Initially September 1999 was the 'accepted' completion date so the first joint intake of students was scheduled for October 2000. The appointed date for merger was to be 1 August 1999 – allowing a year to get the new accommodation functioning properly, and for staff to familiarise themselves with new management systems.[xcii]

However by February 1998 merger fatigue and a sense of planning blight led

---

[32] Robin Fox was RFHSM's Honorary Treasurer for 8 years up to 1992, and was still on Council.

[33] Pattison was awarded a knighthood in the 1998 New Year's Honours.

RFHSM's Education Committee to propose that, without changing the date of the first joint intake, the appointed date should be advanced to 1 August 1998. All the conditions of the Memorandum of Intent would be met, except for completion of the Cruciform Building, and some felt merger would add impetus to curricular development. HoDs and the NHS Hampstead Trust Board supported the idea and Council concurred. 'Royal Free' students were to follow their existing curriculum until the first joint intake in 2000. Then, for a time, there would be students on the new curriculum, on the old UCL curriculum and on the Royal Free curriculum.[xciii]

At its December 1997 meeting Council's attention was drawn to two financial considerations relating to the new curriculum – one the effect of planned changes in teaching methods on resources and costs, and the other the need for adequate funding to cover the proposed six-year course. Even teachers who supported optional intercalated B.Sc. courses were unhappy about extending the course to six years to accommodate an obligatory B.Sc.; they were concerned about the debt many students faced on graduation and/or questioned whether such a course benefited all students. (See above, footnote 21) Some saw the extra year as a way in which UCL could get those who funded the students' education, e.g. local councils, to bolster the income of UCL's preclinical departments. Furthermore there were many, in Britain and in other countries, particularly the USA, who argued that undergraduate medical courses could and should be shortened.[xciv]

After merger Council and the Education Committee would cease to exist and other school committees were to be reduced to a minimum at Hampstead. RFHSM's HoDs and FGPC were to meet for at least the first year of ring-fenced funding, and the Building & Maintenance Committee was to oversee the large-scale building projects shortly to be implemented.[xcv]

At its last meeting on 18 June 1998 Council heard of the death in April of Giles Lascelles, a member for over thirty years and its vice chairman for much of that time. Brian Blatch was to retire as School Secretary on 31 July 1998. Cengiz Tarhan took over his administrative duties and became financial director of the new school. Mark Pepys of Imperial College (Hammersmith campus) was to assume the chair of medicine at Hampstead in October 1999 when McIntyre retired. Humphrey Hodgson, also from Hammersmith, was to head the Liver Unit. He was appointed to the 'Sheila Sherlock Chair in Medicine', newly created to mark the RFHSM President's 80th birthday, and to recognise her outstanding contributions to medicine and to the life of the School. Hodgson was a research fellow on the Unit in 1975.

At the end of May there was a formal announcement that Zuckerman would be Principal and Dean of the Royal Free and University College Medical School, with Professor Bob Souhami as Principal and Dean Elect, and Spyer, Souhami and

David Patterson as campus deans at the Royal Free, UCLH and the Whittington respectively. Spyer remained head of physiology.

Zuckerman, who oversaw the end of of his own alma mater as an independent school, thanked Council, and particularly its officers, for their support while Dean. He paid tribute to the student representatives, and the Presidents of the Students' Union who played such a constructive role in facilitating merger with UCL. Carrier, Chairman of the RFH NHS trust, expressed his appreciation of the close co-operation between School and Trust and hoped it would continue after merger. Council's chairman, sad about the end of an outstanding institution, was encouraged that RFHSM was joining another outstanding institution with similar traditions, both having their origins during a period of liberal advancement.

Most of the School's staff were sad about the fate of LSMW/RFHSM after 124 years, and some regretted that no celebratory wake was held – to mourn its passing and to rejoice in its remarkable history. In keeping with tradition the portrait of Zuckerman, the School's last dean, was painted in 1997 and hangs at the Free alongside those of most of his predecessors. (Fig 16.2, Colour plate) The artist was Susan Ryder who, a year later, painted the portrait of Baroness Trixie Gardner, chairman of the RFH NHS Trust from 1994-97.

Royal Free Association

At Council in December 1995 the President raised the issue of an ongoing role for the Members of the School (MOS), a body which would cease to exist after the appointed date. Scheuer suggested combining it with the Old Students Association (OSA) and the President set up a working party to consider the matter. The merger was relevant to the OSA because students trained at RFHSM, but graduating in or after 1999, would automatically become eligible for membership of UCL's alumnus associations.

Scheuer succeeded Rosemary Radley-Smith as President of the OSA at its November 1997 AGM, which overwhelmingly supported formation of a 'Royal Free Association' (RFA) – comprising OSA and MOS members and others closely associated with RFH. As RFHSM had supported both groups funding was a concern, and some considered an annual subscription inappropriate. It was hoped the RFA would, like the OSA, hold clinical days and dinners, and there was a suggestion (not acted upon) of a dinner with UCL/Middlesex medical alumni. Members of the OSA thought its history should be preserved at all costs.

The working party – three from the OSA, three from MOS, and the School Secretary – reported to the MOS's last AGM in June 1998 and suggested the need for an organisation involved in educational and other activities (e.g. charitable work and fund-raising) that could liaise with similar groups at UCL. The RFA was formally created at that AGM.

The OSA was formally disbanded at its last AGM held on 19 November 1998. The proposals that its members should join the new RFA and that its funds should be transferred to the RFA were passed *nem. con.*, although certain funds (memorial and bursary) were still to be used for their specific purposes.

The RFA's Executive Committee first met on 18 January 1999 in the Sheila Sherlock Education Centre.[34] Three of its members were from the OSA – Scheuer (President), Eve Hammer (Secretary), Rosemary Radley Smith, Rosemarie Baillod and Daniel Hochhauser – and three from the MOS (Roy Pounder, David Jordan and David Dutton), plus John Norton (the Chief Technician in Anatomy), and the School Secretary, Bryan Blatch. A draft constitution was discussed; an amended version was ratified at the first AGM on 18 November 1999. The RFA's full title was "The Royal Free Association (incorporating the RFHSM Old Students Association and MOS)". Its purposes were to support the preservation of the School's history and archives, and to promote relations between school and hospital. New members were to be nominated at an AGM, but the mechanism for including recently qualified students and others was to be sorted out later. The nomination of all present and past RFH consultants and senior managers was approved.

[34] The Sheila Sherlock Education Centre is situated inside the Rowland Hill Street entrance to RFH; it opened early in 1994.

Epilogue

During discussions about the UCL merger there was widespread concern at the Free that, if it went ahead, the School might lose its identity and that its history, and that of RFH, might be neglected and 'forgotten'. Council heard repeated demands that, at all relevant meetings with UCL, the representatives of RFHSM should stress the importance of preserving its identity and of safeguarding the Free's history. A similar fear, that RFH's history might be forgotten after the move to Hampstead, was Cecil Symons's motivation when, in 1972, he commissioned from the artist Peter Jones a series of small paintings of the hospitals in the Royal Free group. Known as the 'Symons Bequest', it is now in the Royal Free library.

After a long and exhausting process RFHSM merged with UCL to create the 'Royal Free and University College Medical School, University College London' (RF&UCMS). The name could not be changed for 10 years from the appointed day. Having been separate schools of the University from 1907 UCHMS and UCL had reunited in 1980 to form the 'Faculty of Clinical Sciences' within a new UCL School of Medicine which in turn merged with Middlesex Hospital Medical School in 1987 to create 'University College and Middlesex School of Medicine' (UCMSM). The fact that 'Middlesex' was not to feature in the school's name after the RFH merger should have alerted those at Hampstead to the possibility (some would have said certainty) that the words 'Royal Free' would follow suit after ten years.

After the RFHSM/UCL merger on 1 August 1998 Zuckerman was, for a year, Principal and Dean of Royal Free & University College Medical School. In 2008, when the ten-year constraint ran out, UCL's Council quickly removed 'Royal Free' from the school's name, leaving it as 'UCL Medical School'. Professor Edward Byrne, then the school's head, apparently said the decision was taken because the existing name (i.e. RF&UCMS) did not reflect the number and range of different locations across UCL where UCL Medical School teaching and research took place. (Neither of course did the acronym UCL).

While UCL seemed keen to rid itself of the names 'Middlesex' and 'Royal Free' that was not true of its medical student body. After the 1998 merger its sports teams identified themselves using the acronym RUMS (for **R**oyal Free & **U**niversity College **M**edical **S**chool), e.g. RUMS Rugby. However, in 2009, a year after the school's name was changed to UCL Medical School, all its sports teams voted to alter the full version of their collective name by adding 'Middlesex' – to honour also the memory of the Middlesex Hospital Medical School. RUMS then meant **R**oyal Free, **U**niversity College and **M**iddlesex Medical **S**tudents – the Union that now runs most of UCLMS's clubs and societies.

The original concerns about the Free's name and history seem justified. On searching UCL's Iris data base for the names of former Royal Free colleagues who transferred to UCL in 1998 I found that they 'Joined UCL' in the year they were appointed to RFHSM – often years before the merger; those of emeritus status did so the year they retired. Zuckerman 'Joined UCL' on 1 October 1999, a year **after** he became Dean of RF&UCMS. It is difficult to understand the rationale for such entries; inaccurate and misleading, they diminish UCL's credibility and the Free's visibility.

In *'The World of UCL 1828-2004'*, published six years after the merger, RFHSM & RFH share six index entries. On p. 17, below a flattering image of RFH, three lines mention the RFHSM/UCL merger and the original link between the Eastman Dental Institute and RFH, and a group photograph on p. 22 includes Professor Michael Spyer, then Dean of RF&UCMS (and a Vice-Provost); p. 86 mentions erroneously that James Robinson, the dentist who first used ether anaesthesia in London in 1846, was attached at the time to RFH (he joined it in 1848). On pages 278-9 a long single paragraph on the foundation of LSMW states that the name 'Royal Free Medical School for Women' was adopted in 1897, and that the last two words were dropped when men were admitted in 1948. That is quite misleading. When the School incorporated in 1898 'London (Royal Free Hospital) School of Medicine for Women' became its 'official' name, but for all practical purposes it remained the 'London School of Medicine for Women' until 1948. On p. 278 there are also three illustrations – a photograph of an early anatomy class at LSMW, and portraits of Jex-Blake and Elizabeth Garrett Anderson. Finally, p. 281 mentions student accommodation at Frances Gardner House (named after an RFHSM dean) and at another hall of residence, Langton Close, formerly the main Nurses Home at the old RFH (but with no indication that Alfred Langton was one of RFH's great benefactors). All in all it is a somewhat parsimonious allocation of space to two institutions whose combined early history, given their role in opening medical (and university) education to women, is arguably as important as that of UCL itself.

The merger with UCL was a *force-majeure* resulting from the Government's implementation of the Tomlinson Report. Academic staff at Hampstead recognised that by merging with UCL they would join one of the world's leading research centres (for medicine and many other disciplines). However, as most of them believed that RFHSM functioned well as an independent school it was hardly surprising that they were (and some still are) unenthusiastic about the merger. There was also a general perception (which remains) that with the much larger number of students at the combined school, staff-student (and probably student-student) relationships could not possibly be as close as they had been previously.

There were other niggles. After the transfer of the preclinical departments and most of the school's administration to Gower Street, RFH's clinical teachers felt less able to influence educational policy, and many thought 'asset stripping' a factor in the two-way traffic of clinical academics between RFH and UCH. Structural changes to the medical school part of the Hampstead building since 1998 have caused some disruption at RFH, and the closing of the senior common room, where preclinical and clinical (academic & NHS) teachers used to meet over lunch, was certainly unpopular. Some thought that the speed with which 'UCL employees' had to change their e-mail addresses, and with which the initials UCL appeared around parts of the Hampstead building, indicated a degree of insensitivity in the corridors at Gower Street. One story, probably apocryphal, was that soon after the merger a carpet displaying those letters was laid within the Rowland Hill Street entrance of the RFH complex (and quickly removed by person or persons unknown!).

One consequence of the merger was the founding in 1998 of the Royal Free Association (RFA) – a combination of the RFHSM Old Students Association (OSA) and the 'Members of the School', the latter having replaced the original Governing Body when LSMW incorporated in 1898. The merger was a sad affair for the OSA which would in future have no 'Royal Free' graduates to replenish its pool of old (some very old) students. The RFA continued the OSA's long tradition of helping students in need. It provides about £8,500 a year to help UCLMS students with the cost of electives, or to support them at times of financial hardship.

A merger of institutions is usually based on the premise that a bigger institution would be cheaper to run, more productive, more efficient and, if in the financial world, more profitable. RFH Hampstead was the eventual result of mergers of the old RFH with Liverpool Road Hospital (1945), North-Western Fever Hospital (1948), Hampstead General Hospital (1948), and Coppetts Wood & New End hospitals (both 1968). Four of them were a consequence, at least in part, of the bomb damage inflicted on RFH Gray's Inn Road in 1944. Profit was not a motive. Saving money was – and there were sound clinical and financial reasons for replacing several small hospitals with a new, larger and better equipped hospital.[1]

---

[1] Liverpool Road and New End hospitals have been converted into residential accommodation, a fate awaiting Coppetts Wood. The North Western Fever Hospital and Hampstead General were demolished with the construction of the new RFH in Hampstead.

The argument for merging small medical schools into one admitting three to four hundred students a year is less convincing. That number is much greater than the annual number of admissions to any of what might be considered as the 'best' American schools. Preclinical teaching is largely dependent on lectures and small group 'theoretical' teaching, techniques that are of less value during the clinical course. The practical training of doctors, like that of scientists, artists, and skilled workmen, has for centuries involved a form of hands-on 'apprenticeship' in which close relationships tend to develop between 'pupils' and their teachers. Students can only learn to care properly for patients by simulating care during clinical attachments, either in hospital or in general practice. Clinical 'knowledge' is best gained by reading around the problems of the patients allocated to them, who should be followed over days or weeks, and having their own 'clinical notes' assessed by some form of supervisor. Clinical skills are acquired by seeing them demonstrated, by practising them repeatedly, and then by displaying them to a teacher who can judge whether performance is satisfactory – and, if it is not, can recommend means of improvement. I think most experienced clinical teachers would agree that the planning, execution and monitoring of such an approach, which calls for a close relationship between the central administration and the 'workers' at the coal face, would be done more easily in a small medical school than in a very large one. The 'workers' include junior doctors, who have traditionally played a major part in teaching both students and their less experienced colleagues – a role typified in the familiar medical school epigram 'See one, do one, teach one'.

Before 1953 students, on qualification, registered fully with the GMC and could enter practice immediately, so it was clearly important that they received a truly practical undergraduate training as well as a theoretical one. After 1953 newly qualified doctors, in order to gain full registration, had to spend one year under supervision as provisionally-registered resident medical officers (housemen[2]). The Government was thus obliged to provide them with their first job and with a year's accommodation. As housemen had done for decades they joined a hospital 'firm' headed by one or more consultants and including other registered junior doctors ('senior house officers', 'registrars' or 'senior registrars'). The houseman clerked all patients allocated to him and would take a patient's history, do a physical examination, make a provisional diagnosis (or diagnoses), suggest appropriate treatment and carry out minor procedures under supervision – all being recorded in the patient's notes – and would receive rapid feedback on his performance from a more senior member of the firm. 'Resident' housemen were available to patients around the clock and learned the importance of continuity of care. Many patients

[2] A gender neutral word.

have more than one problem and, particularly within specialist firms, the houseman was the 'generalist' and was expected to identify problems which might escape the attention of his seniors.

House jobs were often very busy, particularly on general medical and surgical firms, and the long hours worked generated sympathy from relatives, friends and from the press; but it was the busiest jobs, which provided the best experience, that tended to be the most sought after. 'Spare time' was spent with colleagues in the residents' mess. Many considered their year 'on the house' as one of the most enjoyable of their career, but others had difficulty coping with the long hours and the responsibility, and it was particularly hard for married housemen if there was no married accommodation. Some firms had two housemen who could share 'out of hours' work, and sometimes 'single housemen' from different firms arranged a little time off by cross-covering.

Unfortunately there have been dramatic changes in the training of junior hospital doctors which have affected both RFH and UCLMS. They are well documented in Rivett's on-line *National Health Service History* (http://www.nhshistory.net) from which I quote extensively below.

Inevitably the combination of long hours and relatively poor salary led to change. An extra-duty allowance was introduced in 1970, and after industrial action by junior staff in 1975 a new contract gave junior doctors a 'basic' 40-hour week. They continued to work more than 40 hours but for a limited number of the 'extra hours' they received 'overtime' at a third of their normal hourly rate. However, with the change came the introduction of shift systems, particularly at night. Subsequently juniors often dealt with patients they might not see again, and were 'on call with consultants with whom they never did a ward round'. Working relationships were less close and mutual support within teams diminished. The traditional "firm" system began to break down'.

The recommendations in the 'Calman Report' (1993) were meant to promote UK compliance with European Community directives on specialist training and registration. They led to the creation of a sub-group of junior doctors called Specialist Registrars (SpRs) who received educational opportunities but had no responsibility for patients, for the supervision of SHOs and housemen, or for teaching students. Along with bed allocation problems, 'Calman' contributed to the further erosion of firm-based care. Consultants found themselves responsible for 'outlier patients' housed in wards not designed for their specialty and wasted time and energy moving from ward to ward. Doctors worked with many different nurses, and vice versa, a problem aggravated by the introduction of 'team nursing', for no longer could calls be channelled through a single ward sister.

In 2004 another initiative emerged from the Department of Health – where, as Rivett points out, 'medical training traditionally met the needs of the hospitals and the NHS, education sometimes being incidental rather than central'. In the hope of addressing several long-standing problems *'Modernising Medical Careers'* (MMC) suggested that a 'Postgraduate Medical Education and Training Board' should assume the responsibilities of the Specialist Training Authority of the medical Royal Colleges and the Joint Committee on Postgraduate General Practice Training and develop a single framework for postgraduate training. The Board was set up; its powers were transferred to the GMC in 2010.

The SHO grade contained half of all doctors in training, and combined a high work load with relatively poor training. MMC hoped to change that and in 2005 introduced a Foundation Programme Curriculum in the form of a structured two-year training with exposure to a number of specialties including A&E, O&G and anaesthetics as well as primary care. The second year would effectively replace the SHO grade, and offer high quality training with progress dependent on competence rather than time in post. Foundation Programme doctors were meant to progress by becoming either a general practice registrar or a Type 1 or Type 2 specialist registrar (SpR). Problems resulted because young inexperienced doctors rotating through multiple posts contributed less to the actual running of the service, and so trusts employed more consultants and introduced a 'staff grade' offering a permanent position as a middle grade doctor.

Introduced in 2006 the scheme soon ran into difficulties. All new British graduates were expected to apply for the Foundation Programme but other suitably qualified individuals could also do so. 28,000 applied for 15,500 Foundation Programme places, doctors already in SHO posts having to compete with recent UK graduates and with doctors from overseas. The system could not cope; the number of applications doctors could make was restricted, judgments were made on doubtful criteria, and the short lists produced for interviews were inadequate. The careers of some young doctors were imperilled. The medical profession united in protest.

The Department of Health announced an urgent independent review chaired by Sir John Tooke, Dean of the Peninsula Medical School (now UCL's Vice-Provost {Health} and head of UCLMS). His interim report in October 2007 was highly critical. MMC was rushed, poorly led and badly implemented, not flexible enough to meet NHS needs and encouraged premature specialisation. Reforms were needed. Tooke's final report (2008) called for separation of the first two years, allowing universities to guarantee a first medical post to their graduates. He also recommended that management of postgraduate education should be transferred from the Department of Health to a new body, NHS Medical Education England

(MEE). It was established in January 2009 and became 'Health Education England' in 2012.

In 2009 MEE commissioned a formal evaluation of the Foundation Programme by a group led by Professor John Collins. Their description of the Programme ('*Foundation for Excellence*', October 2010) suggested something of a curate's egg. It had established a credible UK-wide, defined, two-year training scheme involving a range of medical specialties (but mainly adult medicine and surgery) and with an emphasis on emergency care to improve identification and handling of acutely ill patients, but it paid insufficient attention to the 'total patient' and to chronic problems. An assessment system was introduced to monitor the acquisition of the key competences called for in the curriculum. However the Programme was thought to lack a clearly articulated and generally accepted purpose, and there was confusion about the role of the trainees. Although educated and trained in the clinical environment, they also made an important contribution to patient care for which they were not considered supernumerary. The demands of the clinical service and their educational requirements had therefore to be balanced, to avoid domination by short-term service requirements. A lack of understanding of the abilities of F1 and F2 doctors (who hailed from various medical schools) may have led to their deployment in inappropriate roles and beyond their level of competence.

The Collins group heard complaints about lack of flexibility. In 2009 just over half of the Foundation Schools (currently numbering twenty-one) had a fixed two-year programme so that F2 specialty placements were decided before the trainees commenced F1. Some trainees complained of boredom owing to overlap with the undergraduate curriculum. Widespread support for the assessment system was lacking; it was thought excessive, onerous and not particularly valuable. The validity of the assessment methods was questioned, and their variable application was attributed to poor preparation of assessors and lack of time to do the assessments properly. Others worried about the quality of the trainees' education and learning, and about inadequate pastoral care. The lack of an agreed purpose made it difficult to measure how well the Foundation Programme delivered against its own objectives. Nevertheless, the Collins group thought there was widespread overall support for the Programme, and indirect evidence that it had delivered successfully against a broad number of objectives.

To exacerbate the situation regarding junior staff the European Working Time Directive (EWTD) came into force in August 2009. It reduced the maximum hours worked over a six-month period from an average of 56 per week to 48. This raised concerns about continuity of care (e.g. patients having to repeat their histories to different doctors), about patient safety (owing to the repeated handovers needed), and about the overall reduction in training experience. Furthermore juniors no longer had the skills of their predecessors because of restrictions on what students were allowed to do on patients (even including simple procedures like venepuncture). A group headed by Sir John Temple reviewed the effect of the EWTD on the training of junior doctors. Its report '*Time for Training*', published in May 2010, showed that despite a 60% increase in consultant numbers over the previous ten years, hospitals still relied too much on junior doctors to provide out of hours services. It suggested that high quality training was compatible with the EWTD but not if trainees were poorly supervised, or had limited access to learning. Increasing hours or lengthening training programmes would not solve existing problems. However a more recent study, published in March 2014,[3] concluded that the EWTD has had an adverse effect on training, and noted that in certain specialties junior doctors, unable to obtain the training they need within the '48 hr week', voluntarily work longer hours to gain the skills they need.

Temple wanted a consultant delivered service, with consultants working more flexibly and being more directly responsible for 24hr care. He thought it would lead to better quality diagnosis, better decision making, and better patient outcomes and safety. However, the issue of consultant-delivered care begs the question 'When did he or she become capable of delivering the care?'. It would be absurd to suggest that successful candidates lack that capability before being appointed as a consultant – and if they have it why should they not deliver the care. An obvious solution would be to reinstate the old post of 'senior registrar' – i.e. 'consultant in waiting'!

In 2011 Medical Education England set up another group – the 'Shape of Training Review' – to suggest the best way of training doctors in the future. Its chairman, Professor David Greenaway, Vice-Chancellor of Nottingham University, is an economist. Its report '*Securing the future of excellent patient care*' was published in October 2013. The group argued – on the basis of a growing number of people with multiple co-morbidities, an ageing population, health inequalities and increasing patient expectations – that the main requirement from the educational system is for more doctors able to provide general care in broad specialties across a range of different settings. It suggested that 'Full registration should move to the point of graduation from medical school, provided there are measures in place to demonstrate graduates are fit to practise at the end of medical school. Patients' interests must be considered first and foremost as part of this change.' Although the last sentence is a statement of the obvious its significance

[3] The 'task force' set up for this study was chaired by Norman Williams PRCS

in this context is not made clear. Following graduation, doctors were to undertake the two-year Foundation Programme. The group thought doctors must have opportunities to support and follow patients through their entire care pathway, both during medical school and in the Foundation Programme.

The recommendation that medical students should become fully registered on graduation leads one to ask 'What privileges would be extended to the "fully registered"?'. Clearly not those associated with 'full registration' after 1858, when registered practitioners could practise in any specialty without a specialist diploma from one of the colleges. The answer seems to be none. The possibility of full registration on qualification has profound implications for future UK medical graduates. Currently, as students, they expect two years of salaried practical experience as NHS doctors after leaving medical school. If Greenaway's proposal is accepted they would have to compete for an F1 post with graduates from foreign medical schools. If unsuccessful they might not be able to practise, even in the UK (except as a registered but 'unapproved' practitioner – a situation analogous to that of the women with foreign MDs who practised in Britain before they could get a qualification 'registrable' with the GMC). (See Chapter 1) At present 'fully registered' British graduates can register in some countries – notably Australasia – without taking further tests; but that might change if the training time towards full registration is reduced. British applicants might decide against spending 5-6 costly years in a UK medical school with no guarantee of a job afterwards.[4]

It is easy to stipulate that medical schools must ensure that medical graduates on registration can work 'safely in a clinical role suitable to their competence level, and have experience of and insight into patient needs'. That judgement could only be made via a good clinically based system of in-course assessment that requires students to simulate patient care. OSCEs[5] would certainly not help, and while 'simulated patients' and mannequins have a place in undergraduate and postgraduate education they are not a substitute for interaction with real patients. I have spent much time in hospital as a patient in recent years, as have some medically qualified friends. Like them, I am puzzled that F1 doctors, although apparently busy, have surprisingly little patient contact – and appear not to take patients' histories or to conduct physical examinations (and are very poor at venepuncture). If, as seems possible, students are following the example set by the F1s those responsible for managing undergraduate and postgraduate curricula should reflect on Osler's words – 'To study the phenomena of disease without books is to sail an uncharted sea, while to study books without patients is not to go to sea at all'.

---

4 See Wakeford's letter *BMJ* 5 Feb 2014

5 OSCE – **O**bjective **S**tructured **C**linical **E**xamination

Given the number of enquiries and half-hearted reports about undergraduate and postgraduate education over the last twenty or so years one could be forgiven for concluding that the situation is chaotic and unlikely to improve with further narrowly based enquiries. A 'national health service' is an ideal system, not only for monitoring and preserving the 'public health', but also for the provision of first class clinical care and for promoting excellent medical education (at undergraduate and postgraduate level). Sadly all 'Ministers of Health' seem compelled to change it in some way (presumably to justify their existence) and blithely disregard potential knock-on effects of their ill-conceived reforms. Lansley's recent plans for the NHS do not take into account the possibility that its privatisation might have deleterious effects on medical education.

The merging of medical schools was not a major issue until 1968 when the 'Royal Commission on Medical Education' ('Todd') recommended reorganizing London's medical schools into six groups that would form the medical faculties of large multi-faculty schools, each with a preclinical intake of 200. RFHSM was to link with UCHMS and merge eventually with UCL. If the medical school, hospital and multi-faculty institution could not co-exist on one site 'Todd' wanted preclinical departments near science departments, not teaching hospitals, a viewpoint diametrically opposed to that of the Goodenough Report in 1944.[6]

Most of London's medical schools (Bart's, Charing Cross, Guy's, The London, Middlesex, St Mary's, and St Thomas' were complete schools with preclinical and clinical faculties. King's College's preclinicals went to King's College Hospital, St George's or Westminster. Most, but not all, of University College's preclinical students moved to University College Hospital Medical School. It was the 'Todd' philosophy that eventually led, via Tomlinson, to the creation of four London medical schools with a very large intake – at UCL, Imperial, KCL, and Queen Mary-Bart's-London, leaving only St George's as a 'single school'. There is of course no evidence that the products of the mega-schools are any better than those who graduated from the original smaller schools.

Within the NHS mergers have remained fashionable, as have transfers and the changing of hospitals' names. In 1991 RFH became the Royal Free Hampstead NHS Trust which also included the Royal National Ear, Nose and Throat Hospital. The last was subsequently transferred to UCL Hospitals NHS Foundation Trust which had earlier, under a different name, merged with the Elizabeth Garrett Anderson Hospital and the Eastman Dental Hospital (both of which have a strong historical connection with the 'Free').

---

[6] See p.134, paras 22-24

The biggest merger involving RFH results from the creation of UCL Partners as an 'Academic Health Science Centre' (AHSC), a term denoting a partnership (between universities and healthcare providers) to focus on research, clinical services, education and training. AHSCs have been established in several countries including Canada and the United States. In October 2007 Imperial College joined up with Hammersmith and St. Mary's hospitals to form Britain's first AHSC. Three months earlier Lord Darzi (of St Mary's), then a Health Minister, had suggested using them to deepen the ties between universities and hospitals – in the hope that they would promote academic and clinical research, improve professional education, help to reform the NHS, and enhance patient care by speeding up the transfer of new ideas from bench to bedside.

UCL Partners, a not-for-profit company based on the Harvard model of an AHSC, was created in 2009 when UCL united with Great Ormond Street, Moorfields Eye Hospital, RFH and UCH. As a group it treated 1.5 million patients a year; employed 3,500 scientists, senior researchers and medical consultants; and had a combined annual budget of around £2 billion. UCL partners decided to concentrate initially on ten research areas: the nervous system, children's health, heart disease, transplantation, immunology, ophthalmology, deafness and hearing impairment, dental and oral disease, cancer and women's health. In October 2011 Bart's and The London NHS Trust and Queen Mary University of London agreed to join UCL Partners, making it the largest AHSC in the world.

The Transfer of the Royal Free Archives

Until recently it was relatively easy to check the accuracy of statements about the history of the Royal Free. Its archives were within walking distance of RFH, and a dedicated archivist could help with enquiries. The responsibility for the housing and uptake of the archives initially rested with RFH, and grants from the Royal Free Charity Trustees and from UCL helped to cover running expenses and the salary of the archivist. In April 1991 RFH metamorphosed into the Royal Free Hampstead NHS Trust and, in 2012, to the Royal Free London NHS Foundation Trust. After an inspection the National Archives told RFH that environmental conditions at The Hoo, particularly in respect of air conditioning, were unsuitable for the storage of important documents and should be improved, but the Foundation Trust decided the cost would be prohibitive. Keen also to save the running costs of the archives, it decided to relocate them. The move of the RFH Archives was brokered by the National Archives and they were transferred to the London Metropolitan Archives in December 2013.

It might be asked why the archives of a London teaching hospital and its medical school should have been relocated in that way. Those of Guy's, King's & St

Thomas' are housed within KCL's 'Foyles Special Collections' in Chancery Lane, while Bart's & The London, although now a combined school, each holds its own school and hospital archives. Of the three former medical schools now within Imperial College, St Mary's has its own archives (school and hospital). Imperial College holds the archives of Charing Cross and Westminster medical schools, but the corresponding hospital records are at the London Metropolitan Archives. St George's has a similar arrangement. The Middlesex archives (hospital and school) are kept with the UCLH archives. Because of the obvious academic link the RFH archives were offered to UCL which declined to take them. As about 60% of the students at UCLMS are women I think that at least some of them might have appreciated the opportunity of exploring, on site, the documents detailing the early stages of women's struggle to get a medical education and to qualify with an appropriate qualification.

A View from the Past

One can but wonder how staff and students from the early days of RFH and LSMW would react on visiting today's RFH. Their pleasure that it remains a 'free hospital' would be diminished somewhat on learning that the present Conservative Government wishes to privatise the NHS. They would be dazzled by the new Royal Free complex and astonished with the facilities now available for patient care. Their delight that School and Hospital eventually lived together in Hampstead would be tempered because that cohabitation lasted for only about twenty years, and because 'Royal Free' was removed from the name of the merged school. They would have been happy that the School became co-educational, given that when that happened all the other London medical schools had to take women. If RFHSM had to merge they would probably be content it was with University College which supplied LSMW with some excellent teachers in the early years. Both institutions were tolerant of religions other than the Anglican Church, and there was little evidence of racial intolerance. They would be bemused that over three hundred students a year are admitted annually to the full course, and that over four hundred enter the clinical part of the curriculum.

Their biggest surprise, particularly for the early LSMW students, would be to find that at British medical schools, including UCL, women now make up around 60% of the students, a figure that had risen from about 15% in 1938-39 (when it was only 11% in London) and about 24% in 1960. Recent predictions suggest that by 2017 more than half of the doctors in Britain will be women. However many, including women doctors, are concerned that a superabundance of women doctors may cause problems. Many of those who are married struggle to combine work and raising a family and, not surprisingly, prefer part time work and work which allows prior planning of the necessary hours. They tend to avoid jobs which might call for a rapid response to emergencies, or which have much on call responsibility, e.g. cardiology and gastro-enterology, and prefer posts like oncology or radiology. One study found that for fifteen years after qualification women on average contribute about 75% of the hours that would have been worked by male doctors, while a census of consultant physicians conducted by the Royal College of Physicians in 2012 found that 39% of the female consultants worked less than whole time (only about 5% of males did so), and that more women (67%) than men (57%) reported a wish to retire early. These figures are worrying in view of the cost of training doctors. An altered gender ratio is not the only significant change in admissions to medical schools. There has been a striking reduction in the number of 'white males' who, in 2004, constituted about 43% of the population but only about 26% of medical students.

Has the merger proved of any financial or educational benefit? As it replaced a basic five-year course with one lasting six years one must assume that the cost to the state of training its students has increased by roughly twenty percent – while students have to find the money for an extra year's tuition, and lose a year's salary from their lifetime's earnings. One would hope therefore that there was some educational benefit. But neither Todd nor Tomlinson put forward any serious *educational* arguments in relation to the merging of medical schools, and the Flowers intervention was openly about reducing the cost of preclinical education. Given the extraordinary changes that have occurred in postgraduate medical education in recent years it would probably be impossible to get a clear idea of the true abilities of modern medical graduates – they certainly seem less prepared for what lies ahead of them.

I am sure that in these uncertain times all 'Royal Free' people wish RFH well for the future and hope it will remember its past, and also feel the same about the new medical school. They may also harbour a slight hope that UCLMS, following the example of RUMS, might at some stage return 'Middlesex' and 'Royal Free' to the name of the school.

Introduction to References

The many references in this book allow readers to check the accuracy of the statements made. The relationship between the references and the relevant statements is usually obvious – but when several points are made within a single paragraph I often, for the sake of convenience, used a single reference number at the end of the paragraph to cover the various sources. For standard references I have tried to follow the Vancouver system. However most references in the book refer to documents in the Royal Free Archives, recently transferred from The Hoo in Hampstead to the London Metropolitan Archives(LMA). For these references I created simple abbreviations to indicate to which documents or sets of documents I was referring. Sometimes I did not insert a reference 'number' when the source of a statement was clear from the text itself.

Working at The Hoo was relatively easy as, with the help of the dedicated archivist, I could move quickly between a variety of documents and so cross-referencing was easy. Such freedom is not feasible at LMA, but the catalogues for the archives of the Royal Free Hospital and Medical School are available online and a limited number of documents for viewing can be ordered in advance. To look at original records at LMA it is necessary to obtain a History Card with one's photograph on it as a means of identification. The card can be issued in advance online or on arrival; an official form of identification (e.g. a passport or driving licence) is required.

To search the LMA catalogue online for documents related to the Royal Free Hospital start at the page headed SIMPLE SEARCH and under 'Search Terms' enter 'Royal Free London' using 'Exact Phrase'. One can then choose between 'Royal Free London NHS Foundation Trust' and 'Royal Free Hospital'. The former encapsulates the latter but also contains materials from other hospitals and institutions associated with the Royal Free Hospital. Click on 'Royal Free Hospital'; this brings up a separate long page. Scroll to the bottom of it and click 'Level Down' to find a list of the various subjects dealing with the Royal Free Hospital's past. Click on a title to find yet another level of choice. To find material about the School of Medicine start the search with 'Royal Free Hospital School of Medicine', 'Exact phrase' and choose the option 'London School of Medicine and Related Collections (H72).

The Royal Free Archives are catalogued at LMA using an alphanumeric system of about six terms – see below. The first five denote a particular subject. 'Documents' for each subject are contained in one or more 'boxes' which tend to be numbered in chronological order – 001 indicating the box containing the 'oldest' items. For example medical school annual reports (AR for LSMW/RFHSM) were produced from 1875 to 1997. There are sixteen boxes, so the last is numbered 016. The catalogue gives the relevant time period for each box, e.g. 001 contains the AR from 1875 to 1898, and 016 those from 1985 to 1997.

The following brief list gives the LMA catalogue references for the most commonly quoted sources in the Royal Free Archive Some material that was in the Archives at The Hoo may not have been transferred to LMA. If a reference to something that 'is in the Royal Free Archives' cannot be found in the LMA catalogue seek help from the RFH library.

AR	**Annual Reports LSMW/RFHSM**
	H72/SM/A/02/01/001 .... 016 (1875-1997)
BoG	**RFH Board of Governors**
	Pre-1948 – H71/RF/A/01/01/001 .... 005 (1839-1946)
	Post-1948 (Royal Free Group) – H71/RF/A/09/01/001 .... 005 (1948-1974)
CM	**Council Minutes ('Executive Council', then 'Council')**
	Executive Council H72/SM/A/02/02/001 .... 007 (1874-1898)
	Council H72/SM/A/02/03/001 .... 023 (1898-1998)
DevComm	**Development Committee**
	H71/RF/A/06/004 (1945-1946)
	H71/RF/A/14/001 (1948-1962)
EC	**LSMW/RFHSM Education Committee (initially School Committee)**
	H72/SM/A/04/01/001 .... 020 (1898-1998)
JMAC	**Joint Advisory Medical Committee**
	H71/RF/A/12/01/001 .... 005 (1948-1972)
LC	**Library Sub-Committee (RFHSM)**
	H72/SM/L/01/01/001 .... 003 (1894-1963)
MAC	**Royal Free Medical Advisory Committee**
	H71/RF/A/32/01/001 (1972-76)
Mag	**Magazine of LSMW & RFH**
	H72/SM/C/03/07/001 .... 033 (1895-1974)
RFH Comm Man	**RFH Committee of Management/Management Committee**
(ManComm)	H71/RF/A/05/01/001 .... 009 (1906-1948)
MC or MedComm	**RFH Medical Committee**
	Pre-1948 – H71/RF/A/01/01/001 .... 008 (1839-1949)
	Post-1948 (Royal Free Group) – H71/RF/A/09/01/001 .... 005 (1948-1974)
PC	**Press Cuttings**
	H72/SM/Y/02/001 ... 014 (1874 – 1983)
Prospectus	**Prospectus LSMW/RFHSM**
	H72/SM/C/01/01/001 .... 007 1874-1988
PUJC	**Pathology Unit Joint Committee**
	H72/SM/A/07/04/001 (1931-1948)

RFH AR	**Royal Free Hospital Annual Reports** H71/RF/A/02/02/001 .... 020 (1848 – 1945) (Annual Reports before 1848 are within the minutes of the Committee of Management – see above)
SCPhys	**Sub-committee of Physicians/Division of Medicine** H71/RF/A/20/01/001 .... 003 (1957-1984)
SU	**Minutes of Students' Union** H72/SM/C/03/03/001 .... 010 (1915-1970)
Union Comm	**LSMW/RFHSM Students' Union Committee minutes** H72/SM/C/03/03/001 .... 010 (1898-1970)
UR	**Union Report**
WB	**RFH Weekly Board** H71/RF/A/03/01/001 .... 022 (1846-1947)

References

Chapter 1

i Du Preez, H.M. Dr James Barry: the early years revealed. *S. Afr. Med J*: 2008; 98: pp. 52-58

ii Sahli N. *Elizabeth Blackwell, MD: A Biography.* Ph.D. Thesis, University of Pennsylvania: 1974

iii Bonner T.N. *To the ends of the earth: Women's search for education in medicine.* Cambridge, Mass: Harvard University Press; 1992. Chapter 1.

iv *Mary Putnam Jacobi,MD: A pathfinder in Medicine.* New York: GP Putnam's Sons, The Knickerbocker Press; 1925.

v Manton J. 1965, *Elizabeth Garrett Anderson*. New York: EP Dutton & Co. 1965.

vi McIntyre N. Britain's first medical marriage: Frances Morgan (1843-1927), George Hoggan (1837-1891) & the mysterious "Elsie". *J Med Biog*. 2004; 12: pp. 105-114.

vii Jex-Blake S. *Medical Women – A Thesis and a History.* Edinburgh: Oliphant, Anderson & Ferrier. 1886 p.5.

viii Hurd-Mead K.C. *A History of Women in Medicine*. Haddam, Conn: The Haddam Press, 1938.

ix Martindale, L. *The Woman Doctor and her future*. London: Mills & Boon: 1922. p30.

x Jex-Blake. op cit. pp.30-31.

xi Jex-Blake, op.cit. p.13.

xii Clark G.A. *History of the Royal College of Physicians of London*. Vol 1, Oxford: Clarendon Press, 1964: p.54.

xiii Op cit ref 8 (Hurd-Mead); Appendix, pp. 521-523.

xiv Geyer-Kordasch J. Women and Medicine. In: Bynum WF & Porter R, eds. *Companion Encyclopedia of the History of Medicine.* Vol 2. London: Routledge;. 1973: pp. 893 & 1052.

xv Jex-Blake, op.cit. p.23.

xvi Martindale. op.cit.p.35.

xvii Newman C. *Evolution of Medical Education in the Nineteenth Century.* London: OUP; 1957: p.59.

xviii Ibid. p.74-5

xix Jex-Blake. op.cit, p.67.

xx Newman. op.cit, Chapter 4.

xxi Boyd J. *The Excellent Doctor Blackwell.* Sutton Publishing, 2005: pp.108-118

xxii Sahli. op.cit., p.87

[xxiii] Boyd , op. cit., p.124.
[xxiv] Sahli. op.cit. p.128.
[xxv] Boyd, J. op.cit pp. 145, 162-3
[xxvi] Sahli, op.cit. p141.
[xxvii] Blackwell E. *Opening the Medical Profession to women*. London: Longmans, Green; 1895. p. 222.
[xxviii] Ibid. pp. 213-219.
[xxix] Daniels EA. *Jessie White Mario: Risorgimento Revolutionary*. Athens: Ohio University Press; 1972.
[xxx] Ibid. pp. 41-43.
[xxxi] Manton, op.cit. (ref 6)
[xxxii] Garrett Anderson, L. *Elizabeth Garrett Anderson 1836-1917*. London: Faber & Faber 1939
[xxxiii] Blackwell, op.cit., p.218.
[xxxiv] Manton, op.cit., p121.
[xxxv] Roberts S. *Sophia Jex-Blake: a woman pioneer in nineteenth-century medical reform*. London: Routledge. 1993: p. 38
[xxxvi] Manton, op.cit., p.155 (quoting letter from EG to ED 27 June 1864. Fawcett Library).
[xxxvii] Crawford E. *Enterprising Women: the Garretts and their Circle*. London: Francis Boutle. 2002: p.76. Franklin A. *A Bart's Woman, 1865*. St Bartholomew's Hospital Journal. 1931: November.
[xxxviii] Cooke, AM. *History of Royal College of Physicians of London*. Oxford: OUP,Vol 3, 1972: pp.832-3.
[xxxix] Crawford, op.cit. pp.242-3.
[xl] Elizabeth Garrett Anderson Letters & Papers, Suffolk Record Office, HA436/1 Correspondence.
[xli] RFH WB 1867: 14 Mar
[xlii] Swain V. Early History to 1914. In Kosky J. ed. *Queen Elizabeth Hospital for Children; 125 years of achievement*. London: The Hospitals for Sick Children, 1992.
[xliii] Allen V. *Lady Trader: a biography of Mrs Sarah Heckford*. London: Collins, 1979.
[xliv] Bonner, op.cit., p.38.
[xlv] McIntyre, op.cit. .
[xlvi] Blake C. *The Charge of the Parasols: Women's entry to the Medical Profession*. London: The Woman's Press; 1990. pp. 80-83.
[xlvii] Elizabeth Garrett Anderson Letters, op cit. (ref 40).
[xlviii] Crawford , op.cit. p.242. See Manton, op.cit. pp.180-183.
[xlix] Todd M. *Life of Sophia Jex-Blake*. London: Macmillan & Co; 1918. p 279.
[l] Garrett E. An enquiry into the nature of the Contagious Diseases Acts. *Pall Mall Gazette*. 1870; 25 January
[li] Sahli, op.cit., p.147.
[lii] Blackwell, op.cit., p.228.
[liii] Todd, op.cit., p.207.
[liv] Sahli, op.cit., p.168 (ref 183 – EB to Bodichon, 16 June 1869).
[lv] Ibid. p.198 & p.206.
[lvi] Ibid. p.202.
[lvii] Blackwell, op.cit., p.250.

Chapter 2

[i] Todd M. *'Life of Sophia Jex-Blake'*. London: Macmillan & Co; 1918.
[ii] Roberts S. *Sophia Jex-Blake: a woman pioneer in nineteenth-century medical reform*. London: Routledge; 1993.
[iii] Jex-Blake S. *Medical Women – A Thesis and a History*. Edinburgh: Oliphant, Anderson & Ferrier; 1886.
[iv] Ibid, p.75.
[v] Todd, op. cit., p.252.

[vi] *Granny Thorne's Diary* – copy in RFH Archives.; Thorne Obit *BMJ* 15 Oct 1910.
[vii] Lutzker E. *Edith Pechey-Phipson, MD: the story of England's foremost pioneering woman doctor.* New York: Exposition Press; 1973.
[viii] Cope Z. *The History of St.Mary's Hospital Medical School.* London: Heinemann; 1954, p.41.
[ix] Anderson L.G. *Elizabeth Garrett Anderson, 1836-1917.* London: Faber & Faber; 1939, p.207
[x] Jex-Blake, op.cit., p.77.
[xi] Thorne I. *Sketch of the Foundation and Development of the London School of Medicine for Women.* London: G Sharrow; 1905, p 27.
[xii] Jex-Blake, op.cit., p.85
[xiii] Ibid. pp. 87-90
[xiv] Ibid. pp. 89-91.
[xv] Todd, op. cit., pp. 291-2.
[xvi] Ibid. pp. 292-4.
[xvii] Ibid, op. cit., pp.296-8.
[xviii] Roberts. op.cit. p.108.
[xix] Todd. Op.cit. p.299.
[xx] Ibid. Chapter IX.
[xxi] Ibid. p.320.
[xxii] Ibid. p331; see also Roberts. op.cit. p.114.
[xxiii] Jex-Blake. op.cit. p.115.
[xxiv] Roberts. op.cit. p.117.
[xxv] Ibid. p118.
[xxvi] Todd, op.cit. .p336.
[xxvii] Ibid. p.337
[xxviii] Jex-Blake, op, cit. pp.119-121.
[xxix] Ibid. p.124.
[xxx] Ibid. pp.125-129.
[xxxi] Ibid. pp.129-132
[xxxii] Ibid. pp.136-144.
[xxxiii] Todd op. cit. Chapter XIV
[xxxiv] McIntyre, N, '*The fate of Rose Anna Shedlock and the medical education of Émile Roux*'. In press J Med Biography.
[xxxv] Roberts, op.cit. p.132.
[xxxvi] Jex-Blake, op.cit. Appendix, .p27-47.
[xxxvii] Todd, op.cit. p.391-392.
[xxxviii] Ibid. p.402.
[xxxix] Ibid. p.403
[xl] *The Times*, 23 August 1873.
[xli] Hammond JE & B. *James Stansfeld: a Victorian champion of sex equality.* London: Longmans, Green & Co; 1932.
[xlii] Todd, op. cit., p389.
[xliii] Ibid. pp. 404-405.
[xliv] Ibid. Chapter XVII
[xlv] Stansfeld, J. *Nineteenth Century*, July 1877
[xlvi] Todd, op. cit., pp.417-418.
[xlvii] Ibid. pp.392-395.
[xlviii] Ibid. pp.419-421.
[xlix] Ibid. pp.423-425.
[l] Willoughby-Lyle, H. (1935) *King's and some King's Men.* Oxford Univ Press, p72
[li] Thorne, op. cit. p.18
[lii] Todd, op, cit. p.380
[liii] Ibid. p.421;see also Jex-Blake, op. cit. p.179.
[liv] *Plarr's Lives of the Fellows of the Royal College of Surgeons of England.* London: Simpkin Marshall; 1930. pp. 265-267.

lv The 'advertisement of sale' notice describing the Pavilion in 1810 is in the Holborn Library

lvi Webb H. *Some Early Recollections of the LSMW.* LSMW Magazine, July 1924, p.58.

lvii Hart, Mrs E. *The London School of them Medicine for Women — Past and Present by a Pioneer.* LSMW Magazine. Nov 1924. p.130.

lviii Sahli N. *Elizabeth Blackwell, MD: A Biography.* Ph.D. Thesis, University of Pennsylvania: 1974. p 217 (Letter from EB to Bodichon, 21 September 1874).

lix Ibid. p 250. (Letter from EB to Bodichon 23 September 1874)

lx *Plarr's Lives of Fellows of RCS England*, Vol II, 1930: pp. 107-8; Zachary Cope, Z *The History of St Mary's Hospital Medical Schoo*l. William Heinemann Ltd. (1954) p. 191; Letter EG to father 12 September 1870; Garrett Anderson Letters & Papers, Suffolk Record Office, HA436/1.

Chapter 3

i Thorne I. *Sketch of the Foundation and Development of the London School of Medicine for Women.* London: G Sharrow; 1905: p.7.

ii Hart, Mrs E. *The London School of them Medicine for Women — Past and Present by a Pioneer.* LSMW Magazine, Nov 1924. p.130.

iii Cope Z. The History of St.Mary's Hospital Medical School. London: Heinemann; 1954: pp.42-43.

iv Letter 26 Oct 1974 from de Meric & Hill. LSMW Letters Books, p. 13.

v CM 1975: 30 Sep.

vi Dupuy's resignation. LSMW Letters Books, p. 17.

vii French, Richard D. *Antivivisection and medical science in Victorian Society.* Princeton:University Press, 1975.

viii CM 1876: 9 Oct; CM 1877: 30 May.

ix Granny Thorne's Diary. LMA (or RFH Library)

x Jewesbury E.C.O. *The Royal Northern Hospital 1856-1956. The story of a hundred years work in North London.* London: H.K. Lewis & Co; 1956. p. 42.

xi Jex-Blake S. *Medical Women – A Thesis and a History.* Edinburgh: Oliphant, Anderson & Ferrier; 1886: pp.184-190

xii Ibid., pp..194-198. (Stansfeld's remarks were in *Nineteenth Century*, July 1877).

xiii Ibid., pp. 200- 202

xiv Ibid., pp. 202-204.

xv CM 1876: 16 Oct

xvi Letter King & Queen's College of Physicians in Ireland. LSMW Letters Books (in LMA). p. 46.

xvii St. John, C. *Christine Murrell, M. D.* London: Williams & Norgate Ltd. 1935, p.18.

xviii Note from Stansfeld , LSMW Letters Books, p. 43.

xix LSMW Letters Books. p. 37.

xx Alice Ker's Diary for 1875. LMA (or try RFH Library)

xxi CM 1876: 27 Apr, 12 May

xxii Quoted in CM 1876: 31 Jul.

xxiii Todd M. *Life of Sophia Jex-Blake.* London: Macmillan & Co; 1918. pp. 441-442.

xxiv Ibid. p. 442.

xxv Ibid. p. 443

xxvi RFH WB 1877: 15 Feb, 1 Mar.

xxvii LSMW Letters Books, p. 49.

xxviii Thorne, op.cit., p.21-22.

xxix Roberts S. *Sophia Jex-Blake: a woman pioneer in nineteenth-century medical reform.* London: Routledge, 1993. pp. 4-5.

xxx Todd, op. cit., pp. 445-447.

xxxi Ibid. p. 447

xxxii Ibid. pp. 447-8

xxxiii Ibid. p. 448.

[xxxiv] Crawford E. *Enterprising Women; the Garretts and their Circle*. London: Francis Boutle; 2002: p 39.
[xxxv] Anderson LG. *Elizabeth Garrett Anderson*. London: Faber & Faber; 1939: p. 205..
[xxxvi] Fawcett, MG , *What I remember* . London. T Fisher Unwin. 1924: p. 106
[xxxvii] Manton J. *Elizabeth Garrett Anderson*. New York: EP Dutton & Co. 1965, p 245.
[xxxviii] Bartrip P. *Themselves Writ Large. The British Medical Association 1832-1966.* London: BMA Publishing,1996. p. 49.
[xxxix] Ibid.: p. 49; see also Report of Annual meeting of BMA. *BMJ* 1878; 17 August; pp. 253-6.
[xl] Anderson, op.cit. p 244. (She states erroneously that Hoggan resigned in 1876)
[xli] Minutes of Managing Committee of New Hospital for Women: 28 April 1877. London Metropolitan Archives. H13/EGA/019.

Chapter 4

[i] Sandwith F. *Surgeon Compassionate*. London: Peter Davies; 1960.
[ii] RFH Comm Man; 1828-39. p.1
[iii] RFH Comm Man; 1828: 14 Feb. (1st Meeting, Gray's Inn Coffee House).
[iv] RFH Comm Man; 1828: 28 Feb; 1830: 2 Dec, 7 Dec; 1831: 13 Jan, 12 Jul, 25 Nov.
[v] RFH Comm Man: 1828-9. pp. 3-5.
[vi] Ibid., p.10.
[vii] RFH AR 1832 (in Comm Man Minute Book)
[viii] RFH AR 1830
[ix] RFH AR 1833, 1834
[x] EGM of Governors, RFH Comm Man: 1832: 4 Oct
[xi] Governors' QGM Comm Man 1833; 3 Jan
[xii] Governors' Special General meeting 1833; 1 Aug
[xiii] RFH Comm Man 1834: 7 Oct; 1835: 5 May, 9 Jun, 21 Jul
[xiv] *Lancet,* 12 Mar 1836, pp. 944-945.;
[xv] Tweedie obituary, *Lancet* 1884; 14 Jun.
[xvi] Harte N, North J. *The World of UCL 1828-2004* (3rd Ed), London, UCL Press. 2004: p. 94; Crawford E. *The Women's Suffrage Movement. A Reference Guide.* London, Routledge, 2001, p.253
[xvii] Governors' Special General meeting 1 Aug 1833.
[xviii] RFH Comm Man 1828-39. General Meeting 1 Sep 1835
[xix] Ibid. General Meeting 3 Oct 1837
[xx] Ibid. QGM, 22 Aug 1839. Board of Gov.1840 5 Mar, p. 22; Building Fund Statement Oct 1839-Jan 1860, p. 40]
[xxi] RFH AR 1841.
[xxii] RFH Comm Man 1841, 2 Dec.
[xxiii] RFH Comm Man 1840; 10 Jan , Medical Staff Report
[xxiv] RFH Comm Man 1841: 13 Apr, p.45
[xxv] RFH AR 1842.
[xxvi] Governors Meeting 1841: 13 Jul.
[xxvii] RFH Comm Man 1842; 12 Jul.
[xxviii] Litchfield F. *Illustrated History of Furniture.* 6th ed. London: Truslove & Hanson; 1907, p.274
[xxix] RFH Comm Man Special Meeting 1842; 4 Aug.
[xxx] RFH Comm. AGM 1843; 28 Feb
[xxxi] RFH Comm Man Special meeting 1842; 13 Sep
[xxxii] RFH AR 1843.
[xxxiii] QGM 11 Feb 1845
[xxxiv] QGM 10 Feb 1846p274
[xxxv] Letter from Wakley Sr declining to join Committee – details in ManComm 5 Mar, pp.151,158: Ref RFH 1/2/1/2.
[xxxvi] RFH Comm Man 1846; 2 Apr.

[xxxvii] RFH Comm Man 1846 4 Jun; Letter from Lord Robert Grosvenor and Kingscote 13 May 1846.
[xxxviii] RFH Comm Man Special meeting 1846; 22 Jun.
[xxxix] RFH Comm Man 1846, 25 Aug.
[xl] *Medical Circular* 1854; 19 Jan. Supplement. p.4.
[xli] WB 1847; 4 Aug.
[xlii] WB 1847: 20 Jan; Merrington WR, *University College Hospital & its Medical School: a history*. London, Heinemann, 1976, pp. 31-3.
[xliii] Obits: Weatherhead, Munk's Roll III, p.213 & DNB; Wilson, Munk's Roll IV, p.221; Peacock, Munk's Roll IV, p.61,
[xliv] WB 1851: 22 Oct, 12 Nov
[xlv] Gray, E.A. *By candlelight: the life of Dr Arthur Hill Hassall*. London, Robert Hale; 1983. Hassall, A.H. *The Narrative of a busy life: an autobiography*. London, Longmans Green & Co., 1893.
[xlvi] *Medical Circular* 1853; 10 Aug, p.111.
[xlvii] Medical Circular 1953; 28 Dec, pp. 480-1.
[xlviii] Gay, obit. *Lancet* 26 September 1885
[xlix] *Medical Circular* 1854, 31 May, 14 Jun, 21 Jun.
[l] *Medical Circular* 1854, 5 Jul, 12 Jul, 19 Jul, 26 Jul, 2 Aug,
[li] WB 1853: 8 Jun, 22 Jun.
[lii] WB 1853: 6 Jul
[liii] RFH Comm Man 1853; 5 Sep.
[liv] RCSEng Council, Thursday, 10 Nov 1853
[lv] Rae I. *Knox: the Anatomist*. Edinburgh: Oliver and Boyd; (1964) pp.135-146.
[lvi] Ibid. p153-4
[lvii] Middlesex Hospital Medical School Committee; 1853; 21 Nov.
[lviii] Gant F.J. *Auto-biography of James Frederick Gant*. London:Bailliere, Tindall & Cox; 1905.
[lix] RCSEng Council 1853; 26 Nov.
[lx] Middlesex Hospital Medical School Committee, 1854: 20 Apr, 5 Oct.
[lxi] WB 1855; 26 Apr, 30 Aug.
[lxii] WB 1856: 2 Oct, 23 Oct
[lxiii] WB 1956: 11 Dec, 18 Dec
[lxiv] Defalque RJ & Wright AJ. The short tragic life of Robert M Glover. *Anaesthesia*, 2004; 59(4): pp. 394-400; Report of inquest, *BMJ*, 30 April 1959, pp 354-6.
[lxv] WB 1855: 13 Sep; WB 1856: 28 Aug
[lxvi] Newman, C. *The evolution of medical education in the nineteenth century*. London, OUP, 1957 p. 136; WB 1858: 10 Jun
[lxvii] RFH Comm Man Special meeting 1844: 10 Jun.
[lxviii] WB 1855; 12 Mar (Building Subcommittee), 19 Jun, 2 Aug; Comm Man 1856:10 Jul; RFH AR 1856
[lxix] WB 1856; 3 Jul, 21 Aug, 27 Nov.
[lxx] LMA, A/NFC/62 (n.d.)]
[lxxi] WB 1857; 19 Mar.
[lxxii] WB 1858; 18 Mar.
[lxxiii] WB 1858; 17 Jun
[lxxiv] Inwood S. *A History of London*. London: Papermac; 2000. p.486
[lxxv] RFH AR 1858
[lxxvi] WB 1862: 8 May, 15 May, 5 Jun, 19 Jun.
[lxxvii] WB 1863: 12 Mar, 26 Mar, 14 May, 18 Jun.
[lxxviii] A copy of Dickens's address is in the RFH Archives.
[lxxix] RFH Quarterly Committee 1863, 9 Jul.
[lxxx] WB 1863; 16 Jul.
[lxxxi] WB 1864, 27 Oct.
[lxxxii] WB 1865, 6 Apr, 13 Apr,

[lxxxiii] WB 1875, 15 Jul.
[lxxxiv] RFH AR 1865.
[lxxxv] RFH AR 1865, 1866.
[lxxxvi] *BMJ* 1868; 21 Mar p. 288, 25 Apr p. 414.
[lxxxvii] *BMJ* 1868; 23 May p521.
[lxxxviii] *The Times* 1868; 10 Jul p10c, 13 Jul p9d.
[lxxxix] WB 1868: 2 Jul; 1869; 28 Jan; 1872; 5 Dec.; 1873, 2 Jan. 9 Jan; RFH AR 1872
[xc] Hassall, op cit. Ref 43.
[xci] WB 1877: 1 Mar
[xcii] Inwood, op. cit. p. 487.
[xciii] WB 1868: 29 Oct, 5 Nov.
[xciv] RFH AR 1868.
[xcv] *Daily Telegraph* 1869; 1 Jan
[xcvi] RFH AR 1869.
[xcvii] RFH AR 1870.
[xcviii] WB 1870: 10 Mar, 7 Apr.
[xcix] UCH Medical Comm 1871; 26 July: RFH WB 1871, 3 Aug.
[c] WB 1871; 10 Aug.
[ci] RFH AR 1870.
[cii] LMA, HI/ST/NC15 13b, June 1875 (2nd ed.) National Association for Providing Trained Nurses for the Sick Poor. p.72.
[ciii] Woodham-Smith C. *Florence Nightingale 1820-1910*. London: Constable & Co; 1950
[civ] LMA, HI/ST/NC2/V3/72, 2 Feb 1872.
[cv] RFH AR 1871.
[cvi] RFH WB 1872; 30 May.
[cvii] LMA A/NFC/22, 2,3 and 4.*General Work and the Nurses Training: Nursing in London Hospitals*. by Florence Lees (with notes & additions by Henry Bonham Carter). [See Appendix 1]
[cviii] RFH AR 1871.
[cix] RFH AR 1876, 1877.
[cx] RFH AR 1876.

Chapter 5

[i] *The Times,* 26 Jun 1877.
[ii] CM 1879: 17 Feb.
[iii] CM 1878: 17 Feb; 1888, 15 Jun
[iv] Press Cuttings vol 3 pg 16 ?c 1882]
[v] CM 1878: 3 Jun.
[vi] *The Times* 13 May 1874.
[vii] *Daily Telegraph* 19 Jan 1876.
[viii] *Standard*, 16 January 1878; Jex-Blake S. *Medical Women – A Thesis and a History.* Edinburgh: Oliphant, Anderson & Ferrier; 1886. p. 216.
[ix] Ibid., (Jex-Blake), pp. 219-220
[x] RFHSM Letters Book, SM/1/7/4. p.68
[xi] Newman C. *The Evolution of Medical Education in the Nineteenth Century.* London: OUP ; 1957, p.231-233.
[xii] Ibid., p.233-235
[xiii] CM 1878: 18 Feb.
[xiv] CM 1879: 15 Mar; Letters Book, Cayley to Heaton 26 Jan 1880.
[xv] RFH AR 1879
[xvi] CM 1880: 19 Oct
[xvii] CM 1880: 14 Dec
[xviii] CM 1881: 15 Feb

xix CM 1881: 17 May; Letter Book. Blyth to Norton 3-6-1881; Blyth to Mrs Thorne 23-10-1881; Blyth to Norton 20-1-1882.

xx CM 1882: 28 Feb.

xxi Barrass, P. *Fifty Years in Midwifery: The Story of Annie McCall, MD*. London: Health for All Publishing; 1950.

xxii CM 1882: 28 Feb.

xxiii CM 1878: 18 Feb.

xxiv RFH WB 1877: 26 April

xxv Results of School Examinations 1874-1916. LMA H72/SM/C/01/04/001 …003

xxvi Chaplin, Matilda. DNB 1885-1900, Vol 02. (On Line) by Sidney Lee.

xxvii *BMJ* 1893, 9 Dec, p. 1296

xxviii *Lancet* 1894 26 May p 1350; *BMJ* 1894 26 May

xxix *The Times*, 1886; 16 May, p.8 col. A.

xxx Ledbetter R. *A History of the Malthusian League*. 1877-1927, Columbus, Ohio State Univ Press.1976

xxxi Manton J. *Elizabeth Garrett Anderson.* New York: EP Dutton & Co. 1965, p. 284.

xxxii CM 1878: 30 Sep, 10 Oct, 21 Oct.

xxxiii Crawford E. *Enterprising Women; the Garretts and their Circle*. London: Francis Boutle; 2002, p.97.

xxxiv Cohen, S.L. *'Walker, Jane Harriett'*. DNB, OUP 2004 (online edition)

xxxv McIntyre N. *Britain's first medical marriage: Frances Morgan, George Hoggan and the mysterious "Elsie". J.Med Biog*. 2004. **12**: 105-114.

xxxvi Scharlieb M. *Reminiscences.* London: Williams and Norgate; 1924, pp.55-62.

xxxvii Thorne I. *Sketch of the Foundation and Development of the London School of Medicine for Women*. London: G Sharrow; 1905, p. 23.

xxxviii CM 1881: 15 Feb.

xxxix P.R.O., T.1/14076. [Lord] R[ichard] Gros[venor]. Memorandum, 3 November 1882. Quoted by Meta Zimmeck , Ch 10 in *Government and expertise; Specialists, administrators and professionals, 1860-1919.* Ed. Roy MacLeod, Camb Univ Press. 1988, p.194.

xl Cooke AM. *A History of the Royal College of Physicians of London*. Vol 3. Oxford: Clarendon Press: 1972, p. 832-4.

xli Maudsley, H. Sex in Mind and Education. *Fortnightly Review,* April 1874.

xlii CM 1882: 20 Apr, 23 May,

xliii CM 1878: 18 Mar

xliv CM 1878: 9 Mar, 18 Mar; 16 Dec; Report LSMW Exec Council to Governing Body, 6 May 1878 (loosely inserted in CM 1878:15 Apr): RFH AR 1872, 1880.

xlv King Chambers, T. Obit. *BMJ* 1889, 31 Aug, pp 506-7

xlvi CM 1878: 9 Mar, 25 Mar, 10 Oct; CM 1882: 28 Feb; Michael Thorn, *Anne Gilchrist*, DNB online.

xlvii Garrett Anderson, Mrs. *The Student's Pocket Book*. London: H K Lewis: 1878. A copy is available for inspection in the British Library, shelf mark 7321.ee.1.

xlviii Minutes of Association of Registered Medical Women, Wellcome Institute

xlix Alan Callender, Special Collections Assistant, Robinson Library, Newcastle University.

l Obituary, Isabella Mears. *The Scotsman,* 13 November 1936, p11.

li CM 1883: 20 Feb

lii Webb H. *Some Early Recollections of the LSMW*. LSMW Magazine, July 1942. p58.

liii Sahli N. *Elizabeth Blackwell, MD: A Biography.* Ph.D. Thesis, Univ of Pennsylvania: 1974. P232.

liv LSMW prospectuses

lv Lancet 18 Sep 1880

lvi John Cockle *Plarr's Lives of FRCSs*. London: Simpkin Marshall; 1930. Vol I. p253-4.

lvii Baxter, Evan Buchanan. In DNB 1885-1900, Vol 02. (on line); RFH AR 1881,1883, 1885.

lviii Gant FJ. *Auto-biography of James Frederick Gant.* London: Bailliere, Tindall & Cox; 1905.

[lix] *Plarr's Lives*, op. cit., Vol II . pp. 242-4
[lx] CM 1882: 20 Apr, 4 Jul, 27 Jul, 31 Oct, 21 Dec
[lxi] RFH AR 1880
[lxii] RFH AR 1879, 1880.
[lxiii] Roberts S. *Sophia Jex-Blake: a woman pioneer in nineteenth-century medical reform*. London: Routledge; 1993. p 166**:** Todd M. *Life of Sophia Jex-Blake*. London: Macmillan & Co; 1918. p 463
[lxiv] Roberts op. cit. pp.168-9.
[lxv] Ibid., p.171.
[lxvi] CM 1883: 13 Mar, 19 Apr.
[lxvii] Roberts op. cit. p.171.

Chapter 6

[i] Harte N. *The University of London 1836-1986*. London: Athlone Press; 1986. p.142
[ii] Ibid. p143-145
[iii] Ibid. p146-7
[iv] Ibid. p150
[v] AR 1892
[vi] Harte, op.cit. p150-154
[vii] Ibid. p154-5
[viii] Ibid. p154-8
[ix] Personal communication. Robert Mills, Librarian, Royal College of Physicians of Ireland.
[x] Widdess JDH, *The Royal College of Surgeons of Ireland and its Medical School 1784-1984.* 3rd ed. Dublin: Royal College of Surgeons in Ireland: 1984. p 97
[xi] Personal communication. Robert Mills, Librarian, Royal College of Physicians of Ireland.
[xii] Ibid.
[xiii] Lyons, JB (1992) 'History of Early Irish Women Doctors', *Irish Medical Times*; Special supp, January 1992, p38-40; Kelly, L (2010); *Medical History*, **54**, 495-516; Logan, MST (1990) The centenary of admission of women to the Belfast medical school. *Ulster Med J*, **59**, pp. 200-3.
[xiv] Craig WS, *History of the Royal College of Physicians of Edinburgh*, Oxford: Blackwell, 1976 p 308
[xv] Comrie, JD *History of Scottish Medicine,* London: Bailliere, Tindall & Cox .Vol 2 . 1932, p 788
[xvi] Roberts S. *Sophia Jex-Blake: a woman pioneer in nineteenth-century medical reform*. London: Routledge; 1993, p.173.
[xvii] Ibid. p.173-4
[xviii] Ibid. p.175.
[xix] CM 1890: 5 Nov, 3 Dec.
[xx] Roberts, op.cit. p176-8
[xxi] Ibid. p. 179.
[xxii] Ibid. pp. 179-180.
[xxiii] Ibid. p. 176; Endeavour 1964: 23; p54 (Editorial)
[xxiv] Michael S Moss, *'Marian Gilchrist'* (1964-1952), DNB 1010447538
[xxv] CM 1893: 27 Sep; 1894: 2 May; CM 1895: 6 Feb, 6 Mar, 1 May, 5 Jun, 4 Dec; CM 1896: 8; Jan
[xxvi] Parker, G. *Schola Medicinæ Bristol; Its History, Lecturers and Alumni, 1833-1933*. Bristol John Wright & Sons. 1935
[xxvii] Davison, Grace C. (1984) in *Newcastle School of Medicine 1834-1984,Sesquicentennial Scrapbook*; eds Dale G, Miller FJW, p 54; Personal communication, Alan Callender, Special Collections Assistant, Robinson Library, Newcastle University.
[xxviii] Mabel Tylecote. *The education of women at Manchester University, 1833-1933*. Univ Manchester Press, 1941. p.50.
[xxix] AR 1883.

[xxx] Crawford, E (2002) *Enterprising Women*. Francis Boutle Publications, London: pp. 59-61
[xxxi] Bartrip P. *Themselves Writ Large. The British Medical Association 1832-1966.* London: BMA Publishing;1996, p 53
[xxxii] Medical Press, 5 July 1893.
[xxxiii] *Nursing Record & Hospital World* 14 Dec 1901; *Daily Sketch*, 31 Dec 1901; 14 Jan 1902: *Daily Telegraph* 31 Dec 1901
[xxxiv] *Liverpool Mercury*, Oct 1901
[xxxv] Lincoln Echo 17 Oct 1901
[xxxvi] CM 1895: 6 Feb. CM 1896: 5 Feb
[xxxvii] Mag: 1898 May, p 414.
[xxxviii] *Grannie Thorne's Diary,1834-1910.* – Copy in RFH Archives at LMA (or try RFH Library)
[xxxix] CM 1886: 10 Mar.
[xl] *The Chronicle* 1884: 16 October
[xli] Mag: 1897: May, Oct; 1899, Jan
[xlii] Thorne I. *Sketch of the Foundation and Development of the London School of Medicine for Women.* London: G Sharrow, 1905, p 27.
[xliii] Anderson, Louisa G. (1939), *Elizabeth Garrett Anderson 1836-1917*, London: Faber & Faber, p. 230-1
[xliv] CM 1888: 29 May, 15 Jun,
[xlv] RFH AR 1888
[xlvi] RFH AR 1892, 1893.
[xlvii] RFH AR 1894, 1895.
[xlviii] CM 1887: 25 Apr; 24 May, 6 Jul; 1890: 4 Jun, 2 Jul; 1891: 7 Jan.
[xlix] CM 1893: 25 Jan, 1 Feb, 20 Feb, 1 Mar
[l] CM 1893: 29 Mar, 3 May
[li] CM 1893: 3 May, 7 Jun
[lii] Scharlieb, M. *Reminiscences*. London: Williams & Norgate, (1924) p. 90
[liii] Ibid. p 95.
[liv] AR 1891
[lv] Ganneri, NR (2007), 'Rakhmabai' in *Dictionary of Medical Biography*, eds. Bynum WF & Bynum H, Vol 4, M-R, p.1045
[lvi] CM 1889: 19 Sep
[lvii] CM 1889: 12 Jun, 9 Jul, 19 Sep
[lviii] CM 1890: 25 Feb
[lix] AR 1890; CM 1891: 1 Jul
[lx] Crawford, E op.cit. pp. 221, 224
[lxi] AR 1890
[lxii] CM 1890: 8 Oct, 5 Nov, 3 Dec; CM 1894: 7 Nov; AR 1899
[lxiii] Anderson, LG, op.cit. p237
[lxiv] Elizabeth Garrett Anderson Letters & Papers, Suffolk Record Office, HA436/1.
[lxv] CM 1890: 25 Feb, 19 Mar; 1991: 4 Mar
[lxvi] CM 1891: 9 Dec: 1892: 6 Jan, 10 Feb, 30 Mar, 28 Sep; AR 1892
[lxvii] CM 1895: 6 Feb
[lxviii] CM 1892 4 May; AR 1892, 1893
[lxix] CM 1896: 30 Sep; 1897: 13 Jan
[lxx] CM 1897: 2 June
[lxxi] CM 1897: 5 May
[lxxii] CM 1897: 28 Jul; CM 1898: 16 Mar
[lxxiii] AR 1898
[lxxiv] CM 1898: 28 Oct (Special meeting)
[lxxv] CM 1896: 2 Dec
[lxxvi] AR 1898
[lxxvii] AR 1898, 1899; Mag 1899. May. Oct; Mag May 1889, pp 536, 564-6

[lxxviii] CM 1898: 6 Jul, 20 Jul
[lxxix] AR 1899
[lxxx] CM 1899: 7 Jun.
[lxxxi] PC Vol 3 pg 80b; CM 1900: 31 Oct; 1901: 27 Mar
[lxxxii] Mag: 1900 Jan
[lxxxiii] Copping, A.M. (1974) *The Story of College Hall 1882-1972*. London: Newman Books. p 29-30.
[lxxxiv] CM 1895: 30 Oct, 4 Dec
[lxxxv] Mag: 1897, Jan; 1902 Oct; 1903 Oct.
[lxxxvi] CM 1894: 6 Jun; 1900: 19 Dec; 1901: 6 Feb,
[lxxxvii] Mag: 1895 Oct; 1896 Oct; 1898 May;1899 Jan.
[lxxxviii] Mag:1898 Jan, May, Oct; 1902 Jan
[lxxxix] Mag :1895 Oct, p 77
[xc] Mag: 1897 Jan
[xci] Mag: 1901 May; Oct; 1902 May.
[xcii] Mag: 1902 Oct
[xciii] Mag: 1903 Jan.
[xciv] CM 1895: 1 May
[xcv] CM 1888: 28 Feb, 20 Mar
[xcvi] Sykes, A.H. (1987) 'A D Waller and the electrocardiogram', 1887. *BMJ*, 30 May p.1396.
[xcvii] CM 1884: 19 Feb, 24 Apr, 27 May, 31 Jul
[xcviii] Thorne, I. op.cit. ref 42, pp. 30-31
[xcix] *St Mary's Hospital Gazette* 1897, iii, 1; *Plarr's Lives* 1930, vol 2, p106.
[c] Minutes Managing Committee New Hospital for Women 1888: 1 Feb, 6 Jun. (LMA).
[ci] Ibid.: 22 Feb 1888; 11 April 1888.
[cii] CM 1900: 9 May
[ciii] CM 1884: 30 Sep; CM1885: 3 Mar
[civ] Stoney obituary, Brit J Radiology, November 1932, Vol 5, pp 853-7
[cv] Munk's Roll Vol IV p.147
[cvi] Munk's Roll Vol IV p.463
[cvii] Cullen, L. (2013) 'The first lady almoner; the appointment, position, and findings of Miss Mary Stewart at the Royal Free Hospital, 1895-99'. *J Hist Med Allied Sci.* 68, pp.551-582
[cviii] Mag: 1904 Jan, p.295.
[cix] Mag: 1902 Jan

Chapter 7

[i] Scharlieb M. *Reminiscences*. London: Williams and Norgate; 1924, p.139.
[ii] 1881 Census.
[iii] Scharlieb, op.cit. p.140.
[iv] *Medical Directory* 1886
[v] Constance Colley Mag May 1907
[vi] Cooke AM. *A History of the Royal College of Physicians of London.* Volume 3. Oxford: Clarendon Press: 1972, p 902.
[vii] Scharlieb op. cit. p140
[viii] CM 1903 4 Feb; CM 1906 7 Feb.
[ix] 1901 Census
[x] AR 1887
[xi] Harte N. *The University of London 1836-1986.* London: Athlone Press; 1986. p 178.
[xii] Ibid. p179.
[xiii] Ensor RCK., *England 1870-1914*,. Oxford:University Press; 1936, p 538
[xiv] Haldane RBS. *Royal Commission on University Education in London. Final Report* – Part III – Faculty of Medicine. p.100-102
[xv] Newman C. *The Evolution of Medical Education in the Nineteenth Century.* London: Oxford University Press; 1957, p.273.

[xvi] Ibid. p 140
[xvii] Cooke op.cit. p 963.
[xviii] Letter filed with her admission form at Royal Free Archives.
[xix] Haldane. Minutes of Evidence. 23 Nov 1911. p.124.
[xx] Haldane Report. Minutes of Evidence, 30 June 1911.
[xxi] Haldane Report. Minutes of Evidence, 10 November 1910. Flexner A. *Medical Education: a comparative study*. New York:Macmillan;1925.
[xxii] Haldane Report. Minutes of Evidence, 21 July 1911.
[xxiii] *The Hospital*, 23 Aug 1913; *Medical Press and Circular*, 7 Oct 1914.
[xxiv] Cooke op.cit. p.972
[xxv] Ibid. pp. 973-4
[xxvi] Ibid. pp. 974-5
[xxvii] Ibid. p. 975
[xxviii] Ibid pp 975-6
[xxix] Ibid. 876; AR 1911
[xxx] CM 1904, 19 Oct
[xxxi] CM 1906 17 Nov
[xxxii] CM 1909 15 Dec
[xxxiii] CM 1912 13 Mar
[xxxiv] AR 1912
[xxxv] UnivLondon Library: Report of principal on work of university, VP 1/1/1
[xxxvi] CM 1906 17 Nov.
[xxxvii] *Henry Cullimore: In Memoriam, 1878-1907.* Printed for private circulation by London and Country Printing Works, London W.C. 1907. Copy in Royal Free Archives/LMA
[xxxviii] CM 1908 4 March
[xxxix] Heaman, E.A. *St Mary's: the history of a London Teaching Hospital.* Liverpool University Press. 2003, p 148; CM 1909: 29 Sep
[xl] CM 1910: 23 Mar, 28 Sep, 12 Oct, 26 Oct,
[xli] CM 1911: 28 Jun, 27 Sep, 20 Dec; CM 1912: 31 Jan, 26 Jun.
[xlii] Mag: May 1903, RFH ARs 1903-8,
[xliii] RFH AR 1870, Mag Oct 1907, Jan 1908.
[xliv] Mag: Jan 1908, May 1908
[xlv] RFH AR for 1906.
[xlvi] RFH AR for 1912.
[xlvii] CM 1912: 25 Sep; 1913, 19 Mar.
[xlviii] CM 1909: 15 Dec.
[xlix] CM 1912, 13 Nov; 1913, 29 Jan. AR for 1913.
[l] Lutzker E. *Edith Pechey-Phipson, MD:* New York: Exposition Press; 1973, p 241-3.
[li] *Sydney Morning Herald*, 24 Aug 1900.
[lii] CM 1904: 9 Mar.
[liii] CM 1912:27 Mar; 1913, 9 Mar, 25 Jun, 24 Sep; 1916, 22 Mar.
[liv] Mag: 1905 May
[lv] CM 1913: 29 Jan. AR 1913, 1914, 1915.
[lvi] CM 1905, 27 Sep; 1906, 24 Sep, 17 Nov, 17 Dec; 1907: 6 Nov;
[lvii] CM 1903, 30 Sep.
[lviii] Winkelstein, W, 'Three firsts by Janet Lane-Claypon'. *Am J Epidemiol.* 2004: 160; 97-101
[lix] LSMW Prospectuses 1903-14; Mag, June 1914.
[lx] Mag: 1911 Mar; 1914 Jun; RFH AR 1910; See *Munk's Roll* for individual physicians.
[lxi] LSMW Prospectuses
[lxii] AR 1904 to 1907
[lxiii] Mag: 1903 Oct, 1904 Oct.
[lxiv] Mag: 1909 May
[lxv] Minutes General Meeting of Students 1905, 1 Nov; 1906 8 Nov

lxvi 'Munk's Roll'. Arthur George Phear. Vol 5, p331-2
lxvii Mag:.1912 Mar
lxviii Franklin AW. A Bart's Woman, 1865. *St Bartholomew's Hospital Journal*, Nov1931, p 31-2
lxix McIntyre N. 'Was Osler opposed to women becoming doctors'. *J Med Biog.* 2007;15; Supp 1, p 22-27.
lxx E.M.Guest, Mag:1908 Jan, p.828-831
lxxi Mag: 1908 May
lxxii *Saturday Review*, 24 Oct 1903
lxxiii *The Times* 11 Oct 1903.
lxxiv *Lives of the Fellows of the Royal College of Surgeons* 1930-1951. Lond: RCS Surgeons;1953, p 367-70.
lxxv Correspondence filed with Lyndall Rice's admission form at RFH Archives (now at LMA)
lxxvi Royal Commission on Vivisection: Final Report. *BMJ.* 1912. 16 Mar, p 623-5.
lxxvii CM 1913: 19 Mar, 24 Sep, 17 Dec; 1914: 21 Jan.
lxxviii LindafHageby L & and Leisa Katarina Schartau LLK *The Shambles of Science – Extracts From the Diary of Two Students of Physiology.* London: Animal Defence & Antivivisection Society; 1903.
lxxix Elston MA. *'Aping the Monstrous Males: Women doctors and vivisection 1870 – 1900'* – unpublished paper, 1985.
lxxx Mag: 1911 Mar
lxxxi CM 1912: 25 Sep; CM 1913: 19 Nov; CM 1914: 18 Mar.
lxxxii CM 1914: 25 Jun (adjourned meeting)
lxxxiii CM 1914: 24 Jun
lxxxiv CM 1924: 5 Nov
lxxxv Augusta U. Landman. Obituary BMJ 26 Jan 1966
lxxxvi Lydia Henry Documents, University of Sheffield web site.
lxxxvii Crawford, E (2002) *Enterprising Women.* Francis Boutle Publications, London, p320, ref 141.
lxxxviii P.R.O., T.1/10818/9533/08. E.W.H. M[illar]. Memorandum, 12 June 1908. Quoted by Meta Zimmeck (1988), Ch 10 *in Government and expertise; Specialists, administrators and professionals, 1860-1919.* Ed. Roy MacLeod. Camb Univ Press.
lxxxix Zimmick M, Op. Cit, p196, ref 85
xc Brit. J Nursing 5 Mar 1904
xci Mag: 1910 May
xcii Bird, Mostyn, M (1911), *Woman at Work*; Chapman & Hall, London; Brooks, LM (letter in) Pall Mall Gazette, 20 Jan, 1912

Chapter 8

i Riddell GA (Lord). *Dame Louisa Aldrich-Blake.* London: Hodder & Stoughton: 1926. p 12.
ii Ibid: pp 15-16
iii Copping AM. *The Story of College Hall 1882-1972.* London: Newman Books: 1974. p 30.
iv www.oxforddnb.com/index/101030367/Louisa-Aldrich-Blake
v Riddell (op. cit. ref 1): p. 47-8
vi CM 1914: 18 Mar.
vii CM 1914: 20 May.
viii CM 1914: 24 Jun.
ix CM 1915: 9 Feb; WB 1915: 17 Feb.
x RFH AR 1915.
xi RFH AR 1916, 1918, 1919.
xii WB 1914: 5 Aug, 16 Sep, 4 Nov; WB 1915 20 Jan
xiii WB 1915: 29 Jan, 12 May. *Sister Wynn Remembers*, Mag: 1939 Jul.
xiv WB 1915: 30 Jun; CM 1915: 23 Jun, 28 Jun.
xv WB 1917: 19 Dec; WB 1918: 2 Jan, 20 Mar
xvi WB 1918: 19 Jun, 31 Jul; CM 1919:18 Dec.

[xvii] AR 1915, 1916, 1917 & 1918.
[xviii] Letter with Helen Ingleby's application form in Students' Files, LMA (RFH Archives). Admission No. 1016, Winter 1911-2.
[xix] WB 1915: 19 May; CM 1915: 23 Jun.
[xx] ibid.
[xxi] BMJ, 1 July 1916, p30.
[xxii] CM 1916: 5 Jan, 26 Jan, 30 Jun.
[xxiii] CM 1916: 23 Feb. Garner J.S. The Great Experiment: the admission of women students to St Mary's Hospital Medical School, 1916-1925. *Medical History*. 1998, 42: 68-88.
[xxiv] Minutes attached to CM 1916: 10 Mar.
[xxv] CM 1916: 5 April.
[xxvi] Garner, op.cit.
[xxvii] CM 1917: 12 Dec; CM 1918: 27 Mar.
[xxviii] *Ida and the Eye: a woman in British ophthalmology. From the autobiography of Ida Mann.* Ed Buckley EI & Potter DU. Tunbridge Wells: Parapress; 1996. p.78.
[xxix] Wilberforce O. *Octavia Wilberforce: the autobiography of a pioneer woman doctor*. Ed Jalland P. London: Cassell; 1989.
[xxx] CM 1914: 18 Mar, 20 May, 1 Jul, 30 Sep.
[xxxi] For details of the meetings see the RFHSM Press Cuttings, Vol 5. RFH Archives.
[xxxii] Mag: 1916 Mar
[xxxiii] CM 1916: 30 Jun
[xxxiv] *Morning Post* 10 June 1916
[xxxv] CM 1914: 15 July; 1915: 14 Apr; 1916 26 Jan, 7 Jun.
[xxxvi] Mag: 1916 Nov
[xxxvii] CM 1917: 14 Nov; 1925: 18 Nov.
[xxxviii] CM 1916: 27 Sep; 1917: 14 Nov
[xxxix] CM 1917: 28 Mar, 27 Jun, 27 Jul, 14 Nov, 12 Dec.
[xl] CM 1916: 22 Mar, 7 Jun; Sir Francis Dyke Acland. DNB doi:10.10/93/ref.odnb/30404.
[xli] Mag: 1918 Mar
[xlii] Heaman EA, *St Mary's: the history of a London Teaching Hospital. Montrea*l: McGill, Queen's University Press; 2003. p152.
[xliii] Brodie, Obit *BMJ* 1916, 2 September
[xliv] Mag: 1937 Mar.
[xlv] CM 1915: 24 Mar, 3 May; CM 1920: 12 May.
[xlvi] Crofton E. *The Women of Royaumont: A Scottish women's hospital on the Western Front*. East Linton, East Lothian:Tuckwell Press;1997. p.137.
[xlvii] Newnham College Register Vol 1 1871-1971; Mag: Mar 1919
[xlviii] Mag: 1932 Nov (Obituary).
[xlix] Mag: 1914 Nov, 1915 Mar; *Munk's Roll of FRCPs*; *Lives of Fellows of the RCS,* 1965-73.
[l] WB 1917: 25 Apr, 23 May, 15 Aug, 12 Sep, 26 Sep
[li] Mag: 1914 Nov, 1915 Mar
[lii] Murray F. *Women as Army Surgeons*. London: Hodder & Stoughton; 1920, p.135.
[liii] Murray, op.cit.
[liv] Murray, op.cit.
[lv] Murray, op cit. p.135
[lvi] Murray, op.cit.
[lvii] Murray, op.cit. p.69
[lviii] Crofton, op.cit.
[lix] Mag 1919: Mar
[lx] Moberly Bell, E. *Storming the Citadel*, pp 152-9; Leah Leneman, 'Inglis, Elsie Maud (1864–1917)', DNB, OUP (www.oxforddnb.com/article/34101)
[lxi] Mag : 1915 Jul, p. 63,68; 1916 Jul, p. 77
[lxii] Berry J, Dickinson Berry FM, Lyon Blease W. *The Story of a Red Cross Unit in Serbia.* London: J & A Churchill, 1916.

lxiii Moberly Bell, op cit. pp.166-7.

lxiv Elston, MA, 'Fairfield, (Josephine) Letitia Denny (1885–1978)', *DNB, OUP,* 2004 (www.oxforddnb.com/article/54196: Bowden, REM 'Hare, Dorothy Christian (1876–1967)', DNB OUP, 2004 (www.oxforddnb.com/article/60911)

lxv Mag: 1917 Jul, Nov

lxvi *Daily Telegraph* 1922: 29 April; Research Defence Society Pamphlet 1930.

lxvii CM 1914: 18 Mar; Mag 1914: Mar, Jun, Nov

lxviii Mag: 1914: Jun, Nov; 1915 Nov.

lxix CM 1914: 11 Nov: Mag: 1915: Jul, Nov.

lxx Mag: 1915 Nov.

lxxi CM 1916: 16 Mar, 30 Jun; CM 1917: 12 Dec

lxxii Mag: 1917 Mar; Mag: 1920 Jul; Mag:1925 Nov.

lxxiii Mag: 1917 Nov

lxxiv CM 1917: 12 Dec.

lxxv CM 1918: 30 Jan, 27 Mar, 18 Dec.

lxxvi CM 1916: 27 Sep; Mag: 1916 Mar; Nov 1917

lxxvii Mag: 1917 Nov; 1919 Dec

lxxviii Mag: 1918 Jul.

lxxix Mag: 1916 Mar; 1917 Jul, Nov.

lxxx Mag: 1918 Mar, Jul

lxxxi Mag: 1914 Jun ; 1915 Mar ; 1918.

lxxxii Mag: 1915 Mar, Jul; 1917 Jun.

lxxxiii Mag: 1916 May; 1917 Jul; 1918 Jul

Chapter 9

i Mag: 1924 Nov

ii *BMJ* 1919: 26 July, p108; Campbell obit *BMJ* 1954: 9 Oct p874; Lambert obit, *BMJ* 1957: 21 Dec; Turnbull obit: *BMJ* 1958: 25 Oct p1046; Eaton obit, *BMJ* 1920: 29 Aug p298.

iii Rowbotham. S. '*A Century of Women*', London, Penguin Books; 1999: p 89

iv Zimmeck, M (1988), Ch 10 in '*Government & expertise; Specialists, administrators & professionals, 1860-1919.* Ed. Roy MacLeod. Camb Univ Press.

v *The Times*, 1921, Oct

vi AR 1919; Taylor, A.J.P. *English History 1914-1945*, Oxford Univ Press; 1965: pp 41, 122.

vii AR 1920, 1921, 1922

viii AR 1922-3, 1923-4

ix ARs from 1922-3 to 1925-6

x CM 1919: 25 Jun

xi CM 1919: 14 May, 23 Jul

xii AR 1919-20, 1920-21

xiii CM 1918: 25 Sep, 9 Oct, 13 Nov

xiv CM 1921: 27 Jul, 5 Oct; CM 1922, 23 Jan, 26 Jun, 4 Oct; CM 1925: 28 Jan

xv CM 1918: 13 Nov

xvi CM 1919: 15 Oct, 19 Nov; CM 1920: 12 May, 21 Jul

xvii Garner JS. The Great Experiment: the admission of women students to St Mary's Hospital Medical School, 1916-1925. *Medical History,* 1998; **42**: 68-88.

xviii Thorne, I. *Sketch of the foundation and development of the London School of Medicine for Women.* G Sharrow, London. 1905; pp. 29-30.

xix Garner, op.cit.

xx Heaman, EA. *St Mary's: The history of a London teaching hospital*. Liverpool University Press. 2003; p. 248

xxi CM 1924: 25 Jun

xxii Merrington, WR. *UniversityCollege Hospital and its Medical School; a history*. London, Heinemann, 1976; pp. 237-9. CMEWU Report 1929: 23 Jan.

xxiii Mag 1921: Mar; CM 1921: 12 May
xxiv Newman, (Sir) G. *'Some Notes on Medical Education'*, HMSO London; 1918.
xxv CM 1919: 5 Mar, 15 Oct; CM 1920: 24 Mar,
xxvi Balsan, C., *The Glitter and the Gold.* Heinemann, London; 1953.
xxvii CM 1920: 24 Mar, 12 May, 8 Jul, 29 Sep,
xxviii CM 1921: 2 Feb, 23 Mar, 12 May.
xxix McIlroy, A. Louise, *From a balcony on the Bosphorus*. London, C. Scribners Sons; 1924.
xxx Mag: 1921 Jul
xxxi RFH AR for 1914, pp.17-18
xxxii Mag: 1915 Mar, p 38
xxxiii Mag: 1926 Mar; Mag: 1936 Mar.
xxxiv CM 1922: 23 Jan
xxxv WB 1925 6 Oct, 13 Oct,
xxxvi WB 1925: 16 Oct, 27 Oct.
xxxvii MedComm 1925: 26 Oct; WB 1925: 27 Oct, 17 Nov
xxxviii CM 1925: 28 Oct, 16 Dec; WB 1925: 1 Dec
xxxix CM 1919: 26 Mar; CM 1921: 26 Jan, 23 Mar
xl Mag: 1952 Dec
xli CM 1918: 18 Dec; Mag: 1919 Mar, Dec; CM 1920: 12 May; CM 1924: 17 Dec.
xlii CM 1919: 17 Dec: CM 1920: 12 May; CM 1922: 29 Mar.
xliii CM 1922: 10 May, 26 Jun; CM 1924: 1 Dec
xliv CM 1925: 14 May
xlv CM 1921: 12 May; CM 1922: 23 Jan
xlvi CM 1922: 10 May, 19 Jul; Saunders obituary, *BMJ* 1923, 10 Nov
xlvii See Footnote 14. Ch 13
xlviii Mag: 1919 Mar; Mag: 1920 Jul; Mag: 1922 Mar.
xlix PC Volume 5, p.145; CM 1925: 25 Mar
l Mag: 1918: Mar; Mag: 1919: Mar; Mag: 1920 Mar; Mag: 1923 Jul; Mag: 1925 Mar.
li Mag: 1919 Mar; Mag: 1921 Jul; Mag: 1922 Mar
lii Mag: 1919 Dec; 1920 Jul; 1921Mar
liii Mag: 1920 Jul; Mag: 1921 Jul
liv Mag: 1919 Mar; Mag: 1920 Mar, Nov; Mag: 1922 Jul.
lv Mag: 1919 Dec; 'Doris Odlum' in '*Women Physicians of the World.* vol 1; Hellstedt, L.M. ed, Taylor & Francis, 1978, pp. 49-54; Odlum, Obit. *BMJ* 1985, 291, p.1356.
lvi Mag: 1920 Nov; Mag: 1921 Mar, Jul; Mag: 1923 Jul; Mag: 1924 Nov
lvii Mag :1921 Jul; Mag: 1922 Jul.
lviii Mag:1924 Nov, pp. 121-8
lix CM 1923: 31 Oct, 12 Dec
lx CM 1924: 25 Jun, 23 Jul.
lxi *'The Women Doctors Jubilee – by a past student*, Mag: 1924 Nov, p.121; AR 1924-5
lxii *Daily Telegraph* 1924: 23 Oct
lxiii *The Times*, 1926, 8 Mar.
lxiv Riddell, Lord. *Dame Louisa Aldrich-Blake.* London, Hodder & Stoughton, 1926.

Chapter 10

i 1881 Census
ii Register of Marriages. Jan/Feb/Mar 1896, Barton Regis 6a 250.
iii UK Census 1901
iv Lady Barrett Obituaries – *BMJ* 1945;18 August; Mag: 1945 Jul-Sep, pp. 49-51.
v Public Record Office. J77/966/9345: Divorce Court File: 9345.
vi Sir William Barrett, Obit – LSMW Magazine July 1925, pp 97-102; Florence Elizabeth Perry, Lady Barrett, *Personality Survives Death; Messages from Sir William Barrett, edited by his wife.* London, Longmans Green & Co; 1937.

[vii] Florence E Barrett, *Conception Control and its effects on the individual and the nation.* London, John Murray, 1922.
[viii] CM 1926: 12 May.
[ix] CM 1925: 24 Jun, 22 Jul, 7 Oct.
[x] CM 1925: 7 Oct, 18 Nov.
[xi] CM 1926: 24 Mar, 14 Jul; CM 1930: 17 Dec; A. Anderson to Miss Brooks 19 Dec 1930.
[xii] CM 1926: 17 Nov.
[xiii] CM 1931: 18 Feb. AR 1927-34. Aitken, Obit, BMJ 1982, 284, p. 1481.
[xiv] CM 1928: 20 Jun; CM 1929: 13 Feb, 19 Jun.
[xv] Mary D Waller, *Practical physics for medical students.* London, H K Lewis; 1927.
[xvi] CM 1925: 7 Oct, 18 Nov; CM 1926: 24 Mar, 30 Jun.
[xvii] CM 1926: 14 Jul.
[xviii] CM 1930: 12 Mar; CM 1931: 18 Feb
[xix] CM 1928: 24 Oct
[xx] Iris Fox, Obit., Mag: 1926 Mar
[xxi] CM 1926: 12 May; CM 1929: 23 Jan; 13 Feb; CM 1930: 23 May, 20 Nov
[xxii] 'Marie Curie Hospital' *BMJ* 1968, 16 Nov; pp. 444-6.
[xxiii] CM 1927, 23 Feb 16 Nov
[xxiv] Mag: 1928 Nov.
[xxv] CM 1930: 19 Mar
[xxvi] CM 1927: 21 Dec; CM 1928: 18 Jan, 3 Oct
[xxvii] CM 1927: 23 Feb
[xxviii] CM 1926: 24 Mar, 30 Jun; CM 1927: 26 Jan, 23 Feb
[xxix] CM 1926: 30 Jun, 14 Jul, 17 Nov, 15 Dec; CM 1927: 11 May, 15 June. Mag 1927 July
[xxx] CM 1926: 15 Dec; Mag Jul 1926
[xxxi] Harte, Negley. *'The University of London 1836-1986'*. London, Athlone Press. 1986; pp. 211-213.
[xxxii] AR 1930-1
[xxxiii] Mag Nov 1926; AR 1927-8
[xxxiv] CM 1928: 21 Mar
[xxxv] SM – 2632, 21 Mar 1928
[xxxvi] CMEWU, Senate House Library – 1929: 23 Jan, 4 May. CMEWU Report SM Nos. 1841-1853
[xxxvii] WB 1926: 23 Nov, 7 Dec: RFH AR 1926, 1927. CM 1926: 15 Dec.
[xxxviii] WB 1927: 11 Jan, 29 Mar; WB 1928: 10 Jan. CM 1927: 18 May
[xxxix] CM 1927: 2 Dec.
[xl] CM 1928: 18 Jan, 18 Jul; CM 1930: 12 Mar (Memo attached)
[xli] WB 1928: 1 June (Special meeting)
[xlii] Mag: 1929 Jul; 1930 Nov
[xliii] RFH AR: 1929, 1930, 1931.
[xliv] Mag: 1930: July, Nov
[xlv] RFH AR: 1929, 1930; Mag 1930 Nov, 1931 Mar, 1932 Jul.
[xlvi] Mag: 1926 Jul , 1927 Nov, 1928 Jul; CM 1928: 21 Mar,
[xlvii] Mag: 1927 Nov.
[xlviii] Winifred Secretan Patch, Obit Mag: 1924 Nov.
[xlix] CM 1927: 16 Nov; CM 1928: 21 Mar
[l] Mag:1929 Jul
[li] CM 1931: 17 Jun; CM 1933: 15 Mar
[lii] CM 1926: 24 Mar, 6 Oct; CM 1927: 23 Feb,
[liii] Mag: 1926: Nov; 1927 Mar, Nov.
[liv] Mag: 1927 Nov; 1929 Jul; 1930 Jul
[lv] Mag: 1928: Mar, Jul; Mag 1931, Mar, Nov
[lvi] Mag: 1927, Nov; 1931, Jul
[lvii] CM 1929: 19 Jun, 17 Jul, 29 Oct, 18 Dec; CM 1930: 26 Feb, 23 May.

[lviii] Mag: 1927: Jul: Mag 1929 Jul, Nov.
[lix] Mag :1926-31.
[lx] Mag: 1926-1931.
[lxi] Mag: 1930 Nov; 1931 Mar.
[lxii] Mag: 1929 Mar
[lxiii] Mag: 1926 Nov
[lxiv] Mag Nov 1931
[lxv] Mag: 1926 Jul; 1927 Nov; 1930 Jul, Nov.
[lxvi] Mag: 1926 Jul; 1928 Jul; 1929 Mar, Dec; 1930 Mar; 1931 Jul.
[lxvii] Mag: 1929 Jul, Nov; 1930 Mar, Nov.
[lxviii] Mag: 1929 Jul.
[lxix] Mag: 1930 Nov.
[lxx] Mag: 1929: Mar; *BMJ* 1928, 15 Dec.
[lxxi] Mag: 1929: Jul, Nov 29; Mag: 1930: Mar.
[lxxii] Mag: 1930: Jul, Nov.
[lxxiii] www.medicalwomensfederation.org.uk/new/about/History.html
[lxxiv] King's College Ladies' Department executive committee minutes, 5 October 1922.
[lxxv] CM 1930: 20 Nov, 17 Dec; CM 1931: 18 Mar
[lxxvi] Taylor, AJP, *'English History 1914-1945*', Oxford, Clarendon Press, 1965; p. 284 et seq.

Chapter 11

[i] Mag: 1945 Jul-Sep, p 41; *BMJ* Obituary 10 Jun 1961, Mag: 1961 Sep
[ii] CM 1930: 29 Oct, 20 Nov, 17 Dec; AR 1930-1, 1931-2.
[iii] CM 1932: 26 Oct; CM 1933: 13 Dec.
[iv] CM 1934: 11 Jul. CM 1935: 10 Jul; CM 1936: 18 Nov.
[v] CM 1933: 15 Nov; CM 1937: 6 Oct, 20
[vi] CM 1936: 16 Dec; CM 1937: 17 Feb, 17 Mar, 19 May
[vii] CM 1937: 17 Mar
[viii] CM 1944: 26 Oct
[ix] CMEWU 1931: 11 Nov
[x] CMEWU 1932: 16 Feb; 10 Mar, 2 May]
[xi] CMEWU 1932: 2 Jun, 24 Jun; SM 3172, 22 Jun 1932.
[xii] CM 1934: 3 Oct; CM 1935: 20 Nov
[xiii] Rivett, G, *From cradle to grave; Fifty years of the NHS.* London, King's Fund. 1998, p 4.; CM 1932: 16 Mar, 27 Apr; MedComm 1932: 14 Mar.
[xiv] WB 1932: 27 Sep
[xv] MedComm 1932: 11 Aug, 7 Oct; WB 1932: 4 Oct
[xvi] Mag: Mar 1933; CM 1933: 15 Nov; CM 1934: 19 Dec]
[xvii] CM 1935: 20 Nov, 16 Dec
[xviii] CM 1936: 17 Feb, 18 Mar; CM 1937: 17 Mar
[xix] Smith, G. Livesonline.rcseng.ac.uk/biogs/E000329b.htm
[xx] RFH ARs 1931-9
[xxi] Ibid.
[xxii] CM 1933:13 Dec; CM 1934: 1 Aug: CM 1938: 5 Oct, 19 Oct, 26 Oct, 16 Nov; 21 Dec; CM 1939: 22 Feb: MedComm 1938: 20 Sep, 12 Oct.
[xxiii] CM 1939: 15 Feb, 22 Feb
[xxiv] CM 1939: 13 Jun, 15 Jun, 20 Jul, 26 Oct; MedComm 1939: 7 Jun
[xxv] Mag:1936 Mar
[xxvi] Mag:1938 Nov
[xxvii] WB 1931: 9 Jun; CM 1931: 17 Jun
[xxviii] WB 1931: 7 Jul, 21 Jul: PUJC 1931: 10 Jul, 5 Aug, 30 Sep, 10 Nov,
[xxix] Mag: Jul 1931; PUJC 1931: 26 Nov
[xxx] PUJC 1931: 15 Dec; 1932: 15 Jan,

[xxxi] Programme for opening of Queen Mary Building (Albert Levy Wing) & laying of foundation stone of Nurses Home Extension. Royal Free Archives at LMA
[xxxii] CM 1932: 27 Apr
[xxxiii] WB 1932: 10 May; CM 1932: 15 Jun; SM 3172, 22 Jun 1932.
[xxxiv] WB 1932: 21 Jun
[xxxv] CM 1932: 20 Jul; WB 1932: 26 Jul
[xxxvi] WB 1932: 27 Sep, 11 Oct, 18 Oct
[xxxvii] PUJC 1932: 7 Nov
[xxxviii] WB 1932: 29 Nov: WB 1933: 17 Jan, 24 Jan, 31 Jan. CM 1933: 15 Feb
[xxxix] PUJC 1933: 13 Feb
[xl] CM 1933: 15 Feb, 17 May; WB 1933: 7 Feb, 15 Feb
[xli] Mag: 1956 Sep
[xlii] Mag: 1933 Dec
[xliii] CM 1933: 13 Dec; Mag: 1935, Mar, Nov
[xliv] 'The Royal Free Hospital: new isolation wards'. *The Hospital*, October 1936, 259-261
[xlv] RFH AR 1936
[xlvi] PUJC 1931: 26 Nov; CM 1933: 13 Dec
[xlvii] CM 1931: 7 Oct
[xlviii] CM 1912: 3 Jul; CM 1915: 24 Mar; CM 1935: 20 Mar
[xlix] CM 1935: 20 Feb, 20 Mar, 19 Jun
[l] CM 1932: 18 May, 20 Jul, 16 Nov
[li] CM 1935: 19 Jun; CM 1936: 19 Feb
[lii] Mag: 1932 Jul; Mag; 1934 Mar; Mag: 1939 Mar, Nov.
[liii] Mag: 1933: Mar
[liv] Mag: 1939: Nov
[lv] Mag: 1935: Nov; Mag: 1945: Jan-Mar
[lvi] Mag: Nov 1937
[lvii] Mag: Nov 1938
[lviii] AR 1931-2
[lix] Mag: 1932 Jul, Mag: 1934 Mar
[lx] Mag: 1932 Mar, Nov: Mag: 1934 Mar
[lxi] Mag: 1934 Mar; Mag: 1935 Nov
[lxii] Mag: 1937 Mar
[lxiii] Mag: 1937 Mar
[lxiv] Mag: 1937 Nov
[lxv] Mag: 1935 Nov; 1939 Jul
[lxvi] Cooke, AM *History of Royal College of Physicians of London,* Vol 3. Oxford, Clarendon Press. 1972, p. 974-7.
[lxvii] Zimmeck, M. 'The "new woman" in the machinery of government: a spanner in the works. In '*Government & expertise: specialists, administrators & professionals, 1860-1919'* Ed. Roy Macleod, Camb Univ. Press. 1988, pp.185-202.
[lxviii] CM 1933: 17 May 1933
[lxix] CM 1938: 15 Jun, 20 Jul, 16 Nov, 21 Dec; CM 1939: 15 Mar
[lxx] CM1936: 17 Jun, 7 Oct, 16 Dec; Mag: 1937 Mar; Kelynack, Obit, *BMJ* 1973, 13 Jan
[lxxi] CM 1936: 17 Jun; CM 1938: 20 Jul, 16 Nov; CM 1939: 15 Feb, 17 May

Chapter 12

[i] CM 1939: 17 May, 15 Jun, 20 Jul, 26 Oct
[ii] CM 1940: 9 Feb, 14 Mar, 23 May
[iii] CM 1940: 23 May, 27 Jun
[iv] CM 1940: 9 Feb; CM 1942: 4 Nov
[v] CM 1939: 17 May; CM 1940: 18 Jul, 10 Oct; CM 1941: 6 Mar; Mag 1956, Mar (Cullis Obit)
[vi] CM 1941: 16 Jan; CM 1942: 29 Jan; CM 1944: 20 Jul, 5 Oct; 26 Oct

[vii] CM 1940: Oct; CM 1941: 1 May, 31 Jul, 16 Oct; CM 1942: 26 Feb; CM 1943: 30 Jun

[viii] CM 1941: 31 Jul

[ix] CM 10 Oct 1940 AR 40/41

[x] CM 14 Nov 1940

[xi] CM 1941: 16 Jan, 31 Jul

[xii] AR 1940/41; CM 1940: 14 Nov; CM 1941: 16 Jan, 1 May

[xiii] Miller, J. *Saints and Parachutes*. Constable, London, (1951) pp. 79-83

[xiv] RFH AR 1940

[xv] CM 1942: 7 May, 26 Jun; AR 41/42

[xvi] Mag: 1942 Jan; 1943 Jan; Green, G. (1999) *The Woman who knew too much: Alice Stewart and the secrets of radiation.* Univ Michigan Press. pp. 56-58.

[xvii] Mag: 1941: Jul; 1943: Jan, July

[xviii] Mag: 1942: Jan, Jul

[xix] Mag: 1942: Jan, Jul

[xx] Mag: 1943 Jan

[xxi] CM 1943: 6 Oct, 27 Oct

[xxii] Mag: 1945 Jan-Mar, AR 1944-5

[xxiii] Rivett, G, *The development of the London Hospital System 1823-1982*. King Edward's Hospital Fund for London (Historical Series No 4), London, (1986) Ch 10 'The Emergency Medical Service and planning during the war.' pp 238-263

[xxiv] AR 1938-39.

[xxv] CM 1939: 21 Sep, 26 Oct, 28 Nov

[xxvi] Mag: 1939 Nov

[xxvii] Mag: 1943: Jan, Jul

[xxviii] MedComm 1940: 10 Jan, 8 May

[xxix] CM 1941: 16 Jan, 6 Mar; AR: 39/40, AR 40/41

[xxx] AR 1941-2; RFH 'Newsletter' 1942 (Wartime substitute for RFH AR)

[xxxi] CM 1940: 14 Nov

[xxxii] CM 1945: 10 May

[xxxiii] CM 1944: 17 Feb

[xxxiv] AR 1940-1

[xxxv] CM 1943: 6 Oct; CM 1944: 18 May

[xxxvi] CM 1941: 16 Oct: CM 1942: 7 Oct; CM 1943: 27 Oct.

[xxxvii] CM 1943: 16 Dec

[xxxviii] Rivett G. *From cradle to grave; Fifty years of the NHS.* London, King's Fund. (1998) p.4. CM:1945: 4 Oct: CM 1947:14 May.

[xxxix] CM 1941: 1 May; CM 1943: 26 May; CM 1943: 3 Mar; CM 1944: 17 Feb; CM 1945: 4 Oct

[xl] CM 1941: 16 Jan

[xli] Blair, JSG.; *In Arduis Fidelis: Centenary History of the Royal Army Medical Corps*. iynx publishing, 2001. p.395.

[xlii] Ibid.

[xliii] CM 1939: 26 Oct; 28 Nov; MedComm 1939: 13 Dec

[xliv] CM 1941: 16 Jan, 6 Mar; AR 1941/42; RFH 'Newsletter' 1942 (Wartime substitute for RFH AR)

[xlv] CM 1943: 1 Dec

[xlvi] Mag: 1944 Jul

[xlvii] Ibid.

[xlviii] Mag: 1939 Nov

[xlix] Mag: 1942 Jul; 1945 Jan-Mar

[l] Mag: 1945: Jan-Mar

[li] Mag: 1944 Jul, 1945 Jan-Mar

[lii] Mag: 1944 Jul; 1945 Jan-Mar

[liii] RFH Newsletter 1944 (Wartime substitute for RFH AR)

[liv] CM 1944: 20 Jul
[lv] AR 43/44; RFH AR 1945
[lvi] RFH AR 1944; CM 1944: 7 Dec
[lvii] CM 1944: 20 Jul; CM 1945: 19 Feb
[lviii] CM 1945; 19 Feb; 9 Mar; 14 Jun; 24 Jul; 6 Dec; CM 1946:14 Mar; 20 Jun
[lix] Rivett, G, (1986) ref 23, op cit pp. 238-263
[lx] Rivett G. (1998), ref 37, op cit, pp. 15-17; 'Report of the Inter-departmental Committee on Medical Schools. ('Goodenough') HMSO, 1944.
[lxi] Rivett, G (1998), ref 37, op.cit. pp. 258-9
[lxii] Rivett, G (1986). ref 23, op cit, p. 242
[lxiii] Memorandum filed c CM 1945: 8 Feb
[lxiv] Development Committee Memorandum (filed with CM 1945: 25 Oct)
[lxv] Mag: 1942 Jan, Jul; Mag: 1943 Jul
[lxvi] CM 1944: 16 Mar, 26 Oct; CM 1945: 8 Mar, 10 May
[lxvii] CM 1945: 12 Jul, 4 Oct
[lxviii] CM 1942: 7 May; CM 1944, 5 Oct; CM 1946: 14 Feb
[lxix] CM 1961: 7 Jun

Chapter 13

[i] Lloyd-Williams, K. Obit. *BMJ*,20 Jan 1973, p. 179; Mag: 1962: Sep, p.48
[ii] CM 1945: 25 Oct; CM 1948:10 Mar; CM 1952: 8 Oct, 8 Dec.
[iii] CM 1951: 9 May; CM 1952: 13 Feb, 12 Mar, 9 Jul, 8 Oct, 29 Oct, 8 Dec; CM 1953: 9 Feb
[iv] CM 1954; 10 May, 14 Jun
[v] CM 1952: 29 Oct; CM 1953: 12 Oct
[vi] CM 1949: 9 Feb, 11 May; CM 1956: 12 Mar; CM 1959: 14 Dec; CM 1960: 9 May; Mag: 1960 Sep, p.20; AR 1959-60
[vii] CM 1951:12 Dec; CM 1956: 7 May; AR 1955-6, 1956-7, 1957-8, 1958-9
[viii] CM 1945: 4 Oct; CM 1947: 11 Jun
[ix] List of admissions, RFH Archives at LMA; AR 1951-2.
[x] List of admissions, RFH Archives at LMA; Danbury Obit, *BMJ* 2008, 26 April.
[xi] CM 1946:11 Jul; CM 1947: 14 May; AR 1949/50, 1950/51
[xii] CM 1950: 12 Jul; AR 1952-3, 1953-4.
[xiii] CM 1946: 24 Oct – attached memo.
[xiv] MedComm 1945: 13 Jun; AR RFH 1945 – dated 1 Oct 1946
[xv] CM 1945: 25 Oct; CM 1946; 14 Mar, 9 May, 20 Jun; CM 1947: 12 Feb. 8 Oct
[xvi] CM 1946: 9 May, 11 Jul, 3 Oct; CM 1947 12 Feb; MedComm 1947: 23 Apr
[xvii] MedComm 1948: 25 Feb
[xviii] CM 1947: 8 Oct
[xix] HGH Council of Management 1947: 17 Mar to 28 Sep; CM 1947: 29 Oct; MedComm 1947: 26 Nov
[xx] CM 1948: 10 Mar; MedComm 1948: 24 Mar
[xxi] CM 1945: 19 Feb, 9 Mar, 14 Jun, 24 July, 6 Dec; CM 1946 14 Mar, 20 Jun; AR: 1945-6
[xxii] CM 1919: 14 May; CM 1933: 13 Dec; CM 1934: 7 Feb; CM 1938: 16 Nov, 21 Dec; CM 1939: 15 Feb, 17 May; CM 1940: 27 Jun
[xxiii] CM 1945: 12 Jul, 4 Oct, 6 Dec; CM 1946 14 Feb, 9 May, 20 Jun, 11 Jul
[xxiv] CM 1946: 11 Jul, 3 Oct, 24 Oct; CM 1947: 12 Feb, 12 Mar, 9 Jul, 3 Dec 1947; CM 1948: 11 Feb, 10 Mar, 12 May
[xxv] CM 1948: 12 May; 9 June
[xxvi] CM 1948: 6 Oct; 27 Oct; Mag: July-Dec 1948, p 55; CM 1949: 11 May
[xxvii] CM 1949: 30 Nov; CM 1950: 12 Jul; CM 1951: 14 Mar; CM 1954: 10 May; CM 1955: 6 June
[xxviii] CM 1949: 9 Mar; CM 1950: 10 May; 7 Jun; 12 Jul, 25 Oct
[xxix] CM 1950: 13 Dec
[xxx] CM 1951: 9 May; Mag: Dec 1951; CM 1954: 14 Jun, 11 Oct, 8 Nov.

[xxxi] CM 1951: 13 Jun; 11 Jul, 12 Dec; CM 1952: 12 Mar

[xxxii] CM 1952: 14 May; 9 Jul; CM 1953: 9 Feb; 11 May

[xxxiii] AR 1952/3; 1953/4; AR54/55

[xxxiv] CM 1939: 21 Sep ; DevCom 1945: 27 Jun; PUJC 1945: 17 Oct; MedComm 1945: 14 Nov; DevComm 1946: 14 Feb

[xxxv] DevCom 1945: 12 Jun, 27 Jun, 16 Oct; DevCom 1946: 14 Feb; PUJC 1945: 17 Oct , 25 Oct; PUJC 1946: 6 Feb.

[xxxvi] PUJC 1945: 17 Oct; PUJC 1946: 6 Feb, 12 Mar ; DevComm 26 Feb 1946; WB 1946: 4 Apr

[xxxvii] WB 1947: 12 Aug, 11 Nov

[xxxviii] WB 1947: 9 Sep, 11 Nov , 9 Dec; MedComm 1947: 24 Sep, 22 Oct,

[xxxix] CM 1942: 7 Oct ; DevCom 1948: 17 May; BoG 1949: 14 Jun, 12 Jul; AR 1949–50

[xl] CM 1956: 11 Jun, 9 Jul, 8 Oct

[xli] DevComm 1956: 8 May; Dev Comm: 1957: 10 Dec

[xlii] CM 1956: 11 Jun

[xliii] AR 1955-56; CM 1956: 9 Jul; CM 1957: 13 May

[xliv] BoG Minutes 1957: 1 Oct

[xlv] CM 1958: 3 Feb

[xlvi] CM 1958: 3 Feb; AR 1957/8; Holborn Guardian 26 May 1973

[xlvii] CM 1958: 3 Feb; 3 Mar; 7 July

[xlviii] CM 1958: 3 Mar

[xlix] CM 1958: 10 Nov

[l] AR 1951-2; CM 1950: 13 Dec; CM 1952: 13 Feb; CM 1954: 10 May; CM 1958: 12 May.

[li] CM 1958 15 Dec: CM 1959: 23 Feb, 16 Mar, 15 Jun

[lii] AR 1959/60, 1960/61; CM 1961: 11 Oct

[liii] CM 11 Jun 1956; CM 1957: 13 May

[liv] CM 1957: 8 Jul; MC 1957: 8 May

[lv] MedComm 1958: 8 Jan, 19 May, 11 Jun, 3 Jul; CM 1958; 13 Oct; AR 1956/7

[lvi] CM 1958; 10 Nov,15 Dec; CM 1959; 23 Feb

[lvii] CM 16 March 1959

[lviii] Munk's Roll, Vol XI, pp. 514-518

[lix] CM 1959:11 May, 15 Jun; BofGov 1959: 12May, 9 Jun; FGPC 1959: 21 Jul, 6 Oct, 1 Dec; FGPC 1960: 5 Jan; FGPC 1961: 18 Jul.

[lx] CM 1960: 13 Jun; AR 1959/60

[lxi] CM 1950: 15 Mar; 10 May; CM 1951: 9 May: 13 Jun; 11 Jul: CM 1957: 8 Jul

[lxii] CM 1959: 16 Mar, 12 Oct ; CM 1960: 15 Feb.

[lxiii] DevCom 1948: 5 Aug; 1950: 5 Dec; 1951: 9 Jan, 13 Mar, 8 May, 12 Jun, 7 Aug

[lxiv] AR 1950-51; CM 1951: 3 Oct, 31 Oct

[lxv] DevCom 1951: 9 Oct, 13 Nov; 1952: 8Jan; CM 1952: 8 Oct; AR 1951-2; RFH Finance Comm 1952: 29 Jul, 30 Sep

[lxvi] LC 1947: 25 Feb; LC 1948: 24 Feb

[lxvii] CM 1951:14 Feb; Mag: 1952 Jun

[lxviii] LC 1959: 2 Mar, 1 Jun; LC Report 1958-9 filed c CM 16 Mar 1959; AR 1958-9

[lxix] LC 1959; 9 Nov; 1960 29 Feb, 20 Jun, Nov; 1961: 28 Feb; 1962: 2 Jul. MedComm 1960: 13 Jan, 10 Feb, 14 Jun, 13 Sep, 11 Oct. Med Comm 1961: 10 May

[lxx] CM 13 Feb 1956

[lxxi] CM 1946: 14 Feb, 14 Mar; Prospectus 1947/8]

[lxxii] AR 1950-51; 1952-3

[lxxiii] AR 1954-55, 1955-56 CM 1957: 4 Feb; Prospectus 1956-7,1971-3

[lxxiv] Prospectuses 1945-6 to 1962-3 ; CM 1957: 4 Feb, 17 Jun

[lxxv] CM 1961: 7 Jun

[lxxvi] CM 1948: 9 Jun, 6 Oct, 27 Oct; CM 1949: 9 Feb

[lxxvii] CM 1949: 9 Mar, 11 May; AR 1949/50; 1950/51, 1953/4

[lxxviii] CM 1956: 9 Jul

[lxxix] CM 1955: 10 Oct, 7 Nov. *The Times* from 25 Jul to 2 Aug 1955; *BMJ* 1957,19 Oct, pp. 895-904.
[lxxx] Ramsay, AM *Postviral Fatigue Syndrome*. Gower Medical Publishing, London. 1986
[lxxxi] CM 1952: 8 Dec; AR 1956-7
[lxxxii] CM 1961: 8 Nov, 6 Dec; CM 1962: 7 Feb; AR 1961-2
[lxxxiii] AR 1958-9; SCPhys 1959: 24 Aug; MedComm:1959: 9 Dec
[lxxxiv] CM 1930: 8 Oct; CM 1947 9 Jul; Dimsdale obit, *Munk's Roll VII* p155.
[lxxxv] CM 1960: 15 Feb, 11 Jul
[lxxxvi] Obit, Martin, BMJ 1953, 11 Jan; AR 1955-6.
[lxxxvii] CM 1957:13 May; Nicol obit, *Munk's Roll VI*, p359.
[lxxxviii] Hopewell, J, Calne, R. Beswick, I. Three clinical cases of transplantation. *BMJ*, 15 Feb, 1964; www.renhist.co.uk
[lxxxix] MedComm 1960: 13 Jan; CM 1960: 15 Feb, 10 Oct. Shaldon, S. The true history of home dialysis. *Nephrol. Dial. Transplant* (2005) 20: 1766–17
[xc] CM 1960: 11 Jul; CM 1961: 1 Feb
[xci] AR 1947-8; 1957-8; 1958-9
[xcii] CM 1946: 24 Oct; CM 1947: 14 May
[xciii] Mag: 1953: Dec; CM 1960: 5 Feb; CM1951: 1 Feb
[xciv] CM 1947: 14 May; CM 1955: 12 Dec; CM 1956: 13 Feb, 9 Jul, 10 Dec
[xcv] AR 1959/60
[xcvi] Obit. Ulysses Williams, BMJ 1961, 19 May; Mag: Jul-Dec 1947
[xcvii] CM 1947: 3 Dec; CM 1959: 13 Jul, 1947
[xcviii] CM 1958: 3 Feb; CM 1959: 14 Dec
[xcix] CM 1949: 11 May, 15 Jun; CM 1950: 7 Jun, 13 Dec; CM 1951: 3 Oct; CM 1962: 10 Oct. Dame Edith Brown obit, *The Times* 1956, 10 Dec
[c] CM 1949: 9 March; CM 1952: 11 Jun; CM 1961: 1 Feb
[ci] AR 1951-2; Sir Roger Bannister, personal communication.
[cii] CM 1949: 12 Oct
[ciii] CM 1949: 13 Jul; AR 1959-60
[civ] CM 1954: 14 Jun; CM 1960: 13 Jun, 11 Jul
[cv] CM 1954: 8 Mar; CM 1956: 11 Jun; CM 1958: 12 May
[cvi] CM 1952: 12 Mar, 14 May; CM 1953: 9 Feb
[cvii] CM 1960: 11 Jul; CM 1961: 1 Feb
[cviii] CM 1946: 24 Oct; CM 1952: 13 Feb, 12 Mar, 11 Jun, 9 Jul, 8 Oct; Mag: 1952: Dec
[cix] CM 1961: 1 Feb; 1 Mar; CM 1962: 9 May
[cx] CM 1948: 11 Feb; Mag: 1948 Jan–Jun (editorial); Prospectus 1953-4
[cxi] CM 1951: 9 May, 13 Jun, 11 Jul, 3 Oct; CM 1953: 9 Mar, 11 May; CM 1954 8 Mar; Mag: 1954 Jun
[cxii] Mag: 1954 Jun, Sep
[cxiii] Mag: 1954 Sep; CM 1954: 10 Nov; AR 1954/5
[cxiv] CM 1955: 7 Feb, 7 Mar, 9 May; CM 1956: 7 May, 11 Jun; AR 1955/56
[cxv] CM 1954: 14 Jun; CM 1955: 9 May,12 Dec; CM 1956: 10 Dec; AR 1956/7
[cxvi] AR 1958-9; 1959-60
[cxvii] AR 1953-4, 1954-5, 1956-7, 1958-9
[cxviii] CM 1960: 9 May; CM 1961: 7 Jun
[cxix] Mag: 1949: Jul – Dec
[cxx] Union Reports – Mag: 1957 Mar, Mag: 1958 Dec, Mag: 1960 Jan, Dec.
[cxxi] Union Reports – Mag: 1956 Sep; Mag: 1958: Sep; AR 1959-60 Dean's Speech Mag: 1961 Dec
[cxxii] Mag: 1953: Jun, Dec; Mag: 1962: Jun (Union Presidents's Report)
[cxxiii] Mag: 1953: Mar, Sep, Dec; Mag: 1954: Mar
[cxxiv] Mag: 1956: Jun; Mag: 1957 Jun, Dec (Dean's Report); Mag: 1960 Sep; Mag: 1961 Sep; AR 1959-60; 1960-1.

[cxxv] Mag: 1947: Jul – Dec 1947; Mag: 1952: Jun; Mag: 1953: Dec
[cxxvi] Tennis Club – Mag: 1952; Jun; Mag: 1953, Sep; Mag: 1954 Jun; Union Report – Mag: 1956, Sep
[cxxvii] Mag: 1946: Jan-Mar; Mag: 1952: Mar – Jun: Mag: 1962: Dec
[cxxviii] Mag: 1946 Jan-Mar; Mag 1952 Mar-Jun
[cxxix] Mag: 1949 Jan–Jun, Mag: 1953 Mar; Mag:1960 Jan, Mag:1962 Dec
[cxxx] Mag: 1956: Dec; Mag: 1957: Mar
[cxxxi] Mag: 1948: Jul-Dec; Mag: 1952: Jun; *Evening Standard* 1953: 10 Feb.
[cxxxii] Mag: 1952: Mar-Jun, Dec
[cxxxiii] Mag: 1953 Jun; Mag 1954 Mar; Mag: 1955 Dec
[cxxxiv] AR 1956/7; Mag: 1956 Jun; Mag: 1960 Jan; Mag:1961 Sep.
[cxxxv] Mag: 1952 Jun; Mag: 1954 Jun, Mag: 1960 Dec; CM 1959: 16 Mar
[cxxxvi] Mag: 1952 Dec; Mag: 1953 June, Dec; Mag: 1956 Mar; Mag: 1957 Jun
[cxxxvii] Mag: 1946: Jan-Mar
[cxxxviii] Mag: March 1956 – The Topical
[cxxxix] Mag: 1957: Mar
[cxl] Mag: 1946 Jan-Mar; Mag:1948 Jan – Jun; Mag:1951 Jan-Mar; Mag: 1958: Mar, Dec; Mag: 1960: Jan;.CM 1958: 3 Mar; AR 1955-6, 1957-8
[cxli] Mag: 1947: Jan-Jun; Mag:1956 Mar; Dec
[cxlii] Mag: 1954 Mar
[cxliii] Mag 1946: Jan-Mar; Mag: 1956 Sep; Mag: 1962: Jun
[cxliv] Mag: 1944 Jul: Mag: 1948 Jul-Dec; Mag: 1957 Mar
[cxlv] P 1947-8, 1948-9. Mag: 1953: Mar, June; Mag: 1955: Dec; Mag: 1956; Mar, Jun, Sep.
[cxlvi] Mag: 1957: Mar
[cxlvii] Mag: 1960: Jun, Sep, Dec. Mag: 1965: Summer
[cxlviii] Mag: 1952 Jun; Mag: 1953 Mar;
[cxlix] Mag: 1949 Jan – Jun; Mag:1950 Jan – Mar; Mag:1952 Mar-Jun; Mag: 1955 Sep; Mag: 1960 Dec
[cl] Mag: 1958, Dec
[cli] Mag: 1959 Jun
[clii] Minutes RFHSM OSA – Executive, 1946-1974; Minutes OSA AGMs 1946-1998.
[cliii] CM 1954:11 Oct
[cliv] OSA – minutes of AGMs and Executive Committee meetings, contact Secretary of RFA
[clv] MedComm: 1957 13 Feb
[clvi] AGM OSA; 28 May 1959, 15 June 1961
[clvii] AGM OSA; 21 Jun 1962
[clviii] CM 1961: 11 Oct
[clix] CM 1952: 11 Jun, 29 Oct, 8 Dec
[clx] CM 1954: 6 Dec; CM 1955: 7 Feb
[clxi] CM 1946: 11 Dec; CM 1947: 12 Feb, 8 Oct; 29 Oct; CM 1948: 11 Feb, 10 Mar
[clxii] CM 1948: 9 Jun; CM 1951:14 Feb, 9 May, 11 Jul; CM 1952: 14 May
[clxiii] CM 1950: 12 Jul; CM 1960: 21 Mar, 7 Dec; CM 1961: 10 May
[clxiv] CM1951: 14 Mar, 13 Jun, 11 Jul, 3 Oct
[clxv] Mag: 1917: Nov; Mag: 1939: Jul; CM 1939: 17 May
[clxvi] CM 1952: 13 Feb; CM 1954: 8 Feb, 14 Jun; CM 1955: 9 May
[clxvii] *Evening Standard* 1960; March 2nd & March 8th.
[clxviii] Mag: 1949: Jan-June
[clxix] Mag: 1958 Jun
[clxx] Mag: 1958 Mar
[clxxi] CM 1960: 2 Nov; CM 1961: 1 Feb.
[clxxii] *Daily Sketch* 1956: 1 Aug; Lloyd-William's Obit *BMJ* 1973: 20 Jan
[clxxiii] Mag: 1962 Sep; CM 1962: 10 Oct
[clxxiv] CM 1963: 19 Mar; CM 1969: 14 May

Chapter 14

i Janet Foster DNB 2004 doi:10.1093/ref:odnb/57538
ii Gilchrist, E. Personal communication
iii Gardner, F, 1949, 'Angiocardiography'. *Postgrad Med J*, 25: 553-564
iv AR 1863-4; CM 1966: 7 Dec
v CM 1965: 10 Nov; CM 1966: 12 Oct, 9 Nov; CM 1968: 12 May,16 Oct; CM 1973: 7 Nov
vi CM 1973: 14 Feb; 11 Jul, 10 Oct; AR 1947-8, 1974-5.
vii CM 1974 13 Mar, 8 May
viii CM 1970: 11 Feb
ix CM 1974: 12 Jun, 10 Jul, 2 Oct; CM 1975 18 Jun, 23 Jul
x AR 1953-54;1964-65; CM 1967: 18 Oct, 13 Dec; CM 1973; 9 May
xi CM 1968: 15 May, 12 Jun
xii CM 1963: 9 Oct, 13 Nov; CM 1964: 10 Jun, 8 Jul, 14 Oct
xiii CM 1962: 7 Feb; 1964:12 Feb; CM 1965:10 Mar
xiv CM 1961: 10 May, 7 Jun; CM 1965: 10 Feb, 7 Jul; AR 1966-7
xv CM 65: 9 Jun; MedComm 1960: 9 Jul, 14 Dec
xvi CM 1965: 13 Oct, 10 Nov, 8 Dec; CM 1966 11 May; AR 1967-8
xvii AR 1970-1
xviii CM 1966: 11 May, 8 Jun, 12 Oct
xix CM 1962: 12 Dec; CM 1965: 13 Oct
xx CM 1962: 12 Dec; CM 1965: 7 Jul; CM 1966: 9 Feb; 9 Mar, 11 May, 8 Jun, 13 Jul; CM 1967: 8 Feb; Mag: 1965 Autumn
xxi CM 1969: 12 Feb, 11 Jun; MedComm 1969: 13 Mar, 12 Jun
xxii Mag: 1961 Sep
xxiii UnionComm 1964: 5 May, 15 Jun; 1965: 16 Feb, 11 May, 8 Jun, 5 Aug; 1966: 11 Oct; CM 1965:9 Jun; Mag: Autumn 1965
xxiv LC 11 March 1963
xxv MedComm 1966:10 Nov
xxvi CM 1965: 10 Mar; LC 1966: 29 Nov; LC 1967:: 6 Mar, 19 Jun, 7 Nov; LC 1968: 6 Mar; EC 1967: 26 Apr; UnionComm 1967:17 Oct
xxvii MedComm 1967: 14 Dec. LC 1968: 24 Jun.
xxviii CM 1970: 11 Feb
xxix AR 1967-8
xxx *Royal Commission on Medical Education 1965-68,* ('Todd') HMSO, London, 1968*; Report of the Inter-Departmental Committee on Medical Schools* ('Goodenough') HMSO, London, 1944; p.134. paras 23 & 24.
xxxi CM 1968: 12 Jun, 10 Jul, 16 Oct
xxxii CM 1968: 16 Oct, 13 Nov, 11 Dec
xxxiii CM 1969: 11 Jun: AR 1968-69
xxxiv AR 1968-69
xxxv CM 1969: 9 Jul; AR 1968-69
xxxvi AR 1968-69
xxxvii CM 1969: 15 Oct; AR 1969-70
xxxviii CM 1970: 11 Mar
xxxix AR 1969-70
xl CM 1966: 9 Nov; CM 1967: 7 Jun; CM 1970: 13 May; CM 1972: 8 Mar; 13 Dec; BoG 1972:29 Feb; AR 1971-2
xli CM 1967: 8 Nov, 13 Dec; CM 1968: 14 Feb, 15 May; CM 1971: 9 Jun
xlii AR 1967-68; CM 1971: 13 Oct
xliii AR 1971-2; 1972-3; 1974-5
xliv CM 1972: 13 Dec
xlv AR 1970-71; 1971-72; CM 1972: 9 Feb
xlvi AR 1971-72, 1973-74

xlvii EC 1973: 24 Oct; AR 1974-75

xlviii AR 1972-73; AR 1973-74; AR 1974-75

xlix EC 1975: 26 Feb, Feasibility Study of April 1975 filed with CM 1975: 18 June

l CM 7 May 1975

li CM 1968: 13 Mar; AR 1967-68; 1968-69; AR 1970-71

lii AR 1973-74; 1974-5

liii AR 1967-68; AR 1972-73

liv Rivett G, *From cradle to grave; Fifty years of the NHS.* (1998) London, King's Fund. Ch 2. 'The renaissance of general practice and the hospitals, pp. 162-172, 184.

lv *Standing Reference on the Pay of University Teachers in Gt Britain, 2nd Report.* 1970, London, HMSO

lvi Rivett, G. (1998) ref 54, op cit. pp. 184, 254.

lvii AR 1965-6, 1966-7; CM 1965: 10 Mar, 8 Dec; CM 1967: 17 May 1967

lviii CM 1968: 12 May

lix CM 1968:13 Mar,15 May

lx CM 1968:15 May; AR 1967-68

lxi CM 1967: 13 Dec; CM 1968: 13 Nov; CM 1969: 14 May; Paper with EC 1975: 29 Jan

lxii EC 1969: 8 Jan; CM 1969: 14 May

lxiii EC 1969: 30 Apr; CM 1969:14 May; AR 1968-69

lxiv EC 1971: 29 Sep; CM 1971: 13 Oct; CM 1972: 9 Feb, 13 Dec; copy of new draft curriculum attached to minutes of CM 1972, 13 Dec.

lxv CM 1972: 9 Feb

lxvi CM 1971: 10 Mar; CM 1972: 9 Feb; AR 1970-71

lxvii EC 1968: 15 May

lxviii SSCME 1968: 2 Jul; CM 1968: 15 May, 13 Nov

lxix AR 1960-1, 1961-2, 1962-3, 1963-4, 1964-5, 1965-6; CM 1961: 5 Jul; Mag March 1962

lxx AR 1962-63,1963-64

lxxi CM 1964: 30 May; AR 1965-66; 1966-67; Prospectus 1965-6

lxxii CM 1971: 10 Mar, 12 May; AR 69-70; 70-1, 71-72.

lxxiii AR 1972-73, 1973-4, 1974-75

lxxiv ARs 1962-3; 63-4; 64-5; 69-70; 1970-71; 72-73. Mag: 1965 Summer 'A Yank's eye view of English Medicine'

lxxv AR 1967-8; CM 1968: 16 Oct.

lxxvi Prospectus 1956-57; 1961-62; 1970-2

lxxvii CM 1964: 12 Feb, 8 Jul

lxxviii AR 1969-70, 1970-71; '*GMC – Recommendations as to the Medical Curriculum*', 1957; GMC – '*Recommendations as to Basic Medical Education*', 1967.

lxxix AASCMed 1970: 16 Feb; EC 1970: 29 Apr, 27 May.

lxxx CM 1970: 10 Jun; CM 1971: 14 Jul

lxxxi CM 1969: 12 Nov; AR 1969-70

lxxxii AR 1973-4

lxxxiii EC 1972: 26 Apr, 28 Jun, 27 Sep

lxxxiv *New England Journal of Medicine* 1968, 278, pp. 593-600, 652-657,

lxxxv MAC 21 Dec 1972; EC 31 Jan 1973

lxxxvi McIntyre, N, Day, RC & Pearson, AJG;, 'Can we write better notes? An introduction to POMR', *British Journal of Hospital Medicine*. 1972 (May), pp. 600-611.

lxxxvii Lloyd, G & McIntyre, N: 'Educational aspects of the problem-orientated medical record', in '*The problem-orientated medical record: its use in hospitals, general practice and medical education*' eds Petrie, JC & McIntyre, N, (1979) Edinburgh, Churchill Livingstone.

lxxxviii EC 1974: 26 Jun, 30 Oct.

lxxxix AABSMed 1975: 15 Apr, 10 Jun: EC 1975: 24 Apr

xc AR 1967-68; AR 1969-70. CM 1966: 7 Dec; CM 1970: 14 Oct; CM 1974: 13 Feb, 2 Oct.

xci CM 1966: 12 Oct; CM 1972: 11 Oct: CM 1973 11 Jul, 7 Nov.

[xcii] CM 1962:7 Nov; CM 1963: 13 Mar; 11 Dec; CM 1964: 30 May; CM 1966: 9 Nov; CM 1967: 17 May; CM 1968: 16 Oct

[xciii] CM 1968 15 May, 12 Jun; CM 1973, 14 Feb; AR 1971-72

[xciv] CM 1955: 12 Dec; CM 1962: 9 May; CM 1966: 13 Jul; CM 1967: 8 Feb, 7 Jun; CM 1970: 9 Dec; CM 1973: 14 Feb

[xcv] Dean's Speech in Mag: 1961 Dec; CM 1963: 6 Feb; CM 1967: 17 May; 18 Oct

[xcvi] CM 1963: 6 Feb; CM 1967: 17 May, 18 Oct; CM 1968: 13 Mar; CM 1973: 11 Jul; 13 Oct; CM 1974: 10 Jul

[xcvii] CM 1963: 13 March; CM 1970: 10 Jun

[xcviii] AR 1969-70

[xcix] CM 1963: 8 May, 11 Dec; CM 1964: 10 Jun; AR 1962-63

[c] CM 1965: 10 Mar; AR 1965-66 ; 1968-69

[ci] AR 1963-64; CM 1963: 9 Oct; CM 1969: 10 Dec; CM 1970: 13 May; 14 Oct; Prospectus: 1970-71, 1971-2, 1973-4

[cii] CM 1963: 10 Jul, 9 Oct; CM 1966: 9 Feb, 11 May

[ciii] CM 1968: 14 Feb,

[civ] CM 1969: 12 Feb

[cv] CM 1971: 13 Oct, 10 Nov

[cvi] CM 1972: 10 May; AR 1974-5; Prospectus: 1974-5, 1975-5

[cvii] AR 1963-64; 1965-66; 1966-67

[cviii] Howells, H. Personal communication.

[cix] MC 1964 11 Jun, 10 Sep, 11 Nov; CM 1964 14 Oct.

[cx] CM 1965: 12 May, 9 Jun, 9 Sep; CM 1966: 13 Jul; CM 1967: 17 May; MC 1965: 9 Sep; AR 1966-7

[cxi] CM 1968: 10 Jul; CM 1973: Oct; CM 1974: 10 Jul.

[cxii] David Skeggs, Obituary. *Daily Telegraph* 20 Jan 2011

[cxiii] AR 1970-1

[cxiv] CM 1972: 14 Jun, 12 Jul; CM 1973: 14 Feb, 14 Mar, 13 Jun

[cxv] CM 1970: 14 Oct; CM 1972: 8 Nov

[cxvi] AR 1962-3, 1964-5, 1969-70, 1974-5

[cxvii] CM 1967: 17 May

[cxviii] AR 1962-63, 1970-71,1972-73

[cxix] AR 1974-5. CM 1964: 11 Nov; CM 1974: 10 July

[cxx] AR 1972-3: CM 1972: 8 Nov

[cxxi] CM 1966: 12 Oct; AR 1966-67

[cxxii] AR 1968 to 1975

[cxxiii] CM 1966: 12 Oct; Report dated 3.9.66 bound with minutes.

[cxxiv] CM 1966: 12 Oct, 9 Nov, 7 Dec

[cxxv] CM 1967: 8 Feb, 17 May

[cxxvi] Hussein Gezairy – Personal communication 2009

[cxxvii] Mag: 1964/5 Winter: AR 62-3 AR 63-4

[cxxviii] ARs 1962-63 to 1971-2. CM 1968: 14 Feb

[cxxix] Mag: 1965 Autumn

[cxxx] AR 1966-7; AR 1970-1; AR 1971-2. CM 1973: 7 Nov

[cxxxi] AR 1968-9, AR 1974-5

[cxxxii] Mag: 1964-5 Winter

[cxxxiii] AR 1972-3

[cxxxiv] Mag: Dec 1962; AR 1967-8,

[cxxxv] CM 1963: 8 May, 12 Jun, 10 Jul; CM 1964: 10 Jun; CM 1965: 10 Mar; CM 1966: 9 Nov

[cxxxvi] CM 1966: 9 Nov; CM 1967: 8 Feb, 17 May, 7 Jun, 18 Oct; CM 1969: 14 May

[cxxxvii] Mag: 1964-5 Winter; Mag: 1965 Summer

[cxxxviii] Mag: 1965-6 Winter/Spring

[cxxxix] AR 1967-8,AR 1969-70. PC Vol 9, pt. 2,p. 220

cxl Mag: 1964/5 Winter; Mag: 1965; Summer, Autumn
cxli AR 1963-4
cxlii Mag: 1962 Dec, 1964-65 Winter, 1965 Autumn; 1965 Summer (Union Progress Report); AR 1962-63; 1963-64, 1965-66.
cxliii Mag: 1962 Dec, Mag 1964-5 Winter
cxliv Mag: 1965 Summer; AR 1967-8
cxlv UnionComm 1963: 10 Dec; AR 1965-6, 1966-7, 1973-4.
cxlvi Mag: 1964-5 Winter
cxlvii Mag: 1965 Summer
cxlviii Mag: 1965 Autumn
cxlix Mag: 1965 Summer
cl ARs from 1967-8 to 1971-2
cli AR 1973-4
clii CM 1972: 14 Jun
cliii AR 1971-2: AR 1972-3
cliv CM 1973: 14 Feb
clv AR 1973-4
clvi EC 1963: 14 Feb; EC 1965: 27 Jan, 24 Feb; CM 1967: 8 Mar
clvii CM 1967: 13 Dec;
clviii CM 1971: 9 Jun
clix CM 1971: 14 Jul, 13 Oct; AR 1971-2
clx CM 1926: 27 Jan; CM 1971: 10 Nov
clxi CM 1972: 14 Jun
clxii CM 1972: 12 Jul
clxiii CM 1972: 8 Nov, 13 Dec
clxiv CM 1973: 14 Feb, 9 May, 11 Jul; AR 1972-3
clxv CM 1973: 14 Feb; CM 1974: 13 Mar
clxvi CM 1974: 8 May
clxvii CM 1974: 12 Jun
clxviii CM 1974: 10 Jul
clxix CM 1974: 4 Dec
clxx CM 1975: 12 Mar
clxxi EC 1975: 2 Jul; CM 1975: 23 Jul

Chapter 15

i CM 1975: 28 Oct; CM 1981: 28 Oct; CM 1982: 11 Feb, 17 Mar, 4 Nov; CM 1987: 5 Nov, 10 Dec; CM 1988: 11 Feb, 10 Mar
ii AR 1983-4, 1984-5
iii CM 1976: 18 Feb, 12 May; CM 1977: 19 Oct; CM 1978: 8 Feb; CM 1982: 4 Nov; CM 1984: 25 Oct
iv CM 1975:19 Nov; CM 1976: 12 May; CM 1978: 18 Oct; CM 1988: 23 Jun; 9 Nov
v RFHSM Annual Reports
vi CM 1982: 23 Jun
vii CM 1975: 22 Oct, 10 Dec
viii CM 1976: 18 Feb
ix CM 1977: 7 Dec; CM 1978, 22 Mar
x CM 1975: 22 Oct, 10 Dec; AR 1985-86
xi CM 1976: 12 May, 13 Oct, 10 Nov; EC 26 May 1976. AR 1975-6
xii CM 1976: 13 Oct, 10 Nov
xiii EC 1977: 5 Oct; CM 1977: 7 Dec
xiv *Evening Standard* 1976, 5 Jul; *Daily Mail, Daily Mirror & Evening News* 1976, 6 Jul; *Ham & High* 1976, 9 July; Murdoch Laing – personal communication .
xv AR 1975-6

[xvi] DHSS *Sharing Resources for Health in England. Report of Resource Allocation Working Party.* London: HMSO, 1976; Rivett G. *From cradle to grave: fifty years of the NHS.* London, King's Fund Publishing. (1998)
[xvii] AR 1976-7; CM 1977: 16 Mar; Bevan, G. *BMJ* 1999;319:908-911
[xviii] CM 1977: 19 Oct, 7 Dec
[xix] CM 1978: 8 Feb, 24 May; AR 1977-8
[xx] AR 1978-9
[xxi] CM 1978: 8 Feb
[xxii] CM 1978: 22 Mar, 24 May, 12 Jul
[xxiii] CM 1978: 6 Dec
[xxiv] CM 1979: 7 Feb,
[xxv] CM 1979: 7 Feb, 21 Mar
[xxvi] CM 1979: 4 Jul, 24 Oct
[xxvii] CM 1979: 24 Oct
[xxviii] *The Times* 1980: 12 Mar.
[xxix] CM 1980: 19 Mar, 21 May, 2 Jul: '*Medical Education in London*' Report of JPC of Court & Senate. October 1980
[xxx] CM 1980: 17 Dec; CM 1981: 4 Feb
[xxxi] CM 1981: 18 Mar, 20 May
[xxxii] CM 1981: 20 May
[xxxiii] CM 1982: 11 Feb; AR 1981-2
[xxxiv] AR 1982-3
[xxxv] CM 1981: 28 Oct, 18 Dec.
[xxxvi] Smith, R. (1982) The Hunter School of Medicine. *BMJ* 285, 11 September; Heffer, S. (1985) Troubles pile up for private medical school project. *Medical News*. 9 May.
[xxxvii] CM 1983: 29 Jun; CM 1984: 1 Feb, 21 Mar, 27 Jun; AR 1983-4
[xxxviii] CM 1985 31 Jan
[xxxix] CM 1985: 5 Jun, 27 Jun, 24 Oct, 12 Dec; CM 1986: 30 Jan.
[xl] AR 1984-5; CM 1985: 24 Oct
[xli] CM 1995: 24 Oct
[xlii] Kogan KM & Hanney S '*Reforming Higher Education*'. Higher Education Policy Series 50, Jessica Kingsley, London. (2000) pp 185 –200
[xliii] CM 1985: 5 Jun; AR 1984-5
[xliv] CM 1986: 26 Jun, 23 Oct, 11 Dec; CM 1987: 10 Dec. AR 1985-86; 1986-7
[xlv] CM 1986: 26 Jun; AR 86-7
[xlvi] CM 1986: 26 Jun
[xlvii] CM 1987: 29 Jan
[xlviii] CM 1987: 29 Jan, 12 Mar
[xlix] AR 1987-8
[l] AR 1975-6, 1976-7, 1977-8, 1979-80; CM 1982: 4 Nov; CM 1985: 27 Jun
[li] CM 1983: 29 Jun
[lii] Dormandy (Obit) – *BMJ* 1978, 24 Jun; *The Times*, 1978, 6 Jun.
[liii] *New Scientist* 3 May 1984
[liv] CM 1984: 25 Oct ; CM 1985: 31 Jan, 14 Mar, 5 Jun; CM 1986: 13 Mar, 26 Jun, 11 Dec; CM 1987: 25 Jun, 5 Nov; CM 1988: 10 Mar, 23 Jun, 10 Nov
[lv] CM 1987: 29 Jan, 25 Jun; AR 1988-9
[lvi] CM 1987: 25 Jun; 5 Nov
[lvii] CM 1987: 5 Nov; CM 1988: 23 Jun
[lviii] CM 1980: 2 Jul; CM 1981: 1 Jul, 28 Oct; CM 1988: 23 Jun
[lix] EC 1977 5 Oct; P 1983-5, 1987-9
[lx] CM 1986: 13 Mar
[lxi] CM 1979: 23 May; CM 1980: 19 Mar; CM 1982: 11 Feb. AR 1978-9; 1979-80
[lxii] CM 1977: 19 Oct; CM 1983: 29 Jun

lxiii AR 1979-80; CM 1980: 21 May, 22 Oct; CM 1981: 20 May. EC 1976: 29 Sep; Dolphin AC 'Eleanor Zaimis (1915-82)' in Bindman L, Brading A, Tansey T. (eds), *Women physiologists: an anniversary celebration of their contributions to British physiology.* (London: Portland), (1993) pp. 129-33.

lxiv CM 1986: 30 Jan, 21 May, 23 Oct. CM 1987: 5 Nov; CM 1989: 22 Jun; CM 1990: 21 Jun.

lxv CM 1987: 5 Nov; CM 1989: 9 Mar, 9 Nov.

lxvi CM 1982: 23 Jun; CM 1986: 23 Oct ,

lxvii CM 1977: 19 Oct; CM 1985: 24 Oct; CM 1986: 21 May

lxviii CM 1986: 13 Mar; CM 1986: 23 Oct; CM 1987: 25 Jun

lxix CM 1976: 7 Jul; CM 1979: 23 May, 4 Jul; CM 1982: 23 Jun, 4 Nov.

lxx CM 1988: 23 Jun

lxxi CM 1979: 4 Jul, 24 Oct, 5 Dec. CM 1980: 19 Mar

lxxii RFHSM Annual Reports & Prospectuses

lxxiii CM 1979: 7 Feb

lxxiv CM 1980: 19 Mar; CM 1988: 23 Jun; AR 1981-2, AR 1983-4.

lxxv Ian James, Obit: *The Independent*, 1998, 7 Oct; *The Guardian*, 1998, 9 Sep; *Munk's Roll XI,* p 297

lxxvi CM 1979: 7 Feb, 21 Mar

lxxvii *Munk's Roll* Vol VIII, pp 103-5103.

lxxviii *Munk's Roll,* Vol VIII, pp 492-3

lxxix Prospectus 1976-8, 1978-80, 1982-4, 1884-6.

lxxx CM 1981: 18 Dec; CM 1986: 23 Oct; CM 1989: 22 Jun

lxxxi RFHSM ARs & Prospectuses

lxxxii CM 1976: 18 Feb; P 1974-6

lxxxiii *The Times* Monday 5 April 1982

lxxxiv *Mail on Sunday, Observer.* 18 July 1982;

lxxxv CM 1982: 4 Nov

lxxxvi CM 1982: 4 Nov, 8 Dec

lxxxvii CM 1976: 15 Dec; CM 1982: 4 Nov, 8 Dec; AR 1984-5

lxxxviii EC 1976: 28 Apr, 29 Sep; AR 1977-8, 1988-9; CM 1984: 27 Jun; CM 1988: 23 Jun, 10 Nov

lxxxix CM 1981: 18 Dec; CM 1988: 10 Mar; CM 1989: 22 Jun AR 1981-2, 1985-6,

xc CM 1973: 10 Oct, 12 Dec; CM 1982: 8 Dec; CM 1984: 25 Oct; CM 1987: 29 Jan; CM 1988: 10 Mar; CM 1989: 22 Jun. AR 1975-6.

xci CM 1979: 21 Mar, 4 Jul; CM 1980: 19 Mar; CM 1981: 18 Mar. CM 1987: 25 Jun; AR 1985-6

xcii CM 1986: 22 Oct; CM 1988: 23 Jun; CM 1989: 9 Nov

xciii CM 1986: 23 Oct.

xciv AR 1985-6; 1986-7; P 1982-4

xcv CM 1988:10 Mar

xcvi MEC 1978: 16 Nov.

xcvii Letter Culyer to McIntyre 23 Jan 1980

xcviii McIntyre, N. (1979) The new clinical curriculum at RFHSM. *Medical Teacher*, 1, pp. 252-7

xcix Lloyd, G & McIntyre, N (1979) 'Educational aspects of the problem-orientated medical record'. In Petrie, J.C. & McIntyre, N (Eds) *'The Problem Orientated Medical Record'*, Edinburgh, Churchill Livingstone. 1979 pp. 143-175; Dearden,G. & Laurillard, D. 1977. Illuminative evaluation in action: an illustration of the concept of progressive focussing. *Research Intelligence* vol 3 pp 3-7.

c Gale J, O'Pray M & Wyn Pugh E (1981) The Importance of Context in the Implementation of a New Curriculum. *Medical Teacher* 3: 29-32; Wyn Pugh E & Engel C. (1978) *J Vis Comm in Med,* Vol 1, pp. 11-14.

ci ARs 1976-1988

cii AR 1988-9

ciii AR 1982-3, 1983-4.

[civ] AR 1976-7
[cv] ARs 1978-9 to 1988-9
[cvi] CM 1978: 6 Dec; CM 1979: 21 Mar, 23 May. AR 1978-9; 1880-1
[cvii] CM 1984: 27 Jun; CM 1986: 13 Mar
[cviii] AR 1977-8
[cix] AR 1974-5; 1975-6; 1979-80; 1985-6; 1987-8.
[cx] AR 1978-9, Free Comment – March 1980
[cxi] CM 1984: 21 Mar; AR 1983-4; *The Times* 1984, 15 March.
[cxii] *The Times* 1988: 3 Mar, 10 Mar; AR 1988-9
[cxiii] *Free Comment* – No. 79 Jun 1981. AR1984-5; 1985-6; 1986-7
[cxiv] *Free Comment* – No. 79 Jun 1981
[cxv] *Free Comment* No. 79 Jun 1981, Boat Club: AR 1980-1; 1982-3; 1983-4: 1984-5: 1985-6; 1986-7.
[cxvi] AR 1884-5; 1988-9; CM 1988 10 Nov
[cxvii] AR 1979-80; 1981-2
[cxviii] Union Comm 1970: 20 Jan; AR 1979-80
[cxix] CM 20 May 1981
[cxx] AR 1981-2, 1982-3, 1983-4
[cxxi] CM 1981: 28 Oct; AR 1980-1, 1981-2, 1982-3
[cxxii] AR 1982-3,1984-5
[cxxiii] ARs from 1984-5 to 1988-9
[cxxiv] CM 1989: 22 Jun; AR 1988-9
[cxxv] CM 1988: 10 Nov
[cxxvi] CM 1988: 10 Nov; AR 1988-9
[cxxvii] CM 1988: 23 Jun; 10 Nov; CM 1989: 22 Jun
[cxxviii] CM 1989: 9 Mar

Chapter 16

[i] CM 1991: 21 Mar; CM 1992: 3 Dec; CM 1997: 4 Dec.
[ii] CM 1989: 9 Nov, 14 Dec; CM 1990: 13 Nov 90; CM 1993: 4 Mar
[iii] CM 1992: 19 Mar 92
[iv] CM 1990: 22 Mar
[v] CM 1989 14 Dec
[vi] CM 1990: 22 Mar, 21 Jun
[vii] CM 1990: 13 Nov, 13 Dec.
[viii] CM 1991 21 Mar, 12 Dec
[ix] CM 1993: 9 Dec
[x] CM 1991: 13 Jun, 12 Dec; AR 93-4
[xi] CM 1993:9 Dec: CM 1994:16 Jun
[xii] CM 1997: 4 Dec
[xiii] CM 1995 14 Dec; CM 1996: 21 Mar, 20 Jun, 5 Dec.
[xiv] CM 1996: 5 Dec; CM 1997: 5 Jun
[xv] CM 1997: 27 Feb, 5 Jun
[xvi] CM 1990 : 22 Mar
[xvii] CM 1991: 21 Mar
[xviii] CM 1990: 13 Nov; CM 1991: 21 Mar
[xix] CM 1993:: 9 Dec; CM 1994: 16 Jun
[xx] CM 1992: 18 Jun, 3 Dec
[xxi] CM 1989: 14 Dec; CM 1992: 18 Jun; CM 1996: 21 Mar
[xxii] CM 1990; 13 Dec; CM 1994: 15 Dec.
[xxiii] CM 1988: 10 Nov; CM 1989: 9 Nov; CM 1990: 22 Mar; 13 Nov ; CM 1997: 4 Dec
[xxiv] CM 1991: 13 Jun; CM 1994: 3 Mar; AR 1993-94
[xxv] CM 1991 : 13 June; AR 1991/92

[xxvi] CM 1993: 4 Mar. CM 1979: 4 Jul
[xxvii] CM 1993: 17 Jun; CM 1996 5 Dec; AR 1996-7
[xxviii] CM 1994: 15 Dec.
[xxix] AR 1988-9, 1995-6
[xxx] CM 1991: 21 Mar; CM 1993: 9 Dec; CM 1997: 5 Jun, 4 Dec
[xxxi] CM 1991: 12 Dec; CM 1992: 19 Mar; AR 1991/92
[xxxii] CM 1994 15 Dec; CM 1996: 21 Mar
[xxxiii] CM 1991: 12 Dec; CM 1992: 3 Dec.
[xxxiv] CM 1993: 17 Jun; CM 1996: 21 Mar
[xxxv] CM 1993: 9 Dec; CM 1997: 5 Jun; CM 1998 5 Mar
[xxxvi] Kernoff , Obit; *BMJ* 2006, 1 April
[xxxvii] CM 1997: 4 Dec; AR 1996-7
[xxxviii] CM 1990: 22 Mar
[xxxix] CM 1989: 9 Nov; CM 1991: 13 Jun.
[xl] CM 1989: 9 Nov, 14 Dec; CM 1990: 21 Jun
[xli] CM 1990: 21 Jun
[xlii] CM 1990: 21 Jun CM 1991: 13 Jun, 12 Dec.
[xliii] CM 1990: 21 Jun
[xliv] CM 1989: 9 Oct; CM 1991: 21 Mar, 13 Jun, 12 Dec.
[xlv] CM 1989: 14 Dec; CM 1991: 21 Mar.
[xlvi] CM 1995: 14 Dec; CM 1996: 20 Jun; CM 1997: 4 Dec
[xlvii] AR 1991-2
[xlviii] AR 1990-1
[xlix] CM 1992: 3 Dec
[l] CM 1992: 3 Dec
[li] CM 1993: 17 Jun
[lii] CM 1993: 9 Dec
[liii] ARs 1991-2 to 1996-7
[liv] AR 1988-9; CM 1989: 9 Nov; CM 1991: 12 Dec; CM 1992 19 Mar, 18 Jun
[lv] CM 1997: 5 Jun
[lvi] CM 1993: 17 Jun, 9 Dec
[lvii] CM 1990: 22 Mar; CM 1991: 21 Mar, 13 Jun, 12 Dec. CM 1992: 19 Mar; 18 Jun.
[lviii] CM 1994: 16 Jun, 15 Dec
[lix] CM 1996: 20 Jun; CM 1997: 5 June; CM 1998: 5 Mar
[lx] Wakefield et al. (1989) Pathogenesis of Crohn's disease: multifocal gastrointestinal infarction. *Lancet* 4 Nov, pp 1957-62.
[lxi] RFH Memos: Bishop to Zuckerman 9 Dec 1997; Bishop to Tarhan 10 Mar 1998: UK patent application 2 300 259A. UK Patent Office. Priority date 28 March 1995
[lxii] Letter from Blatch to Wakefield, 15 March 1995
[lxiii] CM 1995: 2 Mar
[lxiv] Walker-Smith, J (2012) 'Enduring memories, 2nd ed. Ch 15, p.210.
[lxv] GMC Proceedings Day 60: evidence of Andrew Wakefield.
[lxvi] ibid.
[lxvii] ibid. (re Project 172-96)
[lxviii] GMC Proceedings Day 31 –Cengiz Tarhan evidence. RFH Memos: Bishop to Zuckerman 9 Dec 1997; Bishop to Tarhan 10 Mar 1998.
[lxix] Memo : Bishop to Zuckerman 1 Sept 1997
[lxx] GMC Proceedings Day 31 –Cengiz Tarhan evidence; Deer, B 'How the vaccine crisis was meant to make money' *BMJ* 2011, 15 January, 136-142.
[lxxi] DoH, 'Working for Patients', London: HMSO, 1989 (Cm 555)
[lxxii] '*The Best Medicine for London*' (Report of JPC Working Party on an Academic Strategy for Medicine), June 1989; CM 1992: 19 Mar
[lxxiii] CM 1992: 3 Dec

[lxxiv] CM 1992: 3 Dec; CM 1993: 4 Mar
[lxxv] *BMJ* 1993: 6 Mar, p 648
[lxxvi] CM 1993: 17 Jun
[lxxvii] CM 1993: 17 Jun
[lxxviii] CM 1993: 9 Dec
[lxxix] CM 1995: 15 Jun; CM 1996: 5 Dec; CM 1997: 5 Jun, 4 Dec
[lxxx] CM 1990: 21 Jun; CM 1996: 21 Mar, 5 Dec;
[lxxxi] CM 1994: 16 Jun; CM 1995: 14 Dec.
[lxxxii] CM 1990: 13 Nov; CM 1992: 19 Mar
[lxxxiii] CM 1994: 15 Dec
[lxxxiv] CM 1995: 2 Mar, 15 Jun; Letter, Zuckerman to Secretary of HEFCE 25 July 1994 re £546,000
[lxxxv] CM 1995: 15 Jun; CM 1993: 9 Dec
[lxxxvi] CM 1995: 9 Oct
[lxxxvii] CM 1995: 30 Oct
[lxxxviii] CM 1995: 14 Dec
[lxxxix] CM 1997: 27 Feb; CM 1998, 18 Jun
[xc] CM 1995: 14 Dec; 1996: 21 Mar, 20 Jun, 5 Dec
[xci] CM 1995: 14 Dec; CM 1996: 20 Jun; CM 1997: 5 Jun; CM 1998: 5 Mar
[xcii] CM 1996 5 Dec; CM 1997: 27 Feb, 5 Jun, 4 Dec
[xciii] EC 1998: 10 Feb; CM 1998: 5 Mar
[xciv] CM 1997: 4 Dec
[xcv] CM 1998: 5 Mar

Index

Note to reader: any abbreviations used in the index are explained on pp.xiii to xvi. Page numbers in *italics* refer to illustrations. Colour plates appear before pp.290 and 291.